MONOGRAPHS IN STATISTICAL PHYSICS AND THERMODYNAMICS

Volume 1
Non-Equilibrium Statistical Mechanics
by I. PRIGOGINE

Volume 2
Thermodynamics
With quantum statistical illustrations
by P. T. LANDSBERG

Volume 3
Ionic Solution Theory
Based on cluster expansion methods
by HAROLD L. FRIEDMAN

Volume 4
Statistical Mechanics of Charged Particles
by R. BALESCU

Volume 5
Order-Disorder Phenomena
by H. S. GREEN and C. A. HURST

Volume 6
Theory of Spin Relaxation
by W. J. CASPERS

Volume 7
Ergodic Theory in Statistical Mechanics
by I. E. FARQUHAR

Volume 8
The Statistical Mechanics of Simple Liquids
by STUART A. RICE and PETER GRAY

Volume 9
Statistical Continuum Theories
by MARK J. BERAN

MONOGRAPHS IN STATISTICAL PHYSICS AND THERMODYNAMICS

Editor: I. PRIGOGINE

Professor of Physical Chemistry and of Theoretical Physics
Université Libre, Brussels, Belgium

VOLUME 9

STATISTICAL CONTINUUM THEORIES

MARK J. BERAN

Associate Professor of Mechanical Engineering,
The Towne School of Civil and Mechanical Engineering,
University of Pennsylvania,
Philadelphia, Pennsylvania

INTERSCIENCE PUBLISHERS   1968

a division of John Wiley and Sons, New York · London · Sydney

Dedicated to my mother DOROTHY BERAN
and the memory of my father HERMAN BERAN

Preface

This book is primarily intended to acquaint the reader with the problems we face when we formulate a continuum problem from a statistical point of view. In the early chapters I emphasize what is meant by the solution to a statistical continuum problem and in the later chapters we present the techniques of solution that have been used in four separate fields. It is hoped that the book will be suitable for second- or third-year graduate students in engineering and physics and for research workers in the variety of disciplines that use statistical formulations.

The use of the functional formulation in the early chapters is presented in some detail since this formulism is necessary to describe the nature of a statistical solution. In most fields we treat in this book the only statistical equations that are not indeterminate are functional equations. In principle, this means that if we are to extract even the simplest statistical information about some unknown quantity x we must know a very considerable amount of statistical information about the known quantities upon which x depends. In practice this usually requires us to make some sort of approximation in order to make the problem manageable. This point has often not been clear and exact solutions have been sought based on very limited statistical information.

The functional formulation provides a unifying approach since if a statistical problem is formulated in terms of functionals, the basic presentation of the problem is similar in many fields. Unfortunately the use of functionals has not yet proven very fruitful in the solution of statistical problems. Thus once we have formulated the problem to be solved, we derive the associated hierarchy of moment equations and then turn to the various fields in order to see what techniques have been used to obtain approximate solutions.

When I began writing this book I had hoped that I would find many approximate techniques that had been used in a variety of fields. I found instead that with the exception of perturbation and variational procedures each field had concentrated on techniques that were suitable for the particular physical problem under consideration. It is only very recently that people in one field are beginning to consciously borrow the new techniques developed in other fields. In view of the difficulty of presenting general techniques I decided instead to give a fairly complete summary of the approaches used in four different physical areas. It is hoped that by presenting four fields in the same book using the same background formulism the reader will be able to more easily determine if the ideas used in one field are relevant to his own field of interest.

The four fields chosen for study, the theory of partial coherence, the theory of heterogeneous media, flow through porous media, and turbulence, reflect the writer's own interest and experience. It is felt, however, that together these fields are representative of a large class of statistical problems.

The theory of partial coherence as presented here treats the statistical aspects of the classical theory of electromagnetic wave propagation. The quantum theory of coherence, which has been developed in recent years, is omitted since the main lines of research that are currently followed add little that is relevant to the particular problems we consider. It must be noted, however, that in general, quantum field theory, itself, has many similarities to the theories presented here when it is viewed from a functional point of view.

In the chapter on the theory of heterogeneous media and in the chapter on turbulence the reader may feel that the mathematical calculations presented are excessive. I would answer this possible objection by stating that this complexity of calculation seems inherent in most statistical theories and I have included lengthy derivations to show the reader just what is involved in obtaining some statistical solutions. Moreover this labor is many times not in vain. In the theory of heterogeneous media the reader will see that often the end result of a very tedious calculation is a simple algebraic formula that has not been convincingly obtained in any other manner. As a final point I would note that the reader should not confuse complexity of calculation with mathematical rigor. This book is not meant to satisfy the requirements of a mathematician since many of the approximate procedures used can be justified only by an appeal to the physics of the problem.

The chapter on flow through porous media is somewhat different in kind than the other chapters since I have not been able to begin the chapter by setting up a hierarchy of moment equations. I feel, however, that it should be possible to treat flow through porous media from an explicitly statistical continuum point of view and I have included this chapter in the hope that readers will find this problem of interest. In the discussion on dispersion I have presented my own unpublished work since I felt it most clearly showed the relation between the important Taylor pipe dispersion problem and flow through porous media.

I found the chapter on turbulence the most difficult to write since the most recent developments are in a rapid state of change. In the more classical statistical theory I was able to consult Batchelor's book but the more recent work is not yet summarized in such a readable fashion. In order to prevent constant revision I reported in detail on work only through about 1965. I corresponded with a number of workers whose research I commented upon and was made aware by them of the latest developments. I found it too difficult however to present their most recent ideas at this time. Rather I contented myself with the thought that I had presented enough of their work for the reader to become aware of the general approach they followed. I was most particularly concerned that workers in other statistical continuum theories should become acquainted with the type of research being conducted in turbulence theory.

There are many people whose help I would like to acknowledge. In particular I would like to thank Professors Z. Hashin and J. McCoy of the Towne School, University of Pennsylvania for their many critical comments. Professor Hashin and I also taught a course entitled "Statistical Continuum Mechanics" and both he and the students in this course offered a number of important corrections to this text. In addition I want to thank Doctors T. Ho, M. Miller, J. Molyneux, A. Somoroff, and Mr. P. Carson for many valuable technical discussions.

While I was writing this book I also worked on a research contract from the Army Research Office, Durham, N.C. I would like to acknowledge the help this research provided in clarifying for me many of the problems presented in this book.

Presently I am on sabbatical leave from the Towne School, University of Pennsylvania working as a Fulbright Fellow in the Electronics Department of the Weizmann Institute of Science, Rehovoth, Israel. The kind reception I have received has greatly facilitated my completing the final stages of this book.

A number of publishers have given me permission to use material in books they have published. I appreciate this courtesy given to me by: Academic Press Inc., N.Y., American Institute of Physics, N.Y., Cambridge University Press, London and N.Y., Chelsea Publishing Co.,

N.Y., McGraw-Hill Book Co., N.Y., Prentice-Hall Book Co., N.J., and Quarterly Journal of Applied Mathematics, R.I.

Many people have contributed to typing and editing the manuscript over the past years. I want to pay especial thanks in this respect to my secretary Miss K. McGrory.

It is of course a particular pleasure to thank my wife, Barbara, and my children Sarah, Andrew, and Emily for their help. Their interest in my work has always made it very easy for me take the hours necessary to complete this book.

Rehovoth, Israel   MARK J. BERAN
November 1967

Contents

1. Introduction 1

   1.1. Example—One-Dimensional Harmonic Oscillator . . 2
      1.1.1. Constant Coefficients 3
      1.1.2. $k(t)$ and $m(t)$ Are Known Functions of Time . . 7
      1.1.3. $k(t)$ and $m(t)$ Are Statistical Variables . . . 8
      1.1.4. k and m Are Functions of the Dependent Variables . 9
   1.2. A One-Dimensional Continuum Problem 10
   1.3. Discussion 16

2. Definitions and Mathematical Preliminaries 18

   2.1. Probability Theory 18
      2.1.1. Axiomatization and the Concept of an Ensemble . 18
      2.1.2. Conditional Probabilites and Independence . . 21
      2.1.3. Probability Distribution Functions 22
      2.1.4. Probability Density Functions 26
      2.1.5. Mathematical Expectations 30
         2.1.5.1. Characteristic Functions 31
         2.1.5.2. Moments of the Form $\overline{u^n}$ . . . 32
         2.1.5.3. Correlation Functions 35
         2.1.5.4. n-Point Moments 37
      2.1.6. Stationary Processes 38
         2.1.6.1. Ergodic Hypothesis 41
         2.1.6.2. Correlation Functions and Power Spectra . 43
      2.1.7. Gaussian Processes 49
      2.1.8. Definitions of Convergence, Tchebycheff's Inequality,
         and the Karhunen-Loève Theorem . . . 53
         2.1.8.1. Convergence 53
         2.1.8.2. Tchebycheff's Inequality 54
         2.1.8.3. The Karhunen-Loève Theorem . . . 55
   2.2. Theory of Functionals 56
      2.2.1. Continuity 57
      2.2.2. Linear Functionals 59
      2.2.3. Differentiation 62
      2.2.4. Integration of Functionals 67
      2.2.5. Probability Density Functionals 70

3. General Formulations 73

3.1. Derivation of the Functional Equations 75
  3.1.1. Harmonic Oscillator Problem 75
  3.1.2. Maxwell's Equations 81
    3.1.2.1. Static Problem 82
    3.1.2.2. Radiation from a Surface (The Antenna Problem) 83
    3.1.2.3. Propagation through Random Media . 85
  3.1.3. Other Equations 86
  3.1.4. Navier-Stokes Equations 87
3.2. Derivation of the Moment Equations 93
  3.2.1. Derivation of the Moment Equations from Functional Equations 95
    3.2.1.1. Simple Harmonic Oscillator . . . 96
    3.2.1.2. Spatially Variable Permittivity . . . 99
    3.2.1.3. Navier-Stokes Equations 101
  3.2.2. Derivation of the Moment Equations Directly from the Differential Equations 104
    3.2.2.1. Simple Harmonic Oscillator . . . 104
    3.2.2.2. Spatially Variable Permittivity . . . 105
    3.2.2.3. Navier-Stokes Equations 109
  3.2.3. Equations Governing the Fourier Transforms of the Moments 112
3.3. Solution of Moment Equations 116
  3.3.1. Perturbation Techniques for the Solution of the Moment Equations 118
    3.3.1.1. Example of Spatially Variable Permittivity 118
  3.3.2. Cumulant Neglect Hypothesis 121
3.4. Variational Principles 126

4. Theory of Partial Coherence 142

4.1. Introduction 142
  4.1.1. Young's Interference Experiment 142
  4.1.2. Visibility 144
  4.1.3. Coherence Function 145
  4.1.4. Derivation of Equation 4-6 147
  4.1.5. Coherent and Incoherent Fields 149
  4.1.6. Measurement of the Angular Diameter of Two-Point Objects 151
4.2. Mathematical Formulation 155
  4.2.1. Definitions 155
  4.2.2. Derivation of Differential Equations . . . 158

	4.2.3.	Integral Form of Solution	162
4.3.		Radiation from a Plane Finite Surface	165
	4.3.1.	General Form of the Solution	165
	4.3.2.	Quasi-Monochromatic Approximation	166
	4.3.3.	Nature of the Source	169
	4.3.4.	Far-Field Approximation	169
	4.3.5.	Results for Various Source Shapes	171
	4.3.6.	Measurement of Visible Star Diameters	174
4.4.		Coherence of Blackbody Radiation	176
4.5.		Final Remarks	179

5. Theory of Heterogeneous Materials   **181**

5.1.		Introduction	181
	5.1.1.	Effective Constants	181
	5.1.2.	Use of Volume Fractions in Determining Effective Constants	185
	5.1.3.	Electrostatic Effective Constants—Tensor Permittivity	189
	5.1.4.	Definition of Effective Constants Using the Energy Density	191
	5.1.5.	Two Simple Physical Models	192
	5.1.6.	n-Phase Materials	197
	5.1.7.	The Self-Consistent Approximation	199
	5.1.8.	Dilute Suspensions	200
5.2.		Geometry of Heterogeneous Media	202
5.3.		Definition of Effective Constants	210
5.4.		Statistical Moment Equations	215
	5.4.1.	The Electrostatic Case	216
		5.4.1.1. Tensor Permittivity When $\epsilon_{(i)}$ Is Independent of x	225
		5.4.1.2. Scalar Permittivity	230
		5.4.1.3. The Second-Order Perturbation Calculation for Scalar Permittivity	232
	5.4.2.	The Elastic Case	236
5.5.		Variational Procedures	240
	5.5.1.	The Standard Variational Principles	241
	5.5.2.	Brown, Hashin, Shtrikman-Type Variational Principles	247
		5.5.2.1. The Scalar Problem	248
		5.5.2.2. The Tensor Problem	250
		5.5.2.3. The Addition of Correlation Information in the Scalar Problem	255

6. **Flow Through Porous Media** 257

  6.1. Introduction 257
        6.1.1. A Description of Porous Media . . . 258
        6.1.2. Darcy's Law 262
        6.1.3. Dispersion 268
  6.2. Statistical Approaches to the Determination of the Perme-
        ability 274
        6.2.1. Random Capillary Model 275
        6.2.2. Random-Walk Type Theory 278
        6.2.3. Variational Approach for Bounding the Magnitude of
                the Permeability 283
  6.3. Statistical Disperison Theories 288
        6.3.1. Dispersion in Pipe Flow 289
        6.3.2. Dispersion in Granular-Media Continuum Theory . 300
                6.3.2.1. Effects of Molecular Diffusion . . . 304

7. **Turbulence** 311

  7.1. Introduction 311
        7.1.1. Reynolds' Early Studies 312
        7.1.2. Concept of Eddy Viscosity and Mixing Lengths . 318
        7.1.3. Connection between Mixing Lengths, Eddy Viscosity,
                and a Cross-Correlation Function 323
        7.1.4. Experiments in Channel Flow 327
        7.1.5. The Similarity Hypothesis 331
        7.1.6. Further Remarks 333
  7.2. Derivation of Statistical Moment Equations . . . 334
        7.2.1. Homogeneous Turbulence 337
        7.2.2. Homogeneous and Isotropic Turbulence . . 338
        7.2.3. Fourier Transform of $R_{ij}(x_1, x_2)$ and the Transformed
                Moment Equations 343
                7.2.3.1. Qualitative Discussion of "Eddy Sizes" . 344
                7.2.3.2. Transformed Moment Equations . . 347
  7.3. Attempts at Solution of the Statistical Moment Equations . 350
        7.3.1. Final Period of Decay and the Nature of $\Phi_{ij}(k, t)$
                Near $k_i = 0$ 350
        7.3.2. General Remarks 354
        7.3.3. Kolmogorov's Hypothesis 355
        7.3.4. Heisenberg's Theory 358
        7.3.5. Cumulant Neglect Hypothesis 361
  7.4. Recent Approaches 369
        7.4.1. Kraichnan and Related Work 369

Contents

7.4.1.1. Kraichnan (1957, 1958a,b, 1959, 1961, 1964a–c, 1965a,b) 369
7.4.1.2. Wyld (1961) 385
7.4.1.3. Shut'ko (1965) 398
7.4.1.4. Further Remarks 400
7.4.2. Functional Approaches 400
7.4.2.1. Hopf (1952), Hopf and Titt (1953) . . 401
7.4.2.2. Edwards (1964) 402
7.4.2.3. Tatarski (1962) 406
7.4.3. Deissler (1965a) 412
7.4.4. Recent Papers of Interest 413

Bibliography 415
Subject Index 421

CHAPTER 1

Introduction

In the past decades an increasing number of problems in continuum theory have been treated using statistical theories. Statistical theories have been developed in the classical fields of fluid mechanics, elasticity, and electromagnetic theory to consider such diverse phenomena as turbulence, flow through porous media, mechanical and electric properties of heterogeneous media, ionospheric scattering, and black-body radiation. This is but a partial listing,* and it is clear that almost any phenomenon represented by a classical field equation has some subclass of problems that may profitably be treated from a statistical point of view.

The statistical formulation underlying almost all classical field theories may be made the same if we view the problem as one of formally casting the governing partial differential equations into statistical form. This formal manipulation is esthetically very satisfying and yields a set of functional equations that contains within them the solution to our initial statistical problem in the same sense that the original partial differential equations governed the determinate problem. Unfortunately, the governing statistical equations have as yet proved to be of little aid in the solution of problems.

In practice one is forced to seek iterative solutions of the governing statistical equations or to resort to other techniques such as variational principles. In fact, the iterative or variational procedures usually have appeared first in the literature unconnected with a general formulation and have tended to obscure the basic similarity of most statistical formulations.

In this book we shall attempt to treat both the formal and practical aspects of the subject. In Chapters 2 and 3 we shall underscore the basic similarities of most statistical continuum theories. In the remaining chapters, however, we shall discuss the consequences of a statistical theory in a number of particular disciplines. In our treatment of the

* Appropriate references will be given in later chapters.

1

individual disciplines, we shall report on those techniques that have been fruitful for the particular area under study. Some techniques have been used in a number of statistical theories, and we shall emphasize these approaches. More often, unfortunately, the techniques reported on have been used in only one area. Thus, despite the underlying similarity of most statistical theories, little has been developed in the way of general techniques of solution. It is hoped that by reporting on four major statistical theories in the same book, using a common formulation, workers in one area will be made more aware of techniques used in other areas and perhaps find additional application for them.

At this point, we could proceed directly to Chapter 2 in which is given a review of the probability ideas that are necessary to properly understand the type of problem we wish to treat. This approach would be appropriate for those readers largely unfamiliar with probability theory. Some who read this book, however, will be familiar with statistical ideas, and for this audience it is desirable to emphasize immediately the type of problem with which we are faced. We have thus decided to present, next, two simple examples discussing the difficulties occurring in the later chapters. We suggest that the reader unfamiliar with statistical ideas proceed directly to Chapter 2 and read Sections 1.1, 1.2, and 1.3 after reading Chapter 2.

1.1. Example—One-Dimensional Harmonic Oscillator

Since this book is intended for scientists in a wide variety of disciplines, we begin with a model with which everyone has some familiarity. We consider the motion of an harmonic oscillator subjected to a random forcing function. This example does not represent a problem in continuum theory (except in some degenerate sense). It does illustrate a statistical theory in its simplest form, however, and the techniques presented here may be readily generalized to more than one independent variable. The one-dimensional statistical problem is treated in detail in books like Middleton (1960) and Davenport and Root (1958). The harmonic oscillator has been discussed recently by Richardson (1964). We shall consider here an harmonic oscillator with (a) constant coefficients, (b) coefficients that are known functions of time, (c) coefficients that have known statistical properties, and (d) coefficients that are functions of the dependent variable.

1.1.1. Constant Coefficients

The equation governing a one-dimensional harmonic oscillator with no damping and subjected to a force $F(t)$ is

$$(1\text{-}1) \qquad m\frac{d^2x}{dt^2} + kx = F(t)$$

where x is the positional coordinate of the oscillator, t is the time, m is the mass, and k is the spring constant.

Suppose now that m and k are constants and the force $F(t)$ is random. For example, we may consider $F(t)$ to be the force an airplane experiences when passing through turbulent air. We suppose $F(t)$ can only be economically considered in terms of a statistical description. The most direct information we are given about $F(t)$ is contained in functions like $\overline{F(t_1)}$, the average value of $F(t)$ at time t_1; or $\overline{F(t_1)^2}$, the mean square value of $F(t)$ at time t_1; or more generally $P_1(F(t_1))\,dF(t_1)$, the probability that $F(t_1)$ lies between $F(t_1)$ and $F(t_1) + dF(t_1)$. The relation between $P_1(F(t_1))$ and $\overline{[F(t_1)]^n}$ is

$$\overline{[F(t_1)]^n} = \int\limits_{-\infty}^{\infty} [F(t_1)]^n P_1(F(t_1))\,dF(t_1)$$

In order to specify completely $F(t)$ statistically, however, more general functions are necessary. We require, in addition, correlation functions like $\overline{F(t_1)F(t_2)}$ or $\overline{F(t_1)^2F(t_2)^2}$, where

$$\overline{[F(t_1)]^n[F(t_2)]^m} = \int\limits_{-\infty}^{\infty}\!\!\int [F(t_1)]^n[F(t_2)]^m P_2[F(t_1), F(t_2)]\,dF(t_1)\,dF(t_2)$$

$P_2(F(t_1), F(t_2))\,dF(t_1)\,dF(t_2)$ being the probability that $F(t_1)$ lies between $F(t_1)$ and $F(t_1) + dF(t_1)$ and that $F(t_2)$ lies between $F(t_2)$ and $F(t_2) + dF(t_2)$. In fact, the complete specification of $F(t)$ is given by the nth-order probability

$$P_n(F(t_1), F(t_2), \ldots, F(t_n))\,dF(t_1)\,dF(t_2)\cdots dF(t_n)$$

[defined as the probability that $F(t_1)$ lies between $F(t_1)$ and $F(t_1) + dF(t_1)$, that $F(t_2)$ lies between $F(t_2)$ and $F(t_2) + dF(t_2) \cdots$ and that $F(t_n)$ lies between $F(t_n)$ and $F(t_n) + dF(t_n)$] as $n \to \infty$. From this function $\overline{[F(t_1)]^n}$, $\overline{[F(t_1)]^n[F(t_2)]^m}$, $P_1(F(t_1))$, $P_2(F(t_1), F(t_2))$ and higher-order functions may all be derived by integration.

In order to specify the statistical properties of $x(t)$, or the joint statistical properties of $x(t)$ and $F(t)$, we require similar nth-order probability functions. The specification of a random function will be given in detail in Chapter 2. In this introduction the reader is asked to bear with a certain looseness of definition in order to focus on the essential aspects of our solution of Eq. 1-1.

Stated generally the statistical solution of Eq. 1-1 involves finding

$$P_n(x(t_1), x(t_2), \ldots, x(t_n)) \, dx(t_1) \, dx(t_2) \cdots dx(t_n)$$

or
$$P_n(x(t_1), x(t_2), \ldots, x(t_n), F(t_1), F(t_2), \ldots,$$
$$F(t_n)) \, dx(t_1) \, dx(t_2) \cdots dx(t_n) \, dF(t_1) \, dF(t_2) \cdots dF(t_n)$$

as a function of

$$P_n(F(t_1), F(t_2), \ldots, F(t_n)) \, dF(t_1) \, dF(t_2) \cdots dF(t_n)$$

in the limit as $n \to \infty$. *

In the limit $n \to \infty$ we denote these functions by $P[x(t)]$, $P[x(t), F(t)]$, and $P[F(t)]$, respectively. Note now that the P functions are functionals; i.e., $P[x(t)]$ is a function of the function $x(t)$. By the limit $n \to \infty$ we mean here that the succession of times $t_1, t_2, \ldots, t_n$ is replaced by the continuous parameter t.†

It is possible to derive a functional differential equation governing $P[x(t), F(t)]$.‡ $P[F(t)]$ is a functional boundary condition for this equation. We shall not derive this equation in the introduction but rather shall defer this until after Chapter 2 wherein the appropriate mathematical definitions will be given. The reader is asked, however, to remember that the complete statistical solution of the problem requires that we know $P[x(t), F(t)]$ in terms of $P[F(t)]$. Furthermore, it should be remembered that all of the more common statistical functions such as $\overline{x(t_1)}$ or $\overline{x(t_1)x(t_2)}$ or $\overline{x(t_1)F(t_2)}$ or $P_1(x(t_1))$ are derivable by integration from $P[x(t), F(t)]$.

The harmonic oscillator equation given in Eq. 1-1 is of a very special form. Whereas in general it is only possible to derive an equation

* We shall suppose $x(0)$ and $dx/dt(0)$ are specified in a nonrandom manner and hence we shall not stress the dependence of P_n on this boundary condition.

† To proceed from P_n to P requires some care and the limiting procedure is discussed in Chapter 2.

‡ Actually it is usual to derive an equation in terms of the Fourier transform of the joint functional.

between $P[x(t), F(t)]$ and $P[F(t)]$, the form of Eq. 1-1 allows us to derive equations connecting the individual moments of $x(t)$ such as $\overline{x(t_1)}$ and $\overline{x(t_1)x(t_2)}$ with the individual moments of $F(t)$ such as $\overline{F(t_1)}$ and $\overline{F(t_1)F(t_2)}$. It also allows us to derive an equation for the cross correlation, $\overline{x(t_1)F(t_2)}$, in terms of $\overline{F(t_1)F(t_2)}$.

For example, if we average both sides of Eq. 1-1 and interchange the procedures of differentiation and averaging,* we find the following equation between $\overline{x(t)}$ and $\overline{F(t)}$:

(1-2)
$$m \frac{d^2\overline{x(t)}}{dt^2} + k\,\overline{x(t)} = \overline{F(t)}$$

This equation may be solved for $\overline{x(t)}$ in terms of $\overline{F(t)}$. Note that we have not assumed $F(t)$ to be a stationary random process (i.e., the statistical information has not been assumed to be independent of the absolute time, t). Hence $d\overline{x(t)}/dt$ is not in general equal to zero. As a boundary condition we may use the nonrandom set: $x(0) = 0$, $(dx/dt)(0) = 0$.

In order to derive an equation governing the correlation function $\overline{x(t_1)x(t_2)}$ in terms of $\overline{F(t_1)F(t_2)}$, we write Eq. 1-1 in the following two forms:

(1-3)
$$m \frac{d^2x(t_1)}{dt_1^{\,2}} + kx(t_1) = F(t_1)$$

(1-4)
$$m \frac{d^2x(t_2)}{dt_2^{\,2}} + kx(t_2) = F(t_2)$$

We next multiply the left-hand side of Eq. 1-3 by the left-hand side of Eq. 1-4 and the right-hand side of Eq. 1-3 by the right-hand side of Eq. 1-4 and average. This yields

(1-5) $\quad m^2 \dfrac{\partial^4 \overline{x(t_1)x(t_2)}}{\partial t_1^{\,2}\,\partial t_2^{\,2}} + mk\left[\dfrac{\partial^2 \overline{x(t_1)x(t_2)}}{\partial t_1^{\,2}} + \dfrac{\partial^2 \overline{x(t_1)x(t_2)}}{\partial t_2^{\,2}}\right]$

$$+ k^2\,\overline{x(t_1)x(t_2)} = \overline{F(t_1)F(t_2)}$$

* The validity of this interchange is clear if we note that the average operation may be represented as a summation over different members of an ensemble. Thus we write

$$\bar{x} = \lim_{N\to\infty} \frac{1}{N} \sum_{n=1}^{N} x_n$$

This is an equation that determines $\overline{x(t_1)x(t_2)}$ in terms of $\overline{F(t_1)F(t_2)}$. The boundary condition for this equation follows from those given above. It requires some discussion, however, and we shall consider this point in Chapter 3. Proceeding similarly we may find an equation connecting $\overline{x(t_1)x(t_2)\cdots x(t_n)}$ and $\overline{F(t_1)F(t_2)\cdots F(t_n)}$ for every value of n. Note that in the equation governing $\overline{x(t_1)x(t_2)\cdots x(t_n)}$ there do not appear moments of the form $\overline{x(t_1)x(t_2)\cdots x(t_m)}$ if $m \neq n$.

An alternate method of approach for finding $\overline{x(t_1)x(t_2)\cdots x(t_n)}$ in terms of $\overline{F(t_1)F(t_2)\cdots F(t_n)}$ would be to solve Eq. 1-1 and determine $x(t)$ as an integral over $F(t)$. The formal solution of Eq. 1-1 is

$$(1\text{-}6) \qquad\qquad x(t) = \int_0^t G(t, u)F(u)\, du$$

where $G(t, u)$ is an appropriate Green's function. For the boundary condition $x(0) = 0$, $(dx/dt)(0) = 0$, $G(t, u)$ has the form (see, e.g., Hildebrand, 1962)

$$G(t, u) = \frac{1}{m\omega_0} \sin \omega_0(t - u); \qquad \omega_0^2 = \frac{k}{m}$$

In order to find $\overline{x(t)}$, we simply average Eq. 1-6. This yields

$$(1\text{-}7) \qquad\qquad \overline{x(t)} = \int_0^t \overline{F(u)}G(t, u)\, du$$

In order to find $\overline{x(t_1)x(t_2)}$ multiply Eq. 1-6 by itself, using variables t_1 and t_2 and u_1 and u_2, and then average. This yields

$$(1\text{-}8) \qquad \overline{x(t_1)x(t_2)} = \int_0^{t_1} \int_0^{t_2} \overline{F(u_1)F(u_2)}G(t_1, u_1)G(t_2, u_2)\, du_1\, du_2$$

The extension of this procedure yields $\overline{x(t_1)x(t_2)\cdots x(t_n)}$ in terms of $\overline{F(t_1)F(t_2)\cdots F(t_n)}$. It is important to note that $\overline{x(t_1)^n}$ is a function of the full moment $\overline{F(t_1)F(t_2)\cdots F(t_n)}$, *not simply* $\overline{F(t_1)^n}$.

The solution of Eq. 1-1 when m and k are constants presents no difficulties. We reiterate that we may derive, as we shall see later, a relationship between $P[x(t), F(t)]$ and $P[F(t)]$ or we may settle for less information and derive relations such as Eq. 1-5 or Eq. 1-8 by connecting the nth order moment $\overline{x(t_1)x(t_2) \cdots x(t_n)}$ with the nth-order moment $\overline{F(t_1)F(t_2) \cdots F(t_n)}$. The reader will see in Section 1.1.3 that the latter possibility is not open to us when m and k are statistical variables.

1.1.2. $k(t)$ and $m(t)$ Are Known Functions of Time

If $k(t)$ and $m(t)$ are known functions of time, the formal analysis previously given may again be performed. A functional equation governing $P[x(t), F(t)]$ may again be derived. The equation governing $\overline{x(t)}$ has the same form as Eq. 1-2, i.e.,

$$(1\text{-}9) \qquad m(t)\frac{d^2\overline{x(t)}}{dt^2} + k(t)\overline{x(t)} = \overline{F(t)}$$

The analysis of Eq. 1-5 has the slightly more general form

$$(1\text{-}10) \quad m(t_1)m(t_2)\frac{\partial^4\overline{x(t_1)x(t_2)}}{\partial t_1{}^2\,\partial t_2{}^2} + m(t_1)k(t_2)\frac{d^2\overline{x(t_1)x(t_2)}}{dt_1{}^2}$$

$$+ m(t_2)k(t_1)\frac{\partial^2\overline{x(t_1)x(t_2)}}{\partial t_2{}^2} + k(t_1)k(t_2)\overline{x(t_1)x(t_2)} = \overline{F(t_1)F(t_2)}$$

Equations that connect $\overline{x(t_1)x(t_2) \cdots x(t_n)}$ and $\overline{F(t_1)F(t_2) \cdots F(t_n)}$ may easily be derived in exactly the same manner as when m and k are constants.

Since k and m are now arbitrary functions of time, we cannot find a simple solution of Eq. 1-1 such as Eq. 1-6. Formally, since Eq. 1-1 is still linear, we may write

$$(1\text{-}11) \qquad x(t) = \int_0^t F(u)h(t, u)\,du$$

where $h(t, u)$ is a Green's function. Equations such as 1-7 and 1-8 may thus be derived. Conceptually, the statistical aspects of the problem are unaltered if m and k are *known* functions.

1.1.3. $k(t)$ and $m(t)$ Are Statistical Variables

When $k(t)$ and $m(t)$ are statistical variables in addition to $F(t)$, we face a much more difficult problem. We assume here that we know the joint probability density function

$$P_n(m(t_1), m(t_2), \ldots, m(t_n), k(t_1),$$
$$k(t_2), \ldots, k(t_n), F(t_1), F(t_2), \ldots, F(t_n))$$

as $n \to \infty$. We denote this functional as $P[m(t), k(t), F(t)]$.

As we shall show in Chapter 3 it is still possible to determine a functional equation governing $P[x(t), m(t), k(t), F(t)]$, *with* $P[m(t), k(t), F(t)]$ *as a boundary condition. However, we cannot derive equations now similar to Eqs.* 1-2 *and* 1-5 *that would express* $\overline{x(t)}$ *in terms of* $\overline{m(t)}$, $\overline{k(t)}$ *and* $\overline{F(t)}$, *and* $\overline{x(t_1)x(t_2)}$ *in terms of* $\overline{m(t_1)m(t_2)}$, $\overline{m(t_1)k(t_2)}$, *etc.* Consider, for example, averaging Eq. 1-1, where m and k are now functions of t. The result is

$$(1\text{-}12) \qquad \overline{m(t)\frac{d^2x(t)}{dt^2}} + \overline{k(t)x(t)} = \overline{F(t)}$$

where in general

$$\overline{m(t)\frac{d^2x(t)}{dt^2}} \neq \overline{m(t)}\,\overline{\frac{d^2x(t)}{dt^2}}$$

and

$$\overline{k(t)x(t)} \neq \overline{k(t)}\,\overline{x(t)}$$

Hence we do not have an equation that allows us to determine $\overline{x(t)}$ in terms of $\overline{F(t)}$, $\overline{m(t)}$, and $\overline{k(t)}$ alone. Indeed, in general $\overline{x(t)}$ now depends upon the entire functional $P[m(t), k(t), F(t)]$. This same result is true for any nth-order moment $\overline{x(t_1)x(t_2) \cdots x(t_n)}$: it depends upon *all* the statistical information about $m(t)$, $k(t)$, and $F(t)$, not just their nth-order moments.

We could again formally represent $x(t)$ as

$$(1\text{-}13) \qquad x(t) = \int_0^t F(u)h(t, u)\, du$$

where now $h(t, u)$ depends upon $m(t)$ and $k(t)$ and is thus a statistical variable. Little is to be gained by this representation, however, since in general we do not know how to calculate the statistical properties of $h(t, u)F(u)$ in terms of the statistical properties of $m(t)$, $k(t)$, and $F(t)$. The equation

(1-14)
$$\overline{x(t)} = \int_0^t \overline{F(u)h(t, u)} \, du$$

is of little value to us in determining $x(t)$.*

Now, in order to find information about $\overline{x(t_1)x(t_2) \cdots x(t_n)}$ it is in general either necessary to solve for the functional relations between $P[x(t), m(t), k(t), F(t)]$ and $P[m(t), k(t), F(t)]$, or to find some procedure which shows that $\overline{x(t_1)x(t_2) \cdots x(t_n)}$ may be determined to a good approximation by only partial use of the information contained in $P[m(t), k(t), F(t)]$. Except in our study of the propagation of electromagnetic radiation in free space, all the topics that are treated in this book will encounter the difficulty illustrated in this subsection. In lieu of solving the functional equations we shall then be forced to consider iterative, variational, and other procedures to obtain useful information.

1.1.4. k and m Are Functions of the Dependent Variables

When k and m, or either one, are functions of the dependent variable $x(t)$, we have a nonlinear equation and, as we should expect, a statistical formulation is extremely difficult in general. Equation 1-1 now becomes

(1-15)
$$m(x)\frac{d^2x}{dt^2} + k(x)x = F(t)$$

Again a functional formulation is often possible, but the procedure of averaging Eq. 1-15, which gives

(1-16)
$$\overline{m(x)\frac{d^2x}{dt^2}} + \overline{k(x)x} = \overline{F(t)}$$

yields no information about $\overline{x(t)}$. Save in very special cases, we gain no immediate information by multiplying Eq. 1-15 by functions of x at different times and then averaging.

* See, however, Adomian (1963).

It is, of course, sometimes possible to solve for $x(t)$ as a function of $F(t)$ in the form

(1-17) $$x(t) = G(F(t))$$

a form similar to Eq. 1-6. In this event moments of $x(t)$ are determined in terms of moments of $G(F(t))$.

We introduced the nonlinear oscillator in order to prepare the reader for the phenomenon of turbulence. For a one-dimensional analog of turbulence $F(t)$ would usually be taken equal to zero and $m(x)$ and $k(x)$ would be determinate functions. The randomness would occur either because of a stochastic boundary condition $P(x(t_0))$ or, if we have a steady pipe-flow problem in mind, because there exists a stochastic solution to the basic deterministic equation.

I.2. A One-Dimensional Continuum Problem

The first point of the previous section was that a complete solution to a statistical problem means finding the most general probability density function of the dependent variable in terms of the most general probability density functions of any known statistical variables. Furthermore, a functional equation may usually be derived to determine the most general probability density function. (We did not show how this may be done; it will be shown in Chapter 3.)

The second point was to indicate that direct averaging procedures may be used profitably in very simple equations to determine nth-order moments in terms of known nth-order moments, but that in general this technique does not yield a useful set of equations unless approximations are made. In general any nth-order moment is determined by *all* statistical information available in the most general probability density function, *not* by the corresponding nth-order information alone. In order to attempt to find practical calculating techniques, we must make approximations and in this section we consider a simple (mathematically trivial) example to show how averaged equations such as Eq. 1-12 may be made to yield useful information. Note that the techniques given in this section are the prototypes of some of the techniques to be used in many of the later chapters.

Consider now the case of a statistically homogeneous medium with a random dielectric constant $\epsilon(\mathbf{x})$.* We wish to treat the problem of finding the statistical properties of the electric field of the medium if a constant average electric field is impressed upon the medium. We assume that we know all the statistical properties of $\epsilon(\mathbf{x})$. We follow here a discussion given by Beran and Molyneux (1963).

The equations governing the electric field are†

(1-18) $$\nabla \cdot [\epsilon(\mathbf{x})\mathbf{E}(\mathbf{x})] = 0$$

(1-19) $$\nabla \times \mathbf{E}(\mathbf{x}) = 0$$

We assume an infinite medium and suppose we may write the electric field in the form

(1-20) $$E_i(\mathbf{x}) = E_i'(\mathbf{x}) + \bar{E}_3 \delta_{i3}$$

where $\overline{E_i'(x)} = 0$ and $\bar{E}_3$ is a constant. We also write the dielectric constant in the form

(1-21) $$\epsilon(\mathbf{x}) = \bar{\epsilon} + \epsilon'(\mathbf{x})$$

where $\bar{\epsilon}$ is independent of position.

The three-dimensional problem will be treated in detail in Chapter 5. Here we will consider only the one-dimensional problem. In the one-dimensional case Eq. 1-19 is automatically satisfied and Eq. 1-18 reduces to

(1-22) $$\frac{d}{dz} \epsilon(z)E(z) = 0$$

where $E(z) \equiv E_3(z)$. ϵ and E vary only in the z ("three") direction.

Equation 1-20 may be written

(1-23) $$E(z) = \bar{E} + E'(z)$$

* By this we mean that all statistical properties of $\epsilon(\mathbf{x})$ are independent of absolute position. For example, $\bar{\epsilon}$ and $\overline{\epsilon^2}$ do not depend upon $\mathbf{x}$. Furthermore, functions such as $\overline{\epsilon(\mathbf{x}_1)\epsilon(\mathbf{x}_2)}$ depend only upon $\mathbf{x}_1 - \mathbf{x}_2$. This is discussed more fully in Chapter 2.

† Note that the form of the following equations govern the physical problems of heat conduction, electrical conduction, etc. In place of this problem of the electric field the reader may find it convenient to think in terms of variables with which he is more familiar.

The solution of Eq. 1-22 is (we drop the z argument now for convenience)

$$(1\text{-}24) \qquad\qquad \epsilon E = c_1$$

where in general c_1 is a statistical variable like ϵ and E but is independent of z.

In terms of E', $\bar{E}$, ϵ', and $\bar{\epsilon}$ we have

$$(1\text{-}25) \qquad\qquad \bar{\epsilon}E' + \epsilon'\bar{E} + \epsilon'E' = c_2 = c_1 - \bar{\epsilon}\bar{E}$$

Averaging Eq. 1-25 we find

$$\bar{c}_2 = \overline{\epsilon'E'}$$

Suppose, however, we now perform the integration

$$\lim_{Z \to \infty} \frac{1}{Z} \int_0^Z (\quad)\, dz$$

on both sides of Eq. 1-25. Then we should find, since we have assumed spatially homogeneous statistics, that

$$(1\text{-}26) \qquad\qquad \lim_{Z \to \infty} \frac{1}{Z} \int_0^Z E'\, dz = 0$$

$$\lim_{Z \to \infty} \frac{1}{Z} \int_0^Z \epsilon'\, dz = 0$$

$$\lim_{Z \to \infty} \frac{1}{Z} \int_0^Z \epsilon'E'\, dz = \overline{\epsilon'E'}$$

and from Eq. 1-25

$$\bar{c}_2 = \lim_{Z \to \infty} \frac{1}{Z} \int_0^Z c_2\, dz = c_2 = \overline{\epsilon'E'}$$

Thus $c_2 = \bar{c}_2$ and c_2 is not a statistical variable in this case. It is regretted that we had to introduce the concept of *spatial* averaging at this point and forced the reader to distinguish between a spatial average and a probabilistic average, but despite this small complication we could think of no simpler illustrative example.

Returning to Eq. 1-25 we have

(1-27)
$$\bar{\epsilon}E' + \epsilon'\bar{E} + \epsilon'E' = c_2$$

where $c_2 = \overline{\epsilon'E'}$ is a true constant.

Our object is to determine the statistical properties of E' in terms of the statistical properties of ϵ'. [In terms of our previous notation we wish to determine $P[E'(z)]$ in terms of $P[\epsilon'(z)]$.] This may be done in this case by solving Eq. 1-27 for E' in terms of ϵ', or the inverse. We find

(1-28a)
$$E' = \frac{c_2}{\bar{\epsilon} + \epsilon'} - \frac{\bar{E}\epsilon'}{\bar{\epsilon} + \epsilon'}$$

(1-28b)
$$\epsilon' = \frac{c_2}{\bar{E} + E'} - \frac{\bar{\epsilon}E'}{\bar{E} + E'}$$

In order to determine c_2 we average both sides of Eq. 1-28a. This yields

(1-29a)
$$0 = c_2 \overline{\frac{1}{\bar{\epsilon} + \epsilon'}} - \bar{E} \overline{\frac{\epsilon'}{\bar{\epsilon} + \epsilon'}}$$

and

(1-29b)
$$c_2 = \overline{\epsilon'E'} = \bar{E}\left(\frac{\overline{\epsilon'/(\bar{\epsilon} + \epsilon')}}{\overline{1/(\bar{\epsilon} + \epsilon')}}\right)$$

so that c_2 is determined from the known statistical properties of ϵ.

Equation 1-28 represents a transformation of variables between ϵ' and E'. This allows us to directly determine $P[E'(z)]$ from $P[\epsilon'(z)]$. For example if $P_1(\epsilon'(z_1))\,d\epsilon'(z_1)$ is given, then

(1-30)
$$P_1(\epsilon'(z_1))\,d\epsilon'(z_1) = \left\{P_1\left[\frac{c_2}{\bar{E} + E'(z_1)} - \frac{\bar{\epsilon}E'(z_1)}{\bar{E} + E'(z_1)}\right]\left|\frac{d\epsilon'(z_1)}{dE'(z_1)}\right|\right\}dE'(z_1)$$
$$= P_1(E'(z_1))\,dE'(z_1)$$

To calculate $\overline{E'^2}$ we square both sides of Eq. 1-28a and average. The result is

(1-30a) $$\overline{E'^2} = c_2{}^2\overline{\left[\frac{1}{\bar{\epsilon} + \epsilon'}\right]^2} - 2c_2\bar{E}\overline{\frac{\epsilon'}{(\bar{\epsilon} + \epsilon')^2}} + \bar{E}^2\overline{\left[\frac{\epsilon'}{\bar{\epsilon} + \epsilon'}\right]^2}$$

Suppose now that we wished to obtain a result for, say $\overline{\epsilon' E'}$, by directly taking averages of Eq. 1-25 instead of using Eq. 1-28. A procedure such as this is desirable since in more complex problems an equation analogous to Eq. 1-28 cannot be derived. (See Section 1.1.3.) As we have seen, if we average Eq. 1-25 we find that $c_2 = \overline{\epsilon' E'}$. Thus our basic equation is

$$(1\text{-}31) \qquad \bar{\epsilon} E' + \epsilon' \bar{E} + \epsilon' E' = \overline{\epsilon' E'}$$

where $\overline{\epsilon' E'}$ is unknown. In order to find $\overline{\epsilon' E'}$ let us next multiply Eq. 1-31 by ϵ' and then average. This yields

$$(1\text{-}32) \qquad \bar{\epsilon}\,\overline{\epsilon' E'} + \overline{\epsilon'^2}\,\bar{E} + \overline{\epsilon'^2 E'} = 0$$

or

$$(1\text{-}33) \qquad \overline{\epsilon' E'} = -\frac{\bar{E}}{\bar{\epsilon}}\,\overline{\epsilon'^2} - \frac{1}{\bar{\epsilon}}\,\overline{\epsilon'^2 E'}$$

That is, we find $\overline{\epsilon' E'}$ in terms of $\overline{\epsilon'^2}$ *and* $\overline{\epsilon'^2 E'}$ where $\overline{\epsilon'^2 E'}$ is an additional unknown function. If we now attempt to find another equation relating $\overline{\epsilon' E'}$ and $\overline{\epsilon'^2 E'}$, so that we may solve for both, we only compound our difficulties. For example, to find another equation multiply Eq. 1-31 by ϵ'^2 and average. This yields

$$(1\text{-}34) \qquad \bar{\epsilon}\,\overline{\epsilon'^2 E'} + \overline{\epsilon'^3} + \overline{\epsilon'^3 E'} = \overline{\epsilon'^2}\,\overline{\epsilon' E'}$$

which introduces the additional function $\overline{\epsilon'^3 E'}$. No matter how we try we can never get a closed set of equations in this manner; we always have one more unknown than equations.

Nevertheless, if we do proceed in this manner an interesting thing happens. Solving Eq. 1-32 we found

$$(1\text{-}35) \qquad \overline{\epsilon' E'} = -\frac{\bar{E}}{\bar{\epsilon}}\,\overline{\epsilon'^2} - \frac{1}{\bar{\epsilon}}\,\overline{\epsilon'^2 E'}$$

Solving Eqs. 1-33 and 1-34 simultaneously we find

$$(1\text{-}36) \qquad \left(1 + \frac{\overline{\epsilon'^2}}{\bar{\epsilon}^2}\right)\overline{\epsilon' E'} = -\frac{\overline{\epsilon'^2}}{\bar{\epsilon}}\bar{E} + \frac{\overline{\epsilon'^3}}{\bar{\epsilon}^2}\bar{E} + \frac{\overline{\epsilon'^3 E'}}{\bar{\epsilon}^2}$$

Multiplying Eq. 1-31 by ϵ'^3, averaging, and then solving the resultant equation and Eqs. 1-33 and 1-34 simultaneously we find

$$(1\text{-}37) \quad \left(1 + \frac{\overline{\epsilon'^2}}{\bar{\epsilon}^2} - \frac{\overline{\epsilon'^3}}{\bar{\epsilon}^3}\right)\overline{\epsilon'E'} = -\frac{\overline{\epsilon'^2}}{\bar{\epsilon}}\bar{E} + \frac{\overline{\epsilon'^3}}{\bar{\epsilon}^2}\bar{E} - \frac{\overline{\epsilon'^4\bar{E}}}{\bar{\epsilon}^3} - \frac{\overline{\epsilon'^4E'}}{\bar{\epsilon}^3}$$

By looking at Eqs. 1-35, 1-36, and 1-37 in sequence it is easy to see that the next equation involving $\overline{\epsilon'^5E'}$ must be

$$(1\text{-}38) \quad \left(1 + \frac{\overline{\epsilon'^2}}{\bar{\epsilon}^2} - \frac{\overline{\epsilon'^3}}{\bar{\epsilon}^3} + \frac{\overline{\epsilon'^4}}{\bar{\epsilon}^4}\right)\overline{\epsilon'E'} = -\frac{\overline{\epsilon'^2}}{\epsilon}\bar{E} + \frac{\overline{\epsilon'^3}}{\bar{\epsilon}^2}\bar{E} - \frac{\overline{\epsilon'^4\bar{E}}}{\bar{\epsilon}^3}$$
$$+ \frac{\overline{\epsilon'^5\bar{E}}}{\bar{\epsilon}^4} - \frac{\overline{\epsilon'^5E'}}{\bar{\epsilon}^4}$$

and in fact that the term

$$\left(1 + \frac{\overline{\epsilon'^2}}{\bar{\epsilon}^2} - \frac{\overline{\epsilon'^3}}{\bar{\epsilon}^3} + \frac{\overline{\epsilon'^4}}{\bar{\epsilon}^4}\right)$$

is the beginning of a series expansion of $\overline{[1/(1 + \epsilon'/\bar{\epsilon})]}$ and the term

$$E\bar{\epsilon}\left(\frac{\overline{\epsilon'^2}}{\bar{\epsilon}^2} - \frac{\overline{\epsilon'^3}}{\bar{\epsilon}^3} + \frac{\overline{\epsilon'^4}}{\bar{\epsilon}^4} - \frac{\overline{\epsilon'^5}}{\bar{\epsilon}^5}\right)$$

is the beginning of a series expansion of

$$-\left[\bar{E}\,\overline{\frac{\epsilon'^2}{\bar{\epsilon} + \epsilon'}}\right] = -\bar{E}\bar{\epsilon}\,\overline{\frac{\epsilon'}{\bar{\epsilon} + \epsilon'}}$$

From Eq. 1-33 we then find

$$(1\text{-}39) \quad \bar{\epsilon}\left[\overline{\frac{1}{\bar{\epsilon} + \epsilon'}}\right]\overline{\epsilon'E'} = \bar{E}\bar{\epsilon}\,\overline{\frac{\epsilon'}{\bar{\epsilon} + \epsilon'}}$$

Referring to Eq. 1-29, we see that we recover the true solution for $\overline{\epsilon'E'}$ in the limit $n \to \infty$ if we assume that in the limit $n \to \infty$, $\overline{\epsilon'^nE'}$ does not contribute appreciably to the value of $\overline{\epsilon'E'}$.

It is embarrassing to note that if $\overline{\epsilon'^n}/\bar{\epsilon}^n > 1$ the series diverges. Despite this fact, however, the formal summation yields the correct result (Eq. 1-29) even in this case. If we assume that $\overline{\epsilon'^n}/\bar{\epsilon}^n < 1$, no such difficulties arise; it is clear that we have developed a satisfactory iteration procedure for solving for $\overline{\epsilon' E'}$ using the averages of Eq. 1-27. Comparing our iterative solution to the correct solution (Eq. 1-29) we note that Eq. 1-35, neglecting the term $\overline{\epsilon'^2 E'}/\bar{\epsilon}$ is

$$(1\text{-}40) \qquad \overline{\epsilon' E'} = -\frac{\bar{E}}{\bar{\epsilon}}\,\overline{\epsilon'^2}$$

and thus provides a first approximation to the correct solution. Equation 1-36, neglecting the term $\overline{\epsilon'^3 E'}/\bar{\epsilon}^2$, is

$$(1\text{-}41) \qquad \left(1 + \frac{\overline{\epsilon'^2}}{\bar{\epsilon}^2}\right)\overline{\epsilon' E'} = -\bar{E}\left(\frac{\overline{\epsilon'^2}}{\bar{\epsilon}} - \frac{\overline{\epsilon'^3}}{\bar{\epsilon}^2}\right)$$

providing a second approximation to the correct solution. Higher approximations may be derived in a similar manner.

There is, of course, no utility in proceeding in this manner in this particular example. In many problems of interest, however, the equation corresponding to Eq. 1-25 cannot be inverted to yield a solution for E' in terms of ϵ'. It is often a complicated partial differential equation. The only method of attack is some variation of the iterative procedure outlined above or some assumption of closure.* In the three-dimensional problem represented by Eqs. 1-18 and 1-19 we cannot get a solution for $E_i'(\mathbf{x})$ in terms of $\epsilon'(\mathbf{x})$, and an approximation procedure similar to that presented above is the only useful method we have at present for determining statistical information about $E_i'(\mathbf{x})$ from Eqs. 1-18 and 1-19. This procedure will be given in detail in Chapter 5.

1.3. Discussion

In this introduction we have given two very simple examples to illustrate the nature of the statistical solution of a problem. The language has often been imprecise, and minor difficulties have purposely been glossed over in many cases in order to fix our attention on a central

---

* Assumptions of closure will be discussed in later chapters. An assumption of closure is an assumption about the form of an nth-order moment in terms of lower-order moments. For example, we could have derived a determinate set of equations for $\overline{\epsilon' E_1}$ and $\overline{\epsilon'^2 E'}$ by assuming in Eq. 1-36 that $\overline{\epsilon'^3 E'} = \overline{\epsilon'^2}\,\overline{\epsilon' E'}$.

point. We shall now proceed to a more careful presentation of our subject. In Chapter 2 we shall present a discussion of probability theory and functional analysis which we hope will give the reader the mathematical background to understand our subject in detail. In Chapter 3 we shall present various aspects of the general formulations now in use. We shall cover the functional formulation, statistical moment equations, and various variational techniques. In the subsequent chapters we shall discuss the details of solutions of various continuum problems that have been treated statistically. We cannot in single chapters exhaustively cover such voluminous topics as turbulence or the theory of partial coherence. We hope, however, to acquaint the reader with the important ideas in the fields we cover. Chapters 2 and 3 will be rather formal. The latter chapters will be presented from a more physical point of view, and each chapter will begin with a discussion of the basic physical problem.

CHAPTER 2

Definitions and Mathematical Preliminaries

In this chapter we shall review basic ideas in probability theory and in the theory of functionals. The review will be given with the needs of this book clearly in mind and hence will not be comprehensive. For a thorough treatment of probability theory we refer the reader to Cramér (1946), Kolmogorov (1950),* and Loève (1962). In the early sections we shall follow the development of Kolmogorov (1950). For a very readable introduction to probability theory we suggest Davenport and Root (1958). The discussion of the theory of functionals will be based on Volterra (1959).†

2.1. Probability Theory

2.1.1. Axiomatization and the Concept of an Ensemble

Probability theory is properly developed from a series of axioms stating the requisite properties of a non-negative real number called the probability of an occurrence. Kolmogorov (1950) lists the following definitions and axioms (Axiom I is paraphrased): Let E be a collection of elements, ξ, η, ζ, . . . , which we shall call elementary events, and let F be a set of subsets of E; the elements of the set F will be called random events.

    I. F contains within it the sum, difference, and product of all of the subsets of E.

    II. F contains the set E.

    III. To each set A in F is assigned a nonnegative real number $P(A)$. This number is called the probability of the event A.

---

* *Kolmogorov* is often spelled *Kolmogoroff* in English articles.

† 1959 is the date of the Dover edition. The original English edition was published in 1929 and an earlier Spanish edition was published in 1927.

IV. $P(E) = 1$.

V. If A and B have no element in common, then*

$$P(A + B) = P(A) + P(B)$$

A system of sets F, together with a definite assignment of numbers $P(A)$, satisfying Axioms I–V, is called a field of probability.

In tossing a true die, for example, the collection of events in E, ξ, η, $\zeta, \ldots, \omega$ are the six events: $\xi \equiv$ a "one" showing, $\eta \equiv$ a "two" showing, $\zeta \equiv$ a "three" showing, $\ldots, \omega \equiv$ a "six" showing. A set contained in F could be $\eta \equiv$ a "two" showing; or $\eta + \xi \equiv$ (a "two" or a "three" showing); or $\xi + \eta + \omega \equiv$ (a "one" or a "two" or a "six" showing); and so on. The probability associated with the set η is $\frac{1}{6}$, $P(\eta) = \frac{1}{6}$. The probability associated with the set $\eta + \xi$ (a set in F) is $\frac{2}{6}$, $P(\eta + \xi) = \frac{2}{6}$, and since η and ξ have no elements in common we note that $P(\eta + \xi) = P(\eta) + P(\xi) = \frac{1}{6} + \frac{1}{6} = \frac{2}{6}$. Similarly, $P(\xi + \eta + \omega) = \frac{3}{6}$ and

$$P(E) = P(\xi) + P(\eta) + P(\zeta) + \cdots + P(\omega)$$
$$= \frac{1}{6} + \frac{1}{6} + \frac{1}{6} + \cdots + \frac{1}{6} = 1$$

To consider what happens when the die is thrown two times we must have a set of 36 elementary events: the events $(1, 1)$, $(1, 2)$, $\ldots$, $(1, 6)$, $(2, 1)$, $\ldots$, $(6, 6)$. Thus the probability of throwing at least one "four" in the two throws is equal to the probability of one of the following events occurring: $(1, 4)$, $(2, 4)$, $(3, 4)$, $(5, 4)$, $(6, 4)$, $(4, 1)$, $(4, 2)$, $(4, 3)$, $(4, 4)$, $(4, 5)$ or $(4, 6)$. Since the probability of each event is $\frac{1}{36}$ and since the events contain no element in common, the probability of throwing at least one "four" is $\frac{11}{36}$. The set comprising all the elementary events containing a four is a set contained in F.

In order to relate the mathematical formulation to the physical world we identify the elements of E with the possible outcomes of an experiment. In the first of the foregoing paragraphs the experiment was the tossing of the die, and the possible outcomes of the experiment were the showing of a "one," a "two," $\ldots$, or a "six." For the foregoing mathematical formulation to be appropriate for the description of the die problem we sacrificed our usual deterministic approach to nature and assumed that we had no knowledge of the orientation of the die as it was being thrown.

* $A + B$ contains all the elements occurring in either A or B.

In any classical physical problem that we wish to treat statistically we assume that we may make a very large number of experiments that are the same in their large details (macroscopically similar) but vary in an undetermined manner in their small details (microscopically different). This set of experiments is called an ensemble. In the die problem the macroscopic similarities are that the thrower of the die always takes the same die, shakes it in his hand, and throws it. The microscopic differences are that as the thrower shakes the die in his hand the detailed motions of the die are always different and unknown.

If we accept the possibility of randomness arising in our *classical* deterministic universe through this macroscopic–microscopic duality, the next difficulty that we face is the assignment of the numbers $P(A)$. There are quite reasonable grounds for choosing $P(\xi) = \frac{1}{6}$ in the above example, but the problems we shall face in this book are more like the problem of determining $P(\xi)$ for what we think is a loaded die.

The most obvious approach for determining $P(\xi)$ for a loaded die is to toss the die (always in the same macroscopic fashion) a very large number of times (say, n) and note the number of times (say, m) that the event (a "one" showing) has occurred. We then consider it reasonable to set the equality $P(\xi) = m/n$ where the ratio m/n is termed the relative frequency. The difficulty is that the ratio m/n fluctuates as $n \to \infty$ and there is no assurance that it tends to a definite limit. It is easy to imagine the possibility, if not probability, of 1000 successive "ones" showing up even in what we consider to be a true die.

There is a large amount of literature discussing this difficulty and it is not our purpose to discuss the problem here. We adopt a pragmatic approach and assume that the limit m/n does indeed exist. We further assert that we may, with little chance of error, infer $P(\xi)$ (and other needed probabilities) from the ratio m/n (and ratios such as this) if both m and n are very large compared to unity. By little chance of error we mean here that when we predict other statistical quantities using the knowledge $P(\xi) \approx m/n$, our predictions will be experimentally verified.

All the physical problems that we treat in this book will be first set up in terms of an ensemble of experiments. Each experiment will be presumed to be performed the same way macroscopically but to differ from other experiments in a detailed microscopic description. The probability of an occurrence, say the probability of the forcing function $F(t)$ of Chapter 1 having a value between $F(t_1)$ and $F(t_1) + dF(t_1)$ at time t_1, $P_1(F(t_1))\, dF(t_1)$, will be assumed to be the value one would measure experimentally by relative frequency arguments if a very large number of experiments were performed to determine the frequency of the occurrence of $F(t_1)$ at time t_1.*

In terms of the axioms given previously (and in the footnote below) a value between $F(t_1)$ and $F(t_1) + dF(t_1)$ is an elementary event. With the assignment of the positive number $P_1(F(t)) \, dF(t)$ to all such elementary events we may construct a field of probability. (In the axiomatic approach the origin of these numbers is irrelevant.) There are a large number of theorems that have been proved for a field of probability and we may now apply them if the need arises. For example, a number of theorems associated with independence and convergence are available to us. In this chapter we shall not prove any theorems from the axioms. We have set the axioms down, however, to show the reader the nature of the postulates that are necessary for proof of any of the theorems that we shall subsequently state. Much of the chapter will be taken up with the introduction of additional definitions that are useful in physical problems associated with a continuum.

2.1.2. Conditional Probabilities and Independence

Before proceeding to a discussion of probability distribution functions and probability density functions, which we need in order to give a precise meaning to the statistical continuum ideas that we presented in Chapter 1, we shall give here a very brief discussion of conditional probabilities and the concept of independence in terms of discrete events. The conditional probability $P_A(B)$ is defined as

$$P_A(B) = \frac{P(AB)}{P(A)}$$

---

* Axioms I–V given by Kolmogorov (1950) are adequate for a system with a finite number of alternatives. For a system with an infinite number of alternatives (actually the only kind of systems that we shall consider) he presents a sixth axiom which is necessary. Therefore, in order to make our presentation more complete we list this axiom here (somewhat paraphrased):

VI. For a complete sequence of events $A_1, A_2, \ldots, A_n \cdots$ such that the elementary events in A_n are contained among the elementary events in A_m $(m > n)$ (i.e., $A_1 \supset A_2 \supset \cdots \supset A_n \supset \cdots$), then for an event contained in A_1 and A_2 and $\ldots$ and A_n and $\ldots$, $\lim\limits_{n \to \infty} P(A_n) = 0$.

for $P(A) > 0$. The symbol $P(AB)$ represents the probability that the elementary events that lie in *both* A and B occur. This may be written

$$P(AB) = P_A(B)P(A)$$

and interpreted in words as: the probability that A and B both occur, $[P(AB)]$ is equal to the probability of B occurring upon assuming the hypothesis that A has occurred $[P_A(B)]$, multiplied by the probability of A occurring $[P(A)]$.

Noting similarly that

$$P(AB) = P_B(A)P(B)$$

we arrive at a simplified form of Bayes' theorem: i.e.,

$$P_B(A) = \frac{P(A)P_A(B)}{P(B)}$$

A concept of independence follows from consideration of the form of $P(AB)$. We define two events to be mutually independent if

$$P(AB) = P(B)P(A)$$

Hence, if two events are mutually independent, $P_A(B) = P(B)$. That is, the probability of B occurring upon assuming the hypothesis that A has occurred is equal only to the probability of B occurring. It is independent of the hypothesis of the occurrence of A.

2.1.3. Probability Distribution Functions

Consider here that our random elementary event may take on any real number from $-\infty$ to $+\infty$. We denote the possible choices by u and term u a random variable. We may, for example, think of the possible values available for one component of the velocity of a turbulent fluid at some point $\mathbf{x}$ at a particular time. This number may fall anywhere on the real axis (neglecting for the moment the violation of energy conservation for really large magnitudes of velocity). The function that specifies the probability that the event (component of velocity) lies between $-\infty$ and u is denoted by $F_1(u)$ and is termed the probability distribution function. The statement "u lies between a and b" means here that $a \leqslant u < b$.

Since the event must lie somewhere on the real axis, we immediately note from the definition of $F_1(u)$ that

$$\lim_{u \to -\infty} F_1(u) = 0$$

$$\lim_{u \to \infty} F_1(u) = 1$$

The probability that u lies between $u = a$ and $u = b$ $(b > a)$ is the probability that $u < b$ $(-\infty \leqslant u < b)$ minus the probability that $u < a$ $(-\infty \leqslant u < a)$. Thus

$$P_1(a \leqslant u < b) = F_1(b) - F_1(a)$$

is the probability that u lies between a and b.

The definition of $F_1(u)$ ensures that it is always positive. It also ensures that $P_1(a \leqslant u < b)$ is positive since the event $-\infty \leqslant u < b$ includes the event $-\infty \leqslant u < a$ when $b > a$ and hence $F_1(b) \geqslant F_1(a)$. $F_1(u)$ is thus a monotonically increasing function.

If we wish to generalize our distribution function and to determine a joint distribution stating the probabilistic information in all three components of velocity, we need only to consider a three-dimensional space (u, v, w axes). We define $F_3(u, v, w)$ to be the probability that the u event (x component of velocity) lies between $-\infty$ and u, and that the v event (y component of velocity) lies between $-\infty$ and v, and that the w event (z component of velocity) lies between $-\infty$ and w. From this definition we have

$$\lim_{u \to -\infty} F_3(u, v, w) = 0$$

$$\lim_{v \to -\infty} F_3(u, v, w) = 0$$

$$\lim_{w \to -\infty} F_3(u, v, w) = 0$$

$$\lim_{\substack{u \to \infty \\ v \to \infty \\ w \to \infty}} \{F_3(u, v, w)\} = 1$$

The function $\lim_{u \to \infty} F_3(u, v, w)$ is independent of u and may be denoted simply by $F_2(v, w)$. It states the probability that v lies between $-\infty$ and v, and that w lies between $-\infty$ and w, and that u may be *anywhere*. It gives no information about u and is a two-dimensional probability distribution function. Similarly, the function

$$\lim_{\substack{u \to \infty \\ v \to \infty}} F_3(u, v, w)$$

is independent of u and v and may be denoted by $F_1(w)$. It states the probability that w lies between $-\infty$ and w, and that u and v may lie anywhere. It gives no information about u and v and is a one-dimensional probability distribution. The function $F_1(u)$ introduced in the first paragraph of this section is defined as

$$F_1(u) = \lim_{\substack{v \to \infty \\ w \to \infty}} F_3(u, v, w)$$

when considering a three-dimensional velocity field.

The probability that u lies between a and b, and that v lies between c and d, $P_2(a \leqslant u < b, c \leqslant v < d)$, is

$$P_2(a \leqslant u < b, c \leqslant v < d) = F_2(b, d) - F_2(a, d) - F_2(b, c) + F_2(a, c)$$

We give here first the two-dimensional form rather than that of the three-dimensional case since the reader will find it easier to convince himself of its correctness rather than for the three-dimensional case. Here we need only draw a two-dimensional diagram and then subtract areas. In three dimensions we have

$$P_3(a \leqslant u < b, c \leqslant v < d, e \leqslant w < f) = F_3(b, d, f) - F_3(b, d, e)$$

$$- F_3(b, c, f) - F_3(a, d, f) + F_3(b, c, e) + F_3(a, d, e)$$

$$+ F_3(a, c, f) - F_3(a, c, e)$$

The nth-order probability distribution may be defined in the same manner as the one- and three-dimensional forms. Let u_1 be the x component of velocity at the point $\mathbf{x}_1$; u_2, the x component of velocity at point $\mathbf{x}_2$, ... ; and u_n, the x component of velocity of the point $\mathbf{x}_n$. For convenience, here we let the time of measurement at all space points be the same. $F_n(a_1, a_2, \ldots, a_n)$ is the probability that u_1 lies between $-\infty$ and a_1, and that u_2 lies between $-\infty$ and a_2, and that ... , and that u_n lies between $-\infty$ and a_n.

Again

$$\lim_{u_j \to -\infty} [F_n(u_1, u_2, \ldots, u_n)] = 0 \qquad (j = 1, 2, \ldots, n)$$

$$\lim_{\text{all } u_j \to \infty} [F_n(u_1, u_2, \ldots, u_n)] = 1$$

We may also again set any one of the u_j equal to ∞ and thus obtain a probability distribution of dimensionality $n - 1$. That is

$$\lim_{u_n \to \infty} [F_n(u_1, u_2, \ldots, u_{n-1}, u_n)] = F_{n-1}(u_1, u_2, \ldots, u_{n-1})$$

is the probability that u_1 lies between $-\infty$ and $a_1, \ldots,$ and that u_{n-1} lies between $-\infty$ and a_{n-1}, and that u_n may have any value.

A form for

$$P_n(a_1 \leqslant u_1 < b_1, a_2 \leqslant u_2 < b_2, \ldots, a_n \leqslant u_n < b_n)$$

may be derived in terms of the $F_n(u_1, u_2, \ldots, u_n)$; but since it is a somewhat complicated expression, we shall omit it.

In this book we shall need an expression that is even more general than the n-dimensional probability distribution function. In the foregoing we have assumed that n is a finite integer. It was "3" in the case in which we considered three velocity components at one point. If we choose to find the probability distribution function corresponding to the three-dimensional velocities at two distinct points, we should require $n = 6$, for there are three velocity components at each point and there are two points. There is, however, no reason to limit ourselves to only two points. In continuum theory there are an infinite number of points; thus a complete specification of a turbulent velocity field, for example, requires a joint probability distribution over an infinite number of points.

The function $F_n(u_1, u_2, \ldots, u_n)$ is replaced by a functional $F[u(\mathbf{x})]$ when we consider the joint probability distribution over an infinite number of points.* The discrete index n is replaced by the continuous index $\mathbf{x}$. $F[u(\mathbf{x})]$ depends now upon the entire function $u(\mathbf{x})$, not just the value of $u(\mathbf{x})$ at n discrete points $\mathbf{x} = \mathbf{x}_1, \mathbf{x} = \mathbf{x}_2, \ldots, \mathbf{x} = \mathbf{x}_n$. In the case of a turbulent field, $F_n(u_1, u_2, \ldots, u_n)$ may be defined as the probability that u_1 (the x component of velocity at point 1) lies between $-\infty$ and u_1, and that u_2 lies between $-\infty$ and $u_2, \ldots,$ and that u_n lies between $-\infty$ and u_n. Considering the three velocity components (u, v, w), we require $F_{3n}(u_1, u_2, \ldots, u_n, v_1, v_2, \ldots, v_n, w_1, w_2, \ldots, w_n)$. The generalization of $F_{3n}(u_1, u_2, \ldots, u_n, v_1, v_2, \ldots, v_n, w_1, w_2, \ldots, w_n)$ is $F[u(\mathbf{x}), v(\mathbf{x}), w(\mathbf{x})]$, where the n discrete points $1, 2, \ldots, n$ are replaced by the continuum of points $\mathbf{x}$. $F[u(\mathbf{x}), v(\mathbf{x}),$

---

* If this paragraph is unclear, the reader should return to it after reading Section 2.2 on the theory of functionals.

$w(\mathbf{x})$] is the probability of the realization of an *entire* velocity field such that $u(\mathbf{x})$ lies between $-\infty$ and $u(\mathbf{x})$, and that $v(\mathbf{x})$ lies between $-\infty$ and $v(\mathbf{x})$, and that $w(\mathbf{x})$ lies between $-\infty$ and $w(\mathbf{x})$. Despite the compressed notation, $F[u(\mathbf{x})]$ contains infinitely more information than $F_n(u_1, u_2, \ldots, u_n)$. $F_n(u_1, u_2, \ldots, u_n)$ considers the probability of the u component of velocity at n discrete points whereas $F[u(\mathbf{x})]$ considers the probability of the u component of velocity at a continuum of points. $F[u(\mathbf{x})]$ contains within it the information given by $F_n(u_1, u_2, \ldots, u_n)$ and thus we may consider $F[u(\mathbf{x})]$ as a limit of $F_n(u_1, u_2, \ldots, u_n)$ as $n \to \infty$.

We shall consider the notion of a functional in more detail later in this chapter (Section 2.2). Now we shall consider the concept of a probability density and begin with the case of a discrete number of variables.

2.1.4. Probability Density Functions

$F_1(u)$ has been defined as the probability that u lies between $-\infty$ and u. $F_1(b) - F_1(a) = P_1(a \leqslant u < b)$ is thus the probability that u lies between a and b. It is useful to consider the case in which a and b differ by an infinitesimal amount da such that $b = a + da$. Then $F_1(a + da) - F_1(a)$ is the probability that u lies between a and $a + da$. If we may assume that $F_1(u)$ is a continuous function possessing continuous finite derivatives, then we may write

$$F_1(a + da) - F_1(a) = \frac{dF_1}{da}\, da$$

and define dF_1/da, or rather, considering u as our variable, dF_1/du as a probability density. It is common to use the notation

$$P_1(u) \equiv \frac{dF_1}{du}$$

and to describe $P_1(u)\, du$ as the probability that u lies between u and $u + du$.

Conversely

$$F_1(u) = \int\limits_{-\infty}^{u} P_1(u')\, du'$$

We note that by construction, since $F_1(b) \geqslant F_1(a)$, $P_1(u)$ is always positive and

$$\int_{-\infty}^{\infty} P_1(u') \, du' = 1$$

The concept of a probability density function is appropriate for describing the properties of the x component of velocity at some point in a turbulent fluid. We assume that the velocity component is a continuous variable that can take on the value of any one of the real numbers.

The concept of a probability density may be extended to more than one variable. For the two-dimensional case

$$P_2(a \leqslant u < a + da, c \leqslant v < c + dc) = F_2(a + da, c + dc)$$
$$- F_2(a, c + dc) - F_2(a + da, c) + F_2(a, c)$$

In the limit $da \to 0$, $dc \to 0$ we have

$$P_2(a \leqslant u < a + da, c \leqslant v < c + dc)$$
$$= \left[\frac{\partial F_2(a, c + dc)}{\partial a} - \frac{\partial F_2(a, c)}{\partial a} \right] da = \frac{\partial^2 F_2(a, c) \, da \, dc}{\partial a \, \partial c}$$

Proceeding as in the foregoing we define $P_2(u, v)$ as

$$P_2(u, v) \equiv \frac{\partial^2 F_2(u, v)}{\partial u \, \partial v}$$

and say that $P_2(u, v) \, du \, dv$ is the probability that u lies between u and $u + du$ and that v lies between v and $v + dv$. By construction $P_2(u, v)$ is positive and

$$F_2(u, v) = \int_{-\infty}^{u} \int_{-\infty}^{v} P_2(u', v') \, du' \, dv'$$

$$F_2(\infty, \infty) = 1 = \int_{-\infty}^{\infty} \int_{\infty}^{\infty} P_2(u', v') \, du' \, dv'$$

If u and v are the x and y velocity components of the turbulent velocity at some point, this mode of description is appropriate since both components may take on a continuum of values.

This procedure may be extended to the case of n variables. We have

$$P_n(a_1 \leqslant u_1 < a_1 + da_1,\ a_2 \leqslant u_2 < a_2 + da_2,\ \ldots,$$

$$a_n \leqslant u_n < a_n + da_n) = \frac{\partial^n F_n(a_1, a_2, \ldots, a_n)}{\partial a_1\, \partial a_2 \cdots \partial a_n}\, da_1\, da_2 \cdots da_n$$

Denoting the nth derivative of $F_n(u_1, u_2, \ldots, u_n)$ by $P_n(u_1, u_2, \ldots, u_n)$ we have

$$P_n(u_1, u_2, \ldots, u_n) \equiv \frac{\partial^n F_n(u_1, u_2, \ldots, u_n)}{\partial u_1\, \partial u_2 \cdots \partial u_n}$$

and we describe $P_n(u_1, u_2, \ldots, u_n)$ as the probability that u_1 lies between u_1 and $u_1 + du_1$, and that u_2 lies between u_2 and $u_2 + du_2, \ldots,$ and that u_n lies between u_n and $u_n + du_n$.*

The integral relation between $F_n(u_1, u_2, \ldots, u_n)$ and $P_n(u_1, u_2, \ldots, u_n)$ is

$$F_n(u_1, u_2, \ldots, u_n)$$

$$= \int_{-\infty}^{u_n} \cdots \int_{-\infty}^{u_2} \int_{-\infty}^{u_1} P_n(u_1', u_2', \ldots, u_n')\, du_1'\, du_2' \cdots du_n'$$

and we have

$$F_n(\infty, \infty, \ldots, \infty) = 1$$

$$= \int_{-\infty}^{\infty} \cdots \int_{-\infty}^{\infty} \int_{-\infty}^{\infty} P_n(u_1', u_2', \ldots, u_n')\, du_1'\, du_2' \cdots du_n'$$

We have previously denoted $F_n(u_1, u_2, \ldots, u_{n-1}, \infty)$ as simply a function of $n - 1$ variables. We wrote

(2-1) $F_{n-1}(u_1, u_2, \ldots, u_{n-1}) = F_n(u_1, u_2, \ldots, u_{n-1}, \infty)$

This indicated that the variable u_n can take any value between $-\infty$ and $+\infty$ and hence we no longer need to consider it when we determine the

---

* In this description it is proper to say that u_1 lies between u_1 and $u_1 + du_1$. The wording is cumbersome, however, and in later chapters we may on occasion just say that a variable has the probability of having a certain value rather than lying between two values separated by an infinitesmal amount. The correct wording must nevertheless always be understood in these cases.

probability distribution function of the remaining $n - 1$ variables. A similar relationship exists between the probability density functions, but here the relationship requires an integration. We have

$$P_{n-1}(u_1, u_2, \ldots, u_{n-1}) = \int_{-\infty}^{\infty} P_n(u_1, u_2, \ldots, u_{n-1}, u_n)\, du_n$$

This follows directly from Eq. 2-1. In general we have

(2-2) $P_j(u_1, u_2, \ldots, u_j)$

$$= \int_{-\infty}^{\infty} \cdots \int_{-\infty}^{\infty} P_n(u_1, u_2, \ldots, u_j, u_{j+1}, \ldots, u_n)\, du_{j+1} \cdots du_n$$

By construction of P_n we may satisfy ourselves that in general P_n cannot be completely specified by P_{n-j}, $(j > 0)$. P_{n-1} gives us the probability density associated with the $n - 1$ variables, $x_1, x_2, \ldots, x_{n-1}$. The value of x_n is arbitrary. P_n tells us how the probability of obtaining the values of $x_1, x_2, \ldots, x_{n-1}$ is dependent upon a particular value of x_n. Even the knowledge that in some cases the probability of obtaining a sequence of values $x_1, x_2, \ldots, x_{n-1}$ is independent of the value of x_n, is information that is contained in P_n but not in P_{n-1}.

On returning again to the example of a turbulent velocity field, $P_n(u_1, u_2, \ldots, u_n)\, du_1\, du_2 \cdots du_n$ may be interpreted as the probability that the x component of velocity at point $\mathbf{x}_1$ lies between u_1 and $u_1 + du_1$, and that the x component of velocity at point $\mathbf{x}_2$ lies between u_2 and $u_2 + du_2, \ldots$, and that the x component of velocity at point $\mathbf{x}_n$ lies between u_n and $u_n + du_n$.

For continuous fields we require a function such as $P_n(u_1, u_2, \ldots, u_n)$ in the limit as $n \to \infty$. We denote this function as $P[u(\mathbf{x})]$ where the points $\mathbf{x}_1, \mathbf{x}_2, \ldots, \mathbf{x}_n$ are replaced by the continuous variable $\mathbf{x}$. We shall defer discussion of $P[u(\mathbf{x})]$ until we have discussed the concept of functionals and derivatives of functionals. (See Section 2.2.)

It is frequently necessary to determine

$$P_n(s_1, s_2, \ldots, s_n)$$

from

$$P_n(u_1, u_2, \ldots, u_n)$$

if we have n unique relations of the form

$$s_j = g_j(u_1, u_2, \ldots, u_n)$$

where we require that the Jacobian

$$J = \frac{\partial(u_1, u_2, \ldots, u_n)}{\partial(s_1, s_2, \ldots, s_n)}$$

be nonzero at all points.

From the definition of P we have

$$P_n(u_1, u_2, \ldots, u_n) \, du_1 \, du_2 \cdots du_n = P_n(s_1, s_2, \ldots, s_n) \, ds_1 \, ds_2 \cdots ds_n$$

where u_j and s_k are related as given previously. The n-dimensional volume elements are related by the equation

$$du_1 \, du_2 \cdots du_n = |J| \, ds_1 \, ds_2 \cdots ds_n$$

Thus we find

$$P_n(s_1, s_2, \ldots, s_n) = |J| \, P_n(u_1(s_j), u_2(s_j), \ldots, u_n(s_j))$$

2.1.5. Mathematical Expectations

The mathematical expectation E of a function $g(u)$, where u is a random variable, is defined as

$$(2\text{-}3) \qquad \overline{g(u)} \equiv E(g(u)) \equiv \int_{-\infty}^{\infty} g(u) P_1(u) \, du$$

where $P_1(u)$ is the probability density function. When $g(u) = u$, for example,

$$\bar{u} \equiv E(u) \equiv \int_{-\infty}^{\infty} u P_1(u) \, du$$

$\bar{u}$ is called the average value of the random variable u. In the turbulent velocity example $\bar{u}_1$ is the average value of the x component of velocity at the point $\mathbf{x}_1$.

For the nth order case we define the expectation value of the function g of n random variables $u_1, u_2, \ldots, u_n$, as

$$(2\text{-}4) \quad \overline{g(u_1, u_2, \ldots, u_n)} \equiv E(g(u_1, u_2, \ldots, u_n))$$

$$= \int_{-\infty}^{\infty} \cdots \int_{-\infty}^{\infty} \int_{-\infty}^{\infty} g(u_1, u_2, \ldots, u_n) P_n(u_1, u_2, \ldots, u_n) \, du_1 \, du_2 \cdots du_n$$

We defer consideration of the expectation value of the functional $g(u(\mathbf{x}))$ until Section 2.2.

In Chapter 1 we spent much of the time considering the determination of expectation values. We recognize functions such as $\overline{F(t_1)}$, $\overline{F(t_1)F(t_2)}$, etc., as expectation values that are associated with probability density functions of the form $P_n(F(t_1), F(t_2), \ldots, F(t_n))$. For example

$$\overline{F(t_1)} = E(F(t_1)) = \int_{-\infty}^{\infty} F(t_1)P_1(F(t_1))\, dF(t_1)$$

$$\overline{F(t_1)F(t_2)} = E(F(t_1)F(t_2))$$

$$= \int_{-\infty}^{\infty} \int_{-\infty}^{\infty} F(t_1)F(t_2)P_2(F(t_1), F(t_2))\, dF(t_1)\, dF(t_2)$$

We shall now devote a few subsections to a discussion of a number of expectation values that occur very frequently.

2.1.5.1. Characteristic Functions. The characteristic function $M(v)$ is defined in the following manner for the one-dimensional case

$$(2\text{-}5) \qquad M_1(v) \equiv E(e^{ivu}) = \int_{-\infty}^{\infty} e^{ivu}P_1(u)\, du$$

That is, $M_1(v)$ is the Fourier transform of $P_1(u)$. By setting $v = 0$ we note immediately that

$$M_1(0) = \int_{-\infty}^{\infty} P_1(u)\, du = 1$$

Furthermore, since $P_1(u)$ is always positive $|M_1(v)| \leqslant M_1(0) = 1$.

The characteristic function may be defined for n variables $u_1, u_2, \ldots, u_n$ analogously. Here

$$(2\text{-}6) \quad M_n(v_1, v_2, \ldots, v_n) = E\left(\exp\left[i\sum_{k=1}^{n} v_k u_k\right]\right)$$

$$= \int_{-\infty}^{\infty} \cdots \int_{-\infty}^{\infty} \int_{-\infty}^{\infty} \exp\left[i\sum_{k=1}^{n} v_k u_k\right] P_n(u_1, u_2, \ldots, u_n)\, du_1\, du_2 \cdots du_n$$

We have now

$$M_n(0, 0, \ldots, 0) = 1$$

$$|M_n(v_1, v_2, \ldots, v_n)| \leqslant 1$$

Just as the integral

$$\int_{-\infty}^{\infty} P_n(u_1, u_2, \ldots, u_n)\, du_n$$

reduces the probability density function to a function of $n - 1$ variables, we see that setting $v_n = 0$ reduces the function $M_n(v_1, v_2, \ldots, v_{n-1}, v_n)$ to the function $M_n(v_1, v_2, \ldots, v_{n-1})$ where

$$M_n(v_1, v_2, \ldots, v_{n-1}) = \int_{-\infty}^{\infty} \cdots \int_{-\infty}^{\infty} \int_{-\infty}^{\infty} \exp \left[i \sum_{k}^{n-1} v_k u_k \right]$$

$$\times P_n(u_1, u_2, \ldots, u_{n-1})\, du_1\, du_2 \cdots du_{n-1}$$

The extension of M to infinitely many variables involves the concept of a functional and will be considered in Section 2.2. We shall consider next those expectation values called moments. There is an intimate connection between the moments and derivatives of M with respect to v. We shall explore this relation in the next section.

2.1.5.2. Moments of the Form $\overline{u^n}$. The moments of the probability density function, $P(u)$, are defined as the expectation value $E(u^n)$. We have

(2-7) $$\overline{u^n} \equiv E(u^n) = \int_{-\infty}^{\infty} u^n P_1(u)\, du$$

As we mentioned above, $\bar{u}$ is the mean value of u. The moment $\overline{u^2}$ is termed the mean square value of u. The physical interpretation of the second moment ($n = 2$) is best given in terms of the difference of the moments, $\sigma^2 = \overline{u^2} - \bar{u}^2$, which is termed the variance. It is easy to show that

(2-8) $$\sigma^2 = \overline{u^2} - \bar{u}^2 = \int_{-\infty}^{\infty} (u - \bar{u})^2 P_1(u)\, du$$

since in the integral $\bar{u}$ is not a function of u.

The variance σ^2 or its square root σ, called the standard deviation, is a measure of the magnitude of the fluctuations of a random quantity about its mean value. In turbulent flow through a pipe the velocity is usually written in the form $u_1 = \bar{u}_1 + u_1'$ where u_1' is the fluctuation of a velocity component about the mean velocity at the point $\mathbf{x}_1$. Here $\overline{u_1'} = 0$. $\sigma_1 = (\overline{u_1'^2})^{1/2}$ is usually very close in numerical value to the average value of the magnitude of u_1'. That is, σ_1 is usually of the same order as $\overline{|u_1'|}$. We do not often encounter the quantity $\overline{|u'|}$ since the absolute value sign makes it difficult to treat analytically.

The third-order moment $\overline{(u - \bar{u})^3}$ indicates the skewness or lack of symmetry of the distribution. As one would expect, each higher moment in its turn gives some additional information about the structure of $P_1(u)$. In fact, from a complete knowledge of the moments of $P_1(u)$ one can often reconstruct $P_1(u)$. In order to see this let us consider again the one-dimensional characteristic function

$$(2\text{-}9) \qquad M_1(v) = \int_{-\infty}^{\infty} e^{iuv} P_1(u)\, du$$

The exponential function e^{ivu} may be expanded in the series

$$e^{ivu} = \sum_{n=0}^{\infty} \frac{(ivu)^n}{n!}$$

Substituting this series into Eq. 2-9 and assuming that we may interchange the summation and the integration, we have

$$(2\text{-}10) \qquad M_1(v) = \sum_{n=0}^{\infty} \frac{i^n v^n}{n!} \int_{-\infty}^{\infty} u^n P_1(u)\, du$$

or, from the definition of $\overline{u^n}$,

$$(2\text{-}11) \qquad M_1(v) = \sum_{n=0}^{\infty} \frac{i^n v^n \overline{u^n}}{n!}$$

If the series converges we may formally reconstruct $M_1(v)$ from a knowledge of all the moments $\overline{u^n}$. Having $M_1(v)$, we may then take its Fourier transform to formally find $P_1(u)$ since the inverse relation determining $P_1(u)$ is

(2-12) $$P_1(u) = \frac{1}{2\pi} \int\limits_{-\infty}^{\infty} e^{-iuv} M_1(v)\, dv$$

This procedure is formal. It may be shown, however (see Cramér, 1946), that $P_1(u)$ is determined uniquely if all the $\overline{u^n}$ exist and the series on the right-hand side of Eq. 2-11 is absolutely convergent for some $v > 0$.

Equation 2-11 is a Maclaurin series expansion. It may be written

(2-13) $$M_1(v) = \sum_{n=0}^{\infty} \frac{d^n M_1(v)}{dv^n} \bigg|_{v=0} \frac{v^n}{n!}$$

Thus we have the identification

(2-14) $$\frac{d^n M_1(v)}{dv^n} \bigg|_{v=0} = i^n \overline{u^n}$$

2.1.5.2A. Semiinvariants. In addition to the moments $\overline{u^n}$ it is useful to consider a set of related quantities that may be derived from an expansion of $\log M_1(v)$. We may expand $\log M_1(v)$ in the form

(2-15) $$\log M_1(v) = \sum_{n=1}^{\infty} \frac{(iv)^n}{n!} \lambda_n$$

The λ_n are called semiinvariants or cumulants.

Formally comparing Eqs. 2-11 and 2-15, we find after some manipulation the following relations between λ_n and $\overline{u^n}$ (see Cramér, 1946, p. 186)

(2-16) $\lambda_1 = \bar{u}$

$\lambda_2 = \overline{u^2} - \bar{u}^2 = \sigma^2$

$\lambda_3 = \overline{u^3} - 3\bar{u}\overline{u^2} + 2\bar{u}^3$

$\lambda_4 = \overline{u^4} - 3(\overline{u^2})^2 - 4\bar{u}\overline{u^3} + 12\bar{u}^2\overline{u^2} - 6\bar{u}^4$

.

.

.

and inversely

(2-17) $\bar{u} = \lambda_1$

$\overline{u^2} = \lambda_2 + \lambda_1{}^2$

$\overline{u^3} = \lambda_3 + 3\lambda_1\lambda_2 + \lambda_1{}^3$

$\overline{u^4} = \lambda_4 + 3\lambda_2{}^2 + 4\lambda_1\lambda_3 + 6\lambda_1{}^2\lambda_2 + \lambda_1{}^4$

.

.

.

In terms of the moments $\overline{(u - u)^n}$ Eq. 2-16 becomes

(2-18) $\lambda_1 = \bar{u}$

$\lambda_2 = \overline{(u - \bar{u})^2}$

$\lambda_3 = \overline{(u - \bar{u})^3}$

$\lambda_4 = \overline{(u - \bar{u})^4} - 3[\overline{(u - \bar{u})^2}]^2$

.

.

.

2.1.5.3. Correlation Functions.   If we are given the second-order probability density $P_2(u_1, u_2)\, du_1\, du_2$, we may find the following moments, which are usually termed two-point correlation or coherence functions,

(2-19) $E(u_1{}^j u_2{}^k) \equiv \overline{u_1{}^j u_2{}^k} \equiv \int\limits_{-\infty}^{\infty} \int\limits_{-\infty}^{\infty} u_1{}^j u_2{}^k P_2(u_1, u_2)\, du_1\, du_2$

Analogous to the foregoing procedure $\overline{u_1{}^j u_2{}^k}$ may be determined from the characteristic function $M_2(v_1, v_2)$ from the relation

(2-20) $\dfrac{\partial^j\, \partial^k}{\partial v_1{}^j\, \partial v_2{}^k} M_2(v_1, v_2)\,\bigg|_{v_1=v_2=0} = (i)^{j+k}\overline{u_1{}^j u_2{}^k}$

and under suitable conditions of existence and convergence $P_2(u_1, u_2)$ may be determined from $\overline{u_1{}^j u_2{}^k}$.

The function we shall encounter most frequently in the course of this book is the moment $\overline{u_1 u_2}$. In terms of the turbulent velocity example that we have been using we say that the quantity $\overline{u_1 u_2}$ gives the correlation between the x component of velocity at the point $\mathbf{x}_1$ at time t_1 and the x component of velocity at the point $\mathbf{x}_2$ at time t_2. (In the remainder of this chapter we shall consider the general case wherein measurements of u at point $\mathbf{x}_j$ occur at time t_j. For simplicity in the previous sections we have often let $t_j = t_k$.) In the popular sense it helps to answer the question: Is there some relationship between what occurs at the space-time point $(\mathbf{x}_1, t_1)$ and the space-time point $(\mathbf{x}_2, t_2)$? For example, if the magnitude of u_1 is large and its sense positive in an experiment, does the magnitude of u_2 tend also to be large and have positive sense or does it bear no relation at all to the velocity component at u_1? If $\overline{u_1 u_2} = \overline{u_1}\,\overline{u_2}$ we say that the velocity components at u_1 and u_2 are uncorrelated. We must caution the reader, however, against concluding that if $\overline{u_1 u_2} = \overline{u_1}\,\overline{u_2}$, then $P_2(u_1, u_2) = P_1(u_1)P_1(u_2)$ and u_1 bears no relationship at all to u_2. (i.e., u_1 and u_2 are statistically independent.) In general this is not true since we may have $\overline{u_1 u_2} = \overline{u_1}\,\overline{u_2}$ whereas $\overline{u_1^2 u_2^2} \neq \overline{u_1^2}\,\overline{u_2^2}$. The quantity $\overline{u_1 u_2}$ thus gives us a feeling about the extent of the relationship between u_1 and u_2 but by no means represents the entire relationship.*

In the turbulent velocity case, $\overline{u_1 u_2}$ is a function of the eight variables x_1, y_1, z_1, t_1 and x_2, y_2, z_2, t_2, or more compactly, $\mathbf{x}_1$, t_1 and $\mathbf{x}_2$, t_2. Let us write then

$$R(\mathbf{x}_1, t_1; \mathbf{x}_2, t_2) \equiv \overline{u(\mathbf{x}_1, t_1)u(\mathbf{x}_2, t_2)}$$

$R(\mathbf{x}_1, t_1; \mathbf{x}_2, t_2)$ must be known as a function of all its variables before it is completely determined. For example, $R(\mathbf{x}_1, 0; \mathbf{x}_2, 0)$ may be zero whereas $R(\mathbf{x}_1, 0; \mathbf{x}_2, t_2)$ $(t_2 \equiv 0)$ may not be zero. It is convenient sometimes to treat the time and space variables separately. Thus we sometimes find discussions of $R(\mathbf{x}_1, t_1; \mathbf{x}_2, t_2)$ which we denote as the temporal or autocorrelation function at the spatial point $\mathbf{x}$.

Important special cases occur when $R(\mathbf{x}_1, t_1; \mathbf{x}_2, t_2)$ is either spatially homogeneous, so that

$$R(\mathbf{x}_1, t_1; \mathbf{x}_2, t_2) = R(\mathbf{x}_1 - \mathbf{x}_2, t_1, t_2)$$

---

* In the special case of gaussian statistics the relation $\overline{u_1 u_2} = \overline{u_1}\,\overline{u_2}$ does imply statistical independence, but this is a very special case, and in those problems treated in this book the assumption of gaussian statistics must be used with great caution.

or stationary in time so that

$$R(\mathbf{x}_1, t_1; \mathbf{x}_2, t_2) = R(\mathbf{x}_1, \mathbf{x}_2, t_1 - t_2)$$

We shall return to a discussion of these special cases after we have discussed the general notion of a stationary ensemble and considered the ergodic hypothesis.

The higher-order moments $\overline{u_1^j u_2^k}$ are receiving increased attention as measurement procedures are becoming more refined. In particular the moment $\overline{u_1^2 u_2^2}$ is under study in many fields. Since the moment $\overline{u_1^2 u_2^2}$ may be derived from the moment $\overline{u_1 u_2}$ for gaussian processes, it is very important to determine the two moments $\overline{u_1 u_2}$ and $\overline{u_1^2 u_2^2}$ separately and to see whether or not they bear the same relationship as they would in a gaussian process. The gaussian process will be discussed in Section 2.1.7.

2.1.5.4. n-Point Moments. The n-point moment is defined as

$$(2\text{-}21) \quad E(u_1^a u_2^b \cdots u_n^g) = \overline{u_1^a u_2^b \cdots u_n^g}$$

$$= \int_{-\infty}^{\infty} \cdots \int_{-\infty}^{\infty} \int_{-\infty}^{\infty} u_1^a u_2^b \cdots u_n^g P_n(u_1, u_2, \ldots, u_n) \, du_1 \, du_2 \cdots du_n$$

The n-point moment may be derived by differentiation from the n-point characteristic function as in the case of lower moments. We have

$$(i)^{a+b+\cdots+g} \overline{u_1^a u_2^b \cdots u_n^g} = \frac{\partial^a}{\partial v_1^a} \frac{\partial^b}{\partial v_2^b} \cdots \frac{\partial^g}{\partial v_n^g} M_n(v_1, v_2, \ldots, v_n) \Bigg|_{\substack{v_1=0 \\ v_2=0 \\ \vdots \\ v_n=0}}$$

Many-point semiinvariants may be defined by a direct extension of the procedure given in Section 2.1.5.2A.

The many-point moments have not received as much attention as the two-point moments. The reason for this lies in the difficulty of measuring the many-point moments and in the difficulty in treating these analytically. Finally, it lies in the fact that although, as we have emphasized repeatedly, a complete statistical description of a random phenomenon requires knowledge of all the moments, the one-point and two-point moments usually have the most direct physical significance. It is only as measurements become more refined that many-point moments become vital to distinguish between different experimental situations. The significance of some many-point moments will be discussed in subsequent chapters. It is very difficult to consider these moments without a definite physical model in mind.

2.1.6. Stationary Processes

We define here the concept of stationary processes. The n-point probability density function representing a process that is stationary in time is given by the following form:

$$P_n(u(\mathbf{x}_1, t_1), u(\mathbf{x}_2, t_2), \ldots, u(\mathbf{x}_n, t_n))$$
$$= f(\mathbf{x}_1, \mathbf{x}_2, \ldots, \mathbf{x}_n, t_2 - t_1, t_3 - t_1, \ldots, t_n - t_1)$$

This means that the n-point probability density does not depend upon the absolute time, but instead depends only upon the time differences. This may best be illustrated by considering steady turbulent flow through a pipe.

If we keep the pressure differences over the pipe length constant we expect that any average properties of the flow will not depend upon the time. The mean flow rate through the pipe will, for example, be independent of time. Similarly, the mean square value of the x component of the turbulent velocity $\overline{u_1'^2}$ will not depend upon the time but only upon the position within the pipe. (For a very long pipe, it will depend only upon the radial position.) The two point moment $\overline{u_1'u_2'}$ similarly will not depend upon the absolute time but it will depend upon the relative time, $t_2 - t_1$. That is, $\overline{u_1'u_2'} = f(\mathbf{x}_1, \mathbf{x}_2, t_2 - t_1)$. If the pipe flow has been running for a week, $\overline{u_1'u_2'}$ cannot depend upon whether or not the measurements are noted on Monday or Tuesday. It does depend, however, upon whether or not the measurements at $\mathbf{x}_1$ and $\mathbf{x}_2$ are made one second apart or one day apart. Analogous arguments hold for all moments and hence for the n-point probability density.

We may also define a process that is stationary in space. The n-point probability density function representing a process that is stationary in space has the form

$$P_n(u(\mathbf{x}_1, t_1), u(\mathbf{x}_2, t_2), \ldots, u(\mathbf{x}_n, t_n))$$

$$= f(\mathbf{x}_2 - \mathbf{x}_1, \mathbf{x}_3 - \mathbf{x}_1, \ldots, \mathbf{x}_n - \mathbf{x}_1, t_1, t_2, \ldots, t_n)$$

This means that the probability density function does not depend upon the absolute position of the n points in space but only upon the relative configuration of the n points.

The concept of a process that is stationary in space, usually called spatial homogeneity, is used frequently in turbulence theory. We assume that the turbulent fluid covers all space but that no energy is supplied to the fluid and hence the turbulence is gradually decaying. It is assumed, for example, that $\overline{u_1'} = 0$ and that $\overline{u_1'^2(t)} = \overline{u_2'^2(t)}$. In this case, if the fluid was made turbulent by stirring it up on Sunday noon, it does depend upon whether or not we measure $\overline{u_1'^2}$ at 12:05 P.M. or 1:00 P.M. We assume, howevei, that the fluid was stirred up in the same manner at all points in space and hence $\overline{u_1'^2}$ does not depend upon absolute position. The quantity $\overline{u_1'(t_1)u_2'(t_2)}$ will depend upon the relative positions of $\mathbf{x}_1$ and $\mathbf{x}_2$ in addition to t_1 and t_2. This is clear since the correlation of velocity components separated by a distance, $\mathbf{x}_1 - \mathbf{x}_2$, will certainly depend upon this distance. Similarly, the entire probability density function must have the form given in the foregoing.

Occasionally we consider physical problems that may be considered to be stationary in both time and space. The n-point probability density function representing a process that is stationary in both time and space has the form

$$P_n(u(\mathbf{x}_1, t_1), u(\mathbf{x}_2, t_2), \ldots, u(\mathbf{x}_n, t_n))$$

$$= f(\mathbf{x}_2 - \mathbf{x}_1, \mathbf{x}_3 - \mathbf{x}_1, \ldots, \mathbf{x}_n - \mathbf{x}_1, t_2 - t_1, t_3 - t_1, \ldots, t_n - t_1)$$

A simple example of this case is blackbody radiation within a large cavity maintained at a constant temperature T. Since the cavity is taken to be very large the statistical properties of the radiation field will be independent of absolute position and since we always maintain a temperature T, it will be independent of the absolute time.

Whenever we have a process that is stationary in time (or space) it is meaningful to define a set of moments in terms of time (or space) averages. For example, to measure $\overline{u(\mathbf{x}_1, t_1)}$ in the case of turbulent flow through a pipe we must set up an ensemble of pipes and measure

$u(\mathbf{x}_1, t_1)$ at point $\mathbf{x}_1$ and time t_1 in every member of the ensemble. This is a cumbersome procedure, and since $\overline{u(\mathbf{x}_1, t_1)}$ is independent of t_1 for steady flow one wonders whether or not it is perhaps meaningful to measure instead the quantity

$$(2\text{-}23) \qquad \langle u(\mathbf{x}_1, t) \rangle \equiv \lim_{T \to \infty} \frac{1}{2T} \int_{-T}^{T} u(\mathbf{x}_1, t)\, dt$$

termed the time average of $u(\mathbf{x}_1, t)$.

For the pipe flow problem the quantity $\langle u(\mathbf{x}_1, t) \rangle$ is certainly defined (although it is not defined unless the process is stationary). We ask therefore what relationship exists between $\overline{u(\mathbf{x}_1, t_1)}$ and $\langle u(\mathbf{x}_1, t) \rangle$. The intuitive answer is: they are equal. To prove that they are equal, however, is a very difficult matter. It has not been proved for the turbulent case we have used as an illustration, and only in very simple physical cases can the equality be proved.

In general the problem that we face is the identification of the n-point ensemble moment:

$$\overline{u^a(\mathbf{x}_1, t_1) u^b(\mathbf{x}_2, t_1 + \tau_2) \cdots u^g(\mathbf{x}_n, t_1 + \tau_n)}$$

and the n-point time average

$$(2\text{-}24) \quad \langle u^a(\mathbf{x}_1, t_1) u^b(\mathbf{x}_2, t_1 + \tau_2) \cdots u^g(\mathbf{x}_n, t_1 + \tau_n) \rangle$$

$$\equiv \lim_{T \to \infty} \frac{1}{2T} \int_{-T}^{T} u^a(\mathbf{x}_1, t_1) u^b(\mathbf{x}_2, t_1 + \tau_2) \cdots u^g(\mathbf{x}_n, t_1 + \tau_n)\, dt_1$$

Furthermore, since the n-point probability density function may be constructed from the n-point moments if they are suitably well behaved, we are faced with the problem of the identification of the n-point probability density function constructed from ensemble averages with the n-point probability density function constructed from time averages.

The hypothesis that allows us to identify ensemble and time averages is called an ergodic hypothesis. The hypothesis demands that all states available to an ensemble of the systems be available to each system in the ensemble. For example, if $u(\mathbf{x}_1)$ is a possible flow configuration for the x component of turbulent velocity in the ensemble of pipe systems it must be a possible configuration in any pipe with which we choose to experiment. We shall use this type of hypothesis freely throughout this book with no further justification than physical intuition. We shall, however, make a few further remarks in the next subsection.

Just as it is meaningful to speak of time averages when the physical problem is stationary in time, it is meaningful to speak of space averages for systems that are spatially stationary. The n-point space average is defined as

$$(2\text{-}25) \quad [u^a(\mathbf{x}_1, t_1)u^b(\mathbf{x}_1 + \eta_2, t_2) \cdots u_n{}^g(\mathbf{x}_1 + \eta_n, t_n)]$$

$$\equiv \lim_{V \to \infty} \frac{1}{V} \int_V u^a(\mathbf{x}_1, t_1)u^b(\mathbf{x}_1 + \eta_2, t_2) \cdots u^g(\mathbf{x}_1 + \eta_n, t_n) \, d\mathbf{x}_1$$

where the integral is over all space. It is a three-dimensional integral. When necessary in the course of this book we shall assume that the spatial moment given in Eq. 2-25 may be set equal to the ensemble-averaged moment.

Occasionally, as in the case of blackbody radiation in a very large cavity, we have both temporal and spatial stationarity. In such a case we shall equate the moments defined in both Eqs. 2-24 and 2-25 with the ensemble averaged moments.

2.1.6.1. Ergodic Hypothesis. The physical problem that motivated the study of an ergodic hypothesis was the dynamics of a gas contained in a fixed volume. It would carry us too far afield to discuss the ergodic problem in this context, but we refer the reader to the following discussions: Truesdell (1961), D. ter Haar (1960), Farquhar (1964), and the basic article of Birkhoff (1931).

The problems we shall treat in this book have not received the detailed inspection that has been given to the dynamics problem. Only rarely has an ergodic hypothesis been carefully studied in a continuum system. (See Kampé de Feriet, 1962; Hoffman, 1964.) The position usually taken is that it is to be considered an hypothesis subject to experimental verification. We shall make very similar assumptions in the remainder of this book. The reader may, however, find the following few paragraphs helpful in assessing the basic difficulty of establishing an ergodic hypothesis.

In a number of books (see for example Davenport and Root, 1958; Yaglom, 1962) a mathematical discussion is given for processes described by the random function $x(t)$. It is pointed out that if

(2-26) $$\lim_{T \to \infty} \frac{1}{T} \int_0^T (R(\tau) - [\overline{u(t)}]^2)\, d\tau = 0$$

then, in a probabilistic sense, (see Section 2.1.8) we may show that

$$\langle u(t) \rangle = \overline{u(t)}$$

In general (except for gaussian statistics) an additional condition on the fourth-order moment is necessary to show that

$$\langle u(t)u(t + \tau) \rangle = \overline{u(t)u(t + \tau)}$$

A whole sequence of conditions is necessary to prove the identity of ensemble and time averages for all higher moments.

At first glance, Eq. 2-26 seems to be obviously satisfied by just about any physical process we can imagine since we expect

$$\lim_{\tau \to \infty} R(\tau) = [\overline{u(t)}]^2$$

that is, we expect the correlation between $u(t)$ and $u(t + \tau)$ to vanish as $\tau \to \infty$. If, however, all states are not available to all members of the ensemble, some systems may for example have a mean value $\bar{u}_A$ and others, a mean value $\bar{u}_B$. If this is so

$$\lim_{\tau \to \infty} R(\tau) \neq [\overline{u(t)}]^2$$

For example, if half the systems have a mean value $\bar{u}_A$ and half a mean value $\bar{u}_B$

$$\lim_{\tau \to \infty} R(\tau) = \tfrac{1}{2}\bar{u}_A^{\,2} + \tfrac{1}{2}\bar{u}_B^{\,2} \neq \left[\frac{\bar{u}_A}{2} + \frac{\bar{u}_B}{2} \right]^2$$

Thus Eq. 2-26 is by no means an obvious condition for a stationary random process.

Equation 2-26 and other conditions like it enable one to determine if an ensemble has ergodic properties if suitable measurements are made on the ensemble. Only a study of the physical system can tell us beforehand if a condition like Eq. 2-26 is to be expected and at present such a study has not been made for any of the systems treated in this book.

2.1.6.2. Correlation Functions and Power Spectra. *Correlation Functions.* In an ensemble stationary in time the second moment

$$R(\mathbf{x}_1, t_1; \mathbf{x}_2, t_2) = \overline{u(x_1, t_1)u(x_2, t_2)}$$

has the form $R(\mathbf{x}_1, \mathbf{x}_2, \tau)$ where $\tau = t_2 - t_1$. This function has the following properties:

(2-27) $$R(\mathbf{x}_1, \mathbf{x}_2, \tau) = R(\mathbf{x}_2, \mathbf{x}_1, -\tau)$$

(2-28) $$|R(\mathbf{x}_1, \mathbf{x}_2, \tau)| \leqslant [R(\mathbf{x}_1, \mathbf{x}_1, 0)]^{1/2}[R(\mathbf{x}_2, \mathbf{x}_2, 0)]^{1/2}$$

where

$$R(\mathbf{x}_1, \mathbf{x}_1, 0) = \overline{u(\mathbf{x}_1, t_1)u(\mathbf{x}_1, t_1)}.$$

$R(\mathbf{x}_1, \mathbf{x}_2, \tau)$ is termed the cross correlation function. $R(\mathbf{x}_1, \mathbf{x}_1, \tau)$ is termed the autocorrelation function.

Equation 2-27 follows from the definition of stationarity. Since $R(\mathbf{x}_1, \mathbf{x}_2, \tau)$ does not depend upon the absolute origin of time, the equation states that the correlation of $u(\mathbf{x}_1, t_1)$ and $u(\mathbf{x}_2, t_2)$, where t_1 is greater than t_2 by a quantity τ, is the same as the correlation between these quantities when t_2 and t_1 are reduced by a quantity τ. Equation 2-28 follows by noting that

$$\overline{\left\{ \frac{u(\mathbf{x}_1, t_1)}{[\overline{u^2(\mathbf{x}_1, t_1)}]^{1/2}} \pm \frac{u(\mathbf{x}_2, t_2)}{[\overline{u^2(\mathbf{x}_2, t_2)}]^{1/2}} \right\}^2} \geqslant 0$$

Expansion then yields

$$\pm \frac{2R(\mathbf{x}_1, \mathbf{x}_2, \tau)}{[R(\mathbf{x}_1, \mathbf{x}_1, 0)]^{1/2}[R(\mathbf{x}_2, \mathbf{x}_2, 0)]^{1/2}} + 2 \geqslant 0$$

from which Eq. 2-28 follows directly upon taking the plus sign if $R(\mathbf{x}_1, \mathbf{x}_2, \tau)$ is negative and the minus sign if it is positive.

In many applications it is more convenient to work with the complex function

$$v(\mathbf{x}_1, t_1) = u(\mathbf{x}_1, t_1) + iH(u(\mathbf{x}_1, t_1))$$

called the analytic signal. Here $H(u(\mathbf{x}_1, t_1))$ is the Hilbert transform of $u(\mathbf{x}_1, t_1)$ defined as (assuming it exists)

$$H(u(\mathbf{x}_1, t_1)) = \frac{1}{\pi} \int_{-\infty}^{\infty} \frac{u(\mathbf{x}_1, t')}{t' - t_1} dt'$$

where $\int_{-\infty}^{\infty}$ denotes Cauchy's principal value. The analytic signal is a generalization, for a signal with many frequencies, of the usual procedure of association a complex function $e^{i2\pi vt}$ with the real function $\cos 2\pi vt$. If $u(\mathbf{x}_1, t_1) = A(\mathbf{x}_1) \cos(-2\pi vt_1 + \phi(\mathbf{x}_1))$, then

$$H(u(\mathbf{x}_1, t_1)) = A(\mathbf{x}_1) \sin(-2\pi vt_1 + \phi(\mathbf{x}_1))$$

and in general we may obtain $H(u(\mathbf{x}_1, t_1))$ from $u(\mathbf{x}_1, t_1)$ by changing all cosines to sines in a Fourier integral representation of $u(x_1, t_1)$. The analytic signal was introduced by Gabor (1947) and is discussed at length by Beran and Parrent (1964).

There is a problem in determining the correlation function associated with $v(\mathbf{x}_1, t_1)$ since the existence of $H(u(\mathbf{x}_1, t_1))$ is in doubt if we consider infinite time intervals. To circumvent this difficulty we work with a truncated function

$$u_T(\mathbf{x}_1, t) = u(\mathbf{x}_1, t) \qquad |t| \leqslant T$$
$$= 0 \qquad |t| > T$$

$H(u_T(\mathbf{x}_1, t))$ will now exist (although it may extend over an infinite time interval). Using the truncated complex function $v_T(\mathbf{x}_1, t)$ we define the complex correlation function $\Gamma(\mathbf{x}_1, \mathbf{x}_2, \tau)$ as follows

$$(2\text{-}29) \qquad \Gamma(\mathbf{x}_1, \mathbf{x}_2, \tau) = \lim_{T \to \infty} \frac{1}{2T} \int_{-T}^{T} v_T(\mathbf{x}_1, t + \tau) v_T^*(\mathbf{x}_2, t)\, dt$$

where * denotes the complex conjugate.

It may be shown that

$$(2\text{-}30) \qquad \operatorname{Re} \Gamma(\mathbf{x}_1, \mathbf{x}_2, \tau) = 2R(\mathbf{x}_1, \mathbf{x}_2, \tau)$$

where Re denotes the real part.

Everything we have said to this point is applicable to ensembles that are stationary in space. Some care must be taken to account for the vector nature of $\mathbf{x}$, but this consideration introduces no real difficulties. Here we may write the cross correlation function as $R(\boldsymbol{\eta}, t_1, t_2)$ where $\boldsymbol{\eta}$ is $\mathbf{x}_2 - \mathbf{x}_1$.

Power Spectra. It is physically very useful to take the Fourier transform of $R(\mathbf{x}_1, \mathbf{x}_2, \tau)$ with respect to τ. This quantity is defined as

$$(2\text{-}31) \qquad S(\mathbf{x}_1, \mathbf{x}_2, v) = \int_{-\infty}^{\infty} R(\mathbf{x}_1, \mathbf{x}_2, \tau) e^{2\pi iv\tau}\, d\tau$$

and is termed the cross spectral density. $S(\mathbf{x}_1, \mathbf{x}_1, \nu)$ the Fourier transform of the autocorrelation function, is called the spectral density.

The spectral density is very meaningful from a physical point of view. Loosely speaking, it tells us the relative power contained in each frequency component that is included in the signal $u(\mathbf{x}_1, t)$. To see this more clearly let us determine $S(\mathbf{x}_1, \mathbf{x}_2, \nu)$ directly from the signal $u(\mathbf{x}_1, t)$. To do this we first consider the Fourier transform of $u(\mathbf{x}_1, t)$ which we term $\hat{u}(\mathbf{x}_1, \nu)$. Formally we have

$$(2\text{-}32) \qquad \hat{u}(\mathbf{x}_1, \nu) = \int_{-\infty}^{\infty} u(\mathbf{x}_1, t) e^{2\pi i \nu t} \, dt$$

Unfortunately this integral does not exist in the limit as $t \to \infty$. As in the Hilbert transform problem just cited we again work with a truncated function $u_T(\mathbf{x}_1, t)$ in order to avoid this problem.

The function $\hat{u}_T(\mathbf{x}_1, \nu)$ associated with $u_T(\mathbf{x}_1, t)$ exists for finite T.

Let us now form $R(\mathbf{x}_1, \mathbf{x}_2, \tau)$ by considering the limit $T \to \infty$. We have

$$(2\text{-}33) \quad R(\mathbf{x}_1, \mathbf{x}_2, \tau) = \lim_{T \to \infty} \frac{1}{2T} \int_{-T}^{T} u_T(\mathbf{x}_1, t) u_T(\mathbf{x}_2, t + \tau) \, dt$$

$$= \lim_{T \to \infty} \frac{1}{2T} \int_{-T}^{T} \left[\int_{-\infty}^{\infty} \hat{u}_T(\mathbf{x}_1, \nu) e^{-2\pi i \nu t} \, d\nu \right]$$

$$\cdot \left[\int_{-\infty}^{\infty} \hat{u}_T(\mathbf{x}_2, \nu') e^{-2\pi i \nu' t - 2\pi i \nu' \tau} \, d\nu' \right] dt$$

If we assume that we may interchange orders of integration with their corresponding limiting procedures, we have

$$(2\text{-}34)$$

$$R(\mathbf{x}_1, \mathbf{x}_2, \tau) = \int_{-\infty}^{\infty} \int_{-\infty}^{\infty} \lim_{T \to \infty} \frac{1}{2T} \hat{u}_T(\mathbf{x}_1, \nu) \hat{u}_T(\mathbf{x}_2, \nu') e^{-2\pi i \nu' \tau} \, \delta(\nu + \nu') \, d\nu \, d\nu'$$

$$= \int_{-\infty}^{\infty} \lim_{T \to \infty} \left[\frac{1}{2T} \hat{u}_T(\mathbf{x}_1, \nu) \hat{u}_T(\mathbf{x}_2, -\nu) \right] e^{-2\pi i \nu \tau} \, d\nu$$

upon remembering that

$$\lim_{T \to \infty} \int_{-T}^{T} e^{2\pi i(\nu - \nu')t}\, dt = \delta(\nu - \nu')$$

If the function

$$\lim_{T \to \infty} \frac{1}{2T} [\hat{u}_T(\mathbf{x}_1, \nu)\hat{u}_T(\mathbf{x}_2, -\nu)]$$

exists, we may identify it with $S(\mathbf{x}_1, \mathbf{x}_2, \nu)$ upon comparing Eq. 2-34 and Eq. 2-31 (actually its transform pair). When $\mathbf{x}_1 = \mathbf{x}_2$ we see that $S(\mathbf{x}_1, \mathbf{x}_1, \nu)$ thus gives the "power" contained in each frequency component ν.

Unhappily, this limit does not in general exist. The ensemble average of this limit does exist and may be identified with $S(\mathbf{x}_1, \mathbf{x}_2, \nu)$* but it is of interest here to see in what sense this limit exists if we make measurements on only one member of an ensemble.

The nonexistence of the limit is not an academic problem. If we were to plot the function

$$S_T(\mathbf{x}_1, \mathbf{x}_2, \nu) = \frac{1}{2T} [\hat{u}_T(\mathbf{x}_1, \nu)\hat{u}_T(\mathbf{x}_2, -\nu)]$$

as a function of ν for a series of large $T(T_1, T_2, \ldots, T_n)$, we would find that $S_T(\mathbf{x}_1, \mathbf{x}_2, \nu)$ was not a smooth function of ν for a given T_j but that it oscillated violently. Moreover, we would see that the detailed structure of the oscillation varied as a function of T.

To see the nature of the oscillation more clearly, consider the Fourier-series representation of the function $u(\mathbf{x}_1, t)$ in the interval $-T$ to T. For convenience we treat the function $w_T(\mathbf{x}_1, t)$ defined to be equal to $u(\mathbf{x}_1, t)$ in this interval and periodic, with a period $2T$, outside this interval. The Fourier-series representation of $w_T(\mathbf{x}_1, t)$ may be written

(2-35) $$w_T(\mathbf{x}_1, t) = \sum_{n=-\infty}^{\infty} w_{nT}(\mathbf{x}_1)e^{-in\pi t/T}$$

* The identification of the function

$$\overline{\lim_{T \to \infty} \frac{1}{2T} [\hat{u}_T(\mathbf{x}_1, \nu)\hat{u}_T(\mathbf{x}_1, -\nu)]}$$

with the Fourier transform of $R(\mathbf{x}_1, \mathbf{x}_1, \tau)$ is known as the Wiener-Khinchin theorem.

where

$$w_{nT}(\mathbf{x}_1) = \frac{1}{2T} \int_{-T}^{T} w_T(\mathbf{x}_1, t')e^{-in\pi t'/T} \, dt'$$

Calculation of

$$R_F(\mathbf{x}_1, \mathbf{x}_2, \tau) \equiv \lim_{T \to \infty} \frac{1}{2T'} \int_{-T'}^{T'} w_T(\mathbf{x}_1, t)w_T(\mathbf{x}_2, t + \tau) \, dt$$

yields

(2-36) $$R_F(\mathbf{x}_1, \mathbf{x}_2, \tau) = \sum_{n=-\infty}^{\infty} [w_{nT}(\mathbf{x}_1)w_{-nT}(\mathbf{x}_2)]e^{-in\pi\tau/T}$$

From Eq. 2-36 we may calculate

$$S_F(\mathbf{x}_1, \mathbf{x}_2, \nu) = \int_{-\infty}^{\infty} R_F(\mathbf{x}_1, \mathbf{x}_2, \tau)e^{2\pi i \nu \tau} \, d\tau$$

and we find

(2-37) $$S_F(\mathbf{x}_1, \mathbf{x}_2, \nu) = \sum_{n-\infty}^{\infty} [w_{nT}(\mathbf{x}_1)w_{-nT}(\mathbf{x}_2)] \, \delta\left(\nu - \frac{n}{2T}\right)$$

$$\equiv \sum_{n-\infty}^{\infty} S_{nT}(\mathbf{x}_1, \mathbf{x}_2) \, \delta\left(\nu - \frac{n}{2T}\right)$$

In the limit $T \to \infty$ the values ν for which $S_F(\mathbf{x}_1, \mathbf{x}_2, \nu)$ assumes non-zero values (actually infinite values because of the delta function) will become more numerous and hence come closer and closer together. As we approach the limit, however, these values of ν will oscillate along the ν axis since $\nu = n/2T$ changes as T changes. Moreover, in the limit $T \to \infty$, $S_{nT}(\mathbf{x}_1, \mathbf{x}_2)$ will fluctuate since a change in T corresponds to a change in ν for fixed n. $S_F(\mathbf{x}_1, \mathbf{x}_2, \nu)$ approaches no well-defined limit as $T \to \infty$.

In order to get a meaningful physical result for the energy contained in an interval $\Delta\nu$ it thus becomes reasonable* to average $S_F(\mathbf{x}_1, \mathbf{x}_2, \nu)$ over a small region $\Delta\nu$. For fixed T this allows us to integrate out the

---

* Physically reasonable. The subsequent discussion is in no sense mathematically rigorous.

delta function $\delta(v - n/2T)$ and get finite values for $S_F(\mathbf{x}_1, \mathbf{x}_2, v)$. As $T \to \infty$ if Δv is chosen so that

$$\Delta v \gg \frac{n}{2T} - \frac{(n-1)}{2T} = \frac{1}{2T}$$

then many values of n are included in the averaging. We expect that

$$\frac{1}{\Delta v} \int_{v}^{v+\Delta v} S_F(\mathbf{x}_1, \mathbf{x}_2, v') \, dv'$$

will not fluctuate in the limit $T \to \infty$ and will be a well-defined function.

The analyses of $u_T(\mathbf{x}_1, t)$ and $w_T(\mathbf{x}_1, t)$ in the limit $T \to \infty$ are essentially the same. Thus to obtain from $u_T(\mathbf{x}_1, t)$ a smooth function that is independent of T for large T it is necessary to construct a local average of the function $S_T(\mathbf{x}_1, \mathbf{x}_2, v)$. Instead of $S_T(\mathbf{x}_1, \mathbf{x}_2, v)$ consider the function $\bar{S}_T(\mathbf{x}_1, \mathbf{x}_2, v)$ defined as

$$(2\text{-}38) \qquad \bar{S}_T(\mathbf{x}_1, \mathbf{x}_2, v) = \frac{1}{\Delta v} \int_{v}^{v+\Delta v} S_T(\mathbf{x}_1, \mathbf{x}_2, v') \, dv'$$

This function is a smooth function of v for $v_c \gg \Delta v \gg 1/T$ where v_c is the characteristic frequency spread of the spectral density. We imagine the limit of large T taken in the following manner: $\Delta v/v_c \ll 1$, $\Delta v T \gg 1$. For very large T this imposes little restriction on the function $S_T(\mathbf{x}_1, \mathbf{x}_2, v)$ since in any real problem some smoothing is always done. We thus will always assume

$$(2\text{-}39) \qquad S(\mathbf{x}_1, \mathbf{x}_2, v) = \lim_{T \to \infty} \bar{S}_T(\mathbf{x}_1, \mathbf{x}_2, v)$$

In order to make the argument in this section precise it is necessary to introduce the concept of a Fourier-Stieljes integral. The function $u(\mathbf{x}_1, t)$ is represented as

$$u(\mathbf{x}_1, t) = \int_{-\infty}^{\infty} e^{2\pi i v t} \, d\hat{u}(\mathbf{x}_1, v)$$

where the function $d\hat{u}(\mathbf{x}_1, v)$ must be used in place of the function $\hat{u}(\mathbf{x}_1, v) \, dv$ since $\hat{u}(\mathbf{x}_1, v)$ does not exist. The reader is referred to a book such as Kestelman (1960) for a mathematical discussion of

Stieljes integrals. In this book, however, we shall use the notion of a truncated function $u_T(\mathbf{x}_1, t)$, proceed as in Eqs. 2-33 and 2-34, and then posit the existence of the limit $S_T(\mathbf{x}_1, \mathbf{x}_2, \nu)$ by *implicitly* assuming local averaging.

Again we may remark that everything we have said is applicable to ensembles that are stationary in space. In this case, the spectral density associated with the cross-correlation function $R(\boldsymbol{\eta}, t_1, t_2)$ is defined as

$$S(\mathbf{k}, t_1, t_2) = \iiint\limits_{-\infty}^{\infty} R(\boldsymbol{\eta}, t_1, t_2) e^{2\pi i \boldsymbol{\eta} \cdot \boldsymbol{\kappa}} \, d\eta_x \, d\eta_y \, d\eta_z$$

2.1.7. Gaussian Processes

In the course of this book we shall have occasion to consider statistical processes that are termed gaussian (or normal). The one-dimensional probability density function for a random variable that has a gaussian distribution about $\bar{u}_1$ is

(2-40) $P_{1G}(u_1) = \dfrac{1}{\sqrt{2\pi}\sigma} \exp\left[-(u_1 - \bar{u}_1)^2/2\sigma^2\right]$

where $\bar{u}_1$ is the mean value of u_1 and σ is the standard deviation of u_1 (see Eq. 2-8).

The great applicability of the gaussian distribution stems from the central limit theorem which may be stated roughly as follows: If $u_1 = w_1 + w_2 + \cdots + w_n$ and the w_j are independent random variables with mean w_j and standard deviation σ_j then in the limit $n \to \infty$, u_1 has a gaussian distribution if certain conditions on the absolute third moment hold. (The last qualifying phrase is not necessary if the probability density functions of the w_j are the same.)

We refer the reader to Cramér (1946) for a thorough discussion of gaussian processes and the central limit theorem. In addition, in Chapter 16 of his book he shows how some simple discrete distributions become gaussian in the limit of many trials. In particular, we may see there how the binomial distribution (which results from considering the total number of occurrences of an event like obtaining a head in a coin toss) becomes gaussian in an appropriate limit.

The characteristic function $M_{1G}(v)$ associated with $P_{1G}(u_1)$ is (see Eq. 2-5)

(2-41) $M_{1G}(v_1) = \exp\left[iv_1\bar{u}_1 - (\tfrac{1}{2})\sigma^2 v_1^2\right]$

Direct calculation shows that all moments can be calculated in terms of u_1 and σ. We have, from the definition

$$\overline{(u_1 - \bar{u}_1)^n} = \int_{-\infty}^{\infty} (u - \bar{u}_1)^n P_{1G}(u_1)\, du_1$$

the results

$$\overline{(u_1 - \bar{u}_1)^n} = 0 \qquad n \text{ odd}$$

$$\overline{(u_1 - \bar{u}_1)^n} = 1 \cdot 3 \cdot 5 \cdots (n-1)\sigma^n \qquad n \text{ even}$$

When n is even, we note that all moments are expressible in terms of σ, the second moment. For example, a relation that is often useful is the relationship between the second and fourth moments.

$$\overline{(u_1 - \bar{u}_1)^4} = 3\sigma^4$$

We also note that the semiinvariants of a gaussian distribution have the values

$$\lambda_1 = \bar{u}$$

$$\lambda_2 = \sigma^2$$

$$\lambda_j = 0 \qquad j \geqslant 3$$

This may be readily seen from Eqs. 2-41 and 2-15 since the Taylor series expansion or $\log M_G(v)$ does not contain powers in v of higher order than v^2.

The gaussian distribution is readily extended to higher dimensions. In two dimensions we have

(2-42) $P_{2G}(u_1, u_2)\, du_1\, du_2 = \dfrac{1}{2\pi(\mu_{20}\mu_{02} - \mu_{11}^2)^{1/2}}$

$$\times \exp\left\{\frac{-\mu_{02}u_1^2 + \mu_{11}(u_1 - \bar{u}_1)(u_2 - \bar{u}_2) - \mu_{20}u_2^2}{2(\mu_{20}\mu_{02} - \mu_{11}^2)}\right\} du_1\, du_2$$

where

$$\mu_{20} = \overline{(u_1 - \bar{u}_1)^2} = \sigma_1^2$$

$$\mu_{02} = \overline{(u_2 - \bar{u}_2)^2} = \sigma_2^2$$

$$\mu_{11} = \overline{(u_1 - \bar{u}_1)(u_2 - \bar{u}_2)}$$

The associated characteristic function is

(2-43)

$$M_{2G}(v_1, v_2) = \exp\left[i(\bar{u}_1 v_1 + \bar{u}_2 v_2) - \tfrac{1}{2}(\mu_{20}v_1^2 + 2\mu_{11}v_1 v_2 + \mu_{02}v_2^2)\right]$$

The function μ_{11} is termed the correlation coefficient between u_1 and u_2. A nondimensional form of μ_{11} is the function ρ defined as

$$\rho = \frac{\mu_{11}}{\sqrt{\mu_{20}\mu_{02}}} = \frac{\mu_{11}}{\sigma_1 \sigma_2}$$

If the variables u_1 and u_2 are independent, then $\mu_{11} = 0$.

It is useful to note that any linear transformation of the form

$$w_1 = a_{11}u_1 + a_{12}u_2$$

$$w_2 = a_{21}u_1 + a_{22}u_2$$

yields a probability density function that is gaussian in the variables w_1 and w_2. Furthermore, integration over u_1 yields a gaussian density for u_2. The sum of the variables u_1 and u_2 can also be shown to be gaussianly distributed.

The higher order moments μ_{ij} where

$$\mu_{ij} = \overline{(u_1 - \bar{u}_1)^i (u_2 - \bar{u}_2)^j}$$

may be determined from the following formula (derived from Eq. 2-19 or 2-20)

$$\mu_{ij} = 0 \qquad \text{where } i + j = n \qquad \text{for} \qquad n \text{ odd}$$

μ_{ij} = coefficient of $s^i t^j$ in the expression

$$\frac{i!\,j!}{2^n n!} (\mu_{20}s^2 + 2\mu_{11}st + \mu_{02}t^2)^n$$

when $i + j = 2n$ (see Cramér, 1946, p. 317).

As in the one-dimensional case the higher-order moments may be derived from the second-order moments μ_{20}, μ_{11}, μ_{02}. This is clear since the foregoing formula is one for determining all nonzero μ_{ij} in terms of these three moments. For example

$$\mu_{22} = \mu_{20}\mu_{02} + 2\mu_{11}{}^2$$

In subsequent chapters we shall consider the relationship between the full fourth-order moment (see Eq. 2-45 below, $n = 4$)

$$\overline{(u_1 - \bar{u}_1)(u_2 - \bar{u}_2)(u_3 - \bar{u}_3)(u_4 - \bar{u}_4)}$$

and second-order moments of the form $\overline{(u_i - \bar{u}_i)(u_j - \bar{u}_j)}$ for variables obeying gaussian statistics. For convenience we set the formula down here. It is

$$(2\text{-}44) \quad \overline{(u_1 - \bar{u}_1)(u_2 - \bar{u}_2)(u_3 - \bar{u}_3)(u_4 - \bar{u}_4)}$$

$$= [\overline{(u_1 - \bar{u}_1)(u_2 - \bar{u}_2)}][\overline{(u_3 - \bar{u}_3)(u_4 - \bar{u}_4)}]$$

$$+ [\overline{(u_1 - \bar{u}_1)(u_3 - \bar{u}_3)}][\overline{(u_2 - \bar{u}_2)(u_4 - \bar{u}_4)}]$$

$$+ [\overline{(u_1 - \bar{u}_1)(u_4 - \bar{u}_4)}][\overline{(u_2 - \bar{u}_2)(u_3 - \bar{u}_3)}]$$

For n dimensions we have

$$(2\text{-}45) \quad P_{nG}(u_1, u_2, \ldots, u_n)\, du_1\, du_2 \cdots du_n$$

$$= \frac{\exp\left[-\dfrac{1}{2\,|\Lambda|} \sum_{i=1}^{n} \sum_{j=1}^{n} |\Lambda|_{ij}\,(u_i - \bar{u}_i)(u_j - \bar{u}_j)\right]}{(2\pi)^{n/2}\,|\Lambda|^{1/2}}\, du_1\, du_2 \cdots du_n$$

where

$$\Lambda = \begin{bmatrix} \lambda_{11} & \lambda_{12} & \cdots & \lambda_{1n} \\ \lambda_{21} & \lambda_{22} & \cdots & \lambda_{2n} \\ \cdot & & & \cdot \\ \cdot & & & \cdot \\ \cdot & & & \cdot \\ \lambda_{n1} & \lambda_{n2} & \cdots & \lambda_{nn} \end{bmatrix}$$

$|\Lambda|_{ij}$ is the cofactor of λ_{ij}. $|\Lambda|$ is the determinant of Λ. λ_{ij} is defined as

$$\lambda_{ij} = \overline{(u_i - \bar{u}_j)(u_j - \bar{u}_j)}$$

All higher-order moments may be expressed in terms of the λ_{ij}.

The characteristic function $M_G(v_1, v_2, \ldots, v_n)$ is now

$$(2\text{-}46) \quad M_{nG}(v_1, v_2, \ldots, v_n) = \exp\left[i\sum_{j=1}^{n} v_j \bar{u}_j - \frac{1}{2}\sum_{i=1}^{n}\sum_{j=1}^{n}\lambda_{ij}v_i v_j\right]$$

If all λ_{ij} are zero ($i \neq j$) the variables v_n are uncorrelated. It is again sometimes useful to define the nondimensionalized correlation coefficients ρ_{ij} where

$$\rho_{ij} = \frac{\lambda_{ij}}{\sigma_i \sigma_j}$$

As in the two-dimensional case a linear transformation of variables from u_j to w_j yields a gaussian distribution for the w_j. In addition the density

$$P_{nG}(u_1, \ldots, u_j) = \int \cdots \int P_{nG}(u_1, \ldots, u_n)\, du_{j+1} \cdots u_n$$

has a gaussian form.

We shall consider the gaussian distribution in the limit as $n \to \infty$ subsequent to our discussion of functionals. As a final remark, it is of some interest to note that G. Maruyama (1949) has shown that a stationary p-dimensional gaussian process is ergodic if its spectrum is continuous.

2.1.8. Definitions of Convergence, Tchebycheff's Inequality, and the Karhunen-Loève Theorem

We shall conclude this section on probability theory with two definitions stating what is meant by convergence in probability theory, a proof of Tchebycheff's inequality and a statement of the Karhunen-Loève theorem.

2.1.8.1. Convergence. We wish to have a suitable definition that allows us to determine if a sequence of random variables $u_1, u_2, \ldots, u_n, \ldots$ converges to a limiting random variable u_0. We consider two definitions: (1) convergence in probability and (2) convergence in the rth mean.

We say that a sequence of random variables $u_1, u_2, \ldots, u_n, \ldots$ converges in probability to a constant u_0 if for every $\epsilon > 0$ the probability that $|u_n - u_0| \geqslant \epsilon$ approaches zero as $n \to \infty$. That is

$$\lim_{n \to \infty} P_1[|u_n - u_0| \geqslant \epsilon] = 0$$

We say that a sequence of random variables $u_1, u_2, \ldots, u_n, \ldots$ converges in the rth mean to a constant u_0 if the expectation of $|u_n - u_0|^r$ approaches zero as $n \to \infty$. That is

$$\lim_{n \to \infty} E(|u_n - u_0|^r) = 0$$

Usually the statement "convergence in the mean" implies that $r = 2$.

Convergence in probability (or in the mean) is necessary for considering the sequence of random variables obtained in the course of determining the mean occurrence of some process. For example, let u_n equal the fraction of times a "six" occurred when an unloaded die was thrown n times. The u_n sequence might be

$$\{0, 0, \tfrac{1}{3}, \tfrac{1}{4}, \tfrac{2}{5}, \tfrac{2}{6}, \tfrac{2}{7}, \tfrac{2}{8}, \tfrac{2}{9}, \tfrac{3}{10}, \tfrac{3}{11}, \tfrac{4}{12}, \tfrac{4}{13},$$

$$\tfrac{4}{14}, \tfrac{4}{15}, \tfrac{4}{16}, \tfrac{4}{17}, \tfrac{4}{18}, \tfrac{4}{19}, \tfrac{4}{20}, \tfrac{4}{21}, \tfrac{4}{22}, \ldots\}$$

We can, however, assert that

$$\lim_{n \to \infty} P_1(|u_n - \tfrac{1}{6}| \geqslant \epsilon) = 0$$

2.1.8.2. Tchebycheff's Inequality. A generalization of the Tchebycheff inequality may be stated as follows: If $f(u)$ is a non-negative function of the random variable u, and when $u \geqslant a, f(u) \geqslant b$, then

$$(2\text{-}47) \qquad\qquad P_1(u \geqslant a) \leqslant \frac{E[f(u)]}{b}$$

To prove this theorem we simply note

$$(2\text{-}48) \qquad\qquad E[f(u)] = \int_{-\infty}^{\infty} f(u)P_1(u)\, du$$

$$\geqslant \int_{a}^{\infty} f(u)P_1(u)\, du$$

$$\geqslant b\int_{a}^{\infty} P_1(u)\, du = bP_1(u > a)$$

Therefore Eq. 2-47 follows.

If $f(u)$ is even and nondecreasing for positive u, then we have from Eq. 2-47

(2-49)
$$P_1(|u| \geqslant a) \leqslant \frac{E[f(u)]}{f(a)}$$

If we choose $f(u) = u^2$ and $a = \epsilon$ we have

(2-50)
$$P_1(|u| \geqslant \epsilon) \leqslant \frac{\overline{u^2}}{\epsilon^2}$$

Substituting for u the variable $v - \bar{v}$, we have finally Tchebycheff's inequality

(2-51)
$$P_1(|v - \bar{v}| \geqslant \epsilon) \leqslant \frac{\sigma_v^2}{\epsilon^2}$$

Therefore if we have some information about the standard deviation of a random variable v we can place an upper bound on the probability that $|v - \bar{v}|$ exceeds positive number ϵ.

2.1.8.3. The Karhunen-Loève Theorem. A statement of the Karhunen-Loève theorem is given in Loève (1962), Davenport and Root (1958), and Adomain (1963). In Davenport and Root an example is worked out in some detail and Adomian gives a formal application of the theorem. We consider a random function $x(t)$ defined over some interval $a \leqslant t \leqslant b$ and denote its autocorrelation function by $R(t_1, t_2)$. The theorem asserts that $x(t)$ has the orthogonal expansion

(2-52)
$$x(t) = \sum \lambda_n x_n \phi_n(t) \qquad a \leqslant t \leqslant b$$

where

$$E(x_m x_n{}^*) = \delta_{mn}$$

$$\int_a^b \phi_m(t) \phi_n{}^*(t)\, dt = \delta_{mn}$$

if and only if $|\lambda_n|^2$ and $\phi_n(t)$ are the eigenvalues and eigenfunctions of the integral equation

$$\int_a^b R(t_1, t_2)\phi_n(t_2)\, dt_2 = |\lambda_n|^2\, \phi_n(t_1)$$

Convergence of the series in Eq. 2-52 is defined in terms of the second (quadratic) mean.

2.2. Theory of Functionals

In our discussion of the theory of functionals we shall roughly follow the development given by Volterra (1959). The reader is also referred to Evans (1964). *A functional is a quantity which depends upon all the values a function $x(t)$ takes in some interval $a \leqslant t \leqslant b$.* It will often be denoted as $F[x(t)]$. The functional that is perhaps most familiar is the functional appearing in the calculus of variations. In the ordinary Lagrangian formulation of mechanics we seek a stationary value for the functional $I[x(t)]$ where

$$I[x(t)] = \int_a^b L\left[x(t), \frac{dx(t)}{dt}, t \right] dt$$

$L[x(t), dx(t)/dt, t]$ is the Lagrangian.

Referring to our previous discussion we shall be most interested in a functional such as $P[u(t)]$. We remember that this quantity is the probability density that $u(t)$ should take on a particular realization over the whole range of t. It is the limit of the probability density function $P_n(u(t_1), u(t_2), \ldots, u(t_n))$ if the discrete parameter n is replaced by the continuous parameter. $P[u(t)]$ depends upon the value of $u(t)$ at every value of t; it depends upon all values of $u(t)$ in some interval $a \leqslant t \leqslant b$.

The concept of the functional may be extended to several dependent and independent variables. Thus there is no difficulty in considering the functional $F[x(t, u, \ldots), y(t, u, \ldots), \ldots]$. From the probabilistic point of view this means we can consider the probability density functional associated with three components of velocity where each component depends upon three spatial coordinates and one time coordinate. For convenience most of our development in this section, however, will be in terms of the simpler functional $F[x(t)]$.

If we consider an interval (a, b) on the real line (that is, choose $a \leqslant t \leqslant b$), we may define several different functionals depending upon our interest. We may consider, for example: $F[x_c(t)]$, where $x_c(t)$ is the class* of all continuous functions in (a, b); $F[x_i(t)]$, where $x_i(t)$ is the class of all functions that are square integrable in (a, b); $F[x_0(t)]$, where $x_0(t)$ is the class of all functions that are differentiable to some order in (a, b); and so on. We may also choose to consider $F[x_e(t)]$, where $x_e(t)$ is the class of all continuous functions satisfying a particular equation or constraint. We shall be especially concerned with this latter type of functional since the fields we shall treat, such as the velocity field, obey a set of governing equations.

2.2.1. Continuity

We define the continuity of a functional in the following manner: The functional $F[x(t)]$ is continuous at $x(t)$ if

$$\lim_{n \to \infty} F[x_n(t)] = F[x(t)].$$

whenever

$$\lim_{n \to \infty} x_n(t) = x(t)$$

We have to take some care in defining what is meant by the statement that $x_n(t)$ approaches $x(t)$ as $n \to \infty$. A common definition is to state that $\lim_{n \to \infty} x_n(t) \to x(t)$ if the maximum value of $|x_n(t) - x(t)|$ (over the interval (a, b) for which t is defined) approaches 0 as $n \to \infty$. This is called continuity of order zero.

This definition is important in establishing the connection between the functional $P[u(t)]$ and the n-point function $P(u(t_1), u(t_2), \ldots, u(t_n))$ in the limit as $n \to \infty$. We will now point out how, in the sense of the above definition, $F[x(t)]$ may be thought of as the limit of the function, $f(x(t_1), x(t_2), \ldots, x(t_n))$, which has discrete arguments.

Consider $F[x(t)]$ a functional with continuity of order zero, to be

---

* The term class here is meant in a descriptive (not precise) sense.

defined over the range $a \leqslant t \leqslant b$ where the $x(t)$ are real and continuous functions and $A \leqslant x(t) \leqslant B$. Now replace $x(t)$ by the function $x_n(t)$ where $(l = b - a)$

$$\text{(2-53)} \qquad x_n(t) = x\left(a + \frac{l}{n}\right) \equiv \check{x}_1 \qquad a \leqslant t \leqslant a + \frac{l}{n}$$

$$x_n\left(a + \frac{kl}{n}\right) = x\left(a + \frac{kl}{n}\right) \equiv \check{x}_k$$

and $x_n(t)$ varies linearly between $x[a + (kl/n)]$ and $x[a + (k + 1)l/n]$ in the interval

$$a + \frac{kl}{n} \leqslant t \leqslant a + \frac{(k + 1)l}{n} \qquad (k = 1, 2, \ldots, n - 1)$$

$F[x_n(t)]$ is now determined by the n values $\check{x}_k$ and the linearity condition. We may represent $F[x_n(t)]$ by the function

$$f_n(\check{x}_1, \check{x}_2, \ldots, \check{x}_n)$$

Now $\lim_{n\to\infty} x_n(t) \to x(t)$ and since $x(t)$ is continuous and the functional $F[x(t)]$ is assumed continuous of order zero then it may be shown that

$$F[x(t)] = \lim_{n \to \infty} F[x_n(t)]$$

The n values $\check{x}_1, \ldots, \check{x}_n$, together with the statement that $x_n(t)$ varies linearly between $\check{x}_j$ and $\check{x}_{j+1}$, serve to define $x_n(t)$. These n values may be made to correspond to the n points $x(t_1), \ldots, x(t_n)$. The *functional* $F[x_n(t)]$ may thus be represented by the *function*,

$$f_n(\check{x}_1, \ldots, \check{x}_n) = f_n(x(t_1), \ldots, x(t_n)).$$

Since $F[x_n(t)] \to F[x(t)]$ as $n \to \infty$ it is meaningful to think of $F[x(t)]$ as the limit of $f_n(x(t_1), \ldots, x(t_n))$ as $n \to \infty$. The reader is asked to remember, however, that $f_n(x(t_1), \ldots, x(t_n))$ is a *function* and $F[x(t)]$ is a *functional* and that strictly speaking $F[x(t)]$ is defined as the limit of the functional $F[x_n(t)]$. In this book we shall accept a looseness of terminology and term $F[x(t)]$ the limit of $f_n(x(t_1), \ldots, x(t_n))$ as $n \to \infty$, since it is intuitively clear what is meant. Whenever it is necessary to explicitly consider the limit, care must be taken to distinguish between $F[x_n(t)]$ and $f_n(x(t_1), \ldots, x(t_n))$.

2.2.2. Linear Functionals

A linear function of n variables has the form

$$F_1(x_i) = \sum_{i=1}^{n} a_i x_i$$

A linear functional may thus be defined as

(2-54) $$F_1[x(t)] = \int_a^b k(t)x(t)\, dt$$

where we note that if

$$x(t) = \lambda x_1(t) + \mu x_2(t)$$

then

(2-55) $$F_1[x(t)] = \lambda F_1[x_1(t)] + \mu F_1[x_2(t)]$$

There are more general definitions of functionals that are linear in the sense that they satisfy Eq. 2-55 but we shall not consider them here. We refer the reader to Volterra (1959).

Generalizing the homogeneous function of the second order

$$F_2(x_i, x_j) = \sum_{i=1}^{n} \sum_{j=1}^{n} a_{ij} x_i x_j$$

we are led to the functional

(2-56) $$F_2[x(t)] = \int_a^b \int_a^b k(t_1, t_2) x(t_1) x(t_2)\, dt_1\, dt_2$$

where with no loss of generality we choose $k(t_1, t_2) = k(t_2, t_1)$.

Finally the generalization to regular homogeneous functionals of degree n, motivated by the expression

$$F_m(x_i, x_j, \ldots, x_l) = \sum_{i=1}^{n} \sum_{j=1}^{n} \cdots \sum_{l=1}^{n} a_{ij\ldots l} x_i x_j \cdots x_l$$

is

(2-57)

$$F_m[x(t)] = \int_a^b \cdots \int_a^b \int_a^b k(t_1, t_2, \ldots, t_m) x(t_1) x(t_2) \cdots x(t_m) \, dt_1 \, dt_2 \cdots dt_m$$

where again with no loss of generality $k(t_1, t_2, \ldots, t_m)$ is chosen to be symmetric in the t_j.

The functional $G_n[x(t)]$ defined as

(2-58) $G_n[x(t)] = k_0 + F_1[x(t)] + F_2[x(t)] + \cdots + F_n[x(t)]$

is termed a regular functional of degree n.

A theorem of great importance states roughly that many functionals $G[x(t)]$ continuous in the continuous functions $x(t)$ over (a, b) may be represented in the form given in Eq. 2-58 in the limit as $n \to \infty$. $G[x(t)]$ thus may take the form

(2-59) $G[x(t)] = \displaystyle\sum_{n=0}^{\infty} F_n[x(t)]$

$$= k_0 + \int_a^b k_1(t_1) x(t_1) \, dt_1 + \int_a^b \int_a^b k_2(t_1, t_2) x(t_1) x(t_2) \, dt_1 \, dt_2$$

$$+ \cdots + \int_a^b \cdots \int_a^b \int_a^b k_n(t_1, t_2, \ldots, t_n) x(t_1) x(t_2)$$

$$\cdots x(t_n) \, dt_1 \, dt_2 \cdots dt_n + \cdots$$

where the k_n depend only upon the form of the functional $G[x(t)]$ and not upon the particular $x(t)$.

If $x(t)$ is approximated by the form given in Eq. 2-53 we can readily see from Eq. 2-59 precisely how $G[x(t)]$ may be approximated by a function of discrete variables. For example, the integral

$$\int_a^b k_1(t_1) x(t_1) \, dt_1$$

becomes equal to the sum

$$\check{x}_1 \int_a^{a+l/n} k_1(t)\, dt + \sum_{m=1}^{n-1} \int_{a+ml/n}^{a+(m+1)l/n} k_1(t_1)$$

$$\times \left[\check{x}_m - \frac{(\check{x}_{m+1} - \check{x}_m)n}{l}\left(a + \frac{ml}{n}\right) + \frac{n}{l}(\check{x}_{m+1} - \check{x}_m)t_1 \right] dt_1$$

$$= \check{x}_1 \int_a^{a+l/n} k_1(t)\, dt + \sum_{m=1}^{n-1} \check{x}_m \left[\int_{a+ml/n}^{a+(m+1)l/n} k_1(t)\, dt_1 \right] + \sum_{m=1}^{n-1} (\check{x}_m - \check{x}_{m+1})$$

$$\times \left[\frac{n}{l}\left(a + \frac{ml}{n}\right) \int_{a+ml/n}^{a+(m+1)l/n} k_1(t_1)\, dt_1 \right]$$

$$+ \sum_{m=1}^{n-1} \frac{n}{l}(\check{x}_{m+1} - \check{x}_m) \left[\int_{a+ml/n}^{a+(m+1)l/n} k_1(t_1)t_1\, dt_1 \right]$$

where $l = b - a$.

Therefore we have

(2-60) $$\int_a^b k_1(t_1)x(t_1)\, dt_1 \approx \sum_{j=0}^{n-1} \check{x}_j c_j$$

where the c_j depend upon k_1, a, b, and n. Similar analysis may be applied to the mth-order integral terms and we see that we revert back to the forms $F_m(\check{x}_i, \check{x}_j, \ldots, \check{x}_l)$ which suggested the expression $F_m[x(t)]$ originally.

It should be noted that the same type of approximations given in Eq. 2-60 may formally be obtained by the use of delta functions. One could approximate $x(t)$ by

(2-61) $$x(t) = \sum_{m=0}^{n-1} \check{x}_{m+1}\, \delta\left[t - \left(a + \frac{ml}{n}\right) \right]$$

and show that for large n the expression obtained in a good approximation to the expression given in Eq. 2-60.

The expression given in Eq. 2-61 is of great mathematical convenience in formal manipulations compared to the expression given by Eq. 2-53. It is often difficult to see physically, however, just what is happening when such an approximation is used since a continuous function is replaced by a succession of discrete infinite values. We suggest to the reader that when he sees Eq. 2-61 used, he considers this to be an abbreviated notation for the more lengthy process required by Eq. 2-53.

Lastly, we note that whenever necessary we shall let a or b take on infinite values and assume convergence when applying the result to a physical problem.

2.2.3. Differentiation

The concept of differentiation of a functional may be motivated by generalizing the concept of the total differential. The total differential df is defined as

$$(2\text{-}62) \qquad df = \sum_{i=1}^{n} \frac{\partial f}{\partial x_i} \, dx_i$$

where f is a function of $x_1, x_2, \ldots, x_n$.

A generalization of the total differential df is

$$(2\text{-}63) \qquad \delta F = \int_a^b \frac{\delta F}{\delta x(\xi)} \, \delta x(\xi) \, d\xi$$

where the discrete parameter n is replaced by the continuous parameter ξ. The variational symbol δ is used to replace the differential symbol d. $\delta F/\delta x(\xi)$, as yet undefined, replaces the partial derivative $\partial f/\partial x_i$. To indicate the fact that $\delta F/\delta x(\xi)$ is a functional that also depends on the parameter ξ we shall often write

$$F'[x(t), \xi] = \delta F/\delta x(\xi)$$

to make this explicit. (We note that in contrast to the ordinary derivative notation, where dy/dx is also the quotient of differentials, $[\delta F/\delta x(\xi)] \, \delta x(\xi)$ is *not* equal to δF.)

The function $\partial f/\partial x_i$ is defined as $\lim_{\epsilon_i \to 0} (\Delta_i f/\epsilon_i)$ where ϵ_i is the increment in the variable x_i and $\Delta_i f$ is the corresponding increment in f.

When $f(x_1, x_2, \ldots, x_n)$ is replaced by $F[x(t)]$ we must replace the increment ϵ_i by a continuous increment $\delta x(t)$ which we denote by $\theta(t)$. We choose $\theta(t)$ such that it is of constant sign, $|\theta(t)| < \epsilon$, and $\theta(t) = 0$ outside a small interval h within the range of t. We suppose the interval

h contains the point ξ within its interior. With this definition we generalize the concept of the partial derivative $\partial f/\partial x_i$ by defining the functional derivative

$$(2\text{-}64) \quad F'[x(t), \xi] \equiv \lim_{\sigma \to 0} \frac{\Delta F}{\sigma} = \lim_{\sigma \to 0} \left[\frac{F[x(t) + \theta(t)] - F[x(t)]}{\sigma} \right]$$

where

$$\sigma = \int_{\xi - h/2}^{\xi + h/2} \theta(t)\, dt \quad \text{and} \quad \sigma \to 0 \quad \text{means} \quad \epsilon \to 0 \quad \text{and} \quad h \to 0$$

The expression $F'[x(t), \xi]$ depends upon $x(t)$ and additionally upon the point ξ. We suppose that the limit $F'[x(t), \xi]$ is finite and determinate as ϵ and h tend simultaneously to zero and that the approach to the limit is uniform with respect to all functions $x(t)$ and all points ξ.

The functional derivative may also be formally defined by using a Dirac delta function. Schweber (1961), for example, gives the definition

$$(2\text{-}65) \quad F'[x(t), \xi] = \lim_{\substack{\eta \to 0 \\ \epsilon \to 0}} \frac{1}{\epsilon} [F[x(t) + \epsilon \delta_\eta(t - \xi)] - F[x(t)]]$$

where $\delta_\eta(t - \xi)$ is a well-behaved function which tends to the Dirac delta function as $\eta \to 0$.

Using the definition given in Eq. 2-64 to define δF it may be shown that for functionals continuous of order zero, δF is a linear functional of $\delta x(t)$ and that δF differs by infinitesimals of higher order than ϵ from the functional ΔF. $\delta F/\delta x(\xi)$ may thus be calculated using the basic definition Eq. 2-64 or the variational form Eq. 2-63. We shall use Eq. 2-63 in the next few pages since it is so easy to apply when differentiating functionals of the form $F_n(x(t))$. An example of the use of Eq. 2-64 will then be given. [The reader is referred to Hardy (1952), p. 307, for a discussion of the relation between increments and differentials for ordinary functions. This discussion will help clarify the relation between δF and ΔF mentioned previously.]

A specific example of the operation of taking a functional derivative may be given by considering the functional

$$F_1[x(t)] = \int^b k_1(t) x(t)\, dt$$

The variation $\delta F_1[x(t)]$ of the functional $F_1[x(t)]$ is

(2-66) $$\delta F_1[x(t)] = \int_a^b k_1(t)\delta x(t)\, dt$$

Comparison of Eqs. 2-63 and 2-66 shows that

(2-67) $$F_1'[x(t), \xi] = k_1(\xi)$$

so that in this particular case $F'[x(t), \xi]$ reduces to a function of only ξ and is independent of $x(t)$.

From Eq. 2-67 we see that formally at least

(2-68) $$\frac{\delta x(t')}{\delta x(t)} = \delta(t - t')$$

since

$$x(t') = \int_a^b \delta(t' - t)x(t)\, dt \qquad a < t' < b$$

If we consider the functional of degree two

$$F_2[x(t)] = \int_a^b \int_a^b k_2(t_1, t_2)x(t_1)x(t_2)\, dt_1\, dt_2$$

then

(2-69) $$\delta F_2[x(t)] = \int_a^b \int_a^b k_2(t_1, t_2)\delta x(t_1)x(t_2)\, dt_1\, dt_2$$

$$+ \int_a^b \int_a^b k_2(t_1, t_2)x(t_1)\delta x(t_2)\, dt_1\, dt_2$$

$$= 2 \int_a^b \int_a^b k_2(t, \xi)x(t)\delta x(\xi)\, dt\, d\xi$$

so that here

(2-70) $$F_2'[x(t), \xi] = 2 \int_a^b k(t, \xi)x(t)\, dt$$

and $F_2'[x(t), \xi]$ is a functional dependent upon both $x(t)$ and ξ.

In general the derivative of the functional of degree n

$$F_n[x(t)] = \int_a^b \cdots \int_a^b \int_a^b k_n(t_1, t_2, \ldots, t_n)x(t_1)x(t_2) \cdots x(t_n)\, dt_1\, dt_2 \cdots dt_n$$

has the functional derivative

$$(2\text{-}71) \quad F_n'[x(t), \xi] = n\int_a^b \cdots \int_a^b \int_a^b k_n(t_1, t_2, \ldots, t_{n-1}, \xi)x(t_1)x(t_2)$$

$$\cdots x(t_{n-1})\, dt_1\, dt_2 \cdots dt_{n-1}$$

We have pointed out (Eq. 2-59) that many functionals may be represented by the infinite series

$$\sum_{n=0}^{\infty} F_n[x(t)]$$

and Eq. 2-71 gives us the formula for taking the functional derivative of a functional expressed in this manner.

It is instructive to find the functional derivative of $F_1[x(t)]$ by using Eq. 2-64 directly. We have then

$$(2\text{-}72) \quad \lim_{\sigma \to 0} \frac{\Delta F_1}{\sigma} = \lim_{\substack{\epsilon \to 0 \\ h \to 0}} \left[\frac{\displaystyle\int_a^b k_1(t)[x(t) + \theta(t)]\, dt - \int_a^b k_1(t)x(t)\, dt}{\displaystyle\int_{\xi-h/2}^{\xi+h/2} \theta(t)\, dt} \right]$$

$$= \lim_{\substack{\epsilon \to 0 \\ h \to 0}} \left[\frac{\displaystyle\int_a^b k_1(t)\theta(t)\, dt}{\displaystyle\int_{\xi-h/2}^{\xi+h/2} \theta(t)\, dt} \right]$$

$$= \lim_{\substack{\epsilon \to 0 \\ h \to 0}} \left[\frac{\displaystyle\int_{\xi-h/2}^{\xi+h/2} k_1(t)\theta(t)\, dt}{\displaystyle\int_{\xi-h/2}^{\xi+h/2} \theta(t)\, dt} \right]$$

$$= k_1(\xi)$$

since we remember that $\theta(t)$ is nonzero only in the interval $\xi \pm h/2$.

The second derivative of $F[x(t)]$ may be found by considering the first functional derivative of $F'[x(t), \xi]$. We denote this functional $F''[x(t), \xi_1, \xi_2]$. It may be shown that if $F''[x(t), \xi_1, \xi_2]$ is continuous of order 0 and is continuous with respect to both ξ_1 and ξ_2 then

$$(2\text{-}73) \qquad F''[x(t), \xi_1, \xi_2] = F''[x(t), \xi_2, \xi_1]$$

That is, subject to these restrictions, the order of functional differentiation may be interchanged.

In general we may form the nth-order functional derivative

$$F^{(n)}[x(t), \xi_1, \xi_2, \ldots, \xi_n]$$

which under suitable continuity conditions is symmetric in the ξ_j.

We note here that the nth-order functional derivative of the functional

$$F_n[x(t)] = \int_a^b \cdots \int_a^b \int_a^b k_n(t_1, t_2, \ldots, t_n) x(t_1) x(t_2) \cdots x(t_n)\, dt_1\, dt_2 \cdots dt_n$$

is the function

$$(2\text{-}74) \qquad F_n^{(n)}[x(t), \xi_1, \xi_2, \ldots, \xi_n] = n!\, k_n(\xi_1, \xi_2, \ldots, \xi_n)$$

When Eq. 2-74 is used to replace the k_n in Eq. 2-59, we see that Eq. 2-59 is then a generalization of the Taylor series expansion used for discrete variables.

Lastly we note that the functional derivative of the functional

$$G[x(t)] = \int_a^b f[x(t)]\, dt$$

is

$$(2\text{-}75) \qquad G'[x(t), \xi] = \left.\frac{\partial f}{\partial x}\right|_{t=\xi}$$

if $f(x)$ may be expanded in a Taylor series about the point $x = 0$.

Although we shall not require it, the reader will note that the functional formulation has been reviewed in sufficient detail here to allow one to directly derive Euler's equations from the variation $\delta I[x(t)]$.

2.2.4. Integration of Functionals

The indefinite integral of a functional $M'[x(t), \xi]$ may be considered to be the functional $M[x(t)]$. This statement is analogous to stating that the indefinite integral of $\partial f(x_1, \ldots, x_n)/\partial x_i$ is $f(x_1, \ldots, x_n)$. We shall require in our work, however, in addition, the analog of the definite integral

$$\int\limits_{A_n}^{B} \cdots \int\limits_{A_2}^{B_2} \int\limits_{A_1}^{B_1} f_n(x_1, x_2, \ldots, x_n)\, dx_1\, dx_2 \cdots dx_n$$

The integration of the functional $F[x(t)]$ in this sense implies integration in a space of infinite dimensions and it requires some care to provide a useful definition. We remember that $F[x(t)]$ may be represented, approximately, by the function $f_n(\check{x}_1, \check{x}_2, \ldots, \check{x}_n)$ using the methods given in Eq. 2-53. An integral of f_n over some volume in the n-dimensional space spanned by x_j ($j = 1$ to n) is of the form

$$(2\text{-}76) \qquad I_n = \int\limits_{A_n}^{B_n} \cdots \int\limits_{A_2}^{A_2} \int\limits_{A_1}^{B_1} f_n(\check{x}_1, \check{x}_2, \ldots, \check{x}_n)\, d\check{x}_1\, d\check{x}_2 \cdots d\check{x}_n$$

That is, it is an n-fold integral. In the limit $n \to \infty$, through which we recover $F[x(t)]$ from f_n, the n-fold integral becomes an integral in an infinite number of dimensions. We may thus hope to let $\lim_{n\to\infty} I_n$ serve as the definition for the integration of $F[x(t)]$.

Unfortunately $\lim_{n\to\infty} I_n$ will not in general exist. If, for example, $F(t) = \int_a^b k(t)x(t)\, dt$, then I_n will have the form

$$(2\text{-}77) \qquad I_n = \int\limits_{A_n}^{B_n} \cdots \int\limits_{A_2}^{B_2} \int\limits_{A_1}^{B_1} \sum_{j=1}^{n} \check{x}_j c_j\, d\check{x}_1\, d\check{x}_2 \cdots d\check{x}_n$$

Taking for convenience $A_j = 0$, $B_j = B$ we find

$$(2\text{-}78) \qquad I_n = \frac{B^2}{2} c_1 B^{n-1} + \frac{B^2}{2} c_2 B^{n-1} + \cdots + \frac{B^2}{2} c_n B^{n-1}$$

which has the limit 0 or ∞ as $n \to \infty$ depending upon whether or not B is less than or greater than 1.

The difficulty occurs because the volume

$$V_n = \int\limits_{A_n}^{B_n} \cdots \int\limits_{A_2}^{B_2} \int\limits_{A_1}^{B_1} dx_1 \, dx_2 \cdots dx_n$$

does not exist as $n \to \infty$. This difficulty could be overcome here if we have a definition of integration that essentially gives us $\lim_{n\to\infty} I_n/V_n$ rather than $\lim_{n\to\infty} I_n$. In other words we would integrate over the volume element $(dx_1 \, dx_2 \cdots dx_n)/V_n$ rather than simply $dx_1 \, dx_2 \cdots dx_n$. $1/V_n$ would be a weighting function introduced to insure convergence of the integral.

Any definition of integration that is given will have to use some limit of this type. Fortunately for the restricted needs of this book all integrals we consider already include an appropriate weighting function. We consider here only integrals that contain in the integrand the probability density functional $P[x(t)]$. The only integral over $F[x(t)]$ treated will be of the form

$$(2\text{-}79) \quad \lim_{n \to \infty} I_n{}^p = \int\limits_{-\infty}^{\infty} \cdots \int\limits_{-\infty}^{\infty} \int\limits_{-\infty}^{\infty} f_n(\breve{x}_1, \breve{x}_2, \ldots, \breve{x}_n)$$

$$\times P_n(\breve{x}_1, \breve{x}_2, \ldots, \breve{x}_n) \, d\breve{x}_1 \, d\breve{x}_2 \cdots d\breve{x}_n$$

where $P_n(\breve{x}_1, \breve{x}_2, \ldots, \breve{x}_n)$ is determined from $P[x(t)]$ using Eq. 2-53. We suppose that the integral

$$\int\limits_{-\infty}^{\infty} \cdots \int\limits_{-\infty}^{\infty} \int\limits_{-\infty}^{\infty} P_n(\breve{x}_1, \breve{x}_2, \ldots, \breve{x}_n) \, d\breve{x}_1 \, d\breve{x}_2 \cdots d\breve{x}_n$$

is properly normalized to unity for all n. In this book when we write an integral of the form

$$I = \int\limits_{R} F[x(t)] P[x(t)] \, dx(t)$$

we interpret it as $\lim_{n\to\infty} I_n{}^p$. R formally denotes the region over which $x(t)$ varies.

Integrals of the form

$$I' = \int_R g(\xi_1, \ldots, \xi_j) P[x(t)] \, dx(t)$$

where $g(\xi_1, \ldots, \xi_j)$ is an ordinary function of j points will also occur. These integrals may be treated by replacing the function $g(\xi_1, \ldots, \xi_j)$ by the functional

$$G[g(\xi_1, \ldots, \xi_j)]$$
$$= \int g(\xi_1', \ldots, \xi_j') \, \delta_\eta(\xi_1' - \xi_1) \cdots \delta_\eta(\xi_j' - \xi_j) \, d\xi_1' \cdots d\xi_j'$$

where $\delta_\eta(\xi_k' - \xi_k)$ is a well-behaved function which tends to the Dirac delta function as $\eta \to 0$.

Lastly, integrals of the form

$$W[v(t)] = \int_R h\left(\int v(t)u(t) \, dt\right) P[u(t)] \, du(t)$$

must be considered. Here $I_n{}^p$ corresponds to

$$W_n(\breve{v}_1, \ldots, \breve{v}_n) = \int_{-\infty}^{\infty} \cdots \int h(\sum \breve{v}_n \breve{u}_n \, \Delta t_n) P(\breve{u}_1, \ldots, \breve{u}_n) \, d\breve{u}_1 \cdots d\breve{u}_n$$

where $\breve{v}_n$ is a weighting of $v(t)$ in the interval Δt_n. $W_n(\breve{v}_1, \ldots, \breve{v}_n)$ is a function, not a functional. To recover a functional form from this definition we associate $W[v_n(t)]$ with $W_n(\breve{v}_1, \ldots, \breve{v}_n)$. We will assume that this association is implicit in our limiting procedure for integrals of the above type. In this sense $\lim_{n \to \infty} W_n(\breve{v}_1, \ldots, \breve{v}_n)$ yields the functional $W[v(t)]$ represented formally by the above expression.

For a more rigorous discussion of integrals of the type considered here we refer the reader to a paper by Gel'fand and Yaglom (1960) and the report by Friedrichs, Shapiro et al. (1957). In many other developments, I is defined rigorously as a Stieljes integral. We have not done this here since introduction of the Stieljes integral would have required considerable mathematical preparation which we felt would be inappropriate to include in this book. For those readers who find the above definitions somewhat unsatisfactory we refer the reader to some pertinent remarks in Hopf (1952).

2.2.5. Probability Density Functionals

As we pointed out previously we require the probability density function

$$P_n(u(t_1), u(t_2), \ldots, u(t_n))$$

in the limit $n \to \infty$. In the sense given in Section 2.2.1, $P[u(t)]$ may be considered to be this limit and in any physical problem treated in this book we will assume that the limit $P[u_n(t)]_{n \to \infty}$ exists. We thus interpret $P[u(t)]$ as the probability that the field lies between $u(t)$ and $u(t) + \delta u(t)$. $P[u(t)]$ depends upon the value of $u(t)$ for every permissible value of t.* (This treatment may, of course, be extended to functionals of a number of functions like $P[u(t), v(t), w(t)]$.)

We may discuss the correlation function of the form

$$\overline{[u_1(t)][u_2(t_2)] \cdots [u_n(t_n)]}$$

most easily by first considering the functional which may be considered to be the analog of the characteristic function. We remember that we defined the characteristic function $M_n(v_1, v_2, \ldots, v_n)$ as (see Eq. 2-6)

$$M_n(v_1, v_2, \ldots, v_n) = \int\limits_{-\infty}^{\infty} \cdots \int\limits_{-\infty}^{\infty} \int\limits_{-\infty}^{\infty} \exp\left[i \sum_{k=1}^{n} v_k u_k \right]$$

$$\times P_n(u_1, u_2, \ldots, u_n) \, du_1 \, du_2 \cdots du_n$$

In the limit $n \to \infty$ where $P_n(u_1, u_2, \ldots, u_n)$ approaches $P[u(t)]$ the function $M_n(v_1, v_2, \ldots, v_n)$ approaches a functional which may be written as $M[v(t)]$. To write this functional in terms of $P[u(t)]$ we must replace the finite summation

$$\sum_{k=1}^{n} v_k u_k$$

by an integral and replace the integral over $u_1, u_2, \ldots, u_n$ by integration over an infinite-dimensional space.

---

* In the special case when the spectrum of $u(t)$, $S(v)$, is zero outside of some finite interval, $P[u(t)]$ depends on a finite number of parameters. We consider here the general case when $u(t)$ is not band limited.

We thus define

$$(2\text{-}80) \qquad M[v(t)] = \int_R \exp\left[i\int v(t)u(t)\,dt\right]P[u(t)]\,du(t)$$

where R is an integral over the infinite-dimensional function space and $\int v(t)u(t)\,dt$ is an integral over all values of t for which $u(t)$ is defined. (See Section 2.2.4 for a definition of this integral.)

In the n-dimensional case $M_n(v_1, v_2, \ldots, v_n)$ is the expectation value of

$$\exp\left[i\sum_{k=1}^{n} v_k u_k\right]$$

Similarly here $M[v(t)]$ is the expectation value of $\exp[i\int v(t)u(t)\,dt]$.

To derive the correlation functions we take functional derivatives of $M[v(t)]$. The first functional derivative of $M[v(t)]$ with respect to $v(t)$ is (assuming differentiation and our definition of integration, commute)

$$(2\text{-}81) \qquad M'[v(t), \xi] = \int_R iu(\xi)\exp\left[i\int v(t)u(t)\,dt\right]P[u(t)]\,du(t)$$

Proceeding step by step we find that the nth-order functional derivative of $M[v(t)]$ is

$$(2\text{-}82) \quad M^n[v(t), \xi_1, \xi_2, \ldots, \xi_n]$$

$$= \int_R i^n u(\xi_1)u(\xi_2)\cdots u(\xi_n)\exp\left[i\int v(t)u(t)\,dt\right]P[u(t)]\,du(t)$$

The expectation value of $u(\xi)$ is defined as

$$(2\text{-}83) \qquad \overline{u(\xi)} = \int_R u(\xi)P[u(t)]\,du(t)$$

in analogy to the finite-dimensional definition

$$\overline{u(t_1)} = \int_{-\infty}^{\infty}\cdots\int_{-\infty}^{\infty}\int_{-\infty}^{\infty} u(t_1)P_n(u_1, u_2, \ldots, u_n)\,du_1\,du_2\cdots du_n$$

We see immediately then from Eq. 2-81 that

$$(2\text{-}84) \qquad M'[v(t), \xi]\big|_{v=0} = \overline{iu(\xi)}$$

In general

$$(2\text{-}85) \quad \overline{u(\xi_1)u(\xi_2)\cdots u(\xi_n)} = \int_R u(\xi_1)u(\xi_2)\cdots u(\xi_n)P[u(t)]\,du(t)$$

and thus

$$(2\text{-}86) \quad M^n[v(t),\, \xi_1,\, \xi_2,\, \ldots,\, \xi_n]\big|_{v=0} = i^n\overline{u(\xi_1)u(\xi_2)\cdots u(\xi_n)}$$

As an example of a characteristic functional we write the form of the characteristic functional for the case of gaussian statistics. From analogy to Eq. 2-46 we have

$$(2\text{-}87) \quad M_G[v(t)] = \exp\left[i\int\overline{u(t)}v(t)\,dt - \tfrac{1}{2}\iint\lambda(t,s)v(t)v(s)\,ds\,dt\right]$$

In closing we note that for the most part we shall work with the functional $M[v(t)]$ rather than $P[u(t)]$. It is somewhat more useful to derive functional equations governing $M[v(t)]$ since given $M[v(t)]$ the correlation functions may be derived by functional differentiation rather than integration of the type described in Section 2.2.4. In our subsequent developments the definition of integration given in Section 2.2.4 is never explicitly used in calculation. It will only be used formally to find the functional equations governing $M[v(t)]$, from the basic deterministic equations.

CHAPTER 3

General Formulations

In this chapter we will outline general methods of formulation and solution used in treating statistical continuum problems. In Section 3.1 we show how functional equations may be derived for the characteristic functional necessary to describe a particular physical situation. We will present solutions for some simple cases. In Section 3.2 we shall derive from this general formulation and also, in a more direct fashion, the statistical moment equations that are used so commonly in the treatment of many problems. A discussion of perturbation procedures and the cumulant neglect hypothesis will follow in Sections 3.3.1 and 3.3.2. Finally, in Section 3.4 we shall discuss the use of variational principles for extracting useful information from basically statistical problems.

As we have mentioned in Chapter 1, the functional formulation is at present not a very practical method for obtaining useful information in most problems of interest. We have introduced this formulation principally in recognition of the fact that, despite the difficulty in its utilization, it is the formulation that must be given if a complete description is to be obtained for the statistical problem. Since many readers will nevertheless still not wish to master the mathematical details of the functional formulation we have written the majority of the later chapters of the book so that they may be understood without reading Section 3.1 and the first portion of Section 3.2.

In Chapter 1 we stressed the fact that in general functionals are necessary to provide a complete description in a statistical problem. In the harmonic oscillator problem described by the equation

$$m(t) \frac{d^2 x}{dt^2} + k(t)x = F(t)$$

where $m(t)$, $k(t)$, and $F(t)$ are random variables, the problem ideally is to find $P[x(t), m(t), k(t), F(t)]$ in terms of $P[m(t), k(t), F(t)]$. Except as an approximation, it is impossible to find even the moment $\overline{x(t)}$ without a knowledge of the entire functional $P[m(t), k(t), F(t)]$. In addition, if we know less than $P[x(t), m(t), k(t), F(t)]$, we have incomplete statistical information. It thus becomes very desirable to have an equation governing $P[x(t), m(t), k(t), F(t)]$ which we may hope to solve in terms of $P[m(t), k(t), F(t)]$.

It is possible to derive an equation governing $P[x(t), m(t), k(t), F(t)]$ in the harmonic oscillator problem, and it is possible in most statistical problems to derive an equation governing the functional analogous to $P[x(t), m(t), k(t), F(t)]$. This fact is of great conceptual importance, since it allows one to formulate the entire statistical problem in a single equation. Given this equation, all possible information of a statistical nature may be obtained from it and there is no need to refer again to the original deterministic equation. The moment equations that form the heart of many statistical investigations may be derived from this governing functional equation.

We may also derive equations for the generalized Fourier transform of P, termed the characteristic functional and denoted by M. The information contained in M is equivalent to the information contained in P. It is, moreover, somewhat more useful to have the equation governing M since it is very easy to derive the moment equations from this equation. In this chapter we shall for the most part thus derive equations governing M rather than P.

The equation governing either P or M is a functional equation, and up to the present time very little has been done to solve these equations directly. This does not mean, however, that there may not be substantial progress in the future. In fact, the writer believes that progress will indeed occur. Because of this expectation, in addition to the necessity of introducing functionals to provide a complete statistical description, we have included detailed material on functionals in this chapter and in Section 2.2. Some work on the use of functionals in turbulence theory has already been accomplished and is discussed in Chapter 7.

In Section 3.1 we shall derive the functional equations governing the characteristic functional for a number of physical problems, and some solutions will be given for the simpler equations. We shall, in each subsection, give the functions on which the probability density functional must depend if it is to provide complete statistical information in the problem. We shall not prove that all statistical information is in this functional but shall simply assume that the probability functional (or characteristic functional) that has as its arguments all the physical field variables that enter the problem provides us with a complete description. As we pointed out in Section 2.1.4, any less information is insufficient.

3.1. Derivation of the Functional Equations

3.1.1. Harmonic Oscillator Problem

In Chapter 1 we considered the one-dimensional harmonic oscillator subject to a forcing function $F(t)$. To begin our discussion, let us consider this simple case and further restrict our discussion initially to the case in which m and k are independent of x and t. The governing equation of the harmonic oscillator is

$$(3\text{-}1) \qquad m\frac{d^2x}{dt^2} + kx = F(t)$$

We assume that $F(t)$ is a random function of time and that the probability density functional $P[F(t)]$ is known. We desire to calculate the probability density functional $P[x(t), F(t)]$ and the problem we face here is to determine an equation governing $P[x(t), F(t)]$ or equivalently an equation governing the characteristic functional $M[y(t), g(t)]$. We shall now give a procedure for deriving an equation governing $M[y(t), g(t)]$. For developments in this chapter we have relied on the basic paper by Hopf (1952) and a more recent paper by Lewis and Kraichnan (1962). We also wish to acknowledge many private discussions with J. Molyneux on the nature of functional solutions.

We first note that

$$(3\text{-}2) \quad M[y(t), g(t)] = \int_R \exp\left[i\int y(t)x(t)\,dt + i\int g(t)F(t)\,dt\right]$$
$$\cdot P[x(t), F(t)]\,dx(t)\,dF(t)$$

where the integral R is over the infinite-dimensional space taken in the sense given in Section 2.2.4. The other integrals are over all time. For simplicity of notation we shall henceforth write $\int y(t)x(t)\,dt = [y, x]$

and $\int g(t)F(t)\,dt = [g, F]$. We ask the reader to always keep in mind how much information is contained in M or P. The condensed notation should not obscure the fact that $P[x(t)]$ is equivalent to

$$\lim_{n\to\infty} P_n\,(x_1, x_2, \ldots, x_n),$$

(in the sense of Section 2.2.1).

The functional derivative of $M[x(t), F(t)]$ with respect to $y(t)$ will be denoted by the abbreviated form $\delta M/\delta y(\xi)$. Direct calculation shows

$$(3\text{-}3) \qquad \frac{\delta M}{\delta y(\xi)} = i \int_R x(\xi) e^{i[y,x]+i[g,F]} P[x(t), F(t)]\,dx(t)\,dF(t)$$

If we take the ordinary time derivative of $\delta M/\delta y(\xi)$ we have

$$(3\text{-}4) \qquad \frac{d}{d\xi}\frac{\delta M}{\delta y(\xi)} = i \int_R \frac{dx(\xi)}{d\xi}\, e^{i[y,x]+i[g,F]} P[x(t), F(t)]\,dx(t)\,dF(t)$$

where the time has been represented by the variable ξ. The second derivative with respect to ξ yields

$$(3\text{-}5) \qquad \frac{d^2}{d\xi^2}\frac{\delta M}{\delta y(\xi)} = i \int_R \frac{d^2 x(\xi)}{d\xi^2}\, e^{i[y,x]+i[g,F]} P[x(t), F(t)]\,dx(t)\,dF(t)$$

Next let us replace $d^2 x(\xi)/d\xi^2$ in Eq. 3-5 by using Eq. 3-1. We then have

$$(3\text{-}6)$$

$$\frac{d^2}{d\xi^2}\frac{\delta M}{\delta y(\xi)} = \frac{i}{m} \int_R [-kx(\xi) + F(\xi)] e^{i[y,x]+i[g,F]} P[x(t), F(t)]\,dx(t)\,dF(t)$$

We now note that

$$i \int_R x(\xi) e^{i[y,x]+i[g,F]} P[x(t), F(t)]\,dx(t)\,dF(t) = \frac{\delta M}{\delta y(\xi)}$$

and

$$i \int_R F(\xi) e^{i[y,x]+i[g,F]} P[x(t), F(t)]\,dx(t)\,dF(t) = \frac{\delta M}{\delta g(\xi)}$$

We thus have

(3-7) $$m\frac{d^2}{d\xi^2}\frac{\delta M}{\delta y(\xi)} + k\frac{\delta M}{\delta y(\xi)} = \frac{\delta M}{\delta g(\xi)}$$

Equation 3-7 is the functional equation governing the characteristic functional $M[y(t), g(t)]$. The principal boundary condition for the solution to this equation is $P[F(t)]$. Since, however,

$$M[y(t), g(t)] = \int_R e^{i[y,x]+i[g,F]}P[x(t), F(t)] \, dx(t) \, dF(t)$$

and thus

$$M[0, g(t)] = \int_R e^{i[g,F]}P[x(t), F(t)] \, dx(t) \, dF(t)$$

$$= \int_R e^{i[g,F]}P[F(t)] \, dF(t)$$

we may consider the boundary condition to be $M[0, g(t)]$.

In addition to this boundary condition, we specify $x(0) = x_0$ and $dx/dt(0) = x_0'$. This boundary condition could also be made random, but in the developments given here, we shall assume that x_0 and x_0' are the same in all members of the ensemble. Thus we require

$$P_1(x(0)) = \delta(x(0) - x_0)$$

$$P_1\left(\frac{dx}{dt}(0)\right) = \delta\left(\frac{dx}{dt}(0) - x_0'\right)$$

Both $P_1(x(0))$ and $P_1((dx/dt)(0))$ may be derived from $P[x(t)]$, and thus we have imposed a condition on this functional or alternatively on the functional $M[y(t), g(t)]$. The complete solution to the statistical problem is thus obtained by solving Eq. 3-7 subject to the boundary conditions $M[0, g(t)]$ and (x_0, x_0').

It is easy to see from the development how an equation may be derived for any linear equation with constant coefficients subject to a random forcing function. It is instructive to carry our development one step further and derive the functional equation for an harmonic oscillator governed by the equation

(3-8) $$m(t)\frac{d^2x}{dt^2} + k(t)x = F(t)$$

where now $m(t)$ and $k(t)$ are also random variables in addition to $F(t)$. The initial information that we now require is the joint probability density functional $P[m(t), k(t), F(t)]$ and we must find an equation governing the functional $M[y(t), n(t), j(t), g(t)]$ where

$$M[y(t), n(t), j(t), g(t)]$$

$$= \int_R \exp \{i[y, x] + i[n, m] + i[j, k] + i[g, F]\}$$

$$\cdot P[x(t), m(t), k(t), F(t)] \, dx(t) \, dm(t) \, dk(t) \, dF(t)$$

For simplicity we will denote $\exp \{i[y, x] + i[n, m] + i[j, k] + i[g, F]\}$ by $\exp i[\ ]$, omit the arguments of P and write

$$dV \equiv dx(t) \, dm(t) \, dk(t) \, dF(t)$$

Proceeding similarly to our first derivation we first form

(3-9)
$$\frac{\delta M}{\delta y(\xi)} = i \int_R x(\xi) e^{i[\ ]} P \, dV$$

and

(3-10)
$$\frac{d^2}{d\xi^2} \frac{\delta M}{\delta y(\xi)} = i \int_R \frac{d^2 x(\xi)}{d\xi^2} e^{i[\ ]} P \, dV$$

In order to form a term corresponding to $m(t) \, d^2x/dt^2$ we now take a functional derivative of Eq. 3-10 with respect to $n(t)$. This yields

(3-11)
$$\frac{\delta}{\delta n(\xi')} \frac{d^2}{d\xi^2} \frac{\delta M}{\delta y(\xi)} = i^2 \int_R m(\xi') \frac{d^2 x(\xi)}{d\xi^2} e^{i[\ ]} P \, dV$$

In general $\xi' \neq \xi$. Here, however, we will set $\xi' = \xi$, giving

(3-12)
$$\frac{\delta}{\delta n(\xi)} \frac{d^2}{d\xi^2} \frac{\delta M}{\delta y(\xi)} = i^2 \int_R m(\xi) \frac{d^2 x(\xi)}{d\xi^2} e^{i[\ ]} P \, dV$$

Next we use Eq. 3-8 to replace the quantity $m(\xi) \, d^2 x(\xi)/d\xi^2$ by $-k(\xi) x(\xi) + F(\xi)$. Thus

(3-13)
$$\frac{\delta}{\delta n(\xi)} \frac{d^2}{d\xi^2} \frac{\delta M}{\delta y(\xi)} = i^2 \int_R [-k(\xi) x(\xi) + F(\xi)] e^{i[\ ]} P \, dV$$

Finally we note that

$$\frac{\delta}{\delta j(\xi)}\left[\frac{\delta M}{\delta y(\xi)}\right] = i^2 \int_R k(\xi) x(\xi) e^{i[\quad]} {}^1P\, dV$$

and as before

$$\frac{\delta M}{\delta g(\xi)} = i \int_R F(\xi) e^{i[\quad]} {}^1P\, dV$$

giving the functional equation

(3-14) $$\frac{\delta}{\delta n(\xi)}\left[\frac{d^2}{d\xi^2}\frac{\delta M}{\delta y(\xi)}\right] + \frac{\delta}{\delta j(\xi)}\left[\frac{\delta M}{\delta y(\xi)}\right] = i\frac{\delta M}{\delta g(\xi)}$$

The boundary conditions for the solution of Eq. 3-14 are $M[0, n(t), j(t), g(t)]$ and (x_o, x_o').

Little progress has been made in the solution of equations like Eq. 3-14, although something may be said about the simple equation, Eq. 3-7. Unfortunately, most problems of interest in this book are analogous to Eq. 3-14 rather than Eq. 3-7. Nevertheless, we shall conclude this section by showing how equations like Eq. 3-7 may be solved.

First we see that the solution of Eq. 3-7, using a Green's function, $G(t - \alpha)$ (see Eq. 1-6), is

(3-15) $$\frac{\delta M}{\delta y(\xi)} = \int_0^{\xi} \frac{\delta M}{\delta g(\alpha)} G(\xi - \alpha)\, d\alpha$$

Next we write $P[x(t), F(t)]$ in Eq. 3-2 in the form

(3-16) $$P[x(t), F(t)] = P[F(t)]\, \delta[x(t) - \psi(F(t))]$$

Since $x(t)$ and $F(t)$ are causally related through Eq. 3-1, this form is an assertion of the fact that a solution of the form $x(t) = \psi(F(t))$ exists for every function $F(t)$. If Eq. 3-16 is substituted into Eq. 3-2, we find

(3-17)

$$M[y(t), g(t)] = \int_R \exp\left\{i\int y(t)\psi(F(t))\, dt + i\int g(t)F(t)\, dt\right\} P[F(t)]\, dF(t)$$

Substituting Eq. 3-7 into Eq. 3-15 then yields finally (as we might expect from Eq. 3-1) that for Eq. 3-17 to be a solution, we must have

$$(3\text{-}18) \qquad \psi(F(\alpha)) = \int_0^{\xi} F(\alpha)G(\xi - \alpha)\, d\alpha$$

Hence, the solution of Eq. 3-7 is

$$(3\text{-}19) \quad M[y(t), g(t)] = \int_R P[F(t)] \exp\left\{ i \int g(t)F(t)\, dt \right.$$

$$\left. + i \int \left[\int_0^t F(\alpha)G(t - \alpha)\, d\alpha \right] y(t)\, dt \right\} dF(t)$$

We note that obtaining the solution Eq. 3-19 is not dependent on Eq. 3-16. Equation 3-17 may be guessed as the solution form, a technique we often use in solving ordinary differential equations. The expression given in Eq. 3-16 is very useful, however; for instead of proceeding as we did, we might have solved Eq. 3-1 directly, and thus found Eq. 3-18 immediately. We may infer from this method of solution that whenever the basic equation (like Eq. 3-1) may be solved in analytic form, the associated functional equation may also be solved in a form analogous to that given in Eq. 3-17.

As a last remark we note that the taking of the functional Fourier transform of Eq. 3-7 yields

$$(3\text{-}20) \qquad \left(m \frac{d^2x}{d\xi^2} + kx - F \right) P[x(\xi), F(\xi)] = 0$$

which is the functional equation governing $P[x(t), F(t)]$. The solution of this equation is Eq. 3-16. In fact, starting with Eq. 3-16 we could derive Eq. 3-20 since

$$(3\text{-}21) \qquad \left(m \frac{d^2x}{d\xi^2} + kx - F \right) \delta[x(\xi) - \psi(F(\xi))] = 0$$

is a restatement of Eq. 3-1. A similar argument may be used to derive the equation governing $P[x(t), m(t), k(t), F(t)]$. In this latter case, however, an equation like Eq. 3-18 is not available to us and Eq. 3-14 is frequently more useful than the equation governing $P[x(t), m(t), k(t), F(t)]$.

We now turn to the derivation of the functional equations governing some of the physical problems that we shall consider in the remaining chapters of this book.

3.1.2. Maxwell's Equations

In this book we shall have occasion to consider the solution of Maxwell's equations in a number of different physical problems. In order to cover a number of cases we shall consider here the derivation of the functional equations for the electromagnetic field in a medium with a random variable permittivity. We shall not require the most general formulation of this problem, however, and shall restrict ourselves to an ensemble of systems in which the dielectric constants is time independent in each system. There is no difficulty in extending all our derivations to include variable magnetic permeability and conductivity.

Maxwell's equations in the absence of sources are

(3-22)
$$\nabla \times \mathbf{E} = -\frac{\mu}{c}\frac{\partial \mathbf{H}}{\partial t}$$

(3-23)
$$\nabla \times \mathbf{H} = \frac{\epsilon}{c}\frac{\partial \mathbf{E}}{\partial t}$$

$\mathbf{E}$ is the electric field, $\mathbf{H}$ is the magnetic field, μ is the magnetic permeability, and ϵ is the permittivity. We shall use gaussian units in this discussion and thus in the vacuum, $\epsilon = \mu = 1$. Here we take $\mu = 1$.

From Eqs. 3-22 and 3-23 we obtain

(3-24)
$$\text{div } \epsilon\mathbf{E} = 0$$

noting that div $(\nabla \times \mathbf{H}) = 0$ and assuming div $\epsilon\mathbf{E}$ is equal to zero at some time.

In some propagation problems it is desirable to have a wave equation for $\mathbf{E}$ in terms of ϵ. This may be found by taking the curl of Eq. 3-22 and substituting the expression for $\nabla \times \mathbf{H}$ from Eq. 3-23. This yields

(3-25)
$$\nabla \times \nabla \times \mathbf{E} = -\frac{\epsilon}{c^2}\frac{\partial^2 \mathbf{E}}{\partial t^2}$$

Using the vector identity

$$\nabla \times \nabla \times \mathbf{E} = -\nabla^2 E + \nabla(\nabla \cdot \mathbf{E})$$

we have

(3-26) $$\nabla^2 \mathbf{E} = \frac{\epsilon}{c^2} \frac{\partial^2 \mathbf{E}}{\partial t^2} + \nabla(\nabla \cdot \mathbf{E})$$

or noting that $\nabla \cdot \epsilon \mathbf{E} = \mathbf{E} \cdot \nabla \epsilon + \epsilon \nabla \cdot \mathbf{E} = 0$

(3-27) $$\nabla^2 \mathbf{E} = \frac{\epsilon}{c^2} \frac{\partial^2 \mathbf{E}}{\partial t^2} - \nabla(\mathbf{E} \cdot \nabla \ln \epsilon)$$

3.1.2.1. Static Problem.   In problems in which $\partial E/\partial t = 0$, $\partial H/\partial t = 0$ we have from Eq. 3-24 and Eq. 3-22

(3-24) $$\text{div } \epsilon \mathbf{E} = 0$$

(3-28) $$\nabla \times \mathbf{E} = 0$$

The derivation of the functional equations proceeds exactly as in the harmonic oscillator problem. We define here the characteristic functional

(3-29) $$M[\eta(\mathbf{x}), F_i(\mathbf{x})] = \int_R \exp\{i[\eta, \epsilon] + i[F_j, E_j]\}$$

$$\times P[\epsilon(\mathbf{x}), E_i(\mathbf{x})] \, d\epsilon(\mathbf{x}) \, dE_1(\mathbf{x}) \, dE_2(\mathbf{x})dE_3(\mathbf{x})$$

where now

$$[F_j, E_j] = \int_V F_j(\mathbf{x}) E_j(\mathbf{x}) \, dx_1 \, dx_2 \, dx_3$$

The integral over V is a three-dimensional integral over all space, $i = 1, 2, 3$, and the summation convention has been used.

Rather than defining a new notation to express the functional divergence, we shall rewrite Eqs. 3-24 and 3-28 in the form

(3-30) $$\frac{\partial}{\partial x_i}[\epsilon E_i] = 0$$

(3-31) $$\delta_{ijk}\frac{\partial}{\partial x_j} E_k = 0$$

where δ_{ijk} is the antisymmetric tensor of Levi-Civita.

We first form

(3-32) $\quad \dfrac{\delta}{\delta\eta(\xi)}\left[\dfrac{\delta M}{\delta F_i(\xi)}\right] = -\displaystyle\int_R \epsilon(\xi)E_i(\xi)\exp\{i[\eta,\epsilon] + i[F_j, E_j]\}\,P\,d\epsilon\,dE$

Differentiating with respect to $\partial/\partial\xi_i$ and noting the right-hand side is then zero yields

(3-33) $\qquad\qquad\qquad \dfrac{\partial}{\partial\xi_i}\left[\dfrac{\delta}{\delta\eta(\xi)}\dfrac{\delta M}{\delta F_i(\xi)}\right] = 0$

In the same manner, we find for the curl equation

(3-34) $\qquad\qquad\qquad \delta_{ijk}\dfrac{\partial}{\partial\xi_j}\dfrac{\delta M}{\delta F_k(\xi)} = 0$

Equations 3-33 and 3-34 are the governing functional equations.

The boundary conditions for the solution of these equations are $M[\eta(\mathbf{x}), 0]$ and the specification of $n_{Si}E_i(\mathbf{x}_S)$ or $\phi(\mathbf{x}_S)$ (where $E_i = \partial\phi/\partial x_i$) (or some linear combination of these functions) over some surface S. (n_S is the unit normal to S.) We assume the geometry is the same in each member of the ensemble and $\epsilon(\mathbf{x})$ is a constant on S. The condition, $n_{Si}E_i(\mathbf{x}_S)$, for example, is expressed by the functional condition

$$P[n_{Si}E_i(\mathbf{x}_S)] = \delta[n_{Si}E_i(\mathbf{x}_S) - A(\mathbf{x}_S)]$$

where $A(\mathbf{x}_S)$ is a known function. $P[n_{Si}E_i(\mathbf{x}_S)]$ may be derived from the functional $P[E_i(\mathbf{x}_S)]$, and hence its specification imposes a condition on this functional. Actually in the problems treated in this book, we shall consider infinite statistically homogeneous media, and this requires that we only specify the mean value of $E_i(\mathbf{x})$.

To the writer's knowledge no direct solutions of these equations have been found except in the one-dimensional case.

3.1.2.2. Radiation from a Surface (The Antenna Problem).

In this section we consider the radiation from a surface into free space. Referring to Figure 3-1 we suppose that we are given the time-varying tangential electric field over some surface S and wish to determine the electric field at an exterior point P. If the surface S encloses an ordinary light bulb or a star we must treat the problem statistically, since

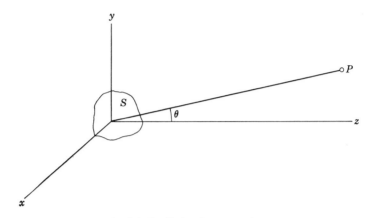

Fig. 3-1. Radiation from a surface.

$E(x_S, t_S)$ (where x_S denotes points on S) is not known. Instead we assume that only $P[E_T(x_S, t_S)]$ is known on S. $E_T(x_S, t_S)$ is the tangential component of E on S. Our problem is to determine $P[E(x, t)]$ where x is any point external to S. We remark again that any statistical information less than $P[E(x, t)]$ does not provide a complete statistical description of this problem.

The equations governing $E(x, t)$ in free space are

$$(3\text{-}35) \qquad \nabla^2 E = \frac{1}{c^2} \frac{\partial^2 E}{\partial t^2}$$

$$(3\text{-}36) \qquad \text{div } E = 0$$

The algebra is very complicated if we consider the full vector problem, and for illustrative purposes we shall consider the simpler scalar problem here. We restrict ourselves to surfaces S that are large compared to a characteristic wavelength and lie in the xy plane. We further consider the radiation only in the neighborhood of the z axis and assume that it is polarized. For this case, we may consider only one component of the E field in the xy plane, say E_x, and neglect the divergence condition. Letting $V(x, t) \equiv E_x(x, t)$ we have the governing equation

$$(3\text{-}37) \qquad \nabla^2 V = \frac{1}{c^2} \frac{\partial^2 V}{\partial t^2}$$

and we seek $P[V(x, t)]$ from a knowledge of $P[V(x_S, t_S)]$. (Note that the equations now also represent an acoustic wave problem).

In order to solve this problem we must consider the joint functional

$$P[V(\mathbf{x}, t), V(\mathbf{x}_S, t_S)]$$

and the associated characteristic functional

(3-38)

$$M[W(\mathbf{x}, t), W(\mathbf{x}_S, t_S)] = \int_R \exp\{i[W, V] + i[W_S, V_S]\}\, P[V, V_S]\, dV\, dV_S$$

where we have set $V_S = V(\mathbf{x}_S, t_S)$ and $W_S = W(\mathbf{x}_S, t_S)$.

We may formally write the solution $V(\mathbf{x}, t)$ in terms of $V(\mathbf{x}_S, t_S)$ by using an appropriate Green's function $G(\mathbf{x}, t; \mathbf{x}_S, t_S)$. Thus we may write

(3-39) $$V(\mathbf{x}, t) = \iint G(\mathbf{x}, t; \mathbf{x}_S, t_S) V(\mathbf{x}_S, t_S)\, d\mathbf{x}_S\, dt_S$$

Proceeding in the same manner as we did in Section 3.1.1, we write

(3-40) $$P[V(\mathbf{x}, t), V(\mathbf{x}_S, t_S)] = P[V(\mathbf{x}_S, t_S^{\cdot})]$$

$$\times \delta\left[V(\mathbf{x}, t) - \iint G(\mathbf{x}, t; \mathbf{x}_S, t_S) V(\mathbf{x}_S, t_S)\, d\mathbf{x}_S\, dt_S\right]$$

and find the solution

(3-41) $$M[W(\mathbf{x}, t), W(\mathbf{x}_S, t_S)]$$

$$= \int_R \exp\left\{i\left[W, \iint GV_S\, d\mathbf{x}_S\, dt_S\right] + i[W_S, V_S]\right\} P[V_S]\, dV_S$$

The Green's function $G(\mathbf{x}, t; \mathbf{x}_s, t_s)$ is a function that may be explicitly determined for radiation from a plane finite surface and thus if $P[V(\mathbf{x}_S, t_S)]$ were known explicit calculations could be made. We note that the functional equation governing M is

(3-42) $$\nabla_\xi^2 \frac{\delta M}{\delta W(\xi, p)} = \frac{1}{c^2} \frac{\partial^2}{\partial p^2} \frac{\delta M}{\delta W(\xi, p)}$$

3.1.2.3. Propagation through Random Media.   The equations governing the propagation of radiation through a random medium are Eqs. 3-24 and 3-27.

Using the procedures already developed, the derivation of the governing functional equations is relatively straightforward. The only point that requires some discussion is the time dependence of **E**. In order to include this dependence we generalize Eq. 3-29 to the form

(3-43) $M[\eta(\mathbf{x}), F_i(\mathbf{x}, t)]$

$$= \int_R \exp \{i[\eta, \epsilon] + i[F_i, E_i]\} P[\epsilon(\mathbf{x}), E_i(\mathbf{x}, t)] \, d\epsilon(\mathbf{x})$$

$$\cdot \, dE_1(\mathbf{x}, t) \, dE_2(\mathbf{x}, t) \, dE_3(\mathbf{x}, t)$$

where

$$[\eta, \epsilon] = \int_V \eta(\mathbf{x})\epsilon(\mathbf{x}) \, dx_1 \, dx_2 \, dx_3$$

and

$$[F_i, E_i] = \int_T \int_V F_i(\mathbf{x}, t)E_i(\mathbf{x}, t) \, dx_1 \, dx_2 \, dx_3 \, dt$$

The functional equation derived using Eq. 3-24 is

(3-44) $$\frac{\partial}{\partial \xi_i} \frac{\delta}{\delta \eta(\boldsymbol{\xi})} \left[\frac{\delta M}{\delta F_i(\boldsymbol{\xi}, p)} \right] = 0$$

When the variation in ϵ for distances of the order of a characteristic radiation wavelength is small the term $\nabla(\mathbf{E} \cdot \nabla \ln \epsilon)$ may be neglected in Eq. 3-27. For simplicity, we consider only this case here. The associated functional equation is

(3-45) $$\nabla_\xi^2 \frac{\delta M}{\delta F_i(\boldsymbol{\xi}, p)} = -\frac{i}{c^2} \frac{\partial^2}{\partial p^2} \frac{\delta}{\delta \eta(\boldsymbol{\xi})} \left[\frac{\delta M}{\delta F_i(\boldsymbol{\xi}, p)} \right]$$

(see Keller (1964) for a similar derivation). The boundary condition for the solution of Eq. 3-45 is $P[\epsilon(\mathbf{x}), E_T(\mathbf{x}_S, t_S)]$ on some surface S, and the Sommerfeld radiation condition.

As in the static case with variable permittivity, no direct solutions have been found for the functional equations.

3.1.3. Other Equations

Using the foregoing procedures it is a simple exercise to derive functional equations for almost any equations in which one may have an interest. Since we shall not be able to solve any but the most simple functional equations we leave this to the reader. We do wish, however, to set down the functional equations associated with the Navier-Stokes equations since these equations were the first considered in Hopf's basic paper (Hopf, 1952) and a number of attempts have been made at approximate solutions. We shall use here initially the formulism given by Lewis and Kraichnan (1962). Further discussion of these functional equations will be given in Chapter 7.

3.1.4. Navier-Stokes Equations

The Navier-Stokes equations and the continuity equation for an incompressible fluid may be written in the following form:

$$(3\text{-}46) \qquad \frac{\partial u_i}{\partial t} + u_j \frac{\partial u_i}{\partial x_j} = \nu \nabla^2 u_i - \frac{\partial p}{\partial x_i}$$

$$(3\text{-}47) \qquad \frac{\partial}{\partial x_i} u_i = 0$$

where ν is the kinematic viscosity and p is here the pressure divided by the density.

The statistical problem that we are going to consider is turbulence. Usually one attempts to treat the decay of turbulence in an infinite medium or the steady state problem of something like turbulent pipe flow. (Lewis and Kraichnan do treat the problem of a random driving force but we shall not consider this here.) In both these cases the only probability density functional of interest is $P[u_i(\mathbf{x}, t), p(\mathbf{x}, t)]$. We must either determine $P[u_i(\mathbf{x}, t), p(\mathbf{x}, t)]$ from a knowledge of this functional at time $t = t_0$ or we must determine $P[u_i(\mathbf{x}, t), p(\mathbf{x}, t)]$ as one of the possible solutions of a steady state flow.

$P[u_i(\mathbf{x}, t), p(\mathbf{x}, t)]$ is the most general functional we need to consider here; but in the literature the velocity functional itself, $P[u_i(\mathbf{x}, t)]$, has usually been considered. The pressure is eliminated by some device so as to arrive at an equation governing the characteristic functional associated with $P[u_i(\mathbf{x}, t)]$. In accordance with common usage we shall here consider $P[u_i(\mathbf{x}, t)]$ rather than $P[u_i(\mathbf{x}, t), p(\mathbf{x}, t)]$.

The characteristic functional associated with $P[u_i(\mathbf{x}, t)]$ is defined as

$$(3\text{-}48) \qquad M[y_i(\mathbf{x}, t)] = \int_R \exp\{i[y_j, u_j]\}\, P[u_i(\mathbf{x}, t)]\, du_i(\mathbf{x}, t)$$

where

$$[y_i, u_i] = \int y_i(\mathbf{x}, t) u_i(\mathbf{x}, t) \, d\mathbf{x} \, dt \qquad \text{(sum over } i = 1, 2, 3)$$

The functional equation associated with the divergence condition Eq. 3-47 is

(3-49)
$$\frac{\partial}{\partial \xi_i} \frac{\delta M}{\delta y_i(\boldsymbol{\xi}, s)} = 0$$

The functional equation associated with Eq. 3-46 is obtained by first writing

(3-50) $$\frac{\delta M}{\delta y_i(\boldsymbol{\xi}, s)} = \int\limits_R i u_i(\boldsymbol{\xi}, s) \exp \{i[y_j, u_j]\} \, P[u_i(\mathbf{x}, t)] \, du_i(\mathbf{x}, t)$$

Differentiating this expression with respect to δs and then using Eq. 3-46 to substitute for $\partial u_i(\boldsymbol{\xi}, s)/\partial s$ under the integral, we obtain

(3-51) $$\frac{\partial}{\partial s} \frac{\delta M}{\delta y_i(\boldsymbol{\xi}, s)} = \int\limits_R i \left[-u_j(\boldsymbol{\xi}, s) \frac{\partial u_i(\boldsymbol{\xi}, s)}{\partial \xi_j} + \nu \nabla_\xi^2 u_i(\boldsymbol{\xi}, s) - \frac{\partial p(\boldsymbol{\xi}, s)}{\partial \xi_i} \right]$$
$$\times \exp \{i[y_j, u_j]\} \, P[u_i(\mathbf{x}, t)] \, du_i(\mathbf{x}, t)$$

This yields then

(3-52) $$\frac{\partial}{\partial s} \frac{\delta M}{\delta y_i(\boldsymbol{\xi}, s)} = i \frac{\partial}{\partial \xi_j} \frac{\delta}{\delta y_j(\boldsymbol{\xi}, s)} \left[\frac{\delta M}{\delta y_i(\boldsymbol{\xi}, s)} \right] + \nu \nabla_\xi^2 \frac{\delta M}{\delta y_i(\boldsymbol{\xi}, s)} - i \frac{\partial \Pi}{\partial \xi_i}$$

where

$$\Pi = \int\limits_R p(\boldsymbol{\xi}, s) \exp \{i[y_j, u_j]\} \, P[u_i(\mathbf{x}, t)] \, du_i(\mathbf{x}, t)$$

and we have made use of the divergence condition to simplify the first term on the right-hand side of Eq. 3-51.

In order to eliminate the pressure term Π we follow Lewis and Kraichnan (1962) and introduce the testing field $\boldsymbol{\gamma}(\mathbf{x}, t)$ which vanishes as rapidly as necessary at infinity and satisfies the divergence condition

$$\frac{\partial \gamma_i(\mathbf{x}, t)}{\partial x_i} = 0$$

Noting then that

$$\int \gamma_i \frac{\partial \Pi}{\partial x_i} \, d\mathbf{x} = \int \frac{\partial \gamma_i \Pi}{\partial x_i} \, d\mathbf{x} - \int \frac{\partial \gamma_i}{\partial x_i} \Pi \, d\mathbf{x} = 0$$

we find from Eq. 3-52

$$(3\text{-}53) \quad \int \gamma_i(\boldsymbol{\xi}, s) \left\{ \frac{\partial}{\partial s} \frac{\delta M}{\delta y_i(\boldsymbol{\xi}, s)} - i \frac{\partial}{\partial \xi_j} \frac{\delta}{\delta y_j(\boldsymbol{\xi}, s)} \left[\frac{\delta M}{\delta y_i(\boldsymbol{\xi}, s)} \right] \right.$$

$$\left. - \nu \nabla_{\xi}^2 \frac{\delta M}{\delta y_i(\boldsymbol{\xi}, s)} \right\} d\boldsymbol{\xi} \, ds = 0$$

Equation 3-53 is the equation governing $M[y_i(\mathbf{x}, t)]$ that we sought. For those readers familiar with Hopf's original paper on this subject (Hopf, 1952) we point out that Hopf's formulation is slightly different from the formulation given here. He considered a probability density functional that depended upon only one time, t. In other words, the moments derivable from Hopf's density functional P_H, are of the restricted form

$$\overline{u_i(\mathbf{x}_1, t) \cdots u_k(\mathbf{x}_n, t)}$$

where the same time is taken at all points $\mathbf{x}_n$. In the formulation given above, the moments derivable from $P[u_i(\mathbf{x}, t)]$ are of the form

$$\overline{u_j(\mathbf{x}_1, t_1) \cdots u_k(\mathbf{x}_n, t_n)}$$

where all the t_j may be different. Interestingly, the original statistical moment formulation given by von Kármán (1937a,b; 1938) was in terms of single-time moments and more general multiple-time moments were not considered until later (see, for example, Chandrasekhar, 1956).

The Hopf formulation requires a slightly different derivation than the foregoing one. The reason for this is that the characteristic functional M_H is defined as a functional of $y_i(\mathbf{x})$ *and* a function of the time t. In the foregoing definition, M was a functional of $y_i(\mathbf{x}, t)$. Hopf defines $M_H[y_i(\mathbf{x}), t]$ as

$$(3\text{-}54) \qquad M_H[y_i(\mathbf{x}), t] = \int_R \exp\left\{i[y_j, u_j]\right\} P[u_i(\mathbf{x}), t] \, du_i(\mathbf{x})$$

where now

$$[y_j, u_j] = \int y_j(\mathbf{x}) u_j(\mathbf{x})\, d\mathbf{x}$$

$u_i(\mathbf{x})$ is the velocity configuration at a fixed time. The key to his derivation is to note that

(3-55) $\displaystyle\int_R f[u_i{}'(\mathbf{x})] \exp\{i[y_j(\mathbf{x}), u_j(\mathbf{x})]\}\, P[u_i(\mathbf{x}), t]\, du_i(\mathbf{x})$

$$= \int_R f[u_i{}'(\mathbf{x}, t)] \exp\{i[y_j(\mathbf{x}), u_j(\mathbf{x}, t)]\}\, P[u_k(\mathbf{x}, 0), 0]\, du_k(\mathbf{x}, 0)$$

Here $u_i(\mathbf{x}, t)$ satisfies the Navier-Stokes equations during the time interval 0 to t, and in the left-hand side we set $u_i(\mathbf{x}) = u_i(\mathbf{x}, t)$.

In order to arrive at Eq. 3-55, we may formally write

(3-56) $\displaystyle P[u_i(\mathbf{x}), t] = \int_R P[u_i(\mathbf{x}, 0), 0]\, \delta[u_i(\mathbf{x}) - u_i(\mathbf{x}, t)]\, du_i(\mathbf{x}, 0)$

This is a mathematical statement of the proposition that the probability of the velocity field having a configuration between $u_i(\mathbf{x}) = u_i(\mathbf{x}, t)$ and $u_i(\mathbf{x}) = u_i(\mathbf{x}, t) + du_i(\mathbf{x}, t)$ at time t is equal to the probability of it having the configuration between $u_i(\mathbf{x}) = u_i(\mathbf{x}, 0)$ and $u_i(\mathbf{x}) = u_i(\mathbf{x}, 0) + du_i(\mathbf{x}, 0)$ at time $t = 0$, *if* $u(\mathbf{x}, t)$ obeys the Navier-Stokes equations during the time interval 0 to t. If Eq. 3-56 is substituted into the left-hand side of Eq. 3-55, we have

(3-57) $\displaystyle\int_R f[u_i(\mathbf{x}')] \exp\{i[y_j(\mathbf{x}), u_j(\mathbf{x})]\}\, P[u_i(\mathbf{x}), t]\, du_i(\mathbf{x})$

$$= \int_R \int_R f[u_i(\mathbf{x}')] \exp\{i[y_j(\mathbf{x}), u_j(\mathbf{x})]\}\, \delta[u_i(\mathbf{x}) - u_i(\mathbf{x}, t)]$$

$$\times\ P[u_i(\mathbf{x}, 0), 0]\, du_i(\mathbf{x})\, du_i(\mathbf{x}, 0)$$

$$= \int_R f[u_i(\mathbf{x}', t)] \exp\{i[y_j(\mathbf{x}), u_j(\mathbf{x}, t)]\}\, P[u_i(\mathbf{x}, 0), 0]\, du_i(\mathbf{x}, 0)$$

In order to evaluate the last term in Eq. 3-57, we must in principle substitute for $u_i(\mathbf{x}, t)$ the solution of the Navier-Stokes equations that has the initial condition $u_i(\mathbf{x}, 0)$.

From the right-hand side of Eq. 3-55 for $f = 1$, we find

(3-58)

$$\frac{\partial M_H}{\partial t} = i \int d\mathbf{x}' y_k(\mathbf{x}') \int_R \frac{\partial u_k(\mathbf{x}', t)}{\partial t} \exp \{i[y_j, u_j(\mathbf{x}, t)]\} \, P[u_i(\mathbf{x}, 0), 0] \, du_i(\mathbf{x})$$

assuming we may interchange the order of integration.

The Navier-Stokes equations may then be used to find an expression for $\partial u_i(\mathbf{x}, t)/\partial t$ yielding

(3-59)

$$\frac{\partial M_H}{\partial t} = i \int d\mathbf{x}' y_k(\mathbf{x}') \int_R \left[-u_j(\mathbf{x}', t) \frac{\partial u_k(\mathbf{x}', t)}{\partial x'_j} + \nu \nabla^2 u_k(\mathbf{x}', t) - \frac{\partial p(\mathbf{x}', t)}{\partial x_k'} \right]$$
$$\times \exp \{i[y_j, u_j(\mathbf{x}, t)]\} \, P[u_i(\mathbf{x}), 0] \, du_i(\mathbf{x})$$

Application of Eq. 3-55 then gives

(3-60)

$$\frac{\partial M_H}{\partial t} = i \int d\mathbf{x}' y_k(\mathbf{x}') \int_R \left[-u_j(\mathbf{x}') \frac{\partial u_k(\mathbf{x}')}{\partial x_j'} + \nu \nabla^2 u_k(\mathbf{x}') - \frac{\partial p(\mathbf{x}')}{\partial x_k'} \right]$$
$$\times \exp \{i[y_j, u_j(\mathbf{x})]\} \, P[u_i(\mathbf{x}), t] \, du_i(\mathbf{x})$$

The right-hand side may now be put in terms of functional derivatives in the usual way. We have finally (dropping the primes)

(3-61) $$\frac{\partial M_H}{\partial t} = \int d\mathbf{x} y_i(\mathbf{x}) \left\{ i \frac{\partial}{\partial x_j} \left(\frac{\delta}{\delta y_j(\mathbf{x})} \left[\frac{\delta M_H}{\delta y_i(\mathbf{x})} \right] \right) + \nu \nabla^2 \frac{\delta M_H}{\delta y_i(\mathbf{x})} - \frac{\partial \Pi_H}{\partial x_i} \right\}$$

where

$$\Pi_H = \int_R p(\mathbf{x}', t) \exp \{i[y_j, u_j(\mathbf{x})]\} \, P[u_i(\mathbf{x}), t] \, du_i(\mathbf{x})$$

The divergence condition yields

(3-62) $$\frac{\partial}{\partial x_i} \frac{\delta M_H}{\delta y_i(\mathbf{x})} = 0$$

and thus in Hopf's formulation, Eqs. 3-61 and 3-62 replace Eqs. 3-52 and 3-49.

An equation for $P_H[u_i(\mathbf{x}), t]$ may also be derived using Eq. 3-54. It is interesting to have such an equation, since it is the analog of Liouville's equation and in fact Liouville's equation may be derived in a corresponding manner (see Beran, 1967). A derivation of the equation governing $P_H[u_i(\mathbf{x}), t]$ using delta functionals is given by Edwards (1964) and the reader is referred to his paper for this approach.

In order to find the equation governing $P_H[u_i(\mathbf{x}), t]$ we first differentiate Eq. 3-54 giving

(3-63) $$\frac{\partial M_H}{\partial t} = \int_R \exp\{i[y_j, u_j]\} \frac{\partial}{\partial t} P_H[u_i(\mathbf{x}), t]\, du_i(\mathbf{x})$$

From Eq. 3-60 we find that

(3-64) $$\frac{\partial M_H}{\partial t} = \int_R \int \left(-u_j(\mathbf{x}) \frac{\partial u_k(\mathbf{x}')}{\partial x_j'} + \nu \nabla^2 u_k(\mathbf{x}') - \frac{\partial p(\mathbf{x}')}{\partial x_k'} \right)$$

$$\times \left\{ \frac{\delta}{\delta u_k(\mathbf{x}')} \exp\{i[y_j, u_j]\} \right\} d\mathbf{x}' P_H[u_i(\mathbf{x}), t]\, du_i(\mathbf{x})$$

performing a functional integration by parts in Eq. 3-64 and assuming the integrated terms vanish yields

(3-65) $$\frac{\partial M_H}{\partial t} = -\int_R \exp\{i[y_j, u_j]\} \int \frac{\delta}{\delta u_k(\mathbf{x}')}$$

$$\times \left[\left(-u_j(\mathbf{x}') \frac{\partial u_k(\mathbf{x})}{\partial x_j'} + \nu \nabla^2 u_k(\mathbf{x}') - \frac{\partial p(\mathbf{x}')}{\partial x_k} \right) P_H[u_i(\mathbf{x}), t] \right] d\mathbf{x}'\, du_i(\mathbf{x})$$

Finally, comparing Eqs. 3-63 and 3-65 and assuming the equation must hold for arbitrary $y(\mathbf{x})$ gives

(3-66) $$\frac{\partial P_H[u(\mathbf{x}), t]}{\partial t} = -\int d\mathbf{x}' \frac{\delta}{\delta u_k(\mathbf{x}')}$$

$$\times \left[\left(-u_j(\mathbf{x}') \frac{\partial u_k(\mathbf{x}')}{\partial x_j'} + \nu \nabla^2 u_k(\mathbf{x}') - \frac{\partial p(\mathbf{x}')}{\partial x_k'} \right) P_H[u_i(\mathbf{x}), t] \right]$$

In order to eliminate the pressure term we may take the divergence of Eq. 3-46 and use a Green's function to formally integrate the resulting Poisson-type equation.

The boundary conditions for the solution of the Navier-Stokes equations are: (*1*) there is no relative motion between a solid and the fluid in contact with it; (*2*) at an interface between the two fluids, the normal pressure and viscous stresses must be continuous; (*3*) $u_i(\mathbf{x}, 0)$ must be given. It is too difficult to catalog here all the possible boundary conditions in analytic form. We note, however, that for statistically homogeneous turbulence, the most studied problem, the boundary condition for the Hopf functional is $P_H[u_i(\mathbf{x}), 0]$.

There have been a number of papers in which attempts have been made to solve the functional equation associated with M or M_H. In addition to the cited papers above, we list Hopf and Titt (1953), Rosen (1960a,b), Hopf (1962), Tatarski (1962), and Edwards (1964). We shall discuss some of these works further in Chapter 7.

3.2. Derivation of the Moment Equations

The complete statistical description of the problems we consider in this book is given by a functional like $P[u(t)]$ or $M[y(t)]$. The moments of the form

$$\overline{u(t_1)u(t_2) \cdots u(t_n)}$$

which may be derived from $P[u(t)]$ or $M[y(t)]$ are, however, the statistical quantities that we encounter most frequently in practice. The low-order moments $\overline{u(t_1)}$, $\overline{u(t_1)u(t_2)}$, $\overline{u(t_1)u(t_2)u(t_3)}$, $\overline{u(t_1)u(t_2)u(t_3)u(t_4)}$ are more easily measured and treated analytically than probability density functions, and a discussion of these moments will form the heart of the later chapters. In Chapter 1 we discussed how the equations governing these moments may be derived in some simple cases. In this section we will present two general methods that may be used. The methods will be outlined by applying them to specific cases.

As we stressed in Chapter 1, we will see again that in general determinate equations *cannot* be obtained for a particular moment. The equation governing the nth-order moment $\overline{u(t_1) \cdots u(t_n)}$ will in general contain the $(n + 1)$th-order moment

$$\overline{u(t_1) \cdots u(t_n)u(t_{n+1})}$$

To obtain an equation containing the nth-order moment alone will require some type of approximation. We shall discuss two methods of approximation in Sections 3.3.1 and 3.3.2, but in this section we shall only derive the governing hierarchy of moment equations.

We should note at this point that moments of the form

$$\overline{u(t_1) \cdots u(t_n)}$$

are not the only moments that may be considered. One might, for example, consider moments like

$$\overline{\left[\frac{u(t_1) \cdots u(t_n)}{u(t_{n+1}) \cdots u(t_{n+m})} \right]}$$

or

$$\overline{\log u(t_1) \cdots \log u(t_n)}$$

Little has been systematically done with these less conventional moments (see, however, Section 5.5; and Tatarski, 1961), and we shall not present any general equations governing their development. One of the purposes of considering functional equations, however, might be to develop expansion techniques that are different from the Taylor series technique we shall present. This would be done in the hope of getting a governing set of less conventional moment equations that will have faster convergence properties than the conventional moment set generated by use of the Taylor series.

The moment equations may be derived from the functional equations by assuming that the characteristic functional may be expanded in the Taylor series form given in Eq. 2-59. We shall present this approach in the next section. The moment equations may also be derived directly, if not so elegantly, from the governing differential equations. We present this more direct approach in Section 3.2.2. This latter section may be read by a reader with no knowledge of functionals. In Section 3.2.3 we shall briefly consider the equations governing the Fourier transform of the moments.

3.2.1. Derivation of the Moment Equations from Functional Equations

In order to derive the moment equations from the functional equations we first note the general relation given in Eq. 2-86

$$(2\text{-}86) \qquad M^n[v(t), \xi_1, \xi_2, \ldots, \xi_n]\big|_{v=0} = i^n \overline{u(\xi_1)u(\xi_2) \cdots u(\xi_n)}$$

This equation is directly generalized to a number of functions $u_1(t), \ldots, u_j(t)$ or a number of independent variables, $t_1, \ldots, t_k$, or both.

As we pointed out in Section 2.2, a functional of suitable regularity may be expanded in the Taylor-type series given in Eq. 2-59. Thus, assuming the characteristic functional to be sufficiently regular we have

$$(3\text{-}67) \quad M[v(t)] = k_0 + \int_a^b m_1(t_1)v(t_1)\,dt_1 + \int_a^b \int_a^b m_2(t_1, t_2)v(t_1)$$

$$\times v(t_2)\,dt_1\,dt_2 + \cdots + \int_a^b \cdots \int_a^b \int_a^b m_n(t_1, t_2, \ldots, t_n)$$

$$\times v(t_1)v(t_2) \cdots v(t_n)\,dt_1\,dt_2 \cdots dt_n + \cdots +$$

For simplicity of notation we denote the nth-order integral by M_n. (We caution the reader against confusing M_n with the nth functional derivative M^n.) Thus we have

$$(3\text{-}68) \qquad M[v(t)] = M_0 + M_1 + \cdots + M_n + \cdots = \sum_{j=0}^{\infty} M_j$$

From Eq. 2-74 we have

$$(3\text{-}69) \qquad M_n{}^n = n!\, m_n(t_1, t_2, \ldots, t_n)$$

Comparison of Eq. 3-69 and Eq. 2-86 thus yields

$$(3\text{-}70) \qquad m_n(t_1, t_2, \ldots, t_n) = \frac{i^n}{n!}\, \overline{u(t_1)u(t_2) \cdots u(t_n)}$$

The generalization of the Taylor series of M to many functions and variables proceeds exactly as in the expansion of ordinary functions.

In this section we shall explicitly treat three problems in order to show the reader the nature of the derivation. He should have no difficulty extending the methods to other cases. We consider here the simple one-dimensional harmonic oscillator, the spatially varying permittivity problem, and turbulence.

3.2.1.1. Simple Harmonic Oscillator. The functional equation governing the one-dimensional harmonic oscillator with constant mass and spring constant subject to a random driving force was given by Eq. 3-7

$$(3\text{-}7) \qquad m \frac{d^2}{d\xi^2} \frac{\delta M}{\delta y(\xi)} + k \frac{\delta M}{\delta y(\xi)} = \frac{\delta M}{\delta g(\xi)}$$

We now assume that M may be expanded in a generalized series of the form Eq. 3-67. Since we have two random variables $x(t)$ and $F(t)$ it is now necessary to have a double Taylor series. Here we require

$$(3\text{-}71) \quad M[y(t), g(t)] = m_{00} + \int_a^b m_{10}(t_1) y(t_1) \, dt_1 + \int_a^b m_{01}(t_1) y(t_1) \, dt$$

$$+ \int_a^b \int_a^b m_{20}(t_1, t_2) y(t_1) y(t_2) \, dt_1 \, dt_2$$

$$+ \int_a^b \int_a^b m_{02}(t_1, t_2) g(t_1) g(t_2) \, dt_1 \, dt_2$$

$$+ \int_a^b \int_a^b m_{11}(t_1, t_2) y(t_1) g(t_2) \, dt_1 \, dt_2 + \cdots +$$

where we now set

$$M[y(t), g(t)] = \sum_{j=0}^{\infty} \sum_{k=0}^{\infty} M_{jk}$$

The j index indicates the number of $y(t)$ repetitions in the integral and the k index indicates the number of $F(t)$ repetitions. We find

$$(3\text{-}72) \quad \frac{1}{j! \, k!} \frac{\delta^j}{\delta y^j} \left[\frac{\delta^k M_{jk}}{\delta g^k} \right] \equiv \frac{M_{jk}^{jk}}{j! \, k!} = m_{jk}(t_1, t_2, \ldots, t_l); \qquad [l = j + k]$$

$$= \frac{i^l}{j! \, k!} \overline{x(t_1) \cdots x(t_j) F(t_{j+1}) \cdots F(t_{j+k})}$$

We have from Eq. 3-71

(3-73)

$$\frac{\delta M}{\delta y(\xi)} = m_{10}(\xi) + 2\int_a^b m_{20}(\xi, t_2)y(t_2)\, dt_2 + \int_a^b m_{11}(\xi, t_2)g(t_2)\, dt_2 + \cdots +$$

(3-74)

$$\frac{\delta M}{\delta g(\xi)} = m_{01}(\xi) + 2\int_a^b m_{02}(\xi, t_2)g(t_2)\, dt_2 + \int_a^b m_{11}(\xi, t_2)y(t_2)\, dt_2 + \cdots +$$

Next we equate like powers of y and g and we find the sequence of equations

(3-75a) $$m\frac{d^2}{d\xi^2}m_{10}(\xi) + km_{10}(\xi) = m_{01}(\xi)$$

(3-75b)

$$\int_a^b \left\{2m\frac{\partial^2}{d\xi^2}m_{20}(\xi, t_2) + 2km_{20}(\xi, t_2) - m_{11}(\xi, t_2)\right\}y(t_2)\, dt_2 = 0$$

(3-75c)

$$\int_a^b \left\{m\frac{\partial^2}{\partial\xi^2}m_{11}(\xi, t_2) + km_{11}(\xi, t_2) - 2m_{02}(\xi, t_2)\right\}g(t_2)\, dt_2 = 0$$

$$\cdot$$
$$\cdot$$
$$\cdot$$

Since the equations must hold for arbitrary $y(t_2)$, $g(t_2)$ we set the integrals in Eq. 3-75b, 3-75c $\cdots$ equal to zero. This yields finally

(3-76a) $$m\frac{d^2}{d\xi^2}m_{10}(\xi) + km_{10}(\xi) = m_{01}(\xi)$$

(3-76b) $$m\frac{\partial^2}{\partial\xi^2}2m_{20}(\xi, t_2) + 2km_{20}(\xi, t_2) = m_{11}(\xi, t_2)$$

(3-76c) $$m\frac{\partial^2}{\partial\xi^2}m_{11}(\xi, t_2) + km_{11}(\xi, t_2) = 2m_{02}(\xi, t_2)$$

$$\cdot$$
$$\cdot$$
$$\cdot$$

In terms of the moments, we have using Eq. 3-72

(3-77a) $\qquad m \dfrac{d^2}{d\xi^2} \overline{x(\xi)} + k\overline{x(\xi)} = \overline{F(\xi)}$

(3-77b) $\qquad m \dfrac{\partial^2}{\partial\xi^2} \overline{x(\xi)x(t_2)} + k\overline{x(\xi)x(t_2)} = \overline{x(\xi)F(t_2)}$

(3-77c) $\qquad m \dfrac{\partial^2}{\partial\xi^2} \overline{x(\xi)F(t_2)} + k\overline{x(\xi)F(t_2)} = \overline{F(\xi)F(t_2)}$

$$\cdot$$
$$\cdot$$
$$\cdot$$

From these equations we can get a set of equations in which cross correlations are omitted. For example, an equation connecting $\overline{x(\xi)x(t_2)}$ and $\overline{F(\xi)F(t_2)}$ may be derived by substituting the expression for $\overline{x(\xi)F(t_2)}$ given in Eq. 3-77b into Eq. 3-77c. These equations are similar to the equations derived in Chapter 1. The fact that $\overline{x(t_1)\cdots x(t_n)}$ may be determined from $\overline{F(t_1)\cdots F(t_n)}$ is a very special circumstance. As we stated in the introduction, this is not possible in general. The moment equations derived in the next sections will not have this simple character.

The boundary conditions for the hierarchy of moment equations are found from the conditions

$$x(0) = x_o$$

$$\frac{dx}{dt}(0) = x_o{}'$$

We stated previously that although x_o and $x_o{}'$ could also be made random variables, we consider them here to be deterministic. To solve the hierarchy, we shall require knowledge of the following class of moments

$$\overline{x(t_1)\cdots x(t_j)x(t_{j+1})\cdots x(t_n)}\Big|_{t_1=\cdots=t_j=0}$$

$$\frac{\partial}{\partial t_1}\cdots\frac{\partial}{\partial t_j}\overline{[x(t_1)\cdots x(t_j)x(t_{j+1})\cdots x(t_n)]}\Big|_{t_1=\cdots=t_j=0}$$

From the boundary conditions x_o and $x_o{}'$ we find

$$\overline{x(0)\cdots x(0)x(t_{j+1})\cdots x(t_n)} = x_0{}^j\overline{x(t_{j+1})\cdots x(t_n)}$$

$$\frac{\partial}{\partial t_1}\cdots\frac{\partial}{\partial t_j}\overline{[x(t_1)\cdots x(t_j)x(t_{j+1})\cdots x(t_n)]}\Big|_{t_1=\cdots=t_j}$$

$$= (x_o{}')^j\overline{x(t_{j+1})\cdots x(t_n)}$$

If the moment equations are solved sequentially, beginning with Eq. 3-77a, it will be seen that these relations are adequate boundary conditions for solution of the hierarchy.

3.2.1.2. Spatially Variable Permittivity. The functional equations governing the problem of determining the statistical electric field variation in a medium with variable permittivity are given by Eqs. 3-33 and 3-34

(3-33)
$$\frac{\partial}{\partial \xi_i}\left[\frac{\delta}{\delta\eta(\xi)}\frac{\delta M}{\delta F_i(\xi)}\right] = 0$$

(3-34)
$$\delta_{ijk}\frac{\partial}{\partial \xi_j}\frac{\delta M}{\delta F_k(\xi)} = 0$$

Just as we do in the harmonic oscillator case we expand M in a Taylor series. Here, however, the variables are $\eta(\xi)$ and $F_i(\xi)$ $(i = 1, 2, 3)$ and integrals must be taken over the three-dimensional volume $d\xi_x\, d\xi_y\, d\xi_z \equiv d\xi$. Thus we have in expanded notation

(3-78)
$$M[\eta(\xi), F_i(\xi)] = m_{0000} + \int_V m_{1000}(\xi)\eta(\xi)\, d\xi + \int_V m_{0100}(\xi)F_1(\xi)\, d\xi$$

$$+ \int_V m_{0010}(\xi)F_2(\xi)\, d\xi + \int_V m_{0001}(\xi)F_3(\xi)\, d\xi + \int_V\int_V m_{2000}(\xi_1, \xi_2)$$

$$\times\, \eta(\xi_1)\eta(\xi_2)\, d\xi_1\, d\xi_2 + \int_V\int_V m_{0200}(\xi_1, \xi_2)F_1(\xi_1)F_1(\xi_2)\, d\xi_1\, d\xi_2 + \cdots$$

$$+ \int_V\int_V m_{1100}(\xi_1, \xi_2)\eta(\xi_1)F_1(\xi_2)\, d\xi_1\, d\xi_2 + \int_V\int_V m_{1010}(\xi_1, \xi_2)$$

$$\times\, \eta(\xi_1)F_2(\xi_2)\, d\xi_1\, d\xi_2 + \cdots + \int_V\int_V m_{0110}(\xi_1, \xi_2)F_1(\xi_1)F_2(\xi_2)\, d\xi_1\, d\xi_2$$

$$+ \cdots + \int_V\int_V\int_V m_{2100}(\xi_1, \xi_2, \xi_3)\eta(\xi_1)\eta(\xi_2)F_1(\xi_3)\, d\xi_1\, d\xi_2\, d\xi_3 + \cdots +$$

$$\equiv \sum_j \sum_k \sum_l \sum_r M_{jklr}$$

The j index of M_{jklr} indicates the number of times $\eta(\xi)$ is repeated in the integral, the k index indicates the number of times $F_1(\xi)$ is repeated in the integral with similar meanings for the l and r indices. We also find

$$(3\text{-}79) \quad \frac{1}{j!\,k!\,l!\,r!} \frac{\delta^j}{\delta\eta^j} \frac{\delta^k}{\delta F_1^{\,k}} \frac{\delta^l}{\delta F_2^{\,l}} \frac{\delta^r}{\delta F_3^{\,r}} M_{jklr} \equiv \frac{M_{jklr}^{jklr}}{j!\,k!\,l!\,r!}$$

$$= m_{jklr}(\xi_1, \xi_2, \ldots, \xi_s); \qquad (s = j + k + l + r)$$

$$= \frac{i^s}{j!\,k!\,l!\,r!}\, \overline{\epsilon(\xi_1) \cdots \epsilon(\xi_j) E_1(\xi_{j+1}) \cdots E_1(\xi_{j+k}) E_2(\xi_{j+k+1}) \cdots E_2(\xi_{j+k+l})}$$

$$\times \overline{E_3(\xi_{j+k+l+1}) \cdots E_3(\xi_{j+k+l+r})}$$

Substituting the form of M given in Eq. 3-78 into Eqs. 3-33 and 3-34 and comparing like powers of $\eta(\xi)$ and $F_i(\xi)$, we have upon setting the integrands of the resulting integrals equal to zero and using Eq. 3-79

$$(3\text{-}80) \quad \frac{\partial}{\partial\xi_i} \overline{\epsilon(\xi)E_i(\xi)} = 0$$

$$\frac{\partial}{\partial\xi_{1i}} \overline{\epsilon(\xi_2)\epsilon(\xi_1)F_i(\xi_1)} = 0$$

$$\vdots$$

$$(3\text{-}81) \quad \delta_{ijk}\frac{\partial}{\partial\xi_j} \overline{E_k(\xi)} = 0$$

$$\delta_{ijk}\frac{\partial}{\partial\xi_{1j}} \overline{\epsilon(\xi_2)E_k(\xi_1)} = 0$$

$$\vdots$$

Expanding Eq. 3-78, using terms like m_{1200}, gives equations for $\overline{\epsilon(\xi_1)E_i(\xi_1)E_j(\xi_2)}$. There is no point in specifically considering these higher-order equations here. In order to find these equations one need only catalog systematically all terms in Eq. 3-78, substitute in Eqs. 3-33 and 3-34, compare like powers, and use Eq. 3-79.

The boundary condition for Eqs. 3-30 and 3-31 is the specification of $n_{Si}E_i(\mathbf{x}_S)$ or $\phi(\mathbf{x}_S)$ (where $E_i = \partial\phi/\partial x_i$) (or some linear combination of these functions) over some surface S. ($\mathbf{n}_S$ is the unit normal to S.) As in the harmonic oscillator problem, we assume these same conditions hold in every member of the ensemble. The geometry is taken to be the same in each member of the ensemble, and we let $\epsilon(\mathbf{x})$ be a constant on S. From these conditions we may find relations among the various moment equations. These relations are the boundary conditions for Eqs. 3-80 and 3-81. Consider the boundary condition $n_{Si}E_i$. A moment of the form

$$\overline{\epsilon(\mathbf{x}_1)\cdots\epsilon(\mathbf{x}_j)E_i(\mathbf{x}_{j+1})\cdots E_p(\mathbf{x}_n)}$$

must satisfy the condition

$$\overline{n_i\epsilon(\mathbf{x}_1)\cdots\epsilon(\mathbf{x}_j)E_i(\mathbf{x}_{j+1})\cdots E_p(\mathbf{x}_n)}\Big|_{\mathbf{x}_{j+1}=\mathbf{x}_S}$$
$$= [n_iE_i(\mathbf{x}_S)][\overline{\epsilon(\mathbf{x}_1)\cdots\epsilon(\mathbf{x}_j)E_k(\mathbf{x}_{j+2})\cdots E_p(\mathbf{x}_n)}]$$

Similar conditions hold for moments in which two or more points lie on S. To use the $\phi(\mathbf{x}_S)$ boundary condition, it is convenient to replace the hierarchy of moment equations (Eqs. 3-80 and 3-81) with a hierarchy in terms of moments of the form

$$\overline{\epsilon(\mathbf{x}_1)\cdots\epsilon(\mathbf{x}_j)\phi(\mathbf{x}_{j+1})\cdots\phi(\mathbf{x}_n)}$$

3.2.1.3. Navier-Stokes Equations. The functional equations governing turbulence are given by Eqs. 3-52 and 3-49:

(3-52)
$$\frac{\partial}{\partial s}\frac{\delta M}{\delta y_i(\boldsymbol{\xi}, s)} = i\frac{\partial}{\partial\xi_j}\frac{\delta}{\delta y_j(\boldsymbol{\xi}, s)}\left[\frac{\delta M}{\delta y_i(\boldsymbol{\xi}, s)}\right] + \nu\nabla_\xi^2\frac{\delta M}{\delta y_i(\boldsymbol{\xi}, s)} - i\frac{\partial\Pi}{\partial\xi_i}$$

(3-49)
$$\frac{\partial}{\partial\xi_i}\frac{\delta M}{\delta y_i(\boldsymbol{\xi}, s)} = 0$$

The function Π plays the same role here that the pressure does in the ordinary Navier-Stokes equations. We shall derive the moment equations assuming it to be an unknown functional.

Since M is a functional of only the vector quantity $y_i(\xi, s)$, we shall use a slightly different notation in expanding M. We set here

$$(3\text{-}82) \quad M[y_i(\xi, s)] = m_0 + \int_{V,T} m_i(\xi, s)y_i(\xi, s)\, d\xi\, ds$$

$$+ \int_{V,T} \int_{V,T} m_{ij}(\xi_1, s_1; \xi_2, s_2)y_i(\xi_1, s_1)y_j(\xi_2, s_2)\, d\xi_1\, ds_1\, d\xi_2\, ds_2$$

$$+ \cdots + \int_{V,T} \cdots \int_{V,T} m_{ij\cdots u}(\xi_1, s_1, \ldots, \xi_n, s_n)$$

$$\times \; y_i(\xi_1, s_1) \cdots y_u(\xi_n, s_n)\, d\xi_1\, ds_1 \cdots d\xi_n\, ds_n + \cdots +$$

We consider Π to also be a functional of $y_i(\xi, s)$, and hence we write analogously

$$(3\text{-}83) \quad \Pi(y_i(\xi, s)] = n_0(\xi, s) + \int_{V,T} n_i(\xi, s; \xi_1, s_1)y_i(\xi_1, s_1)\, d\xi_1\, ds_1 + \cdots$$

$$+ \int_{V,T} \cdots \int_{V,T} n_{ij\cdots u}(\xi, s; \xi_1, s_1; \ldots; \xi_n, s_n)y_i(\xi_1, s_1)$$

$$\cdots y_u(\xi_n, s_n)\, d\xi_1\, ds_1 \cdots d\xi_n\, ds_n + \cdots +$$

$m_{ij\cdots u}$ is related to the moment $\overline{u_i(\xi_1, s_1) \cdots u_u(\xi_n, s_n)}$ by the relation

$$(3\text{-}84) \qquad m_{ij\cdots u} = \frac{i^n}{n!}\overline{u_i(\xi_1, s_1) \cdots u_u(\xi_n, s_n)}$$

We shall discuss the identification of the $n_{ij\cdots u}$ shortly. Note, however, that the $n_{ij\cdots u}$ contain an extra ξ, s argument since Π contains $p(\mathbf{x}, t)$ in its definition (see Eq. 3-52).

We now substitute Eqs. 3-82 and 3-83 into Eqs. 3-52 and 3-49 and compare like powers of y_i. Using Eq. 3-84 we find the following set of equations

$$(3\text{-}85) \quad \frac{\partial}{\partial s} \overline{u_i(\boldsymbol{\xi}, s)} + \frac{\partial}{\partial \xi_j} \overline{u_i(\boldsymbol{\xi}, s)u_j(\boldsymbol{\xi}, s)}$$

$$= \nu \nabla_\xi^2 \overline{u_i(\boldsymbol{\xi}, s)} - \frac{\partial n_0(\boldsymbol{\xi}, s)}{\partial \xi_i} \frac{\partial}{\partial s_1} \overline{u_i(\boldsymbol{\xi}_1, s_1)u_k(\boldsymbol{\xi}_2, s_2)}$$

$$+ \frac{\partial}{\partial \xi_{1j}} \overline{u_i(\boldsymbol{\xi}_1, s_1)u_j(\boldsymbol{\xi}_1, s_1)u_k(\boldsymbol{\xi}_2, s_2)}$$

$$= \nu \nabla_{\xi_1}^2 \overline{u_i(\boldsymbol{\xi}_1, s_1)u_k(\boldsymbol{\xi}_2, s_2)} + i \frac{\overline{\partial n_k(\boldsymbol{\xi}_1, s_1; \boldsymbol{\xi}_2, s_2)}}{\partial \xi_{1i}}$$

$$\cdot$$
$$\cdot$$
$$\cdot$$

+ divergence conditions

In order to determine the $n_{ij\cdots u}$ it is only necessary to expand the exponential term exp $\{i[y_i, u_i]\}$ given in the definition of Π. Comparing this expansion with Eq. 3-83 we find

$$(3.86) \qquad\qquad n_0(\boldsymbol{\xi}, s) = \overline{p(\boldsymbol{\xi}, s)}$$

$$n_k(\boldsymbol{\xi}, s; \boldsymbol{\xi}_1, s_1) = \overline{ip(\boldsymbol{\xi}, s)u_k(\boldsymbol{\xi}_1, s_1)}$$

$$\cdot$$
$$\cdot$$
$$\cdot$$

The boundary conditions for solution of the Navier-Stokes equations are: (1) there is no relative motion between a solid and the fluid in contact with it; (2) at an interface between two fluids the normal pressure and viscous stresses must be continuous; (3) $u_i(\mathbf{x}, 0)$ must be given. If we assume that the same macroscopic geometric configuration is specified in each member of the ensemble, these conditions provide boundary conditions for the hierarchy given in Eqs. 3-85 and 3-86. For example, if all stationary solid surfaces are given by $\mathbf{x}_S$, we have

$$\overline{u_i(\mathbf{x}_1) \cdots u_p(\mathbf{x}_n)}\,\big|_{\mathbf{x}_1 = \mathbf{x}_S} = 0$$

A set of moment equations associated with the Hopf functional, M_H, may be similarly derived. This set will be given by a direct derivation in the next section.

3.2.2. Derivation of the Moment Equations Directly from the Differential Equations

The statistical moment equations may be derived directly from the governing nonstatistical differential equations. In most cases it is simpler to do this than to proceed through the characteristic functional approach. In this section we will derive the moment equations for the simple harmonic oscillator, media with spatially variable permittivity, and the Navier-Stokes equations. The reader who has not read the sections on functionals will have no difficulty in following the derivations.

3.2.2.1. Simple Harmonic Oscillator. The equation governing the simple harmonic oscillator driven by a random force is written in Eq. 3-1.

$$(3\text{-}1) \qquad m\frac{d^2x(t_1)}{dt_1^2} + kx(t_1) = F(t_1)$$

We seek to derive equations for all correlation functions of the form

$$\overline{x(t_1) \cdots x(t_j)F(t_{j+1}) \cdots F(t_n)}$$

from Eq. 3-1. This may be done on multiplying Eq. 3-1 in turn by the following quantities:

$$1$$
$$F(t_2)$$
$$x(t_2)$$
$$F(t_2)F(t_3)$$
$$x(t_2)F(t_3)$$
$$x(t_2)x(t_3)$$
$$x(t_2)x(t_3)$$
$$\cdot$$
$$\cdot$$
$$\cdot$$

and ensemble averaging. This gives the sequence*

$$m \frac{d^2 \overline{x(t_1)}}{dt_1^2} + k\overline{x(t_1)} = \overline{F(t_1)}$$

$$m \frac{\partial^2 \overline{x(t_1)F(t_2)}}{\partial t_1^2} + k\overline{x(t_1)F(t_2)} = \overline{F(t_1)F(t_2)}$$

$$m \frac{\partial^2 \overline{x(t_1)x(t_2)}}{\partial t_1^2} + k\overline{x(t_1)x(t_2)} = \overline{F(t_1)x(t_2)}$$

(3-87)

$$m \frac{\partial^2 \overline{x(t_1)F(t_2)F(t_3)}}{\partial t_1^2} + k\overline{x(t_1)F(t_2)F(t_3)} = \overline{F(t_1)F(t_2)F(t_3)}$$

$$m \frac{\partial^2 \overline{x(t_1)x(t_2)F(t_3)}}{\partial t_1^2} + k\overline{x(t_1)x(t_2)F(t_3)} = \overline{F(t_1)x(t_2)F(t_3)}$$

$$m \frac{\partial^2 \overline{x(t_1)x(t_2)x(t_3)}}{\partial t_1^2} + k\overline{x(t_1)x(t_2)x(t_3)} = \overline{F(t_1)x(t_2)x(t_3)}$$

.
.
.

These are the same equations as derived by the functional approach and already given in part in Chapter 1. They may be solved in sequence, the known functions being the moments of $F(t)$.

3.2.2.2. Spatially Variable Permittivity. The governing equations for the case of a static electric field in a medium with variable spatial

* In order to establish the fact that

$$\frac{\overline{dx(t)}}{dt} = \frac{d}{dt} \overline{x(t)}$$

we note that

$$\overline{x(t)} = \lim_{N \to \infty} \frac{1}{N} \sum_{n=1}^{N} x_n(t)$$

where the summation is over all members of the ensemble. We differentiate $\overline{x(t)}$ and then interchange differentiation and summation. To do this we assume suitable convergence properties for the infinite summation. Similar arguments are used for differentiation of higher-order correlation functions. See Yaglom (1962).

permittivity are given by Eqs. 3-30 and Eq. 3-31

(3-30) $\dfrac{\partial}{\partial x_{1i}} \epsilon(\mathbf{x}_1) E_i(\mathbf{x}_1) = 0$

(3-31) $\delta_{ijk} \dfrac{\partial}{\partial x_{1j}} E_k(\mathbf{x}_1) = 0$

In order to derive a set of statistical moment equations we multiply Eqs. 3-30 and 3-31 in turn by the following sequence of terms

$$1$$
$$\epsilon(\mathbf{x}_2)$$
$$E_j(\mathbf{x}_2)$$
$$\epsilon(\mathbf{x}_2)\epsilon(\mathbf{x}_3)$$
$$\epsilon(\mathbf{x}_2)E_j(\mathbf{x}_3)$$
$$E_j(\mathbf{x}_2)E_k(\mathbf{x}_3)$$
$$\cdot$$
$$\cdot$$
$$\cdot$$

and ensemble average the resulting equations. This yields the set

$$\frac{\partial}{\partial x_{1i}} \overline{\epsilon(\mathbf{x}_1)E_i(\mathbf{x}_1)} = 0$$

$$\frac{\partial}{\partial x_{1i}} \overline{\epsilon(\mathbf{x}_1)E_i(\mathbf{x}_1)\epsilon(\mathbf{x}_2)} = 0$$

$$\frac{\partial}{\partial x_{1i}} \overline{\epsilon(\mathbf{x}_1)E_i(\mathbf{x}_1)E_j(\mathbf{x}_2)} = 0$$

(3-88)

$$\frac{\partial}{\partial x_{1i}} \overline{\epsilon(\mathbf{x}_1)E_i(\mathbf{x}_1)\epsilon(\mathbf{x}_2)\epsilon(\mathbf{x}_3)} = 0$$

$$\frac{\partial}{\partial x_{1i}} \overline{\epsilon(\mathbf{x}_1)E_i(\mathbf{x}_1)\epsilon(\mathbf{x}_2)E_j(\mathbf{x}_3)} = 0$$

$$\frac{\partial}{\partial x_{1i}} \overline{\epsilon(\mathbf{x}_1)E_i(\mathbf{x}_1)E_j(\mathbf{x}_2)E_k(\mathbf{x}_3)} = 0$$

$$\cdot$$
$$\cdot$$
$$\cdot$$

$$\delta_{ijk} \frac{\partial}{\partial x_{1j}} \overline{E_k(\mathbf{x}_1)} = 0$$

$$\delta_{ijk} \frac{\partial}{\partial x_{1j}} \overline{E_k(\mathbf{x}_1)\epsilon(\mathbf{x}_2)} = 0$$

$$\delta_{ijk} \frac{\partial}{\partial x_{1j}} \overline{E_k(\mathbf{x}_1)E_l(\mathbf{x}_2)} = 0$$

(3-89)

$$\delta_{ijk} \frac{\partial}{\partial x_{1j}} \overline{E_k(\mathbf{x}_1)\epsilon(\mathbf{x}_2)\epsilon(\mathbf{x}_3)} = 0$$

$$\delta_{ijk} \frac{\partial}{\partial x_{1j}} \overline{E_k(\mathbf{x}_1)\epsilon(\mathbf{x}_2)E_l(\mathbf{x}_3)} = 0$$

$$\delta_{ijk} \frac{\partial}{\partial x_{1j}} \overline{E_k(\mathbf{x}_1)E_l(\mathbf{x}_2)E_m(\mathbf{x}_3)} = 0$$

.
.
.

These are the same equations as are derived by the functional approach. As we stressed in Chapter 1, a set of equations like Eqs. 3-88 and 3-89 cannot be solved, since in every finite set of equations there are more unknowns than knowns. This statement is clearer if we write

(3-90)
$$\epsilon(\mathbf{x}) = \bar\epsilon(\mathbf{x}) + \epsilon'(\mathbf{x})$$

$$E_i(\mathbf{x}) = \bar E_i(\mathbf{x}) + E_i{}'(\mathbf{x})$$

where $\overline{\epsilon'(\mathbf{x})} = \overline{E_i{}'(\mathbf{x})} = 0$.

We have then

(3-91a) $\dfrac{\partial}{\partial x_{1i}} \overline{[\epsilon(\mathbf{x}_1)\, \overline{E_i(\mathbf{x}_1)}]} + \dfrac{\partial}{\partial x_{1i}} \overline{\epsilon'(\mathbf{x}_1)E_i{}'(\mathbf{x}_1)} = 0$

(3-91b) $\dfrac{\partial}{\partial x_{1i}} [\overline{\epsilon(\mathbf{x}_1)}\, \overline{E_i(\mathbf{x}_1)}\, \overline{\epsilon(\mathbf{x}_2)}] + \dfrac{\partial}{\partial x_{1i}} [\overline{\epsilon'(\mathbf{x}_1)E_i{}'(\mathbf{x}_1)}\, \overline{\epsilon(\mathbf{x}_2)}]$

$$+ \frac{\partial}{\partial x_{1i}} [\overline{\epsilon(\mathbf{x}_1)}\, \overline{E_i{}'(\mathbf{x}_1)\epsilon'(\mathbf{x}_2)}] + \frac{\partial}{\partial x_{1i}} [\overline{\epsilon'(\mathbf{x}_1)\epsilon'(\mathbf{x}_2)}\, \overline{E_i(\mathbf{x}_1)}]$$

$$+ \frac{\partial}{\partial x_{1i}} \overline{\epsilon'(\mathbf{x}_1)E_i{}'(\mathbf{x}_1)\epsilon'(\mathbf{x}_2)} = 0$$

.
.
.

(3-92a) $\delta_{ijk} \dfrac{\partial}{\partial x_{1j}} \overline{E_k(\mathbf{x}_1)} = 0$

(3-92b) $\delta_{ijk} \dfrac{\partial}{\partial x_{1j}} [\overline{E_k(\mathbf{x}_1) \, \epsilon(\mathbf{x}_2)}] + \delta_{ijk} \dfrac{\partial}{\partial x_{1j}} \overline{E_k{}'(\mathbf{x}_1)\epsilon'(\mathbf{x}_2)} = 0$

$$\cdot$$
$$\cdot$$
$$\cdot$$

For the sequence Eqs. 3-91a and 3-92a the unknowns are $\overline{E_k(\mathbf{x}_1)}$ and $\overline{\epsilon'(\mathbf{x}_1)E_i{}'(\mathbf{x}_1)}$. For the sequence Eqs. 3-91a,b and Eqs. 3-92a,b the unknowns are $\overline{E_k(\mathbf{x}_1)}$, $\overline{\epsilon'(\mathbf{x}_1)E_i{}'(\mathbf{x}_2)}$ and $\overline{\epsilon'(\mathbf{x}_1)E_i{}'(\mathbf{x}_1)\epsilon'(\mathbf{x}_2)}$. By induction we see readily that no matter how many equations we use we shall never get a determinate set unless some assumption is made so as to allow us to terminate the set. Two assumptions commonly made are to assume either than higher-order moments are small or that they may be approximated using a relationship derived from gaussianly distributed random variables. We shall discuss both these approximations in later sections.

We should note at this point that these are not the only moment equations that can be derived from Eqs. 3-30 and 3-31; they are only perhaps the most natural. For example, Eq. 3-30 may be expanded in the form

(3-93) $\epsilon(\mathbf{x}_1) \dfrac{\partial}{\partial x_{1i}} E_i(\mathbf{x}_1) + E_i(\mathbf{x}_1) \dfrac{\partial}{\partial x_{1i}} \epsilon(\mathbf{x}_1) = 0$

and rewritten upon dividing through by $\epsilon(x_1)$ to yield

(3-94) $\dfrac{\partial}{\partial x_{1i}} E_i(\mathbf{x}_1) + E_i(\mathbf{x}_1)g_i(\mathbf{x}_1) = 0$

where $g_i(\mathbf{x}_1) \equiv (\partial/\partial x_{1i}) \ln \epsilon(\mathbf{x}_1)$. (This form is used by Prager, 1960.)

A wholly different sequences of moment equations may be derived by multiplication and subsequent ensemble averaging using an approximate sequence of terms. For a particular problem this new sequence may yield a more natural approximation procedure than the set given by Eqs. 3-88 and 3-89. Care must be taken to use a sequence of terms that gives one a usable iteration scheme. For the set of equations 3-94 and 3-31 one could use the sequence

$$1$$
$$g_j(\mathbf{x}_2)$$
$$E_j(\mathbf{x}_2)$$
$$g_j(\mathbf{x}_2)g_k(\mathbf{x}_3)$$
$$g_j(\mathbf{x}_2)E_k(\mathbf{x}_3)$$
$$E_j(\mathbf{x}_2)E_k(\mathbf{x}_3)$$

.
.
.

for some physical problem.

The set of moment equations used for the solution of any physical problem must be based on some physical insight. If the moment equations are used rather than the governing functional equations, some assumption must be made to terminate the set if the equations are to be useful. This closure assumption can only be made intelligently if there is some physical understanding. The assumption that $\overline{\epsilon'^n}/\bar{\epsilon}^n \ll 1$ (all n) often used to terminate a set of equations like 3-91 and 3-92 is a very simple type of physical assumption since it basically assumes that the permittivity variations about the mean are small. If, however, one seeks to make a similar assumption for Eqs. 3-94 and 3-31 using the sequence just cited, the physical interpretation is much more difficult, unless one also makes the assumption $\overline{\epsilon'^n}/\bar{\epsilon}^n \ll 1$ (all n). A modification of the later sequence may be of use in small concentration theory rather than small perturbation theory.

3.2.2.3. Navier-Stokes Equations. The Navier-Stokes equations and the continuity equation for an incompressible fluid are given by Eqs. 3-46 and 3-47

$$(3\text{-}46) \quad \frac{\partial u_i(\mathbf{x}_1, t_1)}{\partial t_1} + u_j(\mathbf{x}_1, t_1)\frac{\partial u_i(\mathbf{x}_1, t_1)}{\partial x_{1j}} = \nu\nabla_1^2 u_i(\mathbf{x}_1, t_1) - \frac{\partial p(\mathbf{x}_1, t_1)}{\partial x_{1i}}$$

$$(3\text{-}47) \quad \frac{\partial}{\partial x_{1i}} u_i(\mathbf{x}_1, t_1) = 0$$

In order to derive the set of moment equations we multiply Eqs. 3-46 and 3-47 by the sequence

$$1$$
$$u_k(\mathbf{x}_2, t_2)$$
$$p(\mathbf{x}_2, t_2)$$
$$u_k(\mathbf{x}_2, t_2)u_l(\mathbf{x}_3, t_3)$$
$$p(\mathbf{x}_2, t_2)u_l(\mathbf{x}_3, t_3)$$
$$p(\mathbf{x}_2, t_2)p(\mathbf{x}_3, t_3)$$

.

.

.

and ensemble average. This yields the set

$$(3\text{-}95) \quad \frac{\partial \overline{u_i(\mathbf{x}_1, t_1)}}{\partial t_1} + \frac{\partial \overline{u_j(\mathbf{x}_1, t_1)u_i(\mathbf{x}_1, t_1)}}{\partial x_{1j}} = \nu \nabla_1^2 \overline{u_i(\mathbf{x}_1, t_1)} - \frac{\partial}{\partial x_{1i}} \overline{p(\mathbf{x}_1, t_i)}$$

$$\frac{\partial \overline{u_i(\mathbf{x}_1, t_1)u_k(\mathbf{x}_2, t_2)}}{\partial t_1} + \frac{\partial}{\partial x_{1j}} \overline{u_j(\mathbf{x}_1, t_1)u_i(\mathbf{x}_1, t_1)u_k(\mathbf{x}_2, t_2)}$$

$$= \nu \nabla_1^2 \overline{u_i(\mathbf{x}_1, t_1)u_k(\mathbf{x}_2, t_2)} - \frac{\partial}{\partial x_{1i}} \overline{p(\mathbf{x}_1, t_1)u_k(\mathbf{x}_2, t_2)}$$

.

.

.

$$(3\text{-}96) \quad \frac{\partial}{\partial x_{1i}} \overline{u_i(\mathbf{x}_1, t_1)} = 0$$

$$\frac{\partial}{\partial x_{1i}} \overline{u_i(\mathbf{x}_1, t_1)u_k(\mathbf{x}_2, t_2)} = 0$$

$$\frac{\partial}{\partial x_{1i}} \overline{u_i(\mathbf{x}_1, t_1)p(\mathbf{x}_2, t_2)} = 0$$

.

.

.

These are the moment equations that are derived by the use of the functional $M[y_i(\mathbf{x}, t)]$ given in Eq. 3-48. As we previously stated, the moment equations of turbulence are commonly derived for only one time t. To derive the set for one time is less straightforward than the many-time case since multiplication of Eq. 3-46 by $u_j(\mathbf{x}_2, t_1)$ yields the term

$$u_j(\mathbf{x}_2, t_1)\frac{\partial}{\partial t_1} u_i(\mathbf{x}_1, t_1)$$

rather than the term

$$\frac{\partial}{\partial t_1} u_i(\mathbf{x}_1, t_1)u_j(\mathbf{x}_2, t_2)$$

To circumvent this difficulty we write two forms of Eq. 3-46 (dropping the 1 subscript on t)

(3-97) $\dfrac{\partial}{\partial t} u_i(\mathbf{x}_1, t) + \dfrac{\partial}{\partial x_{1j}} u_j(\mathbf{x}_1, t)u_i(\mathbf{x}_1, t) = \nu\nabla_1^2 u_i(\mathbf{x}_1, t) - \dfrac{\partial p(\mathbf{x}_1, t)}{\partial x_{1i}}$

(3-98) $\dfrac{\partial}{\partial t} u_k(\mathbf{x}_2, t) + \dfrac{\partial}{\partial x_{2j}} u_j(\mathbf{x}_2, t)u_k(\mathbf{x}_2, t) = \nu\nabla_2^2 u_k(\mathbf{x}_2, t) - \dfrac{\partial p(\mathbf{x}_2, t)}{\partial x_{2k}}$

Now we multiply Eq. 3-97 by $u_k(\mathbf{x}_2, t)$, Eq. 3-98 by $u_i(\mathbf{x}_1, t)$, add the results, and ensemble average. This yields

(3-99) $\dfrac{\partial}{\partial t} \overline{u_i(\mathbf{x}_1, t)u_k(\mathbf{x}_2, t)} + \dfrac{\partial}{\partial x_{1j}} \overline{u_j(\mathbf{x}_1, t)u_i(\mathbf{x}_1, t)u_k(\mathbf{x}_2, t)}$

$\qquad + \dfrac{\partial}{\partial x_{2j}} \overline{u_j(\mathbf{x}_2, t)u_k(\mathbf{x}_2, t)u_i(\mathbf{x}_1, t)} = \nu\nabla_1^2\overline{u_i(\mathbf{x}_1, t)u_k(\mathbf{x}_2, t)}$

$\qquad + \nu\nabla_2^2\overline{u_k(\mathbf{x}_2, t)u_i(\mathbf{x}_1, t)} - \dfrac{\partial}{\partial x_{1i}} \overline{p(\mathbf{x}_1, t)u_k(\mathbf{x}_2, t)}$

$\qquad - \dfrac{\partial}{\partial x_{2k}} \overline{p(\mathbf{x}_2, t)u_i(\mathbf{x}_1, t)}$

There is no difficulty with the divergence condition since there are no t derivatives. Multiplication by $u_k(\mathbf{x}_2, t)$ gives

(3-100) $\qquad \dfrac{\partial}{\partial x_{1i}} \overline{u_i(\mathbf{x}_1, t)u_k(\mathbf{x}_2, t)} = 0$

In order to derive higher-order terms one must write Eq. 3-46a a number of times with different arguments and multiply each form in such a manner as to allow one to form, upon addition of the various equations, terms like

$$\frac{\partial}{\partial t} \overline{u_i(\mathbf{x}_1, t) \cdots u_m(\mathbf{x}_n, t)}$$

The procedure is straightforward though cumbersome, and we need not elaborate upon it here.

It is appropriate to mention that G. I. Taylor and T. von Kármán did the basic work that was needed for deriving suitable moment equations for turbulence. Reference to their many papers is given in Chapter 7. From their work it is easy to see how to proceed in deriving moment equations for other statistical problems.

3.2.3. Equations Governing the Fourier Transforms of the Moments

It is often very convenient, from both a mathematical and a physical point of view, to consider the Fourier transforms of the moments. The transforms may be taken with respect to space or time depending upon the need. In this section we shall consider the transform moments only for the particular case of the spatially variable permittivity problem in which the permittivity statistics are homogeneous. The methods indicated may be used for any of the equations we consider in this book, and in the later chapters we shall consider transform techniques in connection with other statistical problems. The transformed moments have been studied extensively in homogeneous turbulence theory, and we refer the reader to Batchelor (1952) for a thorough discussion of the single-time equations.

In order to avoid difficulties at infinity, it is convenient to work with the correlation functions in terms of $\epsilon'(\mathbf{x})$ and $E_i'(\mathbf{x})$ rather than $\epsilon(\mathbf{x})$ and $E_i(\mathbf{x})$. Thus we consider the set of moment equations given by Eqs. 3-91 and 3-92 rather than Eqs. 3-88 and 3-89. As we just stated, we shall restrict ourselves to the case of permittivity variations that are statistically homogeneous. In order to insure that the joint statistics of $\epsilon'(\mathbf{x})$ and $E_i'(\mathbf{x})$ are homogeneous, we shall also assume that $\overline{E_i(\mathbf{x})}$ is a constant vector, say $\bar{E}\delta_{i3}$.

Since the complete statistics of $\epsilon(\mathbf{x})$ are homogeneous, $\overline{\epsilon(\mathbf{x})}$ is a constant, and Eqs. 3-91 and 3-92 may be written (with the inclusion of an extra equation; the "a" equations are identically zero here).

(3-101a) $\quad \bar{\epsilon} \dfrac{\partial}{\partial x_{1i}} L_i(\mathbf{x}_1, \mathbf{x}_2) + \bar{E} \dfrac{\partial}{\partial x_{13}} C_2(\mathbf{x}_1, \mathbf{x}_2) + \dfrac{\partial}{\partial x_{1i}} P(\mathbf{x}_1, \mathbf{x}_1, \mathbf{x}_2) = 0$

(3-101b) $\quad \bar{\epsilon} \dfrac{\partial}{\partial x_{1i}} P_i(\mathbf{x}_1, \mathbf{x}_2, \mathbf{x}_3) + \bar{E} \dfrac{\partial}{\partial x_{13}} C_3(\mathbf{x}_1, \mathbf{x}_2, \mathbf{x}_3)$

$$+ \dfrac{\partial}{\partial x_{1i}} Q_i(\mathbf{x}_1, \mathbf{x}_1, \mathbf{x}_2, \mathbf{x}_3) = 0$$

$$\cdot$$
$$\cdot$$
$$\cdot$$

(3-102a) $\qquad\qquad \delta_{ijk} \dfrac{\partial}{\partial x_{1j}} L_k(\mathbf{x}_1, \mathbf{x}_2) = 0$

(3-102b) $\qquad\qquad \delta_{ijk} \dfrac{\partial}{\partial x_{1j}} P_k(\mathbf{x}_1, \mathbf{x}_2, \mathbf{x}_3) = 0$

$$\cdot$$
$$\cdot$$
$$\cdot$$

where
$$C_2(\mathbf{x}_1, \mathbf{x}_2) = \overline{\epsilon'(\mathbf{x}_1)\epsilon'(\mathbf{x}_2)}$$
$$L_i(\mathbf{x}_1, \mathbf{x}_2) = \overline{E_i{}'(\mathbf{x}_1)\epsilon'(\mathbf{x}_2)}$$
$$C_3(\mathbf{x}_1, \mathbf{x}_2, \mathbf{x}_3) = \overline{\epsilon'(\mathbf{x}_1)\epsilon'(\mathbf{x}_2)\epsilon'(\mathbf{x}_3)}$$
$$P_i(\mathbf{x}_1, \mathbf{x}_2, \mathbf{x}_3) = \overline{E_i{}'(\mathbf{x}_1)\epsilon'(\mathbf{x}_2)\epsilon'(\mathbf{x}_3)}$$
$$Q_i(\mathbf{x}_1, \mathbf{x}_2, \mathbf{x}_3, \mathbf{x}_4) = \overline{E_i{}'(\mathbf{x}_1)\epsilon'(\mathbf{x}_2)\epsilon'(\mathbf{x}_3)\epsilon'(\mathbf{x}_4)}$$

The condition of homogeneity states that all statistical quantities are independent of absolute position. Thus all statistical functions depend only upon $\mathbf{r}_2 = \mathbf{x}_2 - \mathbf{x}_1$, $\mathbf{r}_3 = \mathbf{x}_3 - \mathbf{x}_1, \ldots$, and

$$C_2(\mathbf{x}_1, \mathbf{x}_2) = C_2(\mathbf{r}_2)$$
$$L_i(\mathbf{x}_1, \mathbf{x}_2) = L_i(\mathbf{r}_2)$$
$$C_3(\mathbf{x}_1, \mathbf{x}_2, \mathbf{x}_3) = C_3(\mathbf{r}_2, \mathbf{r}_3)$$
$$P_i(\mathbf{x}_1, \mathbf{x}_2, \mathbf{x}_3) = P_i(\mathbf{r}_2, \mathbf{r}_3)$$

$$\cdot$$
$$\cdot$$
$$\cdot$$

The independent variables $x_1, x_2, \ldots$, in Eqs. 3-101 and 3-102 may now be replaced by the independent variables $r_2, r_3, \ldots$. This is done by making the following transformation of variables

$$r_2 = x_2 - x_1$$
$$r_3 = x_3 - x_1$$
$$r_4 = x_4 - x_1$$
$$\cdot$$
$$\cdot$$
$$\cdot$$
$$x_1' = x_1$$

All functions will be independent of x_1' and hence all derivatives with respect to x_1' will vanish. In terms of the new variables, Eqs. 3-101 and 3-102 become

(3-103) $\bar{\epsilon}\dfrac{\partial}{\partial r_{2i}} L_i(\mathbf{r}_2) + \bar{E}\dfrac{\partial}{\partial r_{23}} C_2(\mathbf{r}_2) + \dfrac{\partial}{\partial r_{2i}} P_i(0, \mathbf{r}_2) = 0$

$$\bar{\epsilon}\left(\dfrac{\partial}{\partial r_{2i}} + \dfrac{\partial}{\partial r_{3i}}\right) P_i(\mathbf{r}_2, \mathbf{r}_3) + \bar{E}\left(\dfrac{\partial}{\partial r_{23}} + \dfrac{\partial}{\partial r_{33}}\right) C_3(\mathbf{r}_2, \mathbf{r}_3)$$

$$+ \left(\dfrac{\partial}{\partial r_{2i}} + \dfrac{\partial}{\partial r_{3i}}\right) Q_i(0, \mathbf{r}_2, \mathbf{r}_3) = 0$$

$$\cdot$$
$$\cdot$$
$$\cdot$$

$$\delta_{ijk}\dfrac{\partial}{\partial r_{2j}} L_k(\mathbf{r}_2) = 0$$

(3-104)

$$\delta_{ijk}\left(\dfrac{\partial}{\partial r_{2j}} + \dfrac{\partial}{\partial r_{3j}}\right) P_k(\mathbf{r}_2, \mathbf{r}_3) = 0$$

$$\cdot$$
$$\cdot$$
$$\cdot$$

Here we note that

$$\dfrac{\partial}{\partial x_{1i}} = -\sum_{j=2}^{n} \dfrac{\partial}{\partial r_{ji}}$$

We next define the Fourier transforms of $C_2, L_i, \ldots$ We denote the Fourier transforms of these variables by the use of a circumflex accent. Thus we have

$$\hat{C}_2(\mathbf{k}_2) = \int C_2(\mathbf{r}_2) \exp\left[2\pi i\mathbf{k}_2 \cdot \mathbf{r}_2\right] d\mathbf{r}_2$$

(3-105) $\quad \hat{L}_i(\mathbf{k}_2) = \int L_i(\mathbf{r}_2) \exp\left[2\pi i\mathbf{k}_2 \cdot \mathbf{r}_2\right] d\mathbf{r}_2$

$$\hat{C}_3(\mathbf{k}_2, \mathbf{k}_3) = \iint C_3(\mathbf{r}_2, \mathbf{r}_3) \exp\left[2\pi i\mathbf{k}_2 \cdot \mathbf{r}_2 + 2\pi i\mathbf{k}_3 \cdot \mathbf{r}_3\right] d\mathbf{r}_2\, d\mathbf{r}_3$$

$$\cdot$$
$$\cdot$$
$$\cdot$$

where

$$\int d\mathbf{r}_2 \equiv \int_{-\infty}^{\infty} \int_{-\infty}^{\infty} \int_{-\infty}^{\infty} dr_{21}\, dr_{22}\, dr_{23}$$

The inverse transform relations are simply

$$C_2(\mathbf{r}_2) = \int \hat{C}_2(\mathbf{k}_2) \exp\left[-2\pi i\mathbf{k}_2 \cdot \mathbf{r}_2\right] d\mathbf{k}_2$$

(3-106) $\quad L_i(\mathbf{r}_2) = \int \hat{L}_i(\mathbf{k}_2) \exp\left[-2\pi i\mathbf{k}_2 \cdot \mathbf{r}_2\right] d\mathbf{k}_2$

$$C_3(\mathbf{r}_2, \mathbf{r}_3) = \iint \hat{C}_3(\mathbf{k}_2, \mathbf{k}_3) \exp\left[-2\pi i\mathbf{k}_2 \cdot \mathbf{r}_2 - 2\pi i\mathbf{k}_3 \cdot \mathbf{r}_3\right] d\mathbf{k}_2\, d\mathbf{k}_3$$

$$\cdot$$
$$\cdot$$
$$\cdot$$

where

$$\int d\mathbf{k}_2 \equiv \int_{-\infty}^{\infty} \int_{-\infty}^{\infty} \int_{-\infty}^{\infty} dk_{21}\, dk_{22}\, dk_{23}$$

In order to determine the equations governing the transformed variables we take the Fourier transform of Eqs. 3-103 and 3-104. This yields

$$\bar{\epsilon}k_{2i}\hat{L}_i(\mathbf{k}_2) + \bar{E}k_{23}\hat{C}_2(\mathbf{k}_2) + k_{2i}\hat{P}_i(0, \mathbf{k}_2) = 0$$

(3-107) $$\bar{\epsilon}(k_{2i} + k_{3i})\hat{P}_i(\mathbf{k}_2, \mathbf{k}_3) + \bar{E}(k_{23} + k_{33})\hat{C}_3(\mathbf{k}_2, \mathbf{k}_3)$$

$$+ (k_{2i} + k_{3i})\hat{Q}_i(0, \mathbf{k}_2, \mathbf{k}_3) = 0$$

.

.

.

(3-108)
$$\delta_{ijm}k_{2j}\hat{L}_m(\mathbf{k}_2) = 0$$

$$\delta_{ijm}(k_{2j} + k_{3j})\hat{P}_m(\mathbf{k}_2, \mathbf{k}_3) = 0$$

.

.

.

Equations 3-107 and 3-108 are now algebraic equations rather than differential equations. These equations may thus often be more convenient to work with than Eqs. 3-103 and 3-104. Any finite set of the equations is, of course, still indeterminate.

3.3. Solution of Moment Equations

In the physical problems we shall treat in the subsequent chapters we shall for the most part attempt to determine low-order moments like

$$\overline{u(t_1)} \quad \text{and} \quad \overline{u(t_1)u(t_2)}$$

In the harmonic oscillator with constant coefficients, this presents no difficulty, since the equations governing $\overline{x(t)}$ and $\overline{x(t_1)x(t_2)}$ are (see Eq. 3-87)

$$m\frac{d^2\overline{x(t_1)}}{dt_1^2} + k\overline{x(t_1)} = \overline{F(t_1)}$$

$$m\frac{d^2\overline{x(t_1)x(t_2)}}{dt_1^2} + k\overline{x(t_1)x(t_2)} = \overline{F(t_1)x(t_2)}$$

$$m\frac{d^2\overline{x(t_1)F(t_2)}}{dt_1^2} + k\overline{x(t_1)F(t_2)} = \overline{F(t_1)F(t_2)}$$

.

.

.

Thus $\overline{x(t_1)}$ and $\overline{x(t_1)x(t_2)}$ may be found from a knowledge of only $\overline{F(t_1)}$ and $\overline{F(t_1)F(t_2)}$. In the spatially variable permittivity problem and in turbulence, the problem is much more difficult. Referring, for example, to Eqs. 3-91a and 3-92a, we have

$$\frac{\partial}{\partial x_{1i}} \overline{\epsilon(\mathbf{x}_1)} \, \overline{E_i(\mathbf{x}_1)} + \frac{\partial}{\partial x_{1i}} \overline{\epsilon'(\mathbf{x}_1)E_i'(\mathbf{x}_1)} = 0$$

$$\delta_{ijk} \frac{\partial}{\partial x_{ij}} \overline{E_k(\mathbf{x}_1)} = 0$$

and we readily see that $\overline{E_i(\mathbf{x}_1)}$ is not given by $\overline{\epsilon(\mathbf{x}_1)}$ alone. In fact, as we previously stated, we must have knowledge of $P[\epsilon(\mathbf{x})]$ or equivalently all moments of the form $\overline{\epsilon(\mathbf{x}_1) \cdots \epsilon(\mathbf{x}_n)}$ to determine $\overline{E_i(\mathbf{x}_1)}$. In order to solve for $\overline{E_i(\mathbf{x}_1)}$ in terms of a finite set of moments thus requires some method of approximation.

We shall present in the next two sections two methods of approximation that have been used in statistical problems. We consider a perturbation technique and the cumulant neglect method. The methods will be presented by showing how they may be used in the spatially variable permittivity problem, but they may be formally applied to a wide class of statistical problems. The reader should have little difficulty in formally using the methods in many problems he may encounter. The difficulty will be in demonstrating that the approximation used gives good results. The validity of the approximation must be discussed in each particular case. In the perturbation example given, the conditions for applicability are reasonably clear. In the cumulant neglect discussion we shall not be able to comment on the applicability of this method to the permittivity problem, since no work has been done toward obtaining solutions. In Chapter 7, however, the applicability of this method in turbulence studies is considered in some detail.

The reader is also referred to a paper by Richardson (1964) in which he discussed the application of perturbation theory and the cumulant neglect method to the problem of the harmonic oscillator with a random spring constant. He also discussed a third technique which he calls the mean square error procedure. It will be seen from his treatment of perturbation theory that the usual procedure is inapplicable in the case of the harmonic oscillator because of the appearance of a secular term. A recent perturbation theory considered by Brull and

Soler (1966) may, however, circumvent the difficulty. For the purposes of this book we shall only require the conventional type of perturbation theory and hence shall not consider the secular question further.

3.3.1. Perturbation Techniques for the Solution of the Moment Equations

In order to terminate the infinite set of moment equations it is often assumed that some parameter is small and that the solution can be expanded in a power series of this parameter. The formal technique is familiar in most fields of physics. The writer gave some thought to developing a general perturbation formulation to cover a very wide class of problems but he felt that the formulation developed would add little to the discussion. For a general formulation to cover the average propagation of a variety of waves in random media we refer the reader to Karal and Keller (1964). See also Bourret (1962).

The principal difficulty in perturbation procedures is proving convergence of the series solution used. Except in the simplest cases this is usually not possible and the ultimate justification of the procedure is its agreement with experimental results. In this book we shall not be able to present convergence proofs for any of the perturbation series that we use in later chapters.

3.3.1.1. Example of Spatially Variable Permittivity. We write Eqs. 3-30 and 3-31 in terms of the variables

$$\epsilon'(\mathbf{x}) = \epsilon(\mathbf{x}) - \overline{\epsilon(\mathbf{x})}$$

$$E_i'(\mathbf{x}) = E_i(\mathbf{x}) - \overline{E_i(\mathbf{x})}$$

where $\overline{\epsilon'(\mathbf{x})} = \overline{E_i'(\mathbf{x})} = 0$.

For simplicity we shall assume

$$\overline{\epsilon(\mathbf{x})} = \bar{\epsilon} = \text{const}$$

$$\overline{E_i(\mathbf{x})} = \bar{E}\delta_{i3} \qquad \bar{E} = \text{const}$$

We have then

$$(3\text{-}109) \qquad \bar{\epsilon}\frac{\partial E_i'(\mathbf{x}_1)}{\partial x_{1i}} + \bar{E}\frac{\partial \epsilon'(\mathbf{x}_1)}{\partial x_{13}} + \frac{\partial}{\partial x_{1i}}(E_i'(\mathbf{x}_1)\epsilon'(\mathbf{x}_1)) = 0$$

$$(3\text{-}110) \qquad \delta_{ijk}\frac{\partial}{\partial x_{1j}}E_k'(\mathbf{x}_1) = 0$$

In order to use a perturbation procedure we must have a small quantity that is of interest. For this example we consider the variations in permittivity about the mean value $\bar{\epsilon}$ to be small. In statistical terms we assume

(3-111)
$$\frac{\overline{|\epsilon'^n|}}{\bar{\epsilon}^n} \ll 1 \qquad \text{all } n$$

Following Beran and Molyneux (1963) we write

(3-112) $\qquad E_i'(\mathbf{x}) = E_i^{(1)}(\mathbf{x}) + E_i^{(2)}(\mathbf{x}) + \cdots = \sum\limits_{j=1}^{\infty} E_i^{(j)}(\mathbf{x})$

where we assume $E_i^{(j)}(\mathbf{x})$ is of order $\bar{E}(\epsilon'^j/\bar{\epsilon}^j)$.

In this example we shall indicate how to calculate the quantity

$$\overline{E_i'(\mathbf{x})\epsilon'(\mathbf{x_2})} = \sum\limits_{j=1}^{\infty} \overline{E_i^{(j)}(\mathbf{x})\epsilon'(\mathbf{x_2})}$$

The procedure to calculate

$$\overline{E_i'(\mathbf{x_1})E_j'(\mathbf{x_2})}$$

and higher-order moments proceeds analogously.

Let us multiply Eqs. 3-109 and 3-110 by the quantity

$$M(2, n) \equiv \epsilon'(\mathbf{x_2})\epsilon'(\mathbf{x_3}) \cdots \epsilon'(\mathbf{x_n})$$

substitute Eq. 3-112, and ensemble average. This yields

(3-113) $\qquad \sum\limits_{p=1}^{\infty} \bar{\epsilon} \frac{\partial}{\partial x_{1i}} \overline{E_i^{(p)}(\mathbf{x_1})M(2, n)} + \bar{E} \frac{\partial}{\partial x_{13}} \overline{\epsilon'(\mathbf{x_1})M(2, n)}$

$$+ \sum\limits_{p=1}^{\infty} \frac{\partial}{\partial x_{1i}} \overline{E_i^{(p)}(\mathbf{x_1})\epsilon'(\mathbf{x_1})M(2, n)} = 0$$

(3-114) $\qquad \sum\limits_{p=1}^{\infty} \delta_{ijk} \frac{\partial}{\partial x_{1j}} \overline{E_k^{(p)}(\mathbf{x_1})M(2, n)} = 0$

We now equate terms of the same order of smallness for all values of n. For $n = 2$, first order, we have

(3-115) $\qquad \bar{\epsilon} \frac{\partial \overline{E_i^{(1)}(\mathbf{x_1})\epsilon'(\mathbf{x_2})}}{\partial x_{1i}} + \bar{E} \frac{\partial}{\partial x_{13}} \overline{\epsilon'(\mathbf{x_1})\epsilon'(\mathbf{x_2})} = 0$

(3-116) $\qquad \delta_{ijk} \frac{\partial}{\partial x_{1j}} \overline{E_k^{(1)}(\mathbf{x_1})\epsilon'(\mathbf{x_2})} = 0$

For $n = 2$, second order, we have

(3-117) $\bar{\epsilon}\dfrac{\partial}{\partial x_{1i}} \overline{E_i^{(2)}(\mathbf{x}_1)\epsilon'(\mathbf{x}_2)} + \dfrac{\partial}{\partial x_{1i}} \overline{E_i^{(1)}(\mathbf{x}_1)\epsilon'(\mathbf{x}_1)\epsilon'(\mathbf{x}_2)} = 0$

(3-118) $\delta_{ijk}\dfrac{\partial}{\partial x_{1j}} \overline{E_k^{(2)}(\mathbf{x}_1)\epsilon'(\mathbf{x}_2)} = 0$

For $n = 3$, first order, we have

(3-119) $\bar{\epsilon}\dfrac{\partial \overline{E_i^{(1)}(\mathbf{x}_1)E'(\mathbf{x}_2)\epsilon'(\mathbf{x}_3)}}{\partial x_{1i}} + \bar{E}\dfrac{\partial}{\partial x_{13}} \overline{\epsilon'(\mathbf{x}_1)\epsilon'(\mathbf{x}_2)\epsilon'(\mathbf{x}_3)} = 0$

(3-120) $\delta_{ijk}\dfrac{\partial}{\partial x_{1j}} \overline{E_k^{(1)}(\mathbf{x}_1)\epsilon'(\mathbf{x}_2)\epsilon'(\mathbf{x}_3)} = 0$

with similar expressions for higher order $n = 3$ and $n > 3$.

Eqs. 3-135 and 3-136 give a determinate set to solve for the lowest order approximation, $\overline{E_i^{(1)}(\mathbf{x}_1)\epsilon'(\mathbf{x}_2)}$, in terms of the known quantity $\overline{\epsilon'(\mathbf{x}_1)\epsilon'(\mathbf{x}_2)}$. Eqs. 3-117, 3-118, 3-119, and 3-120 provide a determinate set of equations to solve for the next approximation, $\overline{E_i^{(2)}(\mathbf{x}_1)\epsilon'(\mathbf{x}_2)}$, in terms of the known quantity $\overline{\epsilon'(\mathbf{x}_1)\epsilon'(\mathbf{x}_2)\epsilon'(\mathbf{x}_3)}$. This procedure may be continued indefinitely to solve for all terms of the form $\overline{E_i^{(j)}(\mathbf{x}_1)\epsilon'(\mathbf{x}_2)}$. We note that in the absence of approximations, $\overline{E_i'(\mathbf{x}_1)\epsilon'(\mathbf{x}_2)}$ thus depends upon all moments of $\epsilon(\mathbf{x})$—a fact we have repeatedly emphasized.

The moment $\overline{E_i'(\mathbf{x}_1)E_j'(\mathbf{x}_2)}$ may be determined in a similar manner by assuming an expansion of the form

$$\overline{E_i'(\mathbf{x}_1)E_j'(\mathbf{x}_2)} = \sum_{p,q=1}^{\infty}\sum^{\infty} \overline{E_i^{(p)}(\mathbf{x}_1)E_j^{(q)}(\mathbf{x}_2)}$$

The perturbation theory was here cast in the form of a set of differential equations. The set of equations, 3-109 and 3-110, has, however, a simple integral representation. If Eq. 3-109 is written in the form

(3-121) $\dfrac{\partial E_i'(\mathbf{x})}{\partial x_i} = -\dfrac{\bar{E}}{\bar{\epsilon}}\dfrac{\partial \epsilon'(\mathbf{x})}{\partial x_3} - \dfrac{1}{\bar{\epsilon}}\dfrac{\partial}{\partial x_i}(E_i'(\mathbf{x})\epsilon'(\mathbf{x})) = \rho(\mathbf{x})$

one notes that an integral solution to this equation (now in Poisson form since Eq. 3-110 is satisfied) is

(3-122)

$$E_i'(\mathbf{x}) = -\frac{\bar{E}}{4\pi\epsilon} \int\limits_{V'} \frac{\partial \epsilon'(\mathbf{x}')}{\partial x_3'} \frac{r_i}{r^3} dV' - \frac{1}{4\pi\bar{\epsilon}} \int\limits_{V'} \frac{\partial}{\partial x_j'} [E_j'(\mathbf{x}')\epsilon'(\mathbf{x}')] \frac{r_i}{r^3} dV'$$

where $\mathbf{r} = \mathbf{x} - \mathbf{x}'$.

This is an integral equation for $E_i'(x)$ that may be solved (see Brown, 1955) formally by substituting the expansion given in Eq. 3-112 into Eq. 3-122. For example, the first approximation equivalent to Eqs. 3-115 and 3-116 is obtained by neglecting all terms but the first on the right-hand side of Eq. 3-122. Multiplying Eq. 3-122 by $\epsilon'(\mathbf{x}_2)$, ensemble averaging, and keeping only first-order terms yields

(3-123) $$\overline{E_i^{(1)}(\mathbf{x})\epsilon'(\mathbf{x}_2)} = -\frac{\bar{E}}{4\pi\bar{\epsilon}} \int\limits_{V'} \frac{\partial \overline{\epsilon'(\mathbf{x}')\epsilon'(\mathbf{x}_2)}}{\partial x_3'} \frac{r_i}{r^3} dV'$$

which is a solution of Eqs. 3-115 and 3-116.

The second-order term is found to be

(3-124)

$$\overline{E_i^{(2)}(\mathbf{x})\epsilon'(\mathbf{x}_2)} = \frac{\bar{E}}{16\pi^2\bar{\epsilon}^2} \int\limits_{V'} \frac{\partial}{\partial x_j'} \left[\int\limits_{V''} \frac{\partial}{\partial x_3''} \overline{\epsilon'(\mathbf{x}'')\epsilon'(\mathbf{x}')\epsilon'(\mathbf{x}_2)} \frac{s_j \, dV''}{s^3} \right] \frac{r_i}{r^3} dV'$$

where $\mathbf{s} = \mathbf{x}' - \mathbf{x}''$.

The integral equation procedure is equivalent to the differential equation procedure. Which formulation one chooses to use in this problem is determined solely by convenience. If an integral solution to the basic equations is not available, however, one is often forced to use the differential equation formulation. The perturbation techniques currently used in statistical continuum theories will be considered in Chapters 5 and 7.

3.3.2. Cumulant Neglect Hypothesis

Another technique for terminating the infinite set of moment equations is known as the cumulant neglect hypothesis. This is a technique

for expressing higher-order moments in terms of lower order moments
by considering processes that are close to gaussian.

Consider a one-dimensional characteristic function. We may expand
$M_1(v)$ in the following manner (see Cramér, 1946):

$$(3\text{-}125) \qquad M_1(v) = \exp \left[-\tfrac{1}{2}\sigma^2 v^2 + \sum_{n=3}^{\infty} \frac{\lambda_n}{n!}(iv)^n \right]$$

(here we have taken $\bar{v} = 0$). A one-dimensional gaussian distribution
has the form

$$(3\text{-}126) \qquad M_{1G}(v) = \exp \left[-\tfrac{1}{2}\sigma^2 v^2 \right]$$

The moments associated with $M_1(v)$ may be calculated using Eq. 2-13.
We find

$$(3\text{-}127) \qquad \begin{aligned} \overline{u^2} &= \sigma^2 \\ \overline{u^3} &= \lambda_3 \\ \overline{u^4} &= 3\overline{u^2} + \lambda_4 \\ \overline{u^5} &= 10\overline{u^2}\lambda_3 + \lambda_5 \\ &\quad \cdot \\ &\quad \cdot \\ &\quad \cdot \end{aligned}$$

The moments associated with $M_{IG}(v)$ are

$$(3\text{-}128) \qquad \begin{aligned} \overline{u^2} &= \sigma^2 \\ \overline{u^3} &= 0 \\ \overline{u^4} &= 3\overline{u^2} \\ \overline{u^5} &= 0 \\ &\quad \cdot \\ &\quad \cdot \\ &\quad \cdot \end{aligned}$$

Comparison of Eqs. 3-127 and 3-128 thus shows that the semiinvariants
or cumulants, λ_n, measure the degree from which $M_1(v)$ differs from the
gaussian form $M_{1G}(v)$. Concomitantly, λ_n, is a measure of how much
$\overline{u^n}$ differs from $\overline{u_G{}^n}$.

If there is reason to suspect that the process is nearly gaussian $M_1(v)$
may be taken to be of the approximate form

$$(3\text{-}129) \qquad M_1(v) \approx M_{1G}(v) \exp \left[\sum_{n=3}^{N} \frac{\lambda_n}{n!}(iv)^n \right]$$

where we have set $\lambda_n = 0$ for $n > N$. Cramér (1946) discusses conditions under which the series converges to $M_1(v)$ when $N \to \infty$.

Multidimensional distributions may be expanded similarly and a generalization of λ_n defined. If at some point this generalized λ_n is set equal to zero, then the multidimensional characteristic function may be approximated as above. The approximation of setting the multidimensional cumulant equal to zero beyond some point may also be used directly in the moment equations to terminate the hierarchy. The procedure is simply to assume at some point that an nth-order moment is expressible in terms of lower-order moments by choosing the nth order cumulant equal to zero. In order to see this, consider the moment equations associated with the spatially variable permittivity problem.

Consider Eqs. 3-101 and 3-102:

(3-101a) $\quad \bar{\epsilon} \dfrac{\partial}{\partial x_{1i}} L_i(\mathbf{x}_1, \mathbf{x}_2) + \bar{E} \dfrac{\partial}{\partial x_{13}} C_2(\mathbf{x}_1, \mathbf{x}_2) + \dfrac{\partial}{\partial x_{1i}} P_i(\mathbf{x}_1, \mathbf{x}_1, \mathbf{x}_2) = 0$

(3-101b) $\quad \bar{\epsilon} \dfrac{\partial}{\partial x_{1i}} P_i(\mathbf{x}_1, \mathbf{x}_2, \mathbf{x}_3) + \bar{E} \dfrac{\partial}{\partial x_{13}} C_3(\mathbf{x}_1, \mathbf{x}_2, \mathbf{x}_3)$

$$+ \dfrac{\partial}{\partial x_{1i}} Q_i(\mathbf{x}_1, \mathbf{x}_1, \mathbf{x}_2, \mathbf{x}_3) = 0$$

.

.

.

(3-102a) $\qquad\qquad \delta_{ijk} \dfrac{\partial}{\partial x_{1j}} L_k(\mathbf{x}_1, \mathbf{x}_2) = 0$

(3-102b) $\qquad\qquad \delta_{ijk} \dfrac{\partial}{\partial x_{1j}} P_k(\mathbf{x}_1, \mathbf{x}_2, \mathbf{x}_3) = 0$

.

.

.

As these equations are written we cannot find a finite subset of equations to solve. If we desire to terminate the set of equations with Eqs. 3-101a, 3-101b, 3-102a, and 3-102b we must be able to express $Q_i(\mathbf{x}_1, \mathbf{x}_1, \mathbf{x}_2, \mathbf{x}_3)$ in terms of $C_2(\mathbf{x}_1, \mathbf{x}_2)$, $L_i(\mathbf{x}_1, \mathbf{x}_2)$, $P_i(\mathbf{x}_1, \mathbf{x}_2, \mathbf{x}_3)$, and $C_3(\mathbf{x}_1, \mathbf{x}_2, \mathbf{x}_3)$. This may be done by setting equal to zero the cumulant associated with the fourth-order moment.

In order to find the relationship between the fourth-order moment and the lower-order moments, we must expand $M_4(v_1, v_2, v_3, v_4)$ in a form similar to Eq. 3-125. That is, we write

(3-129)

$$M_4(v_1, v_2, v_3, v_4) = \exp\left\{ \sum_{n=0}^{\infty} \sum_{m=0}^{\infty} \sum_{r=0}^{\infty} \sum_{s=0}^{\infty} \frac{\lambda_{nmrs}}{n!\, m!\, r!\, s!}\, i^{n+m+r+s} v_1^{\,n} v_2^{\,m} v_3^{\,r} v_4^{\,s} \right\}$$

From Eq. 3-129 we may find, using Eq. 2-22, the moments

$$\overline{u_1^{\,i} u_2^{\,j} u_3^{\,k} u_4^{\,l}},$$

In particular we find (we take $\bar{u}_1 = \bar{u}_2 = \bar{u}_3 = \bar{u}_4 = 0$ for convenience)

(3-130) $\overline{u_1} = \lambda_{1000} = 0$

.
.
.

$$\overline{u_1 u_2} = \lambda_{1100}$$

.
.
.

$$\overline{u_1 u_2 u_3} = \lambda_{1110}$$

.
.
.

$$\overline{u_1 u_2 u_3 u_4} = \lambda_{1111} + \lambda_{1100}\lambda_{0011} + \lambda_{1010}\lambda_{0101} + \lambda_{1001}\lambda_{0110}$$

Setting the fourth-order cumulant, λ_{1111}, equal to zero, we find

(3-131) $\overline{u_1 u_2 u_3 u_4} = \overline{u_1 u_2}\,\overline{u_3 u_4} + \overline{u_1 u_3}\,\overline{u_2 u_4} + \overline{u_1 u_4}\,\overline{u_2 u_3}$

Thus, we assume

(3-132) $Q_i(\mathbf{x}_1, \mathbf{x}_1, \mathbf{x}_2, \mathbf{x}_3) = \overline{E_i{}'(\mathbf{x}_1)\epsilon'(\mathbf{x}_1)\epsilon'(\mathbf{x}_2)\epsilon'(\mathbf{x}_3)}$

$\qquad\qquad = [\overline{E_i{}'(\mathbf{x}_1)\epsilon'(\mathbf{x}_1)}][\overline{\epsilon'(\mathbf{x}_2)\epsilon'(\mathbf{x}_3)}]$

$\qquad\qquad\quad + [\overline{E_i{}'(\mathbf{x}_1)\epsilon'(\mathbf{x}_2)}][\overline{\epsilon'(\mathbf{x}_1)\epsilon'(\mathbf{x}_3)}]$

$\qquad\qquad\quad + [\overline{E_i{}'(\mathbf{x}_1)\epsilon'(\mathbf{x}_3)}][\overline{\epsilon'(\mathbf{x}_1)\epsilon'(\mathbf{x}_2)}]$

or

$$(3\text{-}133) \quad Q_i(\mathbf{x}_1, \mathbf{x}_1, \mathbf{x}_2, \mathbf{x}_3) = L_i(\mathbf{x}_1, \mathbf{x}_1)C_2(\mathbf{x}_2, \mathbf{x}_3)$$
$$+ L_i(\mathbf{x}_1, \mathbf{x}_2)C_2(\mathbf{x}_1, \mathbf{x}_3) + L_i(\mathbf{x}_1, \mathbf{x}_3)C_2(\mathbf{x}_1, \mathbf{x}_2)$$

Equations 3-101a, 3-102b, 3-102a, 3-102b, and 3-133 form a determinate set which may be solved for $L_i(\mathbf{x}_1, \mathbf{x}_2)$ and $P_i(\mathbf{x}_1, \mathbf{x}_2, \mathbf{x}_3)$ in terms of $C_2(\mathbf{x}_1, \mathbf{x}_2)$ and $C_3(\mathbf{x}_1, \mathbf{x}_2, \mathbf{x}_3)$.

This type of approximation could also have been made at a higher order. For example, the cumulant associated with the sixth-order moment could have been set equal to zero. This would have necessitated considering Eqs. 3-101a,b,c,d and Eqs. 3-102a,b,c,d; but hopefully we would obtain a better approximation than by neglecting the fourth-order cumulants. As a practical matter, however, using this type of approximation is usually excessively cumbersome beyond the fourth order. The reader should note that neglect of the cumulant beyond the fourth order gives, in general, a relationship between higher and lower order moments that is different from the relationship that exists in gaussian statistics (i.e., neglect of the fifth-order cumulant does not result in taking the fifth-order moment equal to zero). Setting the fourth-order cumulant equal to zero does, however, give the convenient result that the fourth-order moment is related to the second-order moment as it would be if the statistics were gaussian (compare Eqs. 2-44 and 3-130).

As we stated above, it is difficult to tell *a priori* whether a cumulant discard assumption is valid or not. In Chapter 7, we shall see that this type of assumption may sometimes yield negative values of the power spectrum. Nevertheless, the idea that it should be a good approximation for processes that are nearly normal leads one to hope that it will be useful in some physical problems. The above set of equations for the permittivity problem has never been investigated to our knowledge for any ϵ fields, but it may certainly warrant consideration for some fields.

The previous example should suffice to allow the reader to apply the method to his problem of interest. The reader is also referred to Kraichnan (1962) for a discussion of the application of this technique to the turbulent diffusion problem and to Richardson (1964), who discusses its use in the harmonic oscillator problem with a random spring constant.

3.4. Variational Principles

Variational principles have been used successfully on problems of a statistical nature in which it is desirable to find only effective physical constants. For the effective constants to be meaningful for a wide range of problems we assume that the joint statistics of the material constants and imposed fields are homogeneous. As an example, we consider again the spatially variable permittivity problem. If a constant field $\bar{E}\delta_{i3}$ is imposed upon a medium wherein $\epsilon'(\mathbf{x}) \equiv 0$ [we remember $\epsilon(\mathbf{x}) = \bar{\epsilon} + \epsilon'(\mathbf{x})$], the average energy density U is given by

$$(3\text{-}134) \qquad\qquad U = \frac{\bar{\epsilon}\bar{E}^2}{2}$$

If, however, $\epsilon'(\mathbf{x})$ is a nonzero random function with homogeneous and isotropic statistics we may write

$$(3\text{-}135) \qquad\qquad \bar{U} = \frac{\epsilon^* \bar{E}^2}{2}$$

where in general $\epsilon^* \neq \bar{\epsilon}$.

The principal purpose of the introduction of a variational principle here is to determine bounds for the constant ϵ^*. In order to see how this may be done, consider Eqs. 3-30 and 3-31:

$$(3\text{-}30) \qquad\qquad \frac{\partial}{\partial x_i} \epsilon E_i = 0$$

$$(3\text{-}31) \qquad\qquad \delta_{ijk} \frac{\partial}{\partial x_j} E_k = 0$$

Equation 3-30 may be derived from variation of the integral

$$(3\text{-}136) \qquad\qquad U = \frac{1}{2V} \int_V \epsilon E_i E_i \, d\mathbf{x}$$

subject to the subsidiary condition

$$\delta_{ijk} \frac{\partial}{\partial x_j} E_k = 0$$

This is true whether or not ϵ may be described statistically.

In order to derive Eqs. 3-30 from the variation of Eq. 3-136 we note that the curl condition implies that

$$E_i = \frac{\partial \phi}{\partial x_i}$$

so that we have

(3-137)
$$U = \frac{1}{2V} \int_V \epsilon \frac{\partial \phi}{\partial x_i} \frac{\partial \phi}{\partial x_i} \, d\mathbf{x}$$

We must assume here that the variation of ϕ vanishes on the boundary S which encloses V.

The variation of Eq. 3-137 yields

(3-138)
$$\delta U = \frac{1}{2V} \int_V 2\epsilon \frac{\partial \phi}{\partial x_i} \, \delta \frac{\partial \phi}{\partial x_i} \, d\mathbf{x}$$

The use of a form of the divergence theorem, noting

$$\delta \frac{\partial \phi}{\partial x_i} = \frac{\partial \delta}{\partial x_i} \phi$$

gives

(3-139)
$$\int_V \left[\frac{\partial}{\partial x_i} \delta\phi \right] \epsilon \frac{\partial \phi}{\partial x_i} \, d\mathbf{x} = -\int_V \delta\phi \frac{\partial}{\partial x_i} \left[\epsilon \frac{\partial \phi}{\partial x_i} \right] d\mathbf{x} + \int_S n_i \epsilon \frac{\partial \phi}{\partial x_i} \, \delta\phi \, dS$$

Since $\delta\phi$ is taken to be equal to zero on S, we have

(3-140)
$$\delta U = \frac{-1}{V} \int_V \delta\phi \frac{\partial}{\partial x_i} \left[\epsilon \frac{\partial \phi}{\partial x_i} \right] d\mathbf{x}$$

By setting $\delta U = 0$ we have, since $\delta\phi$ is an arbitrary variation,

(3-141)
$$\frac{\partial}{\partial x_i} \epsilon \frac{\partial \phi}{\partial x_i} = 0$$

which is just Eq. 3-30 with $E_i = \partial\phi/\partial x_i$.*

---

* It may be shown that this variational principle and the variational principle formulated in terms of D_i (Eq. 3-145) still hold if $\epsilon(x)$ is piecewise continuous.

By taking a second variation of Eq. 3-137 it may be shown that the function determined by Eq. 3-141 yields a minimum value for U. Any other trial (admissible)† function, E_i, substituted into Eq. 3-136 that is derivable from a potential function and meets the boundary conditions will give a value of U which is greater than the minimum value. Thus

(3-142)
$$U \leqslant \frac{1}{2V} \int_V \epsilon E_i E_i \, d\mathbf{x}$$

where E_i is any function such that $E_i = \partial \phi / \partial x_i$ and $\delta \phi_S = 0$. The fact that $\delta \phi = 0$ on the boundary demands that any trial function must also meet the same boundary conditions as the true answer.

As we stated above, Eq. 3-142 is true whether or not ϵ may be described statistically. For the case in which the statistics of $\epsilon(\mathbf{x})$ are homogeneous, we assume that we may, however, equate ensemble and volume averages in the limit $V \to \infty$. This is an ergodic-type hypothesis.

Thus we assume

(3-143)
$$U = \bar{U} = \frac{\epsilon^*}{2} \bar{E}^2 \leqslant \tfrac{1}{2} \overline{\epsilon E_i E_i}$$

As in the volume integral E_i must be the gradient of a scalar function, but the condition for trial functions $\delta \phi_S = 0$, is replaced by the condition that the average value of the trial functions equal the average value of the true functions.‡

† We use the words *trial* and *admissible* interchangeably here.

‡ For the case of homogeneous statistics, the variation may actually be taken directly using ensemble rather than volume averages. We have

$$U = \epsilon \overline{\frac{\partial \phi}{\partial x_i} \frac{\partial \phi}{\partial x_i}}$$

and

$$\delta U = 2\epsilon \overline{\frac{\partial \phi}{\partial x_i} \frac{\partial \delta \phi}{\partial x_i}} = 2 \frac{\partial}{\partial x_i} \left[\overline{\epsilon \frac{\partial \phi}{\partial x_i} \delta \phi} \right] - 2 \overline{\delta \phi \frac{\partial}{\partial x_i} \epsilon \frac{\partial \phi}{\partial x_i}}$$

$$= 0$$

where we take only such variations, $\delta \phi$, that result in joint statistics for ϕ, $\delta \phi$, and ϵ that are homogeneous. For homogeneous statistics

$$\overline{\epsilon \frac{\partial \phi}{\partial x_i} \delta \phi}$$

In order to derive an upper bound for ϵ^* the simplest assumption we may make is to take as a trial function

$$E_i = \bar{E}\delta_{i3}$$

E_i is a constant vector and hence E_i is derivable from a potential. We therefore find here

(3-144) $\epsilon^* \leqslant \bar{\epsilon}$

since for this assumption

$$\overline{\epsilon E_i E_i} = \bar{E}^2 \bar{\epsilon}$$

Despite the simplicity of the result (and a lower bound given below in Eq. 3-152) this is a very elegant result. To this writer's knowledge it has not yet been possible to derive this result from the statistical moment equations. The result was apparently first derived by Wiener (1912) using algebraic means. The variational approach may be found in Brown (1962). The analogous results for bounding the elastic constants were given by Paul (1960).

It is interesting that a lower bound may be derived for ϵ^* by consideration of the energy integral in the form

(3-145) $$U = \frac{1}{2V} \int_V \frac{D_i D_i}{\epsilon}\, d\mathbf{x}$$

subject to the constraint

$$\nabla \cdot \mathbf{D} = 0$$

---

is independent of $\mathbf{x}$. Hence

$$\overline{\delta\phi \frac{\partial}{\partial x_i} \epsilon \frac{\partial \phi}{\partial x_i}} = 0$$

and for arbitrary variations, $\delta\phi$,

$$\frac{\partial}{\partial x_i} \epsilon \frac{\partial \phi}{\partial x_i} = 0$$

If the statistics of $\delta\phi$ are homogeneous, then $\overline{\delta\phi} = $ constant and

$$\frac{\partial}{\partial x_i} \overline{\delta\phi} = \delta \frac{\partial \bar{\phi}}{\partial x_i} = 0$$

Thus it is necessary for an admissible field to have the same average value as the true field.

D_i is simply $D_i = \epsilon E_i$, and we now have a variational principle in terms of the displacement vector rather than the electric vector. The procedure is similar to that given above except that now the curl condition on **E** is replaced by the divergence condition on **D**. The divergence condition implies that

$$\mathbf{D} = \nabla \times \mathbf{A}$$

and we take the variation of the integral

$$(3\text{-}146) \qquad U = \frac{1}{2V} \int_V (\nabla \times \mathbf{A}) \cdot \frac{(\nabla \times \mathbf{A})}{\epsilon}\, dx$$

Thus

$$(3\text{-}147) \qquad \delta U = \frac{1}{2V} \int_V \frac{2(\nabla \times \mathbf{A})}{\epsilon} \cdot \nabla \times \delta A\, dx$$

We must now assume that $\delta\mathbf{A}$ vanishes on the boundary S, surrounding V. Using the vector identity

$$\nabla \cdot (\mathbf{u} \times \mathbf{v}) = \mathbf{v} \cdot (\nabla \times \mathbf{u}) - \mathbf{u} \cdot (\nabla \times \mathbf{v})$$

with $\mathbf{u} = (\nabla \times \mathbf{A})/\epsilon$ and $\mathbf{v} = \delta\mathbf{A}$ we find

$$(3\text{-}148) \quad \delta U = \frac{1}{2V} \int_V -2\nabla \cdot \left[\left(\frac{\nabla \times \mathbf{A}}{\epsilon} \right) \times \delta A \right] dx$$
$$+ \frac{1}{2V} \int_V 2\delta\mathbf{A} \cdot \left[\nabla \times \left(\frac{\nabla \times \mathbf{A}}{\epsilon} \right) \right] dx$$

The first integral on the right-hand side may be shown to be zero by using the divergence condition and the fact that $\delta\mathbf{A} = 0$ on S setting $\delta U = 0$, and noting that $\delta\mathbf{A}$ is arbitrary leads to the condition

$$(3\text{-}149) \qquad \nabla \times \left(\frac{\nabla \times \mathbf{A}}{\epsilon} \right) = 0$$

or equivalently

$$(3\text{-}150) \qquad \nabla \times \frac{\mathbf{D}}{\epsilon} = \nabla \times \mathbf{E} = 0$$

Again it may be shown by considering the second variation that using Eq. 3-149 leads to a minimum value for U.

In order to find a lower bound for ϵ^* we set $D_i = \epsilon^*\bar{E}\delta_{i3}$ in Eq. 3-145. For this assumption D_i is a constant vector, it satisfies the condition $\nabla \cdot \mathbf{D} = 0$,† and we have

$$(3\text{-}151) \qquad U = \epsilon^*\bar{E}^2 \leqslant \epsilon^{*2}\frac{\bar{E}^2}{V}\int_V \frac{1}{\epsilon}\,d\mathbf{x}$$

or upon rearrangement

$$(3\text{-}152) \qquad \epsilon^* \geqslant \frac{1}{\overline{1/\epsilon}}$$

where we have equated the space and ensemble averages. That is, we have assumed

$$\overline{\frac{1}{\epsilon}} = \lim_{V\to\infty}\frac{1}{V}\int_V \frac{1}{\epsilon}\,d\mathbf{x}$$

On using the variational principles expressed in Eqs. 3-136 and 3-145 and their subsidiary conditions we have thus bounded the quantity ϵ^* in the following manner:

$$(3\text{-}153) \qquad \frac{1}{\overline{1/\epsilon}} \leqslant \epsilon^* \leqslant \bar{\epsilon}$$

More stringent bounds may be obtained for ϵ^* by making more sophisticated assumptions for E_i and D_i in the integrals for U. In order to meet the subsidiary curl condition for Eq. 3-136, for example, we need only choose E_i of the form

$$E_i = \frac{\partial\phi}{\partial x_i}$$

In Chapter 5 we shall show how to use the perturbation solution to obtain better bounds than are given in Eq. 3-153.

† It also satisfies the condition that the average value of the trial function equals the average value of the true function. This is true since $\bar{D} = \epsilon^*\bar{E}$. This may be seen from the relation

$$U = \epsilon^*\frac{\bar{E}^2}{2} = \lim_{V\to\infty}\frac{1}{2}\frac{1}{V}\int_V \mathbf{E}\cdot\mathbf{D}\,d\mathbf{x} = \frac{\bar{E}\bar{D}}{2} + \lim_{V\to\infty}\frac{1}{2}\frac{1}{V}\int_V \mathbf{E}'\cdot\mathbf{D}'\,d\mathbf{x}$$

since

$$\lim_{V\to\infty}\frac{1}{V}\int_V \mathbf{E}'\cdot\mathbf{D}'\,d\mathbf{x} = 0.$$

The latter integral may be shown to equal zero by use of the divergence theorem.

There is a wide variety of other problems for which it is desirable to find effective constants. Two such problems that have received attention in the literature are the effective elastic properties of heterogeneous media and the effective resistance to flow through porous media. In both problems one proceeds essentially as we have done for the variable permittivity case. A variational principle based on the energy is used and some trial function is assumed in order to bound the desired effective constant. We shall discuss these problems in more detail in Chapters 5 and 6 and will present the appropriate variational principles at that time.

We should like to conclude this section on variational principles by considering a different type of variational principle that is of special use in considering media composed of a mixture of a finite number of components. We shall again treat the spatially variable permittivity case and shall follow the development given by Hashin and Shtrikman (1962). They consider the problem in the language of magnetic permeability but the governing equations are the same as in the permittivity case. The governing equations are again Eqs. 3-30 and 3-31.

$$(3\text{-}30) \qquad \frac{\partial}{\partial x_i} \epsilon E_i = 0$$

$$(3\text{-}31) \qquad \delta_{ijk} \frac{\partial}{\partial x_j} E_k = 0$$

In order to satisfy Eq. 3-31 we set

$$E_k = \frac{\partial \phi}{\partial x_k}$$

We consider here two media. The first is a reference medium with constant permittivity ϵ_o. In this medium $\mathbf{D}_o = \epsilon_o \mathbf{E}_o$. The second medium is a medium with spatially variable permittivity characterized by the variable permittivity, $\epsilon(\mathbf{x})$. Here $\mathbf{D} = \epsilon \mathbf{E}$. We suppose that the potential ϕ on the surface S of the volume V is the same in both media. In the first medium the potential is denoted ϕ_0 and in the second medium ϕ.

We now define the following quantities

$$\mathbf{T} = \mathbf{D} - \epsilon_o \mathbf{E}$$

$$(3\text{-}154) \qquad \mathbf{E'} = \mathbf{E} - \mathbf{E}_o = \nabla\phi - \nabla\phi_o$$

$$\phi' = \phi - \phi_o$$

The variational principle may now be stated as follows. The integral

$$(3\text{-}155) \quad U_T = \frac{1}{2V} \int_V \left(\epsilon_o \mathbf{E}_o \cdot \mathbf{E}_o - \frac{\mathbf{T} \cdot \mathbf{T}}{\epsilon - \epsilon_o} + 2\mathbf{T} \cdot \mathbf{E}_o + \mathbf{T} \cdot \mathbf{E}' \right) dx$$

subject to the condition

$$(3\text{-}156) \qquad\qquad \epsilon_o \, \text{div } \mathbf{E}' + \text{div } \mathbf{T} = 0$$

and $\phi'(S) = 0$ yields upon variation of $\mathbf{T}$ and $\mathbf{E}'$ the relation

$$(3\text{-}157) \qquad\qquad \mathbf{T} = (\epsilon - \epsilon_o)\mathbf{E}$$

The integral U_T is the average energy density

$$U = \frac{1}{2V} \int_V e\mathbf{E} \cdot \mathbf{E} \, dx$$

that we considered earlier, if we invoke the condition $E_i = \partial\phi/\partial x_i$. In order to see this, first substitute Eq. 3-157 into 3-155 using the definitions given in Eq. 3-154. We find

$$(3\text{-}158) \qquad U_T = \frac{1}{2V} \int_V (\epsilon\mathbf{E} \cdot \mathbf{E} - (\epsilon_o\mathbf{E}_o + \epsilon\mathbf{E}) \cdot \mathbf{E}') \, dx$$

The second term on the right-hand side may be shown to equal zero by using the divergence theorem. We note that $\mathbf{E}' = \nabla\phi'$ and

$$(\epsilon_o\mathbf{E}_o + \epsilon\mathbf{E}) \cdot \nabla\phi' = \nabla \cdot [\phi'(\epsilon_o\mathbf{E}_o + \epsilon\mathbf{E})] - \phi'\nabla \cdot (\epsilon_o\mathbf{E}_o + \epsilon\mathbf{E})$$

$$= \nabla \cdot [\phi'(\epsilon_o\mathbf{E}_o + \epsilon\mathbf{E})]$$

since $\nabla \cdot \epsilon\mathbf{E}$ and $\nabla \cdot \epsilon_o\mathbf{E}_o = 0$.

Thus

$$\int_V (\epsilon_o\mathbf{E}_o + \epsilon\mathbf{E}) \cdot \mathbf{E}' \, dx = \int_S \phi'(\epsilon_o\mathbf{E}_o + \epsilon\mathbf{E}) \cdot \mathbf{n} \, dS = 0$$

since $\phi'(S) = 0$. Finally then

$$(3\text{-}159) \qquad\qquad U_T = \frac{1}{2V} \int_V \epsilon\mathbf{E} \cdot \mathbf{E} \, dx = U$$

We now proceed to establish the above variational principle. Taking the variation of Eq. 3-155 we find

(3-160)

$$\delta U_T = \frac{1}{2V} \int\limits_V \left\{ 2\left[\frac{-\mathbf{T}}{\epsilon - \epsilon_o} + \mathbf{E}_o + \mathbf{E}' \right] \cdot \delta\mathbf{T} - \delta\mathbf{T} \cdot \mathbf{E}' + \mathbf{T} \cdot \delta\mathbf{E}' \right\} d\mathbf{x}$$

We wish next to show

(3-161) $$L = \int (-\delta\mathbf{T} \cdot \mathbf{E}' + \mathbf{T} \cdot \delta\mathbf{E}') \, d\mathbf{x}$$

is zero.

In order to do this consider the auxiliary condition Eq. 3-156. On integrating this expression we find

(3-162) $$\epsilon_o \mathbf{E}' + \mathbf{T} = \mathbf{C}$$

where div $\mathbf{C} = 0$.

By substituting Eq. 3-162 into 3-161, we find

(3-163) $$L = \int (-\delta\mathbf{C} \cdot \mathbf{E}' + \mathbf{C} \cdot \delta\mathbf{E}') \, d\mathbf{x}$$

In the same manner that we showed the second integral in Eq. 3-158 was zero, we may show $L = 0$. We note again $\mathbf{E}' = \nabla\phi'$, $\phi'(S) = 0$ and remember div $\mathbf{C} = 0$.

Thus we have for Eq. 3-160

(3-164) $$\delta U_T = \frac{1}{2V} \int\limits_V 2\left\{ \frac{-\mathbf{T}}{\epsilon - \epsilon_o} + \mathbf{E}_o + \mathbf{E}' \right\} \cdot \delta\mathbf{T} \, d\mathbf{x}$$

For arbitrary variation, $\delta\mathbf{T}$, $\delta U_T = 0$ when

(3-165) $$\mathbf{T} = (\epsilon - \epsilon_o)(\mathbf{E}_o + \mathbf{E}') = (\epsilon - \epsilon_o)\mathbf{E}$$

This establishes the variational principle. In order to make use of the principle we must make a suitable guess for a trial function $\mathbf{T}$. We note finally that it can be shown by considering the second variation that U_T is a maximum if $\epsilon_o < \epsilon$ and a minimum if $\epsilon_o > \epsilon$. This principle may also be shown to be true if $\epsilon(\mathbf{x})$ is piecewise continuous rather than continuous.

As we mentioned above, this variational principle is particularly suited for finding bounds on the effective permittivity for mixtures of materials, where each material has a well-defined permittivity. The permittivity of such a mixture may still be treated as a random function but a function which may only take on n discrete values corresponding to the n materials used to compose the mixture. For example, for a mixture of two materials with permittivities ϵ_1 and ϵ_2 the probability density function $P_1(\epsilon)\,d\epsilon$ is

$$(3\text{-}166) \qquad P_1(\epsilon)\,d\epsilon = [v_1\,\delta(\epsilon - \epsilon_1) + v_2\,\delta(\epsilon - \epsilon_2)]\,d\epsilon$$

where v_1 is the volume fraction of the first material and $v_2 = 1 - v_1$ is the volume fraction of the second material. For an n-phase material (for convenience let $\epsilon_n > \epsilon_{n-1} > \cdots > \epsilon_1$)

$$(3\text{-}167) \qquad P_1(\epsilon)\,d\epsilon = \left[\sum_{j=1}^{n} v_j\,\delta(\epsilon - \epsilon_j)\right] d\epsilon$$

$$\sum_{j=1}^{n} v_j = 1$$

The case of a continuously variable permittivity may be considered in the limit $n \to \infty$. We have had the continuously variable case in mind in previous work. Almost everything we have said heretofore about statistical quantities however applied to the discontinuous case since, even in the discontinuous case the average quantities are in general continuous. There are some difficulties at the origin with correlation functions, but these may be resolved by an ad hoc procedure.

The variational principle just stated is particularly useful in mixtures because $\Delta\epsilon_n = \epsilon_n - \epsilon_1$ is bounded in contrast to the continuous case where usually ϵ has a finite probability of taking on any finite value. To see how this comes about let us represent $\mathbf{T}$ and ϕ' in the following Fourier integral forms:

$$(3\text{-}168) \qquad T_{Vi}(\mathbf{x}) = \int_{-\infty}^{\infty} T_{Vi}'(\mathbf{k})e^{2\pi i\mathbf{k}\cdot\mathbf{x}}\,d\mathbf{k} + T_{VAi}$$

$$(3\text{-}169) \qquad \phi_V'(\mathbf{x}) = \frac{1}{2\pi i} \int_{-\infty}^{\infty} \phi_V'(\mathbf{k})e^{2\pi i\mathbf{k}\cdot\mathbf{x}}\,d\mathbf{k}$$

(note that $\int_{-\infty}^{\infty} d\mathbf{k}$ is a three-dimensional integral).

We have denoted the Fourier transform variables with a subscript V since initially we take a medium with large but finite volume V. We shall soon go to the limit $V \to \infty$. We can treat only the problem of a statistically homogeneous medium subject to a constant average field so that we must take the limit $V \to \infty$. T_{VAi} is a constant.

We can establish a relationship between the variables $T'_{Vi}(\mathbf{k})$ and $\phi_V'(\mathbf{k})$ by invoking the divergence condition given in Eq. 3-156. By substituting Eqs. 3-168 and 3-169 into Eq. 3-156 (noting $E_i' = \nabla\phi'$) and comparing coefficients, we find

(3-170) $$-k_i T_{Vi}' = k^2 \phi_V' \epsilon_o$$

Thus we have

(3-171) $$\phi_V'(\mathbf{x}) = \frac{-1}{2\pi i \epsilon_o} \int_{-\infty}^{\infty} \frac{k_i T_{Vi}'(\mathbf{k})}{k^2} e^{2\pi i \mathbf{k} \cdot \mathbf{x}} \; d\mathbf{k}$$

and

(3-172) $$E_{Vj}'(\mathbf{x}) = -\frac{1}{\epsilon_o} \int_{-\infty}^{\infty} \frac{k_j k_i T_{Vi}'(\mathbf{k})}{k^2} \exp \left[2\pi i \mathbf{k} \cdot \mathbf{x}\right] d\mathbf{k}$$

To use Eq. 3-155 for finding a lower bound we note that

(3-173) $$U_T \leqslant \frac{1}{2V} \int_V \left[\epsilon_o \mathbf{E}_o \cdot \mathbf{E}_o - \frac{\mathbf{T} \cdot \mathbf{T}}{\epsilon - \epsilon_o} + 2\mathbf{T} \cdot \mathbf{E}_o + \mathbf{T} \cdot \mathbf{E}' \right] dx$$

if $\epsilon_o > \epsilon$, for any choice of $\mathbf{T}$ satisfying the condition

(3-166) $$\epsilon \, \text{div} \, \mathbf{E}' + \text{div} \, T = 0$$

The expressions given by Eqs. 3-168 and 3-172 satisfy the necessary requirements, and may be substituted into Eq. 3-173 to formally obtain an upper bound for U_T. For these forms to be useful, however, further assumptions must be made about the nature of the coefficients T_{Vi}'.

To be able to make use of Eq. 3-173, the integral

(3-174) $$J \equiv \frac{1}{V} \int_V \mathbf{T} \cdot \mathbf{E}' \; d\mathbf{x}$$

must be expressed in terms of $\mathbf{T}$, and this can only be done for special forms of T_{Vi}'. In order to see the nature of the problem, let us substitute the expressions given for $\mathbf{T}$ and $\mathbf{E}'$ in Eqs. 3-168 and 3-172, respectively, into the integral J. We have

(3-175)

$$J = -\frac{1}{\epsilon_o}\frac{1}{V}\int\limits_V dx \int\limits_{-\infty}^{\infty} \int\limits_{-\infty}^{\infty} T_{Vj}'(\mathbf{k})T_{Vi}'(\mathbf{k}')\,\frac{k_j'k_i'}{k^2}\,\exp\,[2\pi i(\mathbf{k} + \mathbf{k}')\cdot\mathbf{x}]\,d\mathbf{k}\,d\mathbf{k}'$$

We next suppose that we let $V \to \infty$ and that we may interchange integrals. This yields

(3-176) $$J = -\frac{1}{\epsilon_o}\int\limits_{-\infty}^{\infty}\frac{k_jk_i}{k^2}\lim_{V\to\infty}\left\{\frac{1}{V}T_{Vi}'(\mathbf{k})T_{Vj}'(-\mathbf{k})\right\}d\mathbf{k}$$

since

$$\lim_{V\to\infty}\int\limits_V \exp\,[2\pi i(\mathbf{k} + \mathbf{k}')\cdot\mathbf{x}]\,dx = \delta(\mathbf{k} + \mathbf{k}')$$

As we mentioned in Section 2.1.6.2, the limit does not necessarily exist without ensemble averaging. The difficulty may be avoided without ensemble averaging, however, by noting that whenever the limiting expression occurs it will be integrated over $\mathbf{k}$ and hence the violent oscillations in $\mathbf{k}$ space which are the manifestation of the divergent limit are smoothed out. This smoothing procedure was discussed in Section 2.1.6.2, and we shall assume this smoothing procedure is implied by the limit. We thus write

(3-177) $$J = -\frac{1}{\epsilon_o}\int\limits_{-\infty}^{\infty}\frac{k_ik_j}{k^2}\,Q_{ij}(\mathbf{k})\,d\mathbf{k}$$

where

$$Q_{ij}(\mathbf{k}) = \lim_{V\to\infty}\left\{\frac{1}{V}T_{Vi}'(\mathbf{k})T_{Vj}'(-\mathbf{k})\right\}$$

exists in some smoothed sense.

The same technique may be applied to calculate the integral

$$K = \lim_{V\to\infty}\frac{1}{V}\int\limits_V \mathbf{T}\cdot\mathbf{T}'\,dx$$

We find here

(3-178)
$$K = \int_{-\infty}^{\infty} Q_{ii}(\mathbf{k}) \, d\mathbf{k}$$

We now ask if there is any relation between J and K. The answer is that a simple relationship exists between J and K if we assume that $Q_{ij}(\mathbf{k})$ is of the form

(3-179)
$$Q_{ij}(\mathbf{k}) = \delta_{i3} \, \delta_{j3} B(k)$$

where $B(k)$ is a function only of $k^2 = k_i k_i$. We suppose here that $\mathbf{E}_o$ is in the "three" direction. This form assumes that $Q_{ij}(\mathbf{k})$ is a special form of an axially symmetric tensor and hence that the statistics of the two-point correlation function associated with $T_i(\mathbf{x})$ depend only upon the magnitude of $\mathbf{x}$ and $\mathbf{x} \cdot \mathbf{n}_3$, where $\mathbf{n}_3$ is a unit vector in the direction of $\mathbf{E}_o$.* Using Eq. 3-179 we have

(3-180)
$$K = \int_{-\infty}^{\infty} \delta_{i3} \, \delta_{i3} B(k) \, d\mathbf{k}$$

(3-181)
$$J = -\frac{1}{\epsilon_o} \int_{-\infty}^{\infty} \frac{k_i k_j}{k^2} \delta_{i3} \, \delta_{i3} B(k) \, d\mathbf{k}$$

We next write these integrals in spherical coordinates

$$k_1 = k \sin \theta \cos \phi$$
$$k_2 = k \sin \theta \sin \phi$$
$$k_3 = k \cos \theta$$
$$k^2 = k_1^2 + k_2^2 + k_3^2$$

Thus

(3-182)
$$K = \int_0^{\infty} k^2 B(k) \, dk \int_0^{\pi} \sin \theta \, d\theta \int_0^{2\pi} d\phi$$

$$= \int_0^{\infty} k^2 B(k) \, dk (4\pi)$$

* See the discussion below Eq. 5-216 in connection with this choice.

and

(3-183)
$$J = -\frac{1}{\epsilon_o} \int_0^\infty k^2 B(k)\, dk \int_0^\pi \cos^2\theta \sin\theta \int_0^{2\pi} d\phi$$

$$= -\frac{1}{\epsilon_o} \int_0^\infty k^2 B(k)\, dk (\tfrac{1}{3} 4\pi)$$

Therefore

(3-184)
$$J = -\tfrac{1}{3} K$$

The assumption given by Eq. 3-179 thus reduces Eq. 3-173 to

(3-185)
$$U_T \leqslant I \equiv \frac{1}{2V} \int_V \left(\epsilon_o \mathbf{E}_o \cdot \mathbf{E}_o - \frac{\mathbf{T} \cdot \mathbf{T}}{\epsilon - \epsilon_o} + 2\mathbf{T} \cdot \mathbf{E}_o - \frac{1}{3}\frac{\mathbf{T}' \cdot \mathbf{T}'}{\epsilon_o} \right) d\mathbf{x}$$

In order to find the best possible choice of $\mathbf{T}$ we next take the variation of I for fixed

$$\mathbf{T}_{VA} \equiv \frac{1}{V} \int_V \mathbf{T}\, d\mathbf{x}$$

This gives

(3-186)
$$\delta I = \frac{1}{2V} \int_V \left[-\frac{2\mathbf{T}}{\epsilon - \epsilon_o} + 2\mathbf{E}_o - \frac{2}{3\epsilon_o}\mathbf{T}' \right] \cdot \delta\mathbf{T}'\, d\mathbf{x}$$

and for arbitrary $\delta\mathbf{T}'$

(3-187)
$$\mathbf{T} = \frac{\mathbf{E}_o + \mathbf{T}_{VA}/3\epsilon_o}{1/(\epsilon - \epsilon_o) + 1/3\epsilon_o}$$

$\mathbf{T}_{VA}$ may be found by averaging Eq. 3-187. We find

(3-188)
$$\mathbf{T}_{VA} = \left(\mathbf{E}_o + \frac{\mathbf{T}_{VA}}{3\epsilon_o} \right) A$$

where

(3-189)
$$A = \frac{1}{V} \int_V \frac{d\mathbf{x}}{1/(\epsilon - \epsilon_o) + 1/3\epsilon_o}$$

or

(3-190)
$$\mathbf{T}_{VA} = \frac{\mathbf{E}_o A}{1 - A/3\epsilon_o}$$

On substituting Eqs. 3-187 and 3-190 into Eq. 3-185 we have

(3-191) $$U_T \leqslant \tfrac{1}{2}\epsilon_o \mathbf{E}_o \cdot \mathbf{E}_o \left\{ 1 + \frac{A/\epsilon_o}{1 - A/3\epsilon_o} \right\}$$

Noting again that we define ϵ^* by the relation

(3-192) $$U_T = \tfrac{1}{2}\epsilon^* \mathbf{E}_o \cdot \mathbf{E}_o$$

we have

(3-193) $$\epsilon^* \leqslant \epsilon_o + \frac{A}{1 - A/3\epsilon_o}$$

We remember that the condition for this to be an upper bound is that $\epsilon_o > \epsilon$. The average

(3-189) $$A = \frac{1}{V} \int \frac{d\mathbf{x}}{1/(\epsilon - \epsilon_o) + 1/3\epsilon_o}$$

reduces to a sum for an n-phase material and we choose ϵ_o greater than the maximum finite value of ϵ. Furthermore, it may be noted that the expression

$$\frac{A}{1 - A/3\epsilon_o}$$

is a monotonic function of ϵ_o and therefore the best choice of ϵ_o is the maximum value of ϵ. For a two-phase material with a volume fraction v_1 of ϵ_1 and a volume fraction v_2 of ϵ_2 ($v_1 + v_2 = 1$), Eq. 3-189 reduces to

(3-194) $$A = \frac{v_1}{1/(\epsilon_1 - \epsilon_o) + 1/3\epsilon_o} + \frac{v_2}{1/(\epsilon_2 - \epsilon_o) + 1/3\epsilon_o}$$

For $\epsilon_o = \epsilon_2$

(3-195) $$A = \frac{v_1}{1/(\epsilon_1 - \epsilon_2) + 1/3\epsilon_2}$$

and

(3-196) $$\frac{A}{1 - (1/3\epsilon_o)A} = \frac{v_1}{1/(\epsilon_1 - \epsilon_2) + v_2/3\epsilon_2}$$

The lower bound for ϵ^* may be found in an exactly analogous manner. We need only consider the relation

$$(3\text{-}197) \quad U_T \geqslant \frac{1}{2V} \int_V \left(\epsilon_o \mathbf{E}_o \cdot \mathbf{E}_o - \frac{\mathbf{T} \cdot \mathbf{T}}{\epsilon - \epsilon_o} + 2\mathbf{T} \cdot \mathbf{E}_o + \mathbf{T} \cdot \mathbf{E}' \right) dx$$

in the case when $\epsilon_o < \epsilon$ and follow through as above.

We find

$$(3\text{-}198) \quad \epsilon^* \geqslant \epsilon_o + \frac{A}{1 - A/3\epsilon_o}$$

For a two-phase material ($\epsilon_o = \epsilon_1$)

$$(3\text{-}199) \quad \frac{A}{1 - \tfrac{1}{3}A/\epsilon_o} = \frac{v_2}{1/(\epsilon_2 - \epsilon_1) + v_1/3\epsilon_1}$$

We shall return to a discussion of this variational principle in Chapter 5. In Chapter 5 we shall discuss the experimental verification of this type of result for physical situations in which it is applicable.

CHAPTER 4

Theory of Partial Coherence

4.1. Introduction

The theory of partial coherence is the term used for the formulation that has been developed to treat electromagnetic fields with statistical properties. The classical theory is treated in detail in the following references: Born and Wolf (1959), O'Neill (1963), and Beran and Parrent (1964). We shall consider only the classical theory in this chapter. We shall be principally concerned with the propagation of radiation in free space and as we shall see, any set of finite-order statistical moment equations (e.g., Eqs. 4-28–4-32) is determinate. Thus we present in this chapter an example of the simplest type of statistical continuum theory.

4.1.1. Young's Interference Experiment

To give the reader a physical picture of the problems treated by workers in this field, we begin this chapter with a discussion of a Young's interference experiment such as is commonly performed in optics. We refer to Fig. 4-1.

We suppose that we have a light source of characteristic dimension b, a distance R from a screen A. The screen A is opaque except for two small holes at P_1 and P_2. The light passing through the holes in the screen A impinges upon and is recorded upon a screen B (say a photographic plate). The screen B is in the far field of the pinhole system in screen A (i.e., $R_{AB} \gg d^2/\bar{\lambda}$, where $\bar{\lambda}$ is some mean radiation wavelength). For simplicity, we choose the light source to be self-luminous and filter the radiation so that $\Delta\nu/\bar{\nu} \ll 1$, where $\bar{\nu}$ is the mean radiation frequency and $\Delta\nu$ is some characteristic frequency spread. We term as quasi-monochromatic a source with narrow spectral width. This type of source is particularly useful if the relevant path length differences in a

142

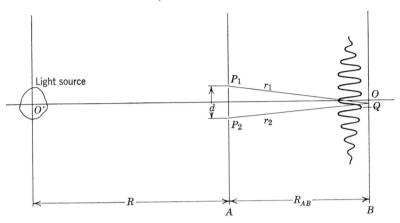

Fig. 4-1. Young's interference experiment.

problem are much less than $c/\Delta\nu$, where c is the velocity of light. Hence in this discussion we shall be most interested in the nature of the intensity distribution on B for those points where $r_1 - r_2 \ll c/\Delta\nu$.

To begin we consider the nature of the intensity distribution on screen B for two positions of the light source: when $R \gg bd/\bar{\lambda}$ and when $R = 0$. In the first case, when $R \gg bd/\bar{\lambda}$ the source could not be resolved by a telescope of diameter d placed near screen A. The sources would appear in such an instrument as a point. Thus if the source is on the axis $O'-O$ (as we have chosen it to be for convenience) the radiation impinging upon screen A is approximately a plane wave traveling in the direction $O'-O$. In this case, since the radiation is quasi-monochromatic and we are considering only the case when $r_1 - r_2 \ll c/\Delta\nu$, we have a textbook interference experiment. The intensity distribution on screen B will exhibit very sharp fringes. At O where $r_1 = r_2$, the radiation from P_1 and P_2 add in phase and the intensity is high. At an adjacent point Q where $r_1 - r_2 = \bar{\lambda}/2$, the radiation from P_1 is out of phase with the radiation at P_2 and they cancel, resulting in a zero intensity at Q. The intensity thus fluctuates sinusoidally in the neighborhood of O. See Fig. 4-2.

When the fringes on B look like those in Fig. 4-2a they are called sharp, and the radiation fields *impinging upon screen A* at P_1 and P_2 are termed coherent. The intensity varies between zero and a maximum intensity that results from the addition of the maximum amplitudes of the radiation at P_1 and P_2.

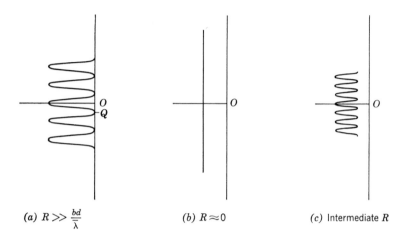

(a) $R \gg \frac{bd}{\lambda}$ (b) $R \approx 0$ (c) Intermediate R

Fig. 4-2. Intensity distribution on recording screen for various positions of the source.

In the second case, when $R = 0$ and the source is placed adjacent to the screen A (we choose d such that $b > d$), the intensity pattern on the screen is quite different. In this case we observe no fringes at all. The intensity is a constant in the neighborhood of O.* The radiation leaving one portion of this type of light source bears no relation to the radiation leaving another portion. The radiation fields *impinging upon screen A at P_1 and P_2* are termed incoherent in this case. See Fig. 4-2b.

For intermediate distances R the intensity distribution on screen B lies somewhere between these two limiting cases. We see fringes but the minimum intensity is not zero and the maximum intensity is not as great as when $R \gg bd/\bar{\lambda}$. In this case we term as partially coherent the radiation fields *impinging upon screen A at P_1 and P_2.*

4.1.2. Visibility

A quantitative measure of fringe strength, called the visibility $\mathscr{V}$, was introduced by Michelson (1890). He defined the function

(4-1) $$\mathscr{V} = \frac{I_{max} - I_{min}}{I_{max} + I_{min}}$$

* This is not true if d is of the order of a wavelength but we exclude such exceptional cases here.

where I_{max} is the maximum intensity in the neighborhood of O and I_{min} is the minimum intensity in the neighborhood of O. (For polychromatic fields this function is not always clearly defined, but for the quasi-monochromatic fields just considered $\mathscr{V}$ is measurable.)

For the foregoing cases we have

$$\mathscr{V} = 1 \qquad\qquad R \gg bd/\bar{\lambda}$$
$$\mathscr{V} = 0 \qquad\qquad R \approx 0$$
$$0 < \mathscr{V} < 1 \qquad \text{Intermediate } R$$

Thus when $\mathscr{V} = 1$, the fields at P_1 and P_2 are termed coherent; when $\mathscr{V} = 0$, the fields at P_1 and P_2 are termed incoherent; and when $0 < \mathscr{V} < 1$, the fields at P_1 and P_2 are termed partially coherent.

We thus note that the coherence of the radiation impinging upon screen A depends not upon the source alone but upon the source *and* the geometry. In addition to the source itself, the coherence of the radiation depends upon R and d. In the foregoing case we held d fixed and varied R. It is most important to note the effect of varying d for fixed R. If we fix R and choose d initially such that $R \gg bd/\bar{\lambda}$, we get the sharp fringes pictured in Fig. 4-2a. As d is increased, however, from this condition to the point where $R \approx bd/\bar{\lambda}$, the fringes become progressively weaker until at some point they vanish completely. Interestingly, if d is increased beyond the point where there are no fringes, fringes will again appear.

4.1.3. Coherence Function

The fringes recorded on screen B are a measure of the coherence, or correlation, of the radiation fields at two points P_1 and P_2. If in a scalar approximation the radiation field at P $(i = 1, 2)$ is represented by $V_i{}^r(t)$,* we should be able to find a relationship between a correlation function determined from $V_i{}^r(t)$ and $V_2{}^r(t)$ and the visibility $\mathscr{V}$ defined above. The radiation field and hence the intensity on the screen B may be determined from $V_1{}^r(t)$ and $V_2{}^r(t)$ since $V^r(t)$ satisfies the wave equation

$$(4\text{-}2) \qquad\qquad \nabla^2 V^r = \frac{1}{c^2}\frac{\partial^2 V^r}{\partial t^2}$$

---

* The r superscript indicates a real field. Later for convenience we shall introduce a complex field.

Since $V^r(t)$ is a function of time, the natural correlation function to define is a function that involves a time average. We may thus consider the function

(4-3) $$\Gamma_{12}^{\ rr}(0) = \langle V_1^{\ r}(t)V_2^{\ r}(t)\rangle$$

where the brackets $\langle\ \rangle$ indicate a time average. (The zero argument in $\Gamma_{12}^{\ rr}(0)$ indicates that both $V_1^{\ r}(t)$ and $V_2^{\ r}(t)$ are taken at the same time. $\Gamma_{12}^{\ rr}(0)$ will be generalized shortly.)

A relationship between $\mathscr{V}$ and a normalized form of $\Gamma_{12}^{\ rr}(0)$ can indeed be found. It turns out however that the relationship is much simpler if a complex form of $V^r(t)$ is introduced. Rather than spending time at this point, giving the appropriate generalization of $V^r(t)$,* let us suppose that $V(t)$ is the proper complex form to associate with $V^r(t)$. We define the quantity

(4-4) $$\Gamma_{12}(0) = \langle V_1(t)V_2^*(t)\rangle$$

[where $V^*(t)$ is the complex conjugate of $V(t)$] and the normalized form of $\Gamma_{12}(0)$, $\gamma_{12}(0)$, where

(4-5) $$\gamma_{12}(0) = \frac{\Gamma_{12}(0)}{\sqrt{I_1' I_2'}}$$

$I_1' = \langle V_1(t)V_1^*(t)\rangle$ and as a result of the complex notation, I_1' turns out to be twice the intensity at P_1; that is, $I' = 2I$.

With these definitions we find for the quasi-monochromatic case that if $I_1' = I_2'$

(4-6) $$\mathscr{V} = |\gamma_{12}(0)|$$

(This relation will be derived shortly.)

Thus we see that there is a very close relationship between visibility and correlation for quasi-monochromatic radiation. We should note however that even in the quasi-monochromatic case the visibility $\mathscr{V}$ is equal to $|\gamma_{12}(0)|$ only in the neighborhood of the point O. At a point T, some distance from O, the fringes will be less sharp than the fringes in the neighborhood of O. The reason for this is that at some point the distance $r_1 - r_2$ becomes of the order of $c/\Delta\nu$ (where we remember that

* It is simply $V(t) = V^r(t) + iV^i(t)$ where $V^i(t)$ is the Hilbert transform of $V^r(t)$. See Section 2.1.6.2.

$\Delta\nu$ is a characteristic spectral spread). $\tau = 1/\Delta\nu$ may also be interpreted as the characteristic correlation time for a quasi-monochromatic signal and when $r_1 - r_2 \approx c/\Delta\nu$, the cross correlation between two signals that are highly correlated when $r_1 - r_2 \ll c/\Delta\nu$ will approach zero.

Once the correlation function is established as the relevant function to study in the Young's interference experiment it becomes natural to seek to extend the definition to include signals of finite spectral width. This was done by Wolf (1955) (see also Blanc-Lapierre and Dumonet, 1955). Wolf defined the cross-correlation function $\Gamma_{12}(\tau)$, termed the mutual coherence function, in the following manner:

$$(4\text{-}7) \qquad \Gamma_{12}(\tau) = \langle V_1(t + \tau)V_2{}^*(t)\rangle$$

where τ is a time delay. The normalized form of $\Gamma_{12}(\tau)$, $\gamma_{12}(\tau)$, is defined as

$$(4\text{-}8) \qquad \gamma_{12}(\tau) = \frac{\Gamma_{12}(\tau)}{\sqrt{\Gamma_{11}(0)\Gamma_{22}(0)}}$$

The function $\gamma_{12}(\tau)$ is not as simply measurable as $|\gamma_{12}(0)|$ was in the quasi-monochromatic case, but Beran and Parrent (1964) have shown that an extension of the procedures that are used in Young's interference experiment may be used to measure the function $\Gamma_{11}(\tau)$. The function $|\gamma_{12}(\tau)|$ lies between 0 and 1 and, using the ideas suggested by the very physical idea of visibility, we may define the concepts of coherence and incoherence for radiation of finite spectral width. Before doing this, however, we should like to outline a derivation of the relation given by Eq. 4-6.

4.1.4. Derivation of Equation 4-6

The complex function $V(t)$ associated with $V^r(t)$ also satisfies a wave equation. We have

$$(4\text{-}9) \qquad \nabla^2 V(t) = \frac{1}{c^2}\frac{\partial^2 V(t)}{\partial t^2}$$

When the radiation is quasi-monochromatic, it can be shown that a solution of Eq. 4-9 which relates $V_B(t)$ on the screen B to $V_1(t)$ and $V_2(t)$

may be written in the form

(4-10) $$V_B(t) = k_1 V_1 \left(t - \frac{r_1}{c} \right) + k_2 V_2 \left(t - \frac{r_2}{c} \right)$$

where k_1 and k_2 are time-independent, pure imaginary functions that reflect the effects of the size of the pinholes, the distance R_{AB}, and the angular spread of the radiation. The intensity of the radiation on screen B, which we denote $I_B{}'$, is the time average of $V_B(t)$ and $V_B{}^*(t)$. Thus

(4-11) $$I_B{}' = \langle V_B(t) V_B{}^*(t) \rangle = \left\langle \left[k_1 V_1 \left(t - \frac{r_1}{c} \right) + k_2 V_2 \left(t - \frac{r_2}{c} \right) \right] \right.$$
$$\left. \cdot \left[k_1{}^* V_1{}^* \left(t - \frac{r_1}{c} \right) + k_2{}^* V_2{}^* \left(t - \frac{r_2}{c} \right) \right] \right\rangle$$

The expansion of the term on the right-hand side of Eq. 4-11 yields

(4-12) $$I_B{}' = I_{1B}{}' + I_{2B}{}' + 2 \operatorname{Re} [k_1 k_2{}^* \langle V_1(t - t_1) V_2{}^*(t - t_2) \rangle]$$

where we have set $t_i = r_i/c$ and Re denotes the real part. $I_{1B}{}'$ is the intensity that would be observed on the screen B if the second pinhole were closed. $I_{2B}{}'$ may be similarly interpreted. Since we have used time averages we have implicitly assumed that the radiation statistics were stationary. Hence

$$\langle V_1(t - t_1) V_2{}^*(t - t_2) \rangle = \langle V_1(t + \tau) V_2{}^*(t) \rangle$$

where $\tau = t_2 - t_1$. Finally then using the definition given in Eq. 4-7

(4-13) $$I_B{}' = I_{1B}{}' + I_{2B}{}' + 2 \operatorname{Re} [k_1 k_2{}^* \Gamma_{12}(\tau)]$$

Since k_1 and $k_2{}^*$ are pure imaginary functions, we may write

(4-14) $$\operatorname{Re} [k_1 k_2{}^* \Gamma_{12}(\tau)] = \operatorname{Re} [k_1 k_2{}^* \sqrt{\Gamma_{11}(0) \Gamma_{22}(0)} \gamma_{12}(\tau)]$$
$$= \operatorname{Re} [\sqrt{|k_1|^2 \, \Gamma_{11}(0) \, |k_2|^2 \, \Gamma_{22}(0)} \gamma_{12}(\tau)]$$
$$= \operatorname{Re} [\sqrt{I_{1B}{}' I_{2B}{}'} \gamma_{12}(\tau)]$$
$$= \sqrt{I_{1B}{}' I_{2B}{}'} \operatorname{Re} [\gamma_{12}(\tau)]$$

Finally then

(4-15) $$I_B{}' = I_{1B}{}' + I_{2B}{}' + 2\sqrt{I_{1B}{}' I_{2B}{}'} \operatorname{Re} [\gamma_{12}(\tau)]$$

The visibility $\mathscr{V}$ is defined in terms of I_B' in the following form

(4-16)
$$\mathscr{V} = \frac{(I_B')_{\max} - (I_B')_{\min}}{(I_B')_{\max} + (I_B')_{\min}}$$

The function $\gamma_{12}(\tau)$ may be written in terms of an amplitude and phase function in the following manner

(4-17)
$$\gamma_{12}(\tau) = |\gamma_{12}(\tau)|\, e^{i\phi_{12}(\tau)}$$

Substituting Eq. 4-17 into Eq. 4-15 we find (assuming for simplicity that $I_{1B}' = I_{2B}' \equiv I'$)

(4-18)
$$I_B' = 2I'(1 + |\gamma_{12}(\tau)| \cos \phi_{12}(\tau))$$

The maximum and minimum values of I_B' are thus

$$(I_B')_{\max} = 2I'(1 + |\gamma_{12}(\tau)|)$$
$$(I_B')_{\min} = 2I'(1 - |\gamma_{12}(\tau)|)$$

and we have finally upon substituting these expressions into Eq. 4-16

(4-19)
$$\mathscr{V} = |\gamma_{12}(\tau)|$$

We caution the reader to remember that the above relation holds only for quasi-monochromatic radiation and small path lengths.

4.1.5. Coherent and Incoherent Fields

Returning to our discussion of coherence and incoherence we make use of the physical picture given by the visibility and say that the radiation fields at two points P_1 and P_2 separated by a time τ are coherent if

$$|\gamma_{12}(\tau)| = 1$$

and incoherent if

$$|\gamma_{12}(\tau)| = 0$$

This definition refers to two specific points P_1, and P_2 and a specific time delay τ. Thus we may have $|\gamma_{12}(\tau)| = 1$ for $P_1 = P_{01}$, $P_2 = P_{02}$, $\tau = \tau_0$ and $|\gamma_{12}(\tau)| = 0.5$ for $P_1 = P_{01}'$, $P_2 = P_{02}'$, $\tau = \tau_0'$. The question that arises is whether or not we can define the concepts of a coherent field and incoherent field, wherein in the coherent case $|\gamma_{12}(\tau)| = 1$ for *all* pairs of points P_1 and P_2 and time delays τ and in the incoherent case $|\gamma_{12}(\tau)| = 0$ for *all* pairs of points P_1 and P_2 and time delays τ.

The answer to this question has been established and the following theorems may be proved (see Beran and Parrent, 1964, Chapter 4; Mehta, Wolf, and Balachandran, 1966.)

THEOREM I. A field has the property $|\gamma_{12}(\tau)| = 1$ for all pairs of points P_1 and P_2 and time delays τ if, and only if, it is monochromatic. By monochromatic we mean that the complex disturbance $V(t)$ is of the form

$$V(t) = A \exp\left[-(2\pi i \nu_0 t + \beta i)\right]$$

where ν_0 is a constant and A and β are functions only of position.

THEOREM II. A non-null field for which $|\gamma_{12}(\tau)| = 0$ for all pairs of points P_1 and P_2 and time delays τ cannot exist in free space.

COROLLARY. If $|\gamma_{12}(\tau)| = 0$ for all pairs of points P_1 and P_2 and time delays τ on some continuous closed surface, then the surface does not radiate.

The reader may roughly convince himself that Theorem I is true by considering a field of the form

$$V(t) = A_1 \exp\left[i\omega_1 t + i\phi_1\right] + A_2 \exp\left[i\omega_2 t + i\phi_2\right] \qquad (\omega_1 \neq \omega_2)$$

It is easy to see that $|\gamma_{12}(\tau)|$ cannot be equal to one for all τ. A rigorous proof was given by Mehta, Wolf, and Balachandran (1966).* The condition that $|\gamma_{12}(\tau)| = 1$ for *all* pairs of points P_1 and P_2 and time delays τ is thus too rigorous a definition to use for the definition of a coherent field since only the special and unphysical case of a pure monochromatic field satisfies this condition. We refer to a pure monochromatic field as unphysical since even the gas laser has a finite bandwidth and can not be called a pure monochromatic field. All physical radiation fields have a finite bandwidth.

The concept of a coherent quasi-monochromatic field may be introduced, however, and it is this definition of a coherent field that is of most use in physical problems. We define a quasi-monochromatic field to be coherent if for every pair of points P_1 and P_2 there exists a

---

* The statement of this theorem given in Beran and Parrent (1964) is correct, but the proof is in error.

time delay $\tau(P_1, P_2)$ such that $|\gamma_{12}[\tau(P_1, P_2)]| = 1$. In this field there will be some time delay for every pair of points for which the interference pattern will exhibit sharp fringes and have a visibility of one. The fact that incoherent fields can not exist in free space is not surprising. We can always find two points in space that receive the radiation that has propagated from a common point or set of points and hence we expect to have some coherence develop even if the initial points were incoherent. What is perhaps more surprising is the corollary which states that the radiation may not be incoherent for all pairs of points on a continuous radiating surface. This theorem may be easily demonstrated by formally calculating the radiation external to a surface for which $|\gamma_{12}(\tau)| = 0$ for all pairs of points and time delays τ on the surface. This may be done in terms of Green's functions and we find directly that the surface does not radiate.

By considering the coherence of the radiation emerging from an excited gas or in the interior of a blackbody cavity we find that a characteristic coherence length on the surface of radiator loosely called incoherent (like the sun) is of the order of a few wavelengths of the dominant radiating components. Thus the best we can do in defining an incoherent radiating surface is to say that the radiation leaving the surface is incoherent if $|\gamma_{12}(\tau)|$ falls essentially to zero in a few wavelengths. For many such purposes it turns out that $|\gamma_{12}(\tau)|$ may be approximated analytically by the Dirac delta function form

$$\Gamma_{12}(\tau) = \delta(P_1 - P_2)G(P_1, \tau)$$

In this case the intensity is infinite over the surface, but since the radiation external to the surface is calculated using an integral relation the radiation field is here finite and depending upon the application, often gives the same result as a coherence function for which $|\gamma_{12}(\tau)|$ approaches zero in the order of a few wavelengths.

4.1.6. Measurement of the Angular Diameter of Two-Point Objects

We should like to conclude this introductory section with perhaps the earliest example illustrating the utility of the ideas of coherence. We wish to outline the procedure for measuring the angular separation of two point objects (like a double-star system) that are not resolvable by ordinary telescopic methods. We follow the simple physical ideas given by Michelson. Let us refer to Fig. 4-3. We suppose that we have two sources S_1 and S_2, a great distance from the screen A. If we are measuring a double-star system, the screen is on the earth and the two sources are S_1 and S_2. We take the sources to be at a great distance so that the radiation from both S_1 and S_2 impinging upon the screen A may be represented by plane waves. We assume that the radiation

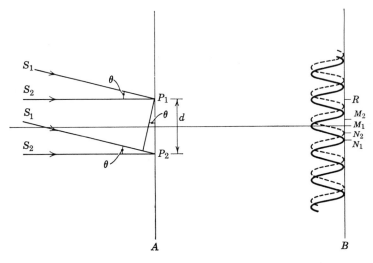

Fig. 4-3. Interference measurement of the radiation from distant point objects.

fields from S_1 and S_2 are incoherent and for convenience we filter the radiation to make it quasi-monochromatic.

In screen A we have two pinholes at P_1 and P_2. The radiation is recorded on a screen B which is in the far field of the pinhole system. Thus we perform a Young's interference experiment. The reason why we perform such a procedure rather than to take a picture of the double star system is that from a practical point of view the distance d may be made considerably larger than an ordinary telescope diameter and hence we can measure the angular diameter θ of systems that could be measured in no other way. This method also has the advantage of being less sensitive to atmospheric turbulence.

The radiation from the source S_1 *alone* forms a classical interference pattern on the screen B. If we keep the path-length differences small the fringe pattern in the neighborhood of O is a cosine pattern and the visibility is equal to one. Similarly, the pattern resulting from the S_2 *alone* will be a cosine pattern with visibility equal to one. The only differences in the patterns is the position of the maximum. The position of the maximum depends upon θ and the distance d which separates the pinholes.

Since the radiation fields from S_1 and S_2 are incoherent the intensities on screen B will add. Thus if M_1 coincides with M_2 we shall have a cosine pattern with minimum intensity zero and visibility one. If M_1 coincides with N_2 the screen B will exhibit no fringes, just a constant intensity; here the visibility will be zero. For fixed θ, the visibility will vary from zero to one depending upon the value of d.

In order to determine whether or not the cosine patterns on B are in phase we consider an arbitrary point R. If $P_1R = P_2R + m\bar{\lambda}$ (m is an integer), then the point R will be a maximum for the source S_2. If $P_1R = P_2R + (m + 1)\bar{\lambda}/2$ then the point R will be a minimum for the source S_2. We now consider the case when $P_1R = P_2R$ and R is a maximum. We call this point $R = M_2$. At this point the radiations from source S_1 passing through P_1 and P_2 will not, in general, be in phase. The path length will differ by the distance $Q_1P_2 = d \sin \theta$. Since we are using a scalar theory we must assume that $\theta \ll 1$ and hence we have $Q_1P_2 = d\theta$.

When $d\theta/\bar{\lambda} \ll 1$, then the radiation originating in S_2 and passing through P_1 and P_2 will be essentially in phase at M_2. That is, M_1 will coincide with M_2. As d is made greater, however, M_1 will move away from M_2 until N_1 coincides with M_2. N_1 will coincide with M_2 if $d\theta = \bar{\lambda}/2$, i.e., when $\theta = \bar{\lambda}/2d$.*

In order to determine the angular diameter θ we thus need only to perform a series of interference experiments with variable d. We begin by choosing d to be very small so that the visibility of fringes is one. We then increase d until the visibility of fringes is zero. The point where the visibility goes to zero, for example, d_0, is then used to determine θ through use of the formula

$$(4\text{-}20) \qquad\qquad \theta = \frac{\bar{\lambda}}{2d_0}$$

This procedure can also be used to determine the angular diameter of incoherent continuous sources when the shape of the intensity

---

* We note that as d changes the distance M_1N_1 changes; but this effect is unimportant for our arguments here.

distribution is known. It is then a question of adding up the effects of the many parts of the source rather than just the two point sources. It is easier however, to treat this problem after the more formal aspects of the theory are presented.

The simple physical picture presented here allows us to consider the effects of atmospheric turbulence on the measurement of angular diameters. If the atmospheric turbulence does not introduce long path-length differences the effect of atmospheric turbulence on the fringe pattern resulting from one source alone is simply to shift the position of the maximum intensity. The visibility in the neighborhood of O still remains one. If we were able to watch the fringe intensity pattern of one source as a function of time, we would see the fringe pattern move laterally (along the screen) as a random function of time.

If the radiation from the two sources experience essentially different turbulent fields, then their respective fringe patterns will move independently and no measurement of the angular diameter is possible. On the other hand, if the radiation from the two sources experience essentially the same turbulent fields, we should expect the fringe patterns to move in the same manner; a measurement of the angular

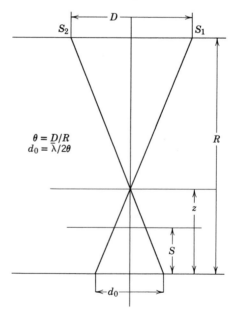

Fig. 4-4. Diagram to determine effects of atmospheric turbulence.

diameter is again possible if fringe intensity measurements are made in times small compared to the characteristic time of significant turbulent fluctuations.

If S is the characteristic depth of the atmosphere we expect measurements to be possible when $\delta \equiv \bar{\lambda}/2S\theta^2 \gg 1$ and to be questionable when $\delta \ll 1$. The parameter δ gives the ratio of the distance z (see Fig. 4-4) to S since $z/R \approx d_0/D$ ($z/R \ll 1$). In a rough sense if $\delta \equiv z/S \gg 1$ the rays from S_1 and S_2 experience essentially the same turbulent field since the turbulence is confined to the region bounded by S. If $\delta \ll 1$ then the rays experience different turbulent fields and if the important characteristic turbulent lengths are less than d_0, we expect the fringe patterns from S_1 and S_2 to move independently. If $\delta \ll 1$ and the important characteristic turbulent length is large compared to d_0 the radiation from S_1 and S_2 may still experience the same turbulent fields and measurement is again possible.

4.2. Mathematical Formulation

In this section we shall be mainly concerned with setting up the formulation to treat the problem of determining the mutual coherence of the free-space radiation in the far field of a source, if the mutual coherence is known for all pairs of points on some surface S. As an explicit example, we give in Section 4.3 the solution for quasi-monochromatic radiation in the field of a plane, finite, incoherent source. We shall conclude the chapter by outlining the method for determining the mutual coherence function for blackbody radiation. We begin the section by considering the problem in rather general terms.

4.2.1. Definitions

As we have implied in the introduction, the radiation in many problems may be conveniently treated from a statistical point of view. The equations governing the electromagnetic field in free space are the Maxwell equations:

(4-21)
$$\nabla \times \mathbf{E}^r = -\frac{1}{c}\frac{\partial \mathbf{H}^r}{\partial t}$$

$$\nabla \times \mathbf{H}^r = \frac{1}{c}\frac{\partial \mathbf{E}^r}{\partial t}$$

where $\mathbf{E}^r$ is the electric field, $\mathbf{H}^r$ is the magnetic field, and c is the velocity of light.

If $\mathbf{E}$ and $\mathbf{H}$ are statistical variables, then we have associated with them the joint probability density functional $P[E_i(\mathbf{x}, t), H_j(\mathbf{x}, t)]$ which was discussed in Chapter 2. Most of the work in this field, however, has been concerned with treating the second and fourth-order moments and we shall restrict ourselves in this chapter to a discussion of these cases. Thus we shall consider here the moments:

$$(4\text{-}22) \quad \mathscr{E}_{ij}{}^E(\mathbf{x}_1, t_1; \mathbf{x}_2, t_2) = \overline{E_i^r(\mathbf{x}_1, t_1)E_j^r(\mathbf{x}_2, t_2)}$$

$$\mathscr{H}_{ij}{}^E(\mathbf{x}_1, t_1; \mathbf{x}_2, t_2) = \overline{E_i^r(\mathbf{x}_1, t_1)E_j^r(\mathbf{x}_2, t_2)}$$

$$\mathscr{G}_{ij}{}^E(\mathbf{x}_1, t_1; \mathbf{x}_2, t_2) = \overline{E_i^r(\mathbf{x}_1, t_1)H_j^r(\mathbf{x}_2, t_2)}$$

$$L_{ijkl}^E(\mathbf{x}_1, t_1; \mathbf{x}_2, t_2; \mathbf{x}_3, t_3; \mathbf{x}_4, t_4)$$
$$= \overline{E_i^r(\mathbf{x}_1, t_1)E_j^r(\mathbf{x}_2, t_2)E_k^r(\mathbf{x}_3, t_3)E_l^r(\mathbf{x}_4, t_4)}$$

$$\cdot$$
$$\cdot$$
$$\cdot$$

where the overbar indicates an ensemble average.

Furthermore, the cases we shall consider will all be stationary in time and hence we assume

$$(4\text{-}23) \quad \mathscr{E}_{ij}{}^E(\mathbf{x}_1, t_1; \mathbf{x}_2, t_2) = \mathscr{E}_{ij}{}^{rr}(\mathbf{x}_1, \mathbf{x}_2, \tau) = \langle E_i^r(\mathbf{x}_1, t + \tau)E_j^r(\mathbf{x}_2, t) \rangle$$

$$\cdot$$
$$\cdot$$
$$\cdot$$

$$L_{ijkl}^E(\mathbf{x}_1, t_1; \mathbf{x}_2, t_2; \mathbf{x}_3, t_3; \mathbf{x}_4, t_4) = L_{ijkl}^{rrrr}(\mathbf{x}_1, \mathbf{x}_2, \mathbf{x}_3, \mathbf{x}_4, \tau_2, \tau_3, \tau_4)$$
$$= \langle E_i^r(\mathbf{x}_1, t)E_j^r(\mathbf{x}_2, t + \tau_2)E_k^r(\mathbf{x}_3, t + \tau_3)E_l^r(\mathbf{x}_4, t + \tau_4) \rangle$$

$$\cdot$$
$$\cdot$$
$$\cdot$$

where the brackets $\langle \ \rangle$ indicate a time average.

As we indicated earlier it most convenient to work with a complex representation. Thus, in our work in this chapter we shall use the complex analytic signal that we introduced in Section 2.1.6.2 rather than $E^r(\mathbf{x}, t)$ and $H^r(\mathbf{x}, t)$. We recall, for example, that the analytic signal $E_j(\mathbf{x}, t)$ associated with the real signal $E_j^r(\mathbf{x}, t)$ is defined as

$$E_j(\mathbf{x}, t) = E_j^r(\mathbf{x}, t) + iE_j^i(\mathbf{x}, t)$$

where $E_j^i(\mathbf{x}, t)$ is the Hilbert transform of $E_j^r(\mathbf{x}, t)$. This procedure is a generalization of the familiar procedure of associating a complex exponential function e^{ivt} with the real function $\cos vt$. In fact, if $E_j^r(\mathbf{x}, t)$ has a Fourier cosine integral representation, we have only to change all cosines to sines in the integral to find $E_j^i(\mathbf{x}, t)$. In Section 2.1.6.2 we discussed the difficulties that occur if we assume that $E_j^r(\mathbf{x}, t)$ exists from $t = -\infty$ to $t = +\infty$, the condition necessary for stationarity. We suppose here that suitable limiting procedures have been introduced and we define here the two-point complex functions (see Roman and Wolf, 1960)

(4-24) $\mathscr{E}_{ij}(\mathbf{x}_1, \mathbf{x}_2, \tau) = \langle E_i(\mathbf{x}_1, t + \tau)E_j^*(\mathbf{x}_2, t)\rangle$

$\quad\quad\quad\quad \mathscr{H}_{ij}(\mathbf{x}_1, \mathbf{x}_2, \tau) = \langle H_i(\mathbf{x}_1, t + \tau)H_j^*(\mathbf{x}_2, t)\rangle$

$\quad\quad\quad\quad \mathscr{G}_{ij}(\mathbf{x}_1, \mathbf{x}_2, \tau) = \langle E_i(\mathbf{x}, t + \tau)H_j^*(\mathbf{x}_2, t)\rangle$

$\quad\quad\quad\quad \tilde{\mathscr{G}}_{ij}(\mathbf{x}_1, \mathbf{x}_2, \tau) = \langle H_i(\mathbf{x}, t + \tau)E_j^*(\mathbf{x}_2, t)\rangle$

as a generalization of the functions $\mathscr{E}_{ij}^{rr}(\mathbf{x}_1, t + \tau; \mathbf{x}_2, t)$. It may be shown (see, for example, Beran and Parrent, 1964) that

$$\mathrm{Re}\,[\mathscr{E}_{ij}(\mathbf{x}_1, \mathbf{x}_2, \tau)] = 2\mathscr{E}_{ij}^{rr}(\mathbf{x}_1, \mathbf{x}_2, \tau)$$

The four-point complex function to associate with L_{ijkl}^{rrrr} is not so easily written down. Beran and Corson (1965) have shown that an acceptable form for L_{ijkl}, the complex function to associate with L_{ijkl}^{rrrr} is

(4-25) $L_{jklm}(\mathbf{x}_1, \mathbf{x}_2, \mathbf{x}_3, \mathbf{x}_4, \tau_2, \tau_3, \tau_4) = \sum\limits_{p=1}^{7} L_{jklm}^{p}(\mathbf{x}_1, \mathbf{x}_2, \mathbf{x}_3, \mathbf{x}_2, \tau_1, \tau_3, \tau_4)$

where

$$L_{jklm}^1 = \langle E_j E_k^* E_l^* E_m\rangle$$

$$L_{jklm}^2 = \langle E_j E_k^* E_l E_m^*\rangle$$

$$L_{jklm}^3 = \langle E_j E_k E_l^* E_m^*\rangle$$

$$L_{jklm}^4 = \langle E_j^* E_k E_l E_m\rangle$$

$$L_{jklm}^5 = \langle E_j E_k^* E_l E_m\rangle$$

$$L_{jklm}^6 = \langle E_j E_k E_l^* E_m\rangle$$

$$L_{jklm}^7 = \langle E_j E_k E_l E_m^*\rangle$$

For this function

$$\text{Re } L_{jklm} = 8L_{jklm}^{rrrr}$$

They do not give the form of mixed coherence functions containing both the $\mathbf{E}$ and $\mathbf{H}$ fields but these functions can be defined analogously.

4.2.2. Derivation of Differential Equations

It may be shown that the analytic signals $\mathbf{E}(\mathbf{x}, t)$ and $\mathbf{H}(\mathbf{x}, t)$ satisfy Maxwell's Equations. Thus

(4-26)
$$\nabla \times \mathbf{E} = -\frac{1}{c}\frac{\partial \mathbf{H}}{\partial t}$$

$$\nabla \times \mathbf{H} = \frac{1}{c}\frac{\partial \mathbf{E}}{\partial t}$$

From Eq. 4-26 differential equations governing the coherence functions may be derived. Once these equations are derived we need not refer back to the functions $\mathbf{E}$ and $\mathbf{H}$ again. Some writers prefer to first find integral solutions for $\mathbf{E}$ and $\mathbf{H}$ and perform the averaging subsequent to this. For free-space propagation problems we feel, however, that the physics of the problem is much more transparent if we derive differential equations for the coherence functions at the onset. *Since the equations are linear with constant coefficients, we are able here to derive a set of differential equations for each order of coherence functions. That is we can derive a finite set of equations containing only second-order coherence functions, another set containing only third-order coherence functions, and so on.* We derive here the set of equations for the second-order coherence functions given in Eq. 4-24. To find the equations for this set we take the curl of the function $\mathscr{E}_{ij}(\mathbf{x}_1, \mathbf{x}_2, \tau)$ with respect to $\mathbf{x}_1$. We have [representing the curl operation as $\epsilon_{ijk}(\partial/\partial x_j)$]

(4-27)
$$\epsilon_{ijk}\frac{\partial}{\partial x_{1j}}\mathscr{E}_{km}(\mathbf{x}_1, \mathbf{x}_2, \tau) = \left\langle \epsilon_{ijk}\frac{\partial}{\partial x_{1j}}E_j(\mathbf{x}_1, t + \tau)E_m{}^*(\mathbf{x}_2, t)\right\rangle$$

Using Eq. 4-26 we find for the right-hand side

$$\left\langle \epsilon_{ijk}\frac{\partial}{\partial x_{1j}}E_k(\mathbf{x}_1, t+\tau)E_m^*(\mathbf{x}_2, t)\right\rangle$$

$$=-\frac{1}{c}\left\langle \frac{\partial}{\partial(t+\tau)}H_i(\mathbf{x}_1, t+\tau)E_m^*(\mathbf{x}_2, t)\right\rangle$$

$$=-\frac{1}{c}\frac{\partial}{\partial\tau}\tilde{\mathscr{G}}_{im}(\mathbf{x}_1, \mathbf{x}_2, \tau)$$

since

$$\frac{\partial}{\partial(t+\tau)}H_j(\mathbf{x}, t+\tau)=\frac{\partial}{\partial\tau}H_j(\mathbf{x}, t+\tau)$$

Thus

(4-28) $$\epsilon_{ijk}\frac{\partial}{\partial x_{1j}}\mathscr{E}_{km}(\mathbf{x}_1, \mathbf{x}_2, \tau)=-\frac{1}{c}\frac{\partial}{\partial\tau}\tilde{\mathscr{G}}_{im}(\mathbf{x}_1, \mathbf{x}_2, \tau)$$

In the same manner, we also find

(4-29) $$\epsilon_{ijk}\frac{\partial}{\partial x_{1j}}\mathscr{H}_{km}(\mathbf{x}_1, \mathbf{x}_2, \tau)=\frac{1}{c}\frac{\partial}{\partial\tau}\mathscr{G}_{im}(\mathbf{x}_1, \mathbf{x}_2, \tau)$$

(4-30) $$\epsilon_{ijk}\frac{\partial}{\partial x_{1j}}\mathscr{G}_{km}(\mathbf{x}_1, \mathbf{x}_2, \tau)=-\frac{1}{c}\frac{\partial}{\partial\tau}\mathscr{H}_{im}(\mathbf{x}_1, \mathbf{x}_2, \tau)$$

(4-31) $$\epsilon_{ijk}\frac{\partial}{\partial x_{1j}}\tilde{\mathscr{G}}_{km}(\mathbf{x}_1, \mathbf{x}_2, \tau)=\frac{1}{c}\frac{\partial}{\partial\tau}\mathscr{E}_{im}(\mathbf{x}_1, \mathbf{x}_2, \tau)$$

Since div $\mathbf{E}$ = div $\mathbf{H}$ = 0, we also find

$$\frac{\partial}{\partial x_{1j}}\mathscr{E}_{jk}(\mathbf{x}_1, \mathbf{x}_2, \tau)=\frac{\partial}{\partial x_{1j}}\mathscr{H}_{jk}(\mathbf{x}_1, \mathbf{x}_2, \tau)$$

$$=\frac{\partial}{\partial x_{1j}}\mathscr{G}_{jk}(\mathbf{x}_1, \mathbf{x}_2, \tau)=\frac{\partial}{\partial x_{1j}}\tilde{\mathscr{G}}_{jk}(\mathbf{x}_1, \mathbf{x}_2, \tau)=0$$

Similar equations may be found if derivatives are taken with respect to $\mathbf{x}_2$ rather than $\mathbf{x}_1$. For the remainder of this chapter we shall work only with the $\mathbf{E}$ field. From Eqs. 4-28 and 4-30 we see that

(4-32) $$\nabla_1^2\mathscr{E}_{jm}(\mathbf{x}_1, \mathbf{x}_2, \tau)=\frac{1}{c^2}\frac{\partial^2}{\partial\tau^2}\mathscr{E}_{jm}(\mathbf{x}_1, \mathbf{x}_2, \tau)$$

$$\frac{\partial}{\partial x_{1j}}\mathscr{E}_{jm}(\mathbf{x}_1, \mathbf{x}_2, \tau)=0$$

To treat the vector aspects of radiation from a closed surface S (see Fig. 4-5) is a very complicated calculation because of the presence of the divergence condition. In principle we may find from Eq. 4-32 $\mathscr{E}_{jm}(\mathbf{x}_1, \mathbf{x}_2, \tau)$ in terms of tangential components of $\mathscr{E}_{jm}(\mathbf{x}_{1S}, \mathbf{x}_{2S}, \tau)$, where $\mathbf{x}_1, \mathbf{x}_2$ are points external to S and $\mathbf{x}_{1S}, \mathbf{x}_{2S}$ are points on S, but in practice it is very involved. Fortunately, in many problems of interest we may introduce a suitable scalar approximation. This type of approximation is appropriate for considering the radiation from S at points $\mathbf{x}_1, \mathbf{x}_2$ such that x_1/R, x_2/R, y_1/R, y_2/R, are much less than one and where $\lambda_c/b \ll 1$, $b/R \ll 1$. (λ_c is a characteristic radiation wavelength.) In this case, the divergence condition is unimportant since the E_z component of the electric field is negligible and the E_x and E_y components of the field vary very slowly in the x and y directions, respectively. In this approximation the j and m indices in $\mathscr{E}_{jm}(\mathbf{x}_1, \mathbf{x}_2, \tau)$ take on only the values 1 and 2 rather than 1, 2, and 3.

The problem in this form may be easily treated using polarization concepts but Parrent and Marathay (1965) have pointed out that a full scalar theory can be achieved under these conditions by considering the trace of $\mathscr{E}_{jm}(\mathbf{x}_1, \mathbf{x}_2, \tau)$. That is, we consider

(4-33) $\Gamma(\mathbf{x}_1, \mathbf{x}_2, \tau) \equiv \mathscr{E}_{11}(\mathbf{x}_1, \mathbf{x}_2, \tau) + \mathscr{E}_{22}(\mathbf{x}_1, \mathbf{x}_2, \tau)$

We use $\Gamma(\mathbf{x}_1, \mathbf{x}_2, \tau)$ in anticipation of identifying this function with the scalar function used in the introduction.

From Eq. 4-32 we see that $\Gamma(\mathbf{x}_1, \mathbf{x}_2, \tau)$ satisfies the wave equation

(4-34) $$\nabla_1^2 \Gamma(\mathbf{x}_1, \mathbf{x}_2, \tau) = \frac{1}{c^2} \frac{\partial^2}{\partial \tau^2} \Gamma(\mathbf{x}_1, \mathbf{x}_2, \tau)$$

Furthermore, $\Gamma(\mathbf{x}_1, \mathbf{x}_2, \tau)$ may be determined from a knowledge of $\Gamma(\mathbf{x}_{1S}, \mathbf{x}_{2S}, \tau_S)$ and hence we need not hark back to $\mathscr{E}_{jm}(\mathbf{x}_1, \mathbf{x}_2, \tau)$ to find its value if $\Gamma(\mathbf{x}_{1S}, \mathbf{x}_{2S}, \tau_S)$ is given. The most important point, however, is the fact that $\Gamma(\mathbf{x}_1, \mathbf{x}_2, \tau)$ may be experimentally determined from measurements of a function like $\Gamma(\mathbf{x}, \mathbf{x}, \tau)$ alone. $\Gamma(\mathbf{x}, \mathbf{x}, 0) = \mathscr{E}_{11}(\mathbf{x}, \mathbf{x}, 0) + \mathscr{E}_{22}(\mathbf{x}, \mathbf{x}, 0)$ is two times the intensity of the radiation (the factor of 2 comes from the use of the complex notation). $\hat{\Gamma}(\mathbf{x}, \mathbf{x}, \nu)$ is the power spectrum of the intensity. An extension of Young's interference experiment (see Beran and Parrent, 1964) may thus be used to find $\Gamma(\mathbf{x}_1, \mathbf{x}_2, \tau)$ over any surface by measuring only $\hat{\Gamma}(\mathbf{x}_1, \mathbf{x}_1, \nu)$ some distance from the surface. (The extension requires first "Fourier analyzing" the field. For quasi-monochromatic radiation the procedure essentially reduces to the ordinary Young's interference experiment; and in order to get a feeling for the measurement we are considering, the reader may recall the introduction wherein we showed how to find $\Gamma(\mathbf{x}_1, \mathbf{x}_2, 0)$ from measurements of intensity alone.)

If the reader is familiar with the problems of the use of scalar theory in optics, he should note that the scalar theory has been achieved here in terms of a scalar coherence function rather than in terms of a scalar field $V(\mathbf{x}, t)$ to replace the vector field $E_i(\mathbf{x}, t)$. The derivation given in the introduction is appropriate when the radiation is polarized and we identify $V(\mathbf{x}, t)$ with $E_j(\mathbf{x}, t)$. The derivation here, however, is more general since the radiation need not be polarized and shows the advantage of introducing the coherence function as soon as possible rather than introducing it subsequent to obtaining an integral solution. In those places in the introduction wherein explicit mention of $V(\mathbf{x}, t)$ is not necessary, the more general trace definition of $\Gamma(\mathbf{x}_1, \mathbf{x}_2, \tau)$ may be used when $\Gamma(\mathbf{x}_1, \mathbf{x}_2, \tau)^*$ is considered.

The fourth-order differential equations governing

$$L_{jklm}(\mathbf{x}_1, \mathbf{x}_2, \mathbf{x}_3, \mathbf{x}_4, \tau_1, \tau_2, \tau_3)$$

may be derived by procedures similar to those used in the foregoing using either Maxwell's equations directly or the set

(4-35)
$$\nabla^2 \mathbf{E}(\mathbf{x}, t) = \frac{1}{c^2} \frac{\partial^2}{\partial t} \mathbf{E}(\mathbf{x}, t)$$

$$\nabla \cdot E(\mathbf{x}, t) = 0$$

We chose to use Maxwell's equations directly in the second-order case just to show how to introduce coherence functions containing both $\mathbf{E}(\mathbf{x}, t)$ and $\mathbf{H}(\mathbf{x}, t)$ but for higher-order functions it is simpler to use the set given by Eq. 4-35. In the second-order case Eq. 4-32 or 4-34 holds if the ∇^2 symbol is replaced by ∇_2^2 but in the fourth-order case an asymmetry develops in the equations. Assuming a scalar-type approximation and polarized radiation, so that for example we have,

$$L'(\mathbf{x}_1, \mathbf{x}_2, \mathbf{x}_3, \mathbf{x}_4, \tau_2, \tau_3, \tau_4)$$
$$= \langle E_1(\mathbf{x}, t) E_1^*(\mathbf{x}_2, t + \tau_2) E_1^*(\mathbf{x}_3, t + \tau_3) E_1(\mathbf{x}_4, t + \tau_4) \rangle$$

* We remind the reader that the notation $\Gamma(\mathbf{x}_1, \mathbf{x}_2, \tau)$, $\Gamma(P_1, P_2, \tau)$, and $\Gamma_{12}(\tau)$ are used interchangeably in the literature.

162   Statistical Continuum Theories

the derived set is

(4-36) $\nabla_i^2 L(\mathbf{x}_1, \mathbf{x}_2, \mathbf{x}_3, \mathbf{x}_4, \tau_2, \tau_3, \tau_4)$

$$= \frac{1}{c^2} \frac{\partial^2}{\partial \tau_i^2} L(\mathbf{x}_1, \mathbf{x}_2, \mathbf{x}_3, \mathbf{x}_4, \tau_2, \tau_3, \tau_4) \qquad (i = 2, 3, 4)$$

$\nabla_1^2 L(\mathbf{x}_1, \mathbf{x}_2, \mathbf{x}_3, \mathbf{x}_4, \tau_2, \tau_3, \tau_4)$

$$= \frac{1}{c^2} \left[\frac{\partial}{\partial \tau_2} + \frac{\partial}{\partial \tau_3} + \frac{\partial}{\partial \tau_4} \right]^2 L(\mathbf{x}_1, \mathbf{x}_2, \mathbf{x}_3, \mathbf{x}_4, \tau_2, \tau_3, \tau_4)$$

We have given the scalar theory in this restricted form since a scalar generalization similar to the second-order case has not yet been worked out.

4.2.3. Integral Form of Solution

An integral solution expressing $\Gamma(\mathbf{x}_1, \mathbf{x}_2, \tau)$ in terms of $\Gamma(\mathbf{x}_{1S}, \mathbf{x}_{2S}, \tau_S)$ (see Fig. 4-5) may be derived using Green's functions. In this section we shall present such a derivation for the second-order coherence function. We shall follow the development given in Beran and Parrent

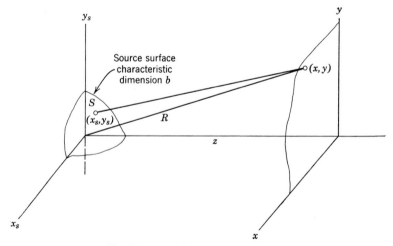

Fig. 4-5. Radiation from a surface S.

(1964). The higher-order derivations proceed similarly and the expressions are available for the restricted scalar theory in the paper by Beran and Corson (1965).

We could use Green's four-dimensional functions but it is easier to interpret the results physically if we first introduce a Fourier transform with respect to time into Eq. 4-34 and then formally solve the resultant equations using three-dimensional Green's functions.

It may be shown that $\Gamma(\mathbf{x}_1, \mathbf{x}_2, \tau)$ is itself an analytic signal (that is, its imaginary part is the Hilbert transform of its real part). Thus we have

$$(4\text{-}37) \qquad \Gamma(\mathbf{x}_1, \mathbf{x}_2, \tau) = \int_0^\infty \hat{\Gamma}(\mathbf{x}_1, \mathbf{x}_2, \nu)e^{-2\pi i\nu\tau}\, d\nu$$

$$(4\text{-}38) \qquad \hat{\Gamma}(\mathbf{x}_1, \mathbf{x}_2, \nu) = \int_{-\infty}^\infty \Gamma(\mathbf{x}_1, \mathbf{x}_2, \tau)e^{2\pi i\nu\tau}\, d\nu \qquad (\nu > 0)$$

$$= 0 \qquad\qquad\qquad (\nu < 0)$$

The fact that $\Gamma(\mathbf{x}_1, \mathbf{x}_2, \nu)$ contains only positive frequencies is very useful when we later introduce the quasimonochromatic approximation.

We can substitute Eq. 4-37 into Eq. 4-34 and obtain

$$(4\text{-}39) \qquad \int_0^\infty [\nabla_1^2 + k^2(\nu)]\hat{\Gamma}(\mathbf{x}_1, \mathbf{x}_2, \nu)e^{-2\pi i\nu\tau}\, d\nu = 0$$

$$k(\nu) = \frac{2\pi\nu}{c}$$

upon interchanging the order of integration and differentiation.

Equation 4-39 must hold for all values of τ and thus we have

$$(4\text{-}40) \qquad [\nabla_1^2 + k^2(\nu)]\hat{\Gamma}(\mathbf{x}_1, \mathbf{x}_2, \nu) = 0$$

As we stated above, Eq. 4-34 holds if ∇_1^2 is replaced by ∇_2^2. Since the derivation is unaffected by this change, we have generally

$$(4\text{-}41) \qquad [\nabla_s^2 + k^2(\nu)]\hat{\Gamma}(\mathbf{x}_1, \mathbf{x}_2, \nu) = 0 \qquad (s = 1, 2)$$

When $s = 1$, Eq. 4-41 has the formal solution

$$(4\text{-}42) \quad \hat{\Gamma}(\mathbf{x}_1, \mathbf{x}_{1S}, \nu) = -\int_S \hat{\Gamma}(\mathbf{x}_{1S}, \mathbf{x}_{2S}, \nu)\frac{\partial G_1(\mathbf{x}_1, \mathbf{x}_1{}', \nu)}{\partial_{1S}}\bigg|_{\mathbf{x}_1{}'=\mathbf{x}_{1S}} d\mathbf{x}_{1S}$$

where the integration is over the surface S. $G_1(\mathbf{x}_1, \mathbf{x}_1', \nu)$ is a Green's function satisfying the equation

(4-43) $$[\nabla_1^2 + k^2(\nu)]G_1(\mathbf{x}_1, \mathbf{x}_1', \nu) = -\delta(\mathbf{x}_1 - \mathbf{x}_1')$$

with the boundary condition

$$G_1(\mathbf{x}_1, \mathbf{x}_1', \nu)\big|_{\mathbf{x}_1'=\mathbf{x}_{1S}} = 0$$

$G_1(\mathbf{x}_1, \mathbf{x}_1', \nu)$ must also be chosen to meet the Sommerfeld radiation condition. This means that we must choose the form of $G_1(\mathbf{x}_1, \mathbf{x}_1', \nu)$ that gives a solution when the energy flows from the surface S to infinity rather than vice-versa. Derivatives with respect to n_{1S} mean derivatives taken in the direction of the outward normal to S.

The solution $\Gamma(\mathbf{x}_1, \mathbf{x}_{2S}, \nu)$ may be looked upon as the boundary condition for the solution of Eq. 4-41 when we set $s = 2$. Proceeding as we did before we find

(4-44) $$\hat{\Gamma}(\mathbf{x}_1, \mathbf{x}_2, \nu) = -\int_S \hat{\Gamma}(\mathbf{x}_1, \mathbf{x}_{2S}, \nu)\frac{\partial G_2(\mathbf{x}_2, \mathbf{x}_2', \nu)}{\partial n_{2S}}\bigg|_{\mathbf{x}_1'=\mathbf{x}_{2S}} d\mathbf{x}_{2S}$$

$G_2(\mathbf{x}_2, \mathbf{x}_2', \nu)$ satisfies the same conditions as $G_1(\mathbf{x}_1, \mathbf{x}_1', \nu)$.

The final solution for $\Gamma(\mathbf{x}_1, \mathbf{x}_2, \tau)$ is thus

(4-45) $$\Gamma(\mathbf{x}_1, \mathbf{x}_2, \tau) = \int_0^\infty \int_S \int_S \hat{\Gamma}(\mathbf{x}_{1S}, \mathbf{x}_{2S}, \nu)\frac{\partial G_1(\mathbf{x}_1, \mathbf{x}_1', \nu)}{\partial n_{1S}}\bigg|_{\mathbf{x}_1'=\mathbf{x}_{1S}}$$

$$\cdot \frac{\partial G_2(\mathbf{x}_2, \mathbf{x}_{21}', \nu)}{\partial n_{2S}}\bigg|_{\mathbf{x}_2'=\mathbf{x}_{2S}} d\mathbf{x}_{1S}\, d\mathbf{x}_{2S} e^{-2\pi i\nu\tau}\, d\nu$$

where

$$\hat{\Gamma}(\mathbf{x}_{1S}, \mathbf{x}_{2S}, \nu) = \int_{-\infty}^\infty \Gamma(\mathbf{x}_{1S}, \mathbf{x}_{2S}, \tau)e^{2\pi i\nu\tau}\, d\nu \qquad (\nu > 0)$$

$$= 0 \qquad\qquad\qquad\qquad\qquad (\nu < 0)$$

Using Eq. 4-45 we shall now consider in the next section the example of radiation from a plane, finite surface. In this case G_1 and G_2 may be given simple analytic expressions.

4.3. Radiation from a Plane Finite Surface

4.3.1. General Form of the Solution

We consider in this section the radiation from a plane, finite surface. We mean by the term plane finite surface an area in the plane $z = 0$ (see Fig. 4-6) bounded by some closed curve C. Within the area

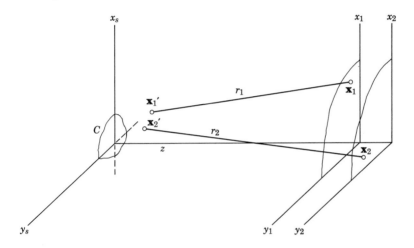

Fig. 4-6. Radiation from a plane finite surface (see Beran and Parrent, 1964, *Theory of Partial Coherence*, Prentice-Hall, Engelwood Cliffs, Fig. 3-1, p. 41).

bounded by C we may specify as a boundary condition any physically realizable mutual coherence function $\Gamma(\mathbf{x}_{1S}, \mathbf{x}_{2S}, \tau)$. Outside this area we assume the radiation intensity (and hence the mutual coherence function) is zero. Actually we do not require the radiation intensity to go abruptly to zero on the boundary C but only in the neighborhood. For the scalar approximation that we consider here to be appropriate, a characteristic dimension of the radiating area must be very much greater than a characteristic radiation wavelength and hence the boundary condition is easy to meet. We consider here the radiation in the region $z > 0$.

For the case of radiation from a plane surface an appropriate set of

Green's functions are

(4-46a) $$G_1 = \frac{\exp[ikr_1]}{4\pi r_1} - \frac{\exp[ikr_1]}{4\pi r_1''}$$

(4-46b) $$G_2 = \frac{\exp[-ikr_2]}{4\pi r_2} - \frac{\exp[-ikr_2'']}{4\pi r_2''}$$

where r_1 and r_2 are defined in Fig. 4-6. r_1'' and r_2'' are the distances to the mirror points (in z) of r_1 and r_2, respectively. We have

$$r_1 = \sqrt{(z_1 - z_1')^2 + (x_1 - x_1')^2 + (y_1 - y_1')^2}$$

$$r_1'' = \sqrt{(z_1 + z_1')^2 + (x_1 - x_1')^2 + (y_1 - y_1')^2}$$

These Green's functions meet the Sommerfeld radiation condition at infinity. That is, all the radiation comes from the plane area in the $z = 0$ plane.

By algebraic manipulation we may then show that substituting the normal derivatives of G_1 and G_2 into Eq. 4-45 yields

(4-47) $$\Gamma(\mathbf{x}_1, \mathbf{x}_2, \tau) = \frac{1}{4\pi^2} \int_0^\infty \int_S \int_S \hat{\Gamma}(\mathbf{x}_{1S}, \mathbf{x}_{2S}, \nu)(1 - ikr_1)(1 + ikr_2)$$

$$\times \cos\theta_1 \cos\theta_2 \frac{\exp[ik(r_1 - r_2)]}{r_1^2 r_2^2} \exp[-2\pi i\nu\tau]\, d\mathbf{x}_{1S}\, d\mathbf{x}_{2S}\, d\nu$$

where

$$\cos\theta_j = \frac{z_j}{r_j} \qquad (j = 1, 2)$$

Equation 4-47 represents the general form of the solution.

4.3.2. Quasi-Monochromatic Approximation

Almost all work in the theory of partial coherence is done by assuming a quasi-monochromatic approximation. Equation 4-47 takes a particularly simple form with respect to the integration over frequency if this approximation in addition to other suitable restrictions is valid. Quasi-monochromatic radiation is radiation in which the mutual power spectrum $\hat{\Gamma}(\mathbf{x}_1, \mathbf{x}_2, \nu)$ is appreciable only for values of ν in the range $\bar{\nu} - \Delta\nu \leqslant \nu \leqslant \bar{\nu} + \Delta\nu$, where $\Delta\nu/\bar{\nu} \ll 1$. In general we may write

$$(4\text{-}48) \quad \Gamma(\mathbf{x}_1, \mathbf{x}_2, \tau) = \int_0^\infty \hat{\Gamma}(\mathbf{x}_1, \mathbf{x}_2, \nu)\, d\nu$$

$$= e^{-2\pi i \bar{\nu}\tau} \int_0^\infty \Gamma(\mathbf{x}_1, \mathbf{x}_2, \nu) e^{-2\pi i(\nu - \bar{\nu})\tau}\, d\nu$$

The quasi-monochromatic approximation simplifies Eq. 4-48 if we restrict ourselves to values of τ for which $\Delta\nu\,|\tau| \ll 1$, for then we have

$$(4\text{-}49) \quad \Gamma(\mathbf{x}_1, \mathbf{x}_2, \tau) \approx e^{-2\pi i \bar{\nu}\tau} \int_0^\infty \hat{\Gamma}(\mathbf{x}_1, \mathbf{x}_2, \nu)\, d\nu \qquad (\Delta\nu\,|\tau| \ll 1)$$

$$\approx e^{-2\pi i \bar{\nu}\tau} \Gamma(\mathbf{x}_1, \mathbf{x}_2, 0) \qquad (\Delta\nu\,|\tau| \ll 1)$$

For the quasi-monochromatic approximation to simplify the propagation equation (Eq. 4-47), similar manipulation must be possible in this equation. Multiplying the right-hand side of Eq. 4-47 by

$$\exp\,[2\pi i \bar{\nu}\tau]\,\exp\,[-2\pi i \bar{\nu}\tau]$$

yields

$$(4\text{-}50) \quad \Gamma(\mathbf{x}_1, \mathbf{x}_2, \tau) = \frac{1}{4\pi^2} e^{-2\pi i \bar{\nu}\tau} \int_S \int_S \frac{\cos\theta_1 \cos\theta_2}{r_1^2 r_2^2}\, d\mathbf{x}_{1S}\, d\mathbf{x}_{2S}$$

$$\cdot \left[\int_0^\infty \Gamma(\mathbf{x}_{1S}, \mathbf{x}_{2S}, \nu)(1 - ikr_1)(1 + ikr_2) \right.$$

$$\left. \cdot \exp\,[ik(r_1 - r_2)]\,\exp\,[-2\pi i(\nu - \bar{\nu})\tau]\, d\nu \right]$$

Restricting ourselves to values of τ such that $\Delta\nu\,|\tau| \ll 1$ will not allow us to perform the ν integration as in Eq. 4-48, since now we have the additional term

$$(1 - ikr_1)(1 + ikr_2)\exp\,[ik(r_1 - r_2)]$$

The term $(1 - ikr_1)(1 + ikr_2)$ is not particularly troublesome; the integral changes very little if the product is replaced by

$$(1 - i\bar{k}r_1)(1 + i\bar{k}r_2)$$

The difficulty occurs in the exponential term since the quantity $\exp[i\,\Delta k(r_1 - r_2)]$ may fluctuate wildly (here, $\Delta k = \Delta\nu/c$) unless we restrict the value of the path difference $|r_1 - r_2|$. If we multiply the right-hand side of Eq. 4-50 (under the space integral) by

$$\exp[i\bar{k}(r_1 - r_2)]\exp[-i\bar{k}(r_1 - r_2)]$$

and replace k by $\bar{k}$ in the term $(1 - ikr_1)(1 + ikr_2)$

$$(4\text{-}51)\quad \Gamma(\mathbf{x}_1, \mathbf{x}_2, \tau) = \frac{1}{4\pi^2}\int_S\int_S \exp\left[-2\pi i\bar{\nu}\left(\tau - \frac{(r_1 - r_2)}{c}\right)\right]$$

$$\times \frac{\cos\theta_1\cos\theta_2}{r_1^2 r_2^2}\,d\mathbf{x}_{1S}\,d\mathbf{x}_{2S}(1 - i\bar{k}r_1)(1 + i\bar{k}r_2)$$

$$\times \left[\int_0^\infty \hat{\Gamma}(\mathbf{x}_{1S}, \mathbf{x}_{2S}, \nu)\exp\left\{-2\pi i(\nu - \bar{\nu})\left[\tau - \frac{(r_1 - r_2)}{c}\right]\right\}d\nu\right]$$

In order to simplify this expression we demand the condition $\Delta\nu\,|\tau - (r_1 - r_2)/c| \ll 1$. Referring to Fig. 4-6 (taking $\mathbf{x}_1{}'$ and $\mathbf{x}_2{}'$ to lie in the plane $z = 0$) we see that when $\tau = 0$ this condition, $\Delta\nu\,|(r_1 - r_2)/c| \ll 1$, requires that all path length differences arising in the radiation problem must be kept small. When $\tau \neq 0$, we may use the somewhat weaker condition $\Delta\nu\,|\tau - (r_1 - r_2)/c| \ll 1$ wherein if the signs are correct a τ variation may be used to compensate for some physical path difference.

In this chapter whenever the quasi-monochromatic approximation is used we shall assume that a condition like $\Delta\nu\,|\tau - (r_1 - r_2)/c| \ll 1$ is fulfilled and hence Eq. 4-51 may be written

$$(4\text{-}52)\quad \Gamma(\mathbf{x}_1, \mathbf{x}_2, \tau) = \frac{1}{4\pi^2}\int_S\int_S \exp\left\{-2\pi i\bar{\nu}\left[\tau - \frac{r_1 - r_2}{c}\right]\right\}\frac{\cos\theta_1\cos\theta_2}{r_1^2}\frac{}{r_2^2}$$

$$\times (1 - i\bar{k}r_1)(1 + i\bar{k}r_2)\Gamma(\mathbf{x}_{1S}, \mathbf{x}_{2S}, 0)\,d\mathbf{x}_{1S}\,d\mathbf{x}_{2S}$$

4.3.3. Nature of the Source

Equation 4-52 is still not too amenable to solution in its present form. If necessary, this equation can be handled by a computer, but for our purposes here it is desirable to obtain an analytic solution. To do this we make two further assumptions. We shall first assume that the source is incoherent and we observe the radiation from the source some distance away from it. In the introduction we discussed the nature of an incoherent source. We stated there that an incoherent source could often be represented by the analytical form

$$(4\text{-}53) \qquad \Gamma(\mathbf{x}_{1S}, \mathbf{x}_{2S}, 0) = \delta(\mathbf{x}_{1S} - \mathbf{x}_{2S}) I(\mathbf{x}_{1S})$$

This form implied an infinite intensity over the surface but since it appeared only under integrals, it offered no difficulty and gave the same results as a more complete analysis. Thus we shall assume that the source may be represented by a mutual coherence function of the form given in Eq. 4-53. Substituting Eq. 4-53 into Eq. 4-52, we find that the $\mathbf{x}_{2S}$ integration may be performed and we have

$$(4\text{-}54) \quad \Gamma(\mathbf{x}_1, \mathbf{x}_2, \tau) = \frac{1}{4\pi^2} \int_S I(\mathbf{x}_{1S}) \exp\left\{-2\pi i\bar{\nu}\left[\tau - \frac{(r_1 - r_2)}{c}\right]\right\}$$

$$\times \frac{\cos\theta_1}{r_1{}^2} \frac{\cos\theta_2}{r_2{}^2} (1 - i\bar{k}r_1)(1 + i\bar{k}r_2) \, d\mathbf{x}_{1S}$$

where now $\mathbf{x}_{2S}$ is replaced by $\mathbf{x}_{1S}$ in the definition of r_2.
We now turn to the far-field approximation.

4.3.4. Far-Field Approximation

The integral given by Eq. 4-54 depends only upon the geometry now and it may be considerably simplified if we assume that the radiation is observed far from the source. The phrase "far from the source" implies immediately that $r_j/\bar{\lambda} \gg 1$ and hence the product

$$(1 - i\bar{k}r_1)(1 + i\bar{k}r_2)$$

may be replaced by $\bar{k}^2 r_1 r_2$. Thus

$$(4\text{-}55) \quad \Gamma(\mathbf{x}_1, \mathbf{x}_2, \tau) = \frac{\bar{k}^2}{4\pi^2} e^{-2\pi i \bar{\nu} \tau} \int_S I(\mathbf{x}_{1S})$$

$$\times \{ \exp [i(r_1 - r_2)\bar{k}] \} \frac{\cos \theta_1 \cos \theta_2}{r_1 r_2} \, d\mathbf{x}_{1S}$$

By the term "far field," however, we demand here also that $R_j/d \gg 1$ where d is a characteristic source size and R_j is a characteristic dimension from the source to the measuring points $\mathbf{x}_j$.* This condition coupled with conditions for the validity of the scalar approximation

$$\frac{x_1 - x_2}{R_1} \ll 1, \qquad \frac{y_1 - y_2}{R_1} \ll 1, \qquad \frac{\sqrt{x_1^2 + y_1^2}}{R_1} \ll 1,$$

allow us to simplify Eq. 4-55 further.

Taking $z_1 = z_2 = z$, for convenience, we may expand the difference of the functions

$$r_1 = \sqrt{(x_1 - x_{1S})^2 + (y_1 - y_{1S})^2 + z^2}$$

$$r_2 = \sqrt{(x_2 - x_{1S})^2 + (y_2 - y_{1S})^2 + z^2}$$

in the following form

$$r_1 - r_2 \approx R_1 - R_2 - \frac{x_{1S}(x_1 - x_2)}{R_1} - \frac{y_{1S}(y_1 - y_2)}{R_1}$$

where

$$R_j = \sqrt{x_j^2 + y_j^2 + z^2}$$

Higher-order terms may be neglected in the exponential term since when multiplied by $2\pi\bar{k}$ it may be shown that the order of magnitude of these terms is much less than one for those regions in which $\Gamma(\mathbf{x}_1, \mathbf{x}_2, \tau)$ is significant.† The term $(\cos \theta_1 \cos \theta_2)/r_1 r_2$ may be replaced by simply z^2/R_1^4 since for this term the approximation

* Note that we will not demand here the usual far field assumption $R/\bar{k}d^2 \gg 1$.
† The argument is one of consistency. The terms are assumed negligible, and inspection of the solution shows that the solution is consistent with this assumption.

$r_1 = r_2 = R_1 = R_2$ is adequate. Equation 4-55 becomes finally then

$$(4\text{-}56) \quad \Gamma(\mathbf{x}_1, \mathbf{x}_2, \tau) = \frac{\bar{k}^2}{4\pi^2 R_1^{\,4}} \exp\left\{-2\pi i \bar{\nu}\left[\tau - \frac{(R_1 - R_2)}{c}\right]\right\} \int_S I(\mathbf{x}_{1S})$$

$$\times \exp\left[-\frac{ik}{R_1}(x_{1S}x_{12} + y_{1S}y_{12})\right] d\mathbf{x}_{1S}$$

where

$$x_{12} \equiv x_1 - x_2$$

$$y_{12} \equiv y_1 - y_2$$

Equation 4-56 is the final form we were seeking. The integral may be easily evaluated for a number of source shapes and intensity distributions. In the next section we consider two examples.

4.3.5. Results for Various Source Shapes

We first evaluate this integral for a circular area of radius a with constant intensity $\bar{I}$. In this case it is convenient to transform to a set of polar coordinates r_S, ϕ, defined by the relations,

$$x_{1S} = r_S \cos\phi$$

$$y_{1S} = r_S \sin\phi$$

The integral over $d\mathbf{x}_{1S}$, denoted by Q, then may be written

$$Q = \int_0^{2\pi} \int_0^a \bar{I}\, d\phi\, dr_S r_S \exp\left[-i\frac{\bar{k}}{R_1}(r_S \cos\phi x_{12} + r_S \sin\phi y_{12})\right]$$

The integral over ϕ may be expressed in terms of a known function since it is one of the forms of the zero-order Bessel function. Thus we have

$$Q = 2\pi\bar{I} \int_0^a r_S\, dr_S J_0\left(\frac{\bar{k}}{R_1} r_{12} r_S\right)$$

$$r_{12} = \sqrt{x_{12}^{\,2} + y_{12}^{\,2}}$$

The integral over r_S then yields

$$Q = 2\pi a^2 I \frac{J_1[(\bar{k}/R_1)r_{12}a]}{(\bar{k}/R_1)r_{12}a}$$

and the final expression for $\Gamma(\mathbf{x}_1, \mathbf{x}_2, \tau)$ is

$$(4\text{-}57) \quad \Gamma(\mathbf{x}_1, \mathbf{x}_2, \tau) = \frac{I}{2\pi} \frac{\bar{k}^2 a^2}{R_1^4} \frac{J_1[(k/R_1)r_{12}a]}{(\bar{k}/R_1)r_{12}a}$$

$$\times \exp\left[-2\pi i\nu\left(\tau - \frac{(R_1 - R_2)}{c} \right) \right]$$

Equation 4-56 may be used to derive the result that the visibility of fringes resulting from the interference of two incoherent point sources goes to zero when

$$\theta = \frac{\bar{\lambda}}{2d_0}$$

This result was obtained by very physical arguments in the introductory section. In order to obtain similar results here we let

$$(4\text{-}58) \quad I(\mathbf{x}_{1S}) = \bar{I}\delta\left(\mathbf{x}_{1S} - \frac{a}{2} \right) \delta(y_{1S}) + \bar{I}\delta\left(x_{1S} + \frac{a}{2} \right) \delta(y_{1S})$$

This expression states that radiation comes from two points of the radiating surface placed on the x axis at $x = \pm a/2$.

Substituting Eq. 4-58 into Eq. 4-56 we find

$$(4\text{-}59) \quad \Gamma(\mathbf{x}_1, \mathbf{x}_2, \tau) = \frac{\bar{k}^2}{4\pi^2 R_1^4} \exp\left[-2\pi i\bar{\nu}\left(\tau - \frac{(R_1 - R_2)}{c} \right) \right]$$

$$\times \left\{ \exp\left[-\frac{i\bar{k}}{R_1} \frac{a}{2} x_{12} \right] + \exp\left[\frac{i\bar{k}}{R_1} \frac{a}{2} x_{12} \right] \right\}$$

$$= \frac{2\bar{k}^2}{4\pi^2 R_1^4} \exp\left[-2\pi i\bar{\nu}\left(\tau - \frac{(R_1 - R_2)}{c} \right) \right] \cos \frac{\bar{k}}{R_1} \frac{a}{2} x_{12}$$

From Eq. 4-59 we find for $|\gamma_{12}(\tau)|$

$$(4\text{-}60) \qquad\qquad |\gamma_{12}(\tau)| = \cos \frac{\bar{k}a x_{12}}{2R_1}$$

The angular diameter θ is defined in this case to be $\theta = a/R_1$. Hence

$$|\gamma_{12}(\tau)| = 0$$

when

$$\frac{\bar{k}\theta x_{12}}{2} = \frac{2\pi}{\bar{\lambda}}\frac{\theta x_{12}}{2} = \frac{\pi}{2}$$

or

(4-61)
$$\theta = \frac{\bar{\lambda}}{2x_{12}}$$

If we know that a source shape is circular and that the intensity distribution is a constant, we may use similar arguments to determine the source radius by making coherence measurements in the far field. For the circular source, Eq. 4-57 shows

(4-62)
$$|\gamma_{12}(\tau)| = \frac{J_1[(\bar{k}/R_1)r_{12}a]}{(\bar{k}/R_1)r_{12}a}$$

We determine the source size by noting when $|\gamma_{12}(\tau)| = 0$. This occurs for a first-order Bessel function when

$$\frac{\bar{k}}{R_1}r_{12}a = 3.83$$

Defining the angular diameter of the circular source θ_c as $\theta_c = 2a/R_1$ this yields

(4-63)
$$\theta_c = \frac{1.22\bar{\lambda}}{r_{12}}$$

It is interesting to note that if $\theta = \theta_c$, then Eqs. 4-61 and 4-63 show that $r_{12} = 2.44x_{12}$. That is, the point at which the coherence goes to zero is over two times as great for a circular source as for two-point sources. This is reasonable since the circular source weights the small diameter central regions of the source more heavily than the two-point source configuration which gives no weight to the central region.

Lastly, suppose that $I(\mathbf{x}_{1S})$ is of arbitrary shape but falls effectively to zero in distances such that the far-field approximation may be used.

The surface integral in Eq. 4-56 may then be written

$$\int\limits_{-\infty}^{\infty}\int dx_{1S}\, dy_{1S} I(\mathbf{x}_{1S}) \exp - \left[\frac{i\bar{k}}{R_1} x_{12}\right] x_{1S} - \left[\frac{i\bar{k}}{R_1} y_{12}\right] y_{1S}$$

and we see that this integral is the Fourier transform of $I(\mathbf{x}_{1S})$ in terms of the transform variables $(\bar{k}/R_1)x_{12}$ and $(\bar{k}/R_1)y_{12}$. Treating the term

$$\frac{\bar{k}^2}{4\pi^2 R_1{}^2} \exp\left[-2\pi i\bar{\nu}\left(\tau - \frac{R_1 - R_2}{c}\right)\right]$$

as a known function, $I(\mathbf{x}_{1S})$ may be determined from the measurement of $\Gamma(\mathbf{x}_1, \mathbf{x}_2, \tau)$ by calculating the inverse transform. Thus we have for fixed $\mathbf{x}_1$

$$(4\text{-}64) \quad I(x_{1S}, y_{1S}) = \frac{1}{4\pi^2} \int\limits_{-\infty}^{\infty}\int \frac{4\pi^2 R_1{}^4}{\bar{k}^2}$$

$$\times \exp\left[2\pi i\bar{\nu}\left(\tau - \frac{(R_1 - R_2)}{c}\right)\right] \Gamma(\mathbf{x}_{12}, \mathbf{y}_{12}, \tau)$$

$$\times \exp\left\{i\left(x_{1S}\left[\frac{\bar{k}x_{12}}{R_1}\right] + y_{1S}\left[\frac{\bar{k}y_{12}}{R_1}\right]\right)\right\} d\left[\frac{\bar{k}x_{12}}{R_1}\right] d\left[\frac{\bar{k}y_{12}}{R_1}\right]$$

This Fourier-transform relationship between $I(\mathbf{x}_{1S})$ and $\Gamma(\mathbf{x}_{12}, \mathbf{y}_{12}, \tau)$ is known as one form of the van Cittert-Zernike theorem.

Although in principle it is possible to determine $I(\mathbf{x}_{1S})$ from the measurement of $\Gamma(\mathbf{x}_1, \mathbf{x}_2, \tau)$ under the assumptions cited in the foregoing in practice, however, it is very difficult and measurements are usually confined to measuring the first zero of $\Gamma(\mathbf{x}_1, \mathbf{x}_2, \tau)$. In the next section we shall show how Eq. 4-63 may be used to measure the diameter of visible stars that are not resolvable by telescopes that are presently available.

4.3.6. Measurement of Visible Star Diameters

The measurement of visible star diameters by interferometric techniques is accomplished by assuming the star is a sphere but then, in order to use the previously developed theory, making some additional assumption to determine the intensity across an osculating disk. Let us refer to Fig. 4-7. In the two-dimensional figure the star is represented by a circle of radius a. The osculating circular disk is represented by the line AB. We wish to determine the intensity across the disk by making some assumption about the radiation leaving the sphere's surface. If the intensity distribution over the disk AB is known, then Eq. 4-63 may be used to find the disk diameter by measuring the first

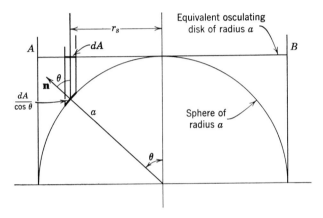

Fig. 4-7. Equivalent disk used in determining radiation from a spherical object (see Beran and Parrent, 1964, *Theory of Partial Coherence*, Prentice-Hall, Engelwood Cliffs, Fig. 5-2, p. 76).

zero of $|\Gamma(\mathbf{x}_1, \mathbf{x}_2, 0)|$. The validity of the scalar approximation and indeed the whole formulation we have given in the past few sections demands that we consider radiation passing through AB in the direction $\theta \approx 0$. This means that we must know the radiation intensity as a function of local angle to the normal $\mathbf{n}$, leaving any portion of the sphere. The radiation reaching our measuring instruments ($\theta = 0$) from an element of surface area an angle θ from the z axis must leave the surface element at an angle θ to the local normal. The distribution of radiation about $\mathbf{n}$ is not known in detail for a star and is indeed dependent upon frequency. Often, however, the radiation is assumed to be Lambertian; that is, $I(\theta) = I \cos \theta$. For this case, the radiation leaving the disk AB is seen to uniform over AB. We have

$$I \cos \theta (dA/\cos \theta) = I \, dA$$

If the intensity is uniform across the disk AB, $|\gamma_{12}(0)|$ is given by Eq. 4-62 (for filtered light)

$$(4\text{-}62) \qquad |\gamma_{12}0)| = \frac{J_1[(\bar{k}/R_1)r_{12}a]}{(\bar{k}/R_1)r_{12}a}$$

and hence we have for the angular diameter of the star θ

$$(4\text{-}63) \qquad \theta = \frac{1.22\bar{\lambda}}{r_{12}}$$

where r_{12} is the distance for which the coherence falls to zero.

Using this formula Michelson and Peace (1921) found that for α Orion's, $\theta = 0.055$ sec. It should be noted however that if we had taken $I(\alpha) = I\cos^2\theta$ we should have found

$$\theta = \frac{1.4\lambda}{r_{12}}$$

giving about a 17% error.

We note that since up to the present time only $|\gamma_{12}(0)|$ has been measured, it is not too critical to align the base line or the collecting apertures. Any small tilting of the base line simply shifts the center of the fringe pattern. If we wished to determine $\Gamma(\mathbf{x}_1, \mathbf{x}_2, 0)$, a much more stringent set of conditions would be necessary.

The question of the effect of turbulence on star measurements has always been difficult to answer and is presently under study. We believe, however, that the crude picture given at the end of Section 4.1 gives a proper criterion for determining when turbulence is important in measurement of $|\gamma_{12}(0)|$. This discussion does not apply to the measurement of $\Gamma(\mathbf{x}_1, \mathbf{x}_2, 0)$.

4.4. Coherence of Blackbody Radiation

The formulation that we have set up is convenient for calculating $\mathscr{E}_{ij}(\mathbf{x}_1, \mathbf{x}_2, \tau)$ for blackbody radiation. For the blackbody case we assume that the radiation statistics are homogeneous and isotropic. Beyond this the only information that we require is the frequency spectrum $\mathscr{E}_{ii}(\mathbf{x}_1, \mathbf{x}_1, \nu)$ determined from the Planck distribution. We follow a development given by Bourret (1960). Similar calculations were made prior to this date, however, and these references may be found in Landau and Lifshitz (1960) in Chapter XIII.

The equation governing $\mathscr{E}_{ij}(\mathbf{x}_1, \mathbf{x}_2, \tau)$ are given by Eq. 4-32

(4-32)
$$\nabla_1^2 \mathscr{E}_{ij}(\mathbf{x}_1, \mathbf{x}_2, \tau) = \frac{1}{c^2} \frac{\partial^2}{\partial \tau^2} \mathscr{E}_{ij}(\mathbf{x}_1, \mathbf{x}_2, \tau)$$

$$\frac{\partial}{\partial x_{1i}} \mathscr{E}_{ij}(\mathbf{x}_1, \mathbf{x}_2, \tau) = 0$$

Since the equations are homogeneous $\mathscr{E}_{ij}(\mathbf{x}_1, \mathbf{x}_2, \tau)$ is a function only of $\mathbf{x}_1 - \mathbf{x}_2 = \mathbf{r}$ and τ. Thus we have

(4-65a)
$$\nabla^2 \mathscr{E}_{ij}(\mathbf{r}, \tau) = \frac{1}{c^2} \frac{\partial^2}{\partial \tau^2} \mathscr{E}_{ij}(\mathbf{r}, \tau)$$

(4-65b)
$$\frac{\partial}{\partial r_i} \mathscr{E}_{ij}(\mathbf{r}, \tau) = 0$$

where $\mathbf{r} = (x, y, z)$.

The isotropy condition on $\mathscr{E}_{ij}$ may be introduced most conveniently by first noting that the solution of Eq. 4-65a may be written in the form

(4-66)
$$\mathscr{E}_{ij}(\mathbf{r}, \tau) = \int\!\!\!\int\!\!\!\int_{-\infty}^{\infty} \exp\left[i(\mathbf{k} \cdot \mathbf{r} - ck\tau)\right] f_{ij}(\mathbf{k}) \, dk_1 \, dk_2 \, dk_3$$

$(k = |\mathbf{k}|)$.

Direct substitution of $f_{ij}(\mathbf{k}) \exp i(\mathbf{k} \cdot \mathbf{r} - ck\tau)$ into Eq. 4-65a shows that this expression is indeed a solution and the linearity of the equation allows us to integrate over all values of $\mathbf{k}$.

Since the radiation is isotropic, $f_{ij}(\mathbf{k})$ must be an isotropic tensor. The form of the isotropic tensor is given in Batchelor (1953). (See also Chapter 7.) He shows that $f_{ij}(\mathbf{k})$ has the form

(4-67)
$$f_{ij}(\mathbf{k}) = A'(k) k_i k_j + B(k) \delta_{ij}$$

The divergence condition given by Eq. 4-65b serves to introduce a relationship between $A'(k)$ and $B(k)$. Equation 4-65b yields for $f_{ij}(\mathbf{k})$ the condition

$$k_i f_{ij}(\mathbf{k}) = 0$$

which requires that

$$B(k) = -k^2 A'(k)$$

Thus finally we find

(4-68) $f_{ij} = A(k)(k^2\delta_{ij} - k_i k_j)$

where $A(k) = -A'(k)$. The expression for $\mathscr{E}_{ij}(\mathbf{r}, \tau)$ is now

(4-69)

$$\mathscr{E}_{ij}(\mathbf{r}, \tau) = \int\!\!\!\int\!\!\!\int_{-\infty}^{\infty} \exp\left[i(\mathbf{k} \cdot \mathbf{r} - ck\tau)\right]A(k)(k^2\delta_{ij} - k_i k_j)\, dk_1\, dk_2\, dk_3$$

In order to determine $A(k)$ we require a knowledge of Planck's distribution. To put this in appropriate form we consider

(4-70) $\mathscr{E}_{ij}(0, \tau) = \int\!\!\!\int\!\!\!\int_{-\infty}^{\infty} \exp\left[-ick\tau\right]A(k)(k^2\delta_{ij} - k_i k_j)\, dk_1\, dk_2\, dk_3$

in terms of spherical coordinates

$$k_1 = k \sin\phi \sin\theta$$
$$k_2 = k \cos\phi \sin\theta$$
$$k_3 = k \cos\theta$$

Integration then yields

(4-71) $\mathscr{E}_{ij}(0, \tau) = \dfrac{8\pi}{3}\delta_{ij}\displaystyle\int_0^{\infty} k^4 A(k) e^{-ick\tau}\, dk$

Now for blackbody radiation the energy density U has the form

(4-72) $U = \dfrac{\hbar c}{\pi^2}\displaystyle\int_0^{\infty} \dfrac{k^3\, dk}{e^{\alpha k} - 1}$

where $\alpha = \hbar c/KT$, $h = 2\pi\hbar$ is Planck's constant, and K is Boltzmann's constant. We also note that here

(4-73) $U = \dfrac{1}{8\pi}\, \text{Trace}\, \mathscr{E}_{ij}(0, 0)$

[A factor of $\frac{1}{2}$ is introduced by the complex notation but this is cancelled by noting that Trace $\mathscr{E}_{ij}(0, 0) = $ Trace $\mathscr{H}_{ij}(0, 0)$.] The use of Eqs.

4-71, 4-72, and 4-73 show that

$$A(k) = \frac{1}{\pi^2} \frac{\hbar c}{k} \frac{1}{e^{\alpha k} - 1}$$

and finally

(4-74) $\mathcal{E}_{ij}(\mathbf{r}, \tau)$

$$= \beta \iiint\limits_{-\infty}^{\infty} \exp\left[i(\mathbf{k} \cdot \mathbf{r} - ck\tau)\right]\left(k\delta_{ij} - \frac{k_i k_j}{k}\right)[1/(e^{\alpha k} - 1)] \, dk_1 \, dk_2 \, dk_3$$

(where β is a constant).

Equation 4-74 may be evaluated for arbitrary $\mathbf{r}$ and τ. (See Beran and Parrent, 1964, Chapter 11, for a fuller discussion.) Here, however, we will set down the solution for $\mathcal{E}_{ij}(\mathbf{r}, 0)$ in the case when the components i and j lie along $\mathbf{r}$. This is called the longitudinal coherence function and is denoted $\mathcal{E}_{33}^{\text{long}}(\mathbf{r}, 0)$ if $\mathbf{r}$ is taken along the z (or 3) axis. The result of integrating Eq. 4-74 is

(4-75) $\text{Re } \mathcal{E}_{33}^{\text{long}}(\mathbf{r}, 0) = \frac{4\hbar c}{\alpha} \frac{1}{r^3}\left(1 - r\frac{\partial}{\partial r}\right)\left[\text{cotgh}\,(\pi r/\alpha) - \frac{1}{(r\pi/\alpha)}\right]$

The interesting thing about this solution is that $\mathcal{E}_{33}^{\text{long}}(\mathbf{r}, 0)$ goes to zero when r is of the order of a few mean wavelengths. (By the mean wavelength we mean here the average wavelength for the blackbody distribution at a particular temperature.) This is the condition we require for an incoherent source.

The higher-order moments have not yet been calculated in this classical manner although it can be shown that the gaussian functional is *a* solution to the functional equations governing blackbody radiation. Using quantum field theory, however, Glauber (1964) has shown that the gaussian solution is *the* solution to the problem and hence Eq. 4-74 is all the further information we require for the statistical description of blackbody radiation.

4.5. Final Remarks

The theory of partial coherence as presented in this chapter is representative of the simplest form of statistical theory since there is no indeterminacy in the statistical moment equations. In addition, the functional solution is available and could be used to obtain complete statistical information external to the source if it were given over the source surface.

If the radiation is not propagating in free space but rather in a medium with a random $\epsilon(\mathbf{x})$ field, the character of the problem is changed radically. Then the statistical moment equations are indeterminate and some approximation procedure is necessary to obtain a useful solution. The problem of propagation of radiation through a turbulent atmosphere has been treated from a coherence point of view by assuming the variation about $\epsilon(\mathbf{x})$ is small and by using perturbation theory. The techniques are similar to those to be presented in the next chapter but it would carry us too far afield to present the details here. The reader is referred to Beran (1966) for a treatment of this problem. A statistical treatment of this problem from a different point of view is given by Furutsu (1963).

CHAPTER 5

Theory of Heterogeneous Materials

5.1. Introduction

We shall now consider heterogeneous materials that may be conveniently treated from a statistical point of view. We shall specifically discuss the elastic and electrical properties of these materials. By heterogeneous materials we mean here materials in which the macroscopic electric or elastic properties vary from point to point within a material sample. We shall restrict ourselves to cases in which this variation is independent of time.

In a sense, all samples of materials are heterogeneous if we make fine enough measurements. The principal practical application of this chapter, however, is intended for materials in which the variation of material properties is an obvious macroscopic property of the material. We will not consider variations resulting from atomic effects.* For example, we consider here inclusions of one material in another, multiphase material mixtures and polycrystals. In all these cases the composition of these materials may have either an ordered or a random character, but we consider here only the latter case.

5.1.1. Effective Constants

In the introductory chapters of this book we stressed what is meant by a proper description of a continuum problem that has statistical aspects. Although heterogeneous materials were later conveniently described from a statistical point of view, most early investigations were concerned with determining effective constants of such media. A discussion of these constants provides, perhaps, the best physical introduction to the theory of heterogeneous materials.

---

* For a discussion of atomic effects we refer the reader to Burgess, Ed., *Fluctuation Phenomena in Solids* (1965).

The concept of effective constants is superficially quite intuitive, but under deeper analysis many subtleties appear. On the surface the problem is simply to take a sample of a material within which some material constant varies with position and determine the overall constant of the sample in the same manner that we would if the constant were independent of position within the sample. For example, we consider the problem of determining the Young's modulus E of a material sample.

If Young's modulus is independent of position, we determine it by subjecting a material sample of length l and cross-sectional area A to a tensile force F. We measure the change in length Δl and determine E from the formula

(5-1) $$E = \frac{F/A}{\Delta l/l}$$

If Young's modulus is dependent upon position, we may determine an effective constant E^* in exactly the same manner. We again chose a sample of length l and cross-sectional area A and determine E^* from the equation†

(5-2) $$E^* = \frac{F/A}{\Delta l^*/l}$$

where Δl^* is the change in length of this heterogeneous sample. (We note that E^* determined in this manner will not in general equal $\bar{E}$ where $\bar{E}$ is the volume average value of E in the sample.)

Now having determined E^* in this manner, we hope it will have applicability beyond the confines of this particular experiment. We would certainly hope that E^* would not depend upon the values of A and l that we chose as our sample size. If we cut the sample in four equal parts we would hope that if experiments were made on each sample individually that the value of E^* obtained would be the same in all four samples. It is possible however that this would not be so. In making tests on heterogeneous materials to determine effective constants of general applicability the assumption must always implicitly be made that the samples are in some sense "homogeneous."

† See Section 3.3 for a remark on the connection between this type of definition and an energy-type definition. This point will also be discussed later in this chapter (Secs. 5.1.4, 5.3).

By "homogeneous" in the sense used above we mean *statistically homogeneous*. Further, we mean *statistically homogeneous* in a volume-averaged sense, not in an ensemble-averaged sense. What is meant is twofold. First, all characteristic lengths that appear in a problem of a material under stress must be large compared to a distance, for example, d_M, within which the modulus E undergoes considerable variation about its mean value. Second, loosely speaking, the character of the variations in a volume element of size d_M^3 in one part of the sample must be of the same sort as the variations in another part of the sample. The latter condition is usually met if the sample is uniformly mixed when it is manufactured but if care is not taken gravitational effects, for example, can sometimes introduce nonuniformities.

In the test cited above we would demand that l and $A^{1/2}$ be much larger than d_M. If we wish to use the results obtained here on samples one fourth the size, then

$$\frac{A^{1/2}}{4} \gg d_M, \qquad l/4 \gg d_M$$

It is easy to see the difficulty that would arise if $A^{1/2}$ and l were much less than d_M. In one sample E could then be a constant E_1; in another, a constant E_2; in another, perhaps vary linearly between the values E_3 and E_4; and so on. There would be no chance for the variations of E to average out within a single sample and every sample would yield a different value for E^*.

The effective constants determined by the above experiment are also expected to have validity in materials subjected to nonconstant external forces. In this case we must meet the condition that the average stress does not change appreciably over distances large compared to d_M. For the effective constant E^*, determined in the above manner, to be meaningful within a material, the average stress must encounter the same material conditions that were encountered during the determination of E^*. In other words, the stress must be essentially constant in distances over which significant variations of E occur.

In most practical cases the conditions given above are easily realized and the experimenter knows intuitively that if he is using a mixture it must be well mixed within a sample. Unless one is especially aware of this problem, however, there is a tendency to forget that the above conditions may easily be violated in regions of very strong stress concentration. If the above conditions are violated, then one cannot consider a heterogeneous material by simply replacing E by E^* whenever Young's modulus occurs in the theory of homogeneous materials. In these cases the concept of an effective constant breaks down.

Although we did not wish to complicate the above discussion by stating further conditions it is also necessary in most instances that the sample be statistically isotropic. It should not matter on which faces of the sample we apply forces to measure E^* provided only that all dimensions are large compared to d_M. If the orientation of the sample was important, the concept of an effective constant would be severely limited.

In the classical theory of elasticity we assume the following relation between stress and strain for a homogeneous isotropic elastic body.

(5-3) $$\tau_{ij} = \lambda e_{ll}\delta_{ij} + 2\mu e_{ij}$$

where τ_{ij} is the stress tensor, e_{ij} is the strain tensor, μ is the shear modulus and λ is related to the bulk modulus k, by the relation $k = \lambda + 2/3\mu$. We also have

$$E = \frac{\mu(3\lambda + 2\mu)}{\lambda + \mu}$$

The constants λ and μ may be determined by finding E in the method outlined above and perhaps finding μ in a torsion experiment.

If all characteristic lengths appearing in consideration of the problem of a heterogeneous material under stress are large compared to d_M and the orientation of the sample is unimportant, the assumption is usually made that

(5-4) $$\langle \tau_{ij} \rangle = \lambda^* \langle e_{ll} \rangle \delta_{ij} + 2\mu^* \langle e_{ij} \rangle$$

Here $\langle \tau_{ij} \rangle$ and $\langle e_{ij} \rangle$ denote the stress and strain averaged over a local volume large compared to d_M.† λ^* and μ^* are the effective elastic constants determined by experiments identical to those used in the analysis of homogeneous materials. In experiments such as these the characteristic sample lengths are large compared to d_M. We remember that two types of characteristic lengths enter the problem. We must consider characteristic lengths associated with the size of the

† In this chapter the angular brackets denote a local volume average. The reader is cautioned not to confuse this notation with the use of angular brackets in the previous chapter where they denoted a time average.

medium under study and we must consider characteristic lengths associated with distances over which the stress and strain field vary appreciably. If either characteristic length of the problem is less than d_M there is no basis for postulating an equation like Eq. 5-4.

We note again that the constants λ^* and μ^* are not equal to $\langle\lambda\rangle$ and $\langle\mu\rangle$, respectively. This may be seen by writing

(5-5)
$$\lambda(\mathbf{x}) = \langle\lambda(\mathbf{x})\rangle + \lambda'(\mathbf{x})$$
$$\mu(\mathbf{x}) = \langle\mu(\mathbf{x})\rangle + \mu'(\mathbf{x})$$
$$e_{ij}(\mathbf{x}) = \langle e_{ij}(\mathbf{x})\rangle + e_{ij}'(\mathbf{x})$$
$$\tau_{ij}(\mathbf{x}) = \langle\tau_{ij}(\mathbf{x})\rangle + \tau_{ij}'(\mathbf{x})$$

where $\langle\lambda'(\mathbf{x})\rangle = \langle\mu'(\mathbf{x})\rangle = \langle e_{ij}'(\mathbf{x})\rangle = \langle\tau_{ij}'(\mathbf{x})\rangle = 0$. Again the brackets denote a local volume average.

Substituting the expressions given in Eq. 5-5 into Eq. 5-3 and taking a local volume average, we find

(5-6) $\langle\tau_{ij}\rangle = \bar{\lambda}\langle e_{ll}\rangle\delta_{ij} + \langle\lambda'e_{ll}'\rangle\delta_{ij} + 2\mu\langle e_{ij}\rangle + 2\langle\mu e_{ij}'\rangle$

In general the terms $\langle\lambda'e_{ll}'\rangle$ and $\langle\mu'e_{ij}'\rangle$ are not zero and hence to make Eqs. 5-4 and 5-6 compatible, λ^* and μ^* cannot be equal to $\langle\lambda\rangle$ and $\langle\mu\rangle$, respectively. The relationship that does exist between λ^* and μ^* and $\langle\lambda\rangle$, $\langle\mu\rangle$, $\langle\lambda'e_{ll}'\rangle$ and $\langle\mu'e_{ij}'\rangle$ requires discussion of a mathematical nature and we shall defer this point until later in the chapter. In this introduction we need to note only the fact that some relationship does exist.

As a last remark we note that in this chapter we shall only consider effective constants for heterogeneous materials that are statistically homogeneous and isotropic. We shall not consider here what must be done to treat materials that do not satisfy this condition. (If, however, the material properties vary "slowly" with position, then it is possible to define local effective constants $\langle\lambda\rangle$ and $\langle\mu\rangle$ that vary with position.) In the statistical analyses that follow, we shall sometimes treat aspects of the statistically nonhomogeneous problem which need not be discussed in terms of effective constants.

5.1.2. Use of Volume Fractions in Determining Effective Constants

When attempting to determine constants like E^*, λ^*, and μ^* for an inclusion of one material within another or a mixture of two materials, the most easily measurable quantity is the volume fraction of each material. It is thus most natural to attempt to find E^*, λ^*, and μ^* in terms of volume fractions.

Unfortunately these constants are not determined by the volume fractions alone but depend upon the geometry associated with the material mixture. To see this intuitively consider the following limiting cases given in Fig. 5-1.

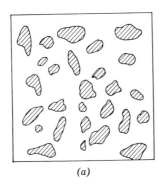   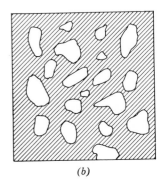

(a)   (b)

Fig. 5-1. Limiting types of inclusions. a. Young's modulus of inclusion E_1. Young's modulus of matrix E_2. $E_1 \gg E_2$. b. Young's modulus of inclusion E_2. Young's modulus of matrix E_1. $E_1 \gg E_2$.

We suppose that the sample in Fig. 5-1a is composed of a matrix material with Young's modulus E_2 and an inclusion with Young's modulus E_1, where $E_1 \gg E_2$. We think of the matrix as being composed of a soft material like lead and the inclusion as being composed of a hard material like steel. The sample size is taken to be very large compared to a characteristic inclusion size or average distance between inclusions. The inclusions are spread randomly throughout the sample and the sample is constructed so that it appears the same when viewed from any angle. In statistical language the sample is statistically homogeneous and isotropic. The second sample has similar properties except that in this case the matrix material has the Young's modulus E_1 and the inclusion the Young's modulus E_2. We choose the volume fractions in both samples to be 50% matrix and 50% inclusion.

We now wish to determine E^* for both samples by using the simple tension experiment described above. In the first case, the Young's modulus of the inclusion is much greater than the Young's modulus of the matrix. We may think of steel pellets in a lead matrix. Under tension the steel will provide resistance to elongation but since the matrix provides continuous paths of lead from one face of the sample to the other, the lead will "provide" more of the resistance to elongation. In the second case, the Young's modulus of the matrix is much greater than the Young's modulus of the inclusion. We expect here that the resistance that the sample gives to elongation will again be governed principally by the matrix. In this case the steel will "provide" more of the resistance to elongation.

The reader should note that the above statements are meant to appeal to only intuition and in no sense provide proof. If the reader does not find the above statements convincing, he might consider for a moment a steel–rubber combination rather than a steel–lead combination.

In the above samples the volume fractions of lead and steel were the same in each case. Since E^* will be different in the two cases we conclude that volume fractions are not sufficient to determine E^* for a mixture. Evidently the specific geometrical arrangement is also important in determining E^*. The effect is certainly not limited to the inclusion–matrix concept. We would expect, for example, that if lead and steel were mixed in equal proportions by volume in such a manner that neither could be considered to be an inclusion in the matrix of the other that a third value of E^* would be obtained.

The possible ways in which two materials may be mixed together in equal volume proportions is countless. To describe the geometrical arrangement when the mixture is random we rely on the concept of correlation functions or, more generally, probability density functions. The volume fraction of material 1 and material 2 may be represented by the following probability density function

$$P_1[E(\mathbf{x})] \, dE(\mathbf{x})$$

defined roughly as the probability that we find the material with Young's modulus E at point $\mathbf{x}$. Since $E(\mathbf{x})$ may take on only two values, E_1 and E_2, we may write

$$(5\text{-}7) \qquad P_1[E(\mathbf{x})] = v_1 \delta[E(\mathbf{x}) - E_1] + v_2 \delta[E(\mathbf{x}) - E_2]$$

The Dirac delta function indicates that the probability density function is nonzero only when $E(\mathbf{x})$ is equal to E_1 or E_2. v_1 and v_2 are the volume fractions of material 1 and 2, respectively. The probability that the value of $E(\mathbf{x})$ is E_1 at point $\mathbf{x}$ is obtained by evaluating the integral

$$(5\text{-}8) \qquad\qquad P(E_1) = \int_{E_1 - \Delta E}^{E_2 + \Delta E} P_1[E(\mathbf{x})]\, dE(\mathbf{x})$$

for small values of ΔE; that is, in the neighborhood of E_1. The result is

$$(5\text{-}9) \qquad\qquad P(E_1) = v_1$$

In other words, we have the obvious result that the probability of finding the value E_1 at some point $\mathbf{x}$ is equal to the volume fraction of that material.

To introduce the concept of the probability density function with the attendant delta functions is of course pointless to obtain the result given in Eq. 5-9. The probability density concept is necessary, however, for obtaining more information about the geometrical arrangement of the mixture. More information about the geometrical arrangement is given by the two-point probability density function

$$P_2[E(\mathbf{x}_1), E(\mathbf{x}_2)]\, dE(\mathbf{x}_1)\, dE(\mathbf{x}_2)$$

defined roughly as the probability that the value of E at $\mathbf{x}_1$ is $E(\mathbf{x}_1)$ and the probability of E at $\mathbf{x}_2$ is $E(\mathbf{x}_2)$. The relation between P_1 and P_2 is

$$(5\text{-}10) \quad P_1[E(\mathbf{x}_1)]\, dE(\mathbf{x}_1) = \int_{\substack{\text{all values} \\ \text{of } E(\mathbf{x}_2)}} P_2[E(\mathbf{x}_1), E(\mathbf{x}_2)]\, dE(\mathbf{x}_1)\, dE(\mathbf{x}_2)$$

The probability density function P_2 indicates how quickly the value of E changes with separation $|\mathbf{x}_2 - \mathbf{x}_1|$. From $P_2[E(\mathbf{x}_1), E(\mathbf{x}_2)]$, for example, we can determine the probability that $E(\mathbf{x}_2)$ will have the value E_1 at point $\mathbf{x}_2$ if it has the value E_1 at point $\mathbf{x}_1$. The correlation function $R(\mathbf{x}_1, \mathbf{x}_2)$, defined as

$$(5\text{-}11) \quad R(\mathbf{x}_1, \mathbf{x}_2) = \overline{E(\mathbf{x}_1)E(\mathbf{x}_2)}$$

$$= \iint E(\mathbf{x}_1)E(\mathbf{x}_2)P_2[E(\mathbf{x}_1), E(\mathbf{x}_2)]\, dE(\mathbf{x}_1)\, dE(\mathbf{x}_2)$$

is a measure of this type of relatedness between the value of E at point $\mathbf{x}_1$ and the value of E at point $\mathbf{x}_2$. We also note that since the statistical characteristics of a material sample are taken here to be the same in all parts of the sample and are independent of orientation, $R(\mathbf{x}_1, \mathbf{x}_2)$ depends only upon $|\mathbf{r}|$ where $\mathbf{r} = \mathbf{x}_2 - \mathbf{x}_1$.

Beyond knowing the volume fractions v_1 and v_2 of a mixture of two materials the next piece of information that is commonly sought is a correlation function such as $R(|\mathbf{r}|)$. Of course, the volume fraction and $R(|\mathbf{r}|)$ alone do not completely characterize the geometry and it is easy to imagine that an infinite number of higher-order correlation functions are required for a complete specification of the geometry. In fact, E^* depends upon the volume fractions of materials and all correlation functions describing the geometry of the mixture.† In practice we cannot of course know all the correlation functions describing the geometry but we can hope to measure or predict the lower-order correlation functions upon which E^* often strongly depends.

Having made the foregoing statement, however, we must point out to the reader that most of the work to date on the determination of effective constants has been done solely in terms of volume fractions. This is true from both a measurement and a theoretical point of view. The measurement of correlation functions is very tedious and there is virtually no theory to guide one in predicting correlation functions for a given mixing process. We shall discuss what little has been accomplished later in this chapter.

5.1.3. Electrostatic Effective Constants—Tensor Permittivity

The effective constants that we have discussed above are for elastic media that are locally isotropic; that is, they obey a stress–strain relation like that given in Eq. 5-3. The counterpart of this local isotropy in electrostatic problems is the relation

$$(5\text{-}12) \qquad\qquad \mathbf{D}(\mathbf{x}) = \epsilon(\mathbf{x})\mathbf{E}(\mathbf{x})$$

where $\mathbf{D}(\mathbf{x})$ is the electric displacement, $\mathbf{E}(\mathbf{x})$ is the electric field, and $\epsilon(\mathbf{x})$ is the variable permittivity in the medium. A very important heterogeneous medium that we frequently encounter is the polycrystal. Often the individual crystal is not locally isotropic and Eqs. 5-3 and 5-12 must be replaced by a more general relationship. In this introduction we will briefly consider the generalization of Eq. 5-12 since the mathematics is simpler than in the elastic case that requires two

---

† For exactness we note that E^* depends in general upon the joint moments involving E and another constant like μ, not just on the moments of E alone.

constants. If the reader prefers not to think in electrical terms, he might consider the medium to have a variable heat conductivity wherein Eq. 5-12 is replaced by

$$(5\text{-}13) \qquad \mathbf{q}(\mathbf{x}) = k(\mathbf{x})\nabla T(\mathbf{x})$$

where $\mathbf{q}(\mathbf{x})$ is the heat flux vector, $k(\mathbf{x})$ is the conductivity, and $T(\mathbf{x})$ is the temperature.

If the local properties of the medium are not isotropic, it is often appropriate to replace Eq. 5-12 by the tensor relation

$$(5\text{-}14) \qquad D_i(\mathbf{x}) = \epsilon_{ij}(\mathbf{x})E_j(\mathbf{x})$$

where $\mathbf{D}(\mathbf{x})$ and $\mathbf{E}(\mathbf{x})$ retain their original meanings but the scalar permittivity $\epsilon(\mathbf{x})$ must be replaced by the tensor permittivity $\epsilon_{ij}(\mathbf{x})$. In the isotropic case the electric displacement existed only in the direction of the electric field. Equation 5-14, however, allows the possibility of the displacement field existing in a direction that is different from the electric field. For example, if $E_j(\mathbf{x})$ only has a component in the $j = 3$ direction, $D_i(\mathbf{x})$ has components in all three directions

$$(5\text{-}15) \qquad \begin{aligned} D_1(\mathbf{x}) &= \epsilon_{13}(\mathbf{x})E_3(\mathbf{x}) \\ D_2(\mathbf{x}) &= \epsilon_{23}(\mathbf{x})E_3(\mathbf{x}) \\ D_3(\mathbf{x}) &= \epsilon_{33}(\mathbf{x})E_3(\mathbf{x}) \end{aligned}$$

provided $\epsilon_{i3}(\mathbf{x})$ is not zero for $i = 1, 2, 3$.

Although the local properties of the medium are not isotropic, the macroscopic properties of the medium are expected to be isotropic. In a polycrystal we will assume here that the crystals are oriented at random and thus if we average a quantity over a volume that contains many crystals, we expect the result to be independent of orientation. Exactly as in the case of a medium that is locally isotropic we need define only one effective constant ϵ^*, given by the relation

$$(5\text{-}16) \qquad \langle D_i \rangle = \epsilon^* \langle E_i \rangle$$

Note again that ϵ^* may only be defined if $\overline{E}_i(\mathbf{x})$ is essentially constant over volumes of space that contain many crystals.

If we rewrite Eq. 5-14 using the definitions

$$(5\text{-}17) \qquad \begin{aligned} D_i(\mathbf{x}) &= \langle D_i \rangle + D_i'(\mathbf{x}) \\ E_i(\mathbf{x}) &= \langle E_i \rangle + E_i'(\mathbf{x}) \\ \epsilon_{ij}(\mathbf{x}) &= \langle \epsilon_{ij} \rangle + \epsilon_{ij}'(\mathbf{x}) \end{aligned}$$

we have upon averaging

(5-18) $D_i = \langle \epsilon_{ij} \rangle \langle E_j \rangle + \langle \epsilon_{ij}' E_j' \rangle$

If the crystals in the polycrystal are oriented at random then the off-diagonal terms of $\langle \epsilon_{ij} \rangle$ are zero and we find

(5-19) $\langle \epsilon_{ij} \rangle = \frac{1}{3}(\langle \epsilon_{11} \rangle + \langle \epsilon_{22} \rangle + \langle \epsilon_{33} \rangle)\delta_{ij} = \frac{1}{3}\langle \epsilon_{11} \rangle \delta_{ij}$

On the average $\langle D_i \rangle$ cannot have a component in a direction other than the direction of $\langle E_i \rangle$ since there is no reason to prefer the negative or positive directions for $\langle D_i \rangle$ along any other axis. For example, suppose $\langle E_i \rangle$ was directed along the z axis; i.e., $\langle E_3 \rangle \neq 0$, $\langle E_1 \rangle = \langle E_2 \rangle = 0$. There is no difficulty in stating that $\langle D_3 \rangle \neq 0$ since $\langle E_3 \rangle$ defines a sense along the "three" axis. If, however, we say that $\langle D_1 \rangle$ or $\langle D_2 \rangle \neq 0$ and the crystals are oriented in a random manner we have no physical reason for stating that, for example, $\langle D_1 \rangle$ should lie in the direction of the positive x axis rather than the negative x axis. We can only conclude that it must be zero. Finally we note that $\langle \epsilon_{ij}' E_j' \rangle$ must be proportional to the electric field since the equations are linear. Equation 5-18 may thus be written in the form

(5-20) $\langle D_i \rangle = [\frac{1}{3}\langle \epsilon_{11} \rangle + \epsilon^\dagger]\langle E_i \rangle = \epsilon^* \langle E_i \rangle$

where $\langle \epsilon_{ij}' E_j' \rangle = \epsilon^\dagger \delta_{ij} \langle E_j \rangle$ and $\epsilon^\dagger$ depends upon the detailed geometric arrangement of the crystals within the polycrystal.

As we shall see later in the chapter the dependence on the geometry of ϵ^* in the polycrystal case may occur even in the limit of small deviations from local isotropy. This is contrasted to the locally isotropic case in which the geometric effects (beyond volume fractions) may be shown to become progressively less important as deviation from the average permittivity approaches zero.

5.1.4. Definition of Effective Constants Using the Energy Density

The effective permittivity ϵ^* has been defined in Eq. 5-16 by the relation

(5-16) $\langle D_i \rangle = \epsilon^* \langle E_i \rangle$

The effective elastic constants have been defined in Eq. 5-4 by the relation

(5-4) $\langle \tau \rangle_{ij} = \lambda^* e_{11} \delta_{ij} + 2\mu^* \langle e_{ij} \rangle$

These constants could alternatively have been defined by the energy relations

(5-20) $$\frac{\epsilon^*\langle E_i\rangle\langle E_i\rangle}{2} = \tfrac{1}{2}\langle E_i D_i\rangle$$

and

(5-21) $\tfrac{1}{2}\lambda^*\langle e_{ij}\rangle\langle e_{ll}\rangle\delta_{ij} + \tfrac{1}{2}[2\mu^*\langle e_{ij}\rangle\langle e_{ij}\rangle] = \tfrac{1}{2}\langle \lambda e_{ij}e_{ll}\rangle\delta_{ij} + \langle 2\mu e_{ij}e_{ij}\rangle$

We pointed out in Chapter 3 (footnote, below Eq. 3-151) that the definitions in Eq. 5-16 and Eq. 5-20 are equivalent, since $\langle E_i' D_i'\rangle = 0$. A similar type proof will establish the equivalence of the definitions given in Eq. 5-4 and 5-21, since $\langle e_{ij}' \tau_{ij}'\rangle = 0$. We shall use the two definitions interchangeably in the remainder of the chapter.

5.1.5. Two Simple Physical Models

Because of the difficulty of theoretically and experimentally determining the effect of geometry on the effective constants of a medium a considerable amount of effort has been directed to determining bounds for the effective constants in terms of volume fractions (see Hashin, 1964, for appropriate references) and more recently in terms of low-order correlation functions (see *Transactions of the Rheology Society*, 1965, Pt. 9, No. 1). Later in the chapter we shall show how the bounds may be derived from variational principles (a preliminary discussion was already given in Chapter 3). Here we should like to consider two simple physical models which are sometimes taken as limiting cases of the many geometrical arrangements possible for a homogeneous isotropic mixture of dissimilar materials. The models themselves are not isotropic but they give some indications of limiting behavior of isotropic arrangements. In order to keep the example as simple as possible we consider initially a mixture of two materials and analyze the electrical permittivity case.

The limiting cases that we wish to consider are most easily described by referring to Fig. 5-2a and b. We consider an infinite number of infinite two-dimensional slabs with variable thicknesses. We suppose the cross-hatched slabs have permittivity ϵ_1 and the plain slabs have permittivity ϵ_2. We construct our samples by alternately placing one

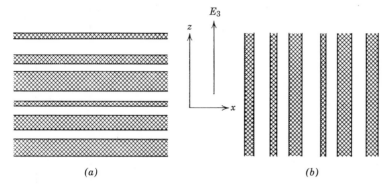

Fig. 5-2. Infinite slab models of a random medium.

type of slab upon the other as indicated in the diagram. The slab thicknesses are chosen at random. The permittivity ϵ thus varies in a random manner in one dimension as a result of the random slab thicknesses. A typical pattern for the permittivity of the medium represented by Fig. 5-2a is given as a function of z in Fig. 5-3. A similar pattern would be obtained by considering the variation of ϵ in the x direction in Fig. 5-2b. Both material samples are, of course, statistically the same; they only differ in their orientation to the z axis.

We suppose that an electric field E_3 is applied to the geometrical arrangements given in Figs. 5-2a and 5-2b. We wish to calculate ϵ^* in both cases, denoted for convenience by ϵ_a^* and ϵ_b^*, respectively. We note again that the samples are not statistically isotropic and thus the effective permittivity depends upon orientation. We wish to

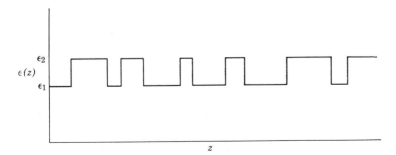

Fig. 5-3. One-dimensional permittivity pattern.

consider the behavior of these two cases, however, as rough limiting behavior possibilities of statistically isotropic material mixtures.

Let us consider the calculation of $\epsilon_a{}^*$. In this case, the variables are independent of **x**. We note from either physical reasoning or reference to the governing equation

$$\frac{\partial}{\partial z}\,\epsilon(z)E(z) = 0$$

that the displacement

(5-22) $$D(z) = \epsilon(z)E(z)$$

is equal to a constant. (In terms of a heat-conductivity problem this means that the flow of heat q is constant in the z direction; an obvious fact since q cannot depend upon x or y and there are no sinks or sources to collect or emit heat.) We call this constant D and, since the average of a constant is just the constant itself, we note that $D = \langle D \rangle$. From Eq. 5-22, we then find

(5-23) $$E(z) = \langle D \rangle / \epsilon(z)$$

If we now take the volume average of both sides of Eq. 5-23, we find

(5-24) $$\langle E(z) \rangle = \langle D \rangle [\langle 1/\epsilon(z) \rangle]$$

The defining equation for $\epsilon_b{}^*$ is

(5-25) $$D = \epsilon_a{}^* E$$

and thus a comparison of Eqs. 5-24 and 5-25 yields

(5-26) $$\epsilon_a{}^* = \frac{1}{\langle 1/\epsilon(z) \rangle}$$

The average $\langle 1/\epsilon(z) \rangle$ may be written in terms of volume fractions v_1 and v_2 as

(5-27) $$\left\langle \frac{1}{\epsilon(z)} \right\rangle = \frac{v_1}{\epsilon_1} + \frac{v_2}{\epsilon_2}$$

where v_1 is the fraction of volume in the sample occupied by one material (say the cross-hatched material) with permittivity ϵ_1 and v_2 in the fraction of volume occupied by the other material with permittivity ϵ_2.

The reader will note that this is just the type of formula that is derived in elementary circuit theory for the effective resistance if a voltage is put across a number of resistances in parallel.

The determination of $\epsilon_b{}^*$ proceeds even more directly. In this case the electric field is the same constant in each phase of the material. We have

(5-28) $\langle E(x, z) \rangle = \langle E \rangle$

The displacement is a function of x since ϵ is here a function of x. All the variables are independent of z. Thus

(5-29) $D(x) = \epsilon(x) \langle E \rangle$

Averaging Eq. 5-29, we find

(5-30) $\langle D(x) \rangle = \langle \epsilon(x) \rangle \langle E \rangle$

From the defining relation

$$\langle D \rangle = \epsilon_b{}^* \langle E \rangle$$

we thus find here that

(5-31) $\epsilon_b{}^* = \langle \epsilon(x) \rangle$

The same results (Eq. 5-26 and Eq. 5-31) would have been obtained if instead of two-phase materials we had considered n-phase materials. That is, we could have made composite materials from an infinite number of two-dimensional slabs in which a percentage v_1 of the slabs had permittivity ϵ_1, a percentage v_2 had permittivity $\epsilon_2, \ldots$, and a percentage v_n had permittivity ϵ_n. In fact, we could let $n \to \infty$ and find the same answers for $\epsilon_a{}^*$ and $\epsilon_b{}^*$. We could have considered in the first case a material sample for which ϵ was a random function of z and in the second case a material sample for which ϵ was a random function of x. In the latter case ϵ could have taken any value between 0 and ∞, provided only that the integral

$$\int_0^\infty P_1(\epsilon) \, d\epsilon$$

was equal to unity, where $P_1(\epsilon) \, d\epsilon$ is the probability that the material has a value of ϵ between ϵ and $\epsilon + d\epsilon$.

We have shown in Chapter 3, using variational principles, that for a statistically homogeneous isotropic medium

$$(5\text{-}32) \qquad \frac{1}{\langle 1/\epsilon \rangle} \leqslant \epsilon^* \leqslant \langle \epsilon \rangle$$

The relationship holds for the case of continuous variation of ϵ or for the special case of an n-phase material. The relationship was obtained using only a knowledge of volume fractions. Better bounds may be obtained for the case of an n-phase material, as we shall discuss in a moment, but it appears that for the general case in which all values of permittivity are permitted Eq. 5-32 is the most we can say about the range of ϵ^* from just a consideration of volume fractions.

Since the material geometries given in Fig. 5-2 yield the limiting values $1/\langle 1/\epsilon \rangle$ and $\langle \epsilon \rangle$ for Figs. 5-2a and 5-2b, respectively, we may hope that in some sense these geometries represent the limiting behavior of geometries that could exist in a statistically homogeneous and isotropic material. The first case (Fig. 5-2a) indicates a geometrical arrangement in which it is necessary that an electric field path pass sequentially through the entire range of permittivity values. There is no possibility of the electric field path passing through a continuous region with only one value of permittivity as in Fig. 5-2b. Moreover, the geometrical arrangement in Fig. 5-2a tends to emphasize the behavior of regions with low values of permittivity. This may be seen from Eqs. 5-26 and 5-27 in the two-phase case where

$$(5\text{-}33) \qquad \epsilon_a^* = \frac{1}{(v_1/\epsilon_1) + (v_2/\epsilon_2)}$$

In the limit $\epsilon_2/\epsilon_1 \gg 1$ (v_1 and v_2 of the same order)

$$(5\text{-}34) \qquad \epsilon_a^* \approx \frac{\epsilon_1}{v_1}$$

A statistically isotropic material that corresponded to the limit of Fig. 5-2a would thus tend to make regions of low permittivity readily accessible and regions of high permittivity (through which the field would normally tend to pass) relatively inaccessible. An extreme example of such a material would be to form a material from discrete fragments of all sizes such that in each fragment the outer portion of the fragment had low values of permittivity and the inner portions had high values of permittivity. In this case, since low permittivity volumes would have a larger surface area than high permittivity volumes electric field paths would tend to pass through both high and low permittivity regions. On the other hand if the surface availability of both low and high permittivity regions were equal the electric field would tend to pass through regions of high permittivity with a consequent high effective permittivity.

In the second case, paths are available for the electric field that lie entirely in regions of high permittivity or entirely in regions of low permittivity. In the two-phase case

$$(5\text{-}35) \qquad \epsilon_b{}^* = v_1\epsilon_1 + v_2\epsilon_2$$

Thus if $\epsilon_2 \gg \epsilon_1$ (and v_1 and v_2 are of the same order)

$$(5\text{-}36) \qquad \epsilon_b{}^* \approx v_2\epsilon_2$$

This geometrical arrangement tends to emphasize the behavior of regions with high permittivity. An extreme example of such a geometry for a statistically isotropic medium would be just the inverse of material constructed above. In this case we would construct fragments with an outer coating of high permittivity and an inner core of low permittivity. In this medium the electric field path would tend to lie principally in regions of high permittivity.

When applying these limiting ideas to specific geometrical arrangements great care must, of course, be taken. For example, if the material has permittivity fluctuations that are small and thus all values of the permittivity lie in the neighborhood of the mean value the above limits are never appropriate. In this case we will show later in the chapter that the formula for ϵ^* is always

$$(5\text{-}37) \qquad \epsilon^* = \langle \epsilon \rangle - \frac{1}{3} \frac{\langle \epsilon'^2 \rangle}{\langle \epsilon \rangle}$$

where $\langle \epsilon'^2 \rangle$ is the mean square fluctuation in permittivity. One could interpret this result to indicate a tendency for the electric field paths to lie in regions of high permittivity but the tendency is certainly not overwhelming.

5.1.6. n-Phase Materials

In the special case of an n-phase material or the case when the permittivity takes on continuous values but lies between two finite values ϵ_m and ϵ_n, Hashin and Shtrikman (1962) have shown that better bounds may be derived in terms of volume fractions than those given in Eq. 5-32. For example, they have shown that for a statistically homogeneous and isotropic two-phase medium that ϵ^* is bounded in the following manner

$$(5\text{-}38) \quad \epsilon_1 + \frac{v_2}{1/(\epsilon_2 - \epsilon_1) + v_1/3\epsilon_1} \leqslant \epsilon^* \leqslant \epsilon_2 + \frac{v_1}{1/(\epsilon_1 - \epsilon_2) + v_2/3\epsilon_2}$$

$$(\epsilon_2 > \epsilon_1)$$

This result has been derived in Chapter 3 and will be discussed again later in this chapter.

As Hashin and Shtrikman point out it is particularly interesting that the bounds given in Eq. 5-38 correspond to two different geometric arrangements for which an exact determination of ϵ^* is possible. Consider a material made up of composite spheres of all different sizes so arranged that the void (air volume/sphere volume) ratio approaches zero. A composite sphere is composed of an inner core of radius r_a and permittivity ϵ_a and an outer shell extending from radius r_a to r_b and having a permittivity ϵ_a such that $r_a/r_b = \alpha$ (a constant). The total volume of each sphere is $\frac{4}{3}\pi r_b^3$ and thus the volume fractions v_a and v_a are

$$v_a = \left[\frac{r_a}{r_b}\right]^3 \quad \text{and} \quad v_b = 1 - \left[\frac{r_a}{r_b}\right]^3$$

Hashin and Shtrikman (1962) show that the effective permittivity of such a two-phase material is

$$(5\text{-}39) \qquad \epsilon^* = \epsilon_b + \frac{v_a}{1/(\epsilon_a - \epsilon_b) + v_b/3\epsilon_b}$$

They do this in a very ingenious manner. They show that if one composite sphere is imbedded in a strictly homogeneous medium with permittivity ϵ^* given by Eq. 5-39 then for a uniform field, the field on the surface of the composite sphere is the same as it would be if the sphere was not there. They reason then that if this holds for one sphere it will hold for two spheres or n spheres and that eventually the entire homogeneous medium with permittivity ϵ^* may be replaced by the composite medium with no change in the average field. Hence, the effective permittivity of the composite sphere medium is given by Eq. 5-39.

Depending upon whether or not ϵ_a/ϵ_b is greater or less than 1, Eq. 5-39 may be made to correspond to either the upper or lower bound of Eq. 5-38. We obtain an upper bound for the effective permittivity when $\epsilon_b > \epsilon_a$; that is when the composite sphere is made of an inner core of low permittivity material and an outer core of high permittivity material. Based upon our previous discussion we expect this case to have a higher effective permittivity than the reverse possibility since in this case more paths through high permittivity material are available to the electric field than if the sphere shells were of low permittivity material. If the sphere shells were of low permittivity material every electric field path must pass through low permittivity material with a consequent reduction of the effective permittivity.

5.1.7. The Self-Consistent Approximation

When we have a statistically homogeneous and isotropic material composed of n phases whose component geometries are not too irregular, we may determine an effective constant for the material by a consistency argument. This approach has been developed in elastic problems by Budiansky (1965) and Hill (1965), and we will outline Budiansky's type of treatment in terms of the simpler dielectric problem. The reader is also referred to Landauer (1952) and Kerner (1956) for similar-type analyses.

In general we define ϵ^* by the relation

(5-40) $$\langle D_3 \rangle = \epsilon^* \langle E_3 \rangle$$

where $\langle E_3 \rangle$ is a constant field in the z direction. We may also write

(5-41) $$U = \tfrac{1}{2}\epsilon^* \langle E_3 \rangle^2 = \tfrac{1}{2}\langle D_3 \rangle \langle E_3 \rangle$$

where U is the energy/unit volume. (See Eq. 5-20.) If we rewrite Eq. 5-41 in the form

(5-42) $$U = \frac{1}{2V} \int_V \langle E_3 \rangle \epsilon_N E_3 \, dV + \frac{1}{2V} \int \langle E_3 \rangle (\langle D_3 \rangle - \epsilon_N E_3) \, dV$$

(where the subscript N denotes the Nth phase), then by explicitly considering the other $N - 1$ phases, we find

(5-43) $$U = \frac{\epsilon^*}{2} \langle E_3 \rangle^2 = \frac{\langle E_3 \rangle^2}{2} \left[\epsilon_N + \sum_{i=1}^{n-1} p_i \left(1 - \frac{\epsilon_N}{\epsilon_i} \right) \frac{\langle D_{3i} \rangle}{\langle E_3 \rangle} \right]$$

where p_i is the volume fraction of the ith phase and D_{3i} is the average value of D_3 in the ith phase.

There are no approximations in Eq. 5-43. For this expression to be useful, however, we must determine $\langle D_{3i} \rangle$. In the self-consistency approximation $\langle D_{3i} \rangle$ is determined by assuming that the ith inclusion is immersed in a continuous matrix of the other $N - 1$ phases; the matrix having a constant dielectric constant ϵ^*. If the inclusion is assumed to have some average shape, $\langle D_{3i} \rangle$ may then be found. If the shape is assumed spherical, then we find (see Stratton, 1941)

$$(5\text{-}44) \qquad\qquad \langle D_{3i} \rangle = \frac{3\epsilon_i \epsilon^* \langle E_3 \rangle}{\epsilon_i + 2\epsilon^*}$$

If the n phases are roughly symmetric and if we assume all inclusions are roughly spherical, we find

$$(5\text{-}45) \qquad \epsilon^* = \left[\epsilon_N + \sum_{i=1}^{N-1} p_i \left(1 - \frac{\epsilon_N}{\epsilon_i} \right) \frac{3\epsilon_i \epsilon^*}{(\epsilon_i + 2\epsilon^*)} \right]$$

This expression may be used to find ϵ^*.

In the limit of small perturbations, this formula yields the exact result given in Eq. 5-37. In the elastic case this relation was noted to lie within bounds that are the analog of those given in Eq. 5-32. Similar reasoning should show that Eq. 5-45 lies within the bounds given in Eq. 5-32.

It is not clear at present whether or not this procedure may be reasonably extended to irregular geometries (except if $p_i \ll 1$ for all except one component). Since Eq. 5-43 is correct independently of the detailed geometry, it is certainly worth investigating the relation between $\langle D_{3i} \rangle$ and the geometry of the ith phase. If this is done, however, a more explicitly statistical formulation will probably be necessary.

5.1.8. Dilute Suspensions

As a final remark in this introductory section we note that one limiting case of a two-phase material has received considerable attention in the literature. This is the case of dilute suspensions, or what is often termed small concentration theory. Here a small percentage of one material is considered as an inclusion in the matrix of another material. Numerous references to work in this area are given by Hashin (1964) and it appears that one of the earliest investigations was by Einstein (1906) in his studies of Brownian motion. The analysis just given for the self-consistent approximation may also be utilized to treat this problem.

This particular limit is easy to handle since the effects of each inclusion may be considered individually. Since the percentage of inclusions is small each included particle may be considered to lie in an infinite matrix of the imbedding material. In the electrostatic

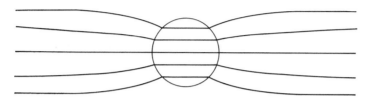

Fig. 5-4. Small concentration theory—field about a single inclusion (see Stratton, J., *Electromagnetic Theory*, McGraw-Hill, 1941, p. 207).

problem the electric field in the neighborhood of the particle may be solved as a straightforward boundary value problem, if the particle geometry is not too complicated. In Fig. 5-4 we show how the electric field would look in the neighborhood of a sphere with permittivity ϵ_1 in a matrix with permittivity ϵ_2 where $\epsilon_1 > \epsilon_2$. The formula for the electric field is derived in Stratton (1941).

From a knowledge of the solution for the boundary value problem we may determine the difference between the energy of the field in the presence of the inclusion and the energy of the field in the absence of the inclusion. Let us term this energy $\Delta\mathscr{E}$. If we have n inclusions per unit volume, then the change in energy as a result of the presence of the inclusion in a volume V will be $n\Delta\mathscr{E}V$. The energy of the field in the absence of the inclusions is $\frac{1}{2}\epsilon_2 E_{i0}E_{i0}V$ where E_{i0} is the field at great distances from the particles. We may thus define an effective constant ϵ^* by the relation†

(5-46) $$\frac{1}{2}\epsilon^* E_{i0}E_{i0}V = \frac{1}{2}\epsilon_2 E_{i0}E_{i0}V + n\Delta\mathscr{E}V$$

or upon rearrangement

(5-47) $$\epsilon^* = \epsilon_2 + \frac{2n\Delta\mathscr{E}}{E_{i0}E_{i0}}$$

† See Eq. 5-20.

From the linearity of the Laplace equation it is easily seen that $\Delta\mathscr{E}$ must be proportional $E_{i0}E_{i0}$. Thus we may write

(5-48) $\epsilon^* = \epsilon_2(1 + n\alpha)$

where α is a constant that depends upon ϵ_1, ϵ_2, and the geometry of the included particles.

5.2. Geometry of Heterogeneous Media

As we pointed out in the introduction we here consider a hetero-geneous material to be a material in which the electric or elastic properties of the material vary from point to point in a manner that may best be treated from a statistical point of view. In this section we wish to discuss what is known about the geometry of such materials. In part we shall follow the discussions given in papers by Beran (1965b) and Frisch (1965). Since most attention has been paid to two-phase materials our discussion will be principally directed toward this special case.

It is clear, of course, that if we have a single sample of a material we never need consider the problem from a statistical point of view. In principal we may measure the elastic or electric constants of the sample as a function of position to any desired accuracy. The information may be stored in tabular form or perhaps in an analytic expression that is obtained by expansion in some set of complete functions. When treating heterogeneous media, however, this is usually not what we wish to do. We are almost never concerned with the detailed variation of a single sample but rather with the properties of a large class of samples that were prepared in the same overall or macroscopic manner.

For example, we may prepare a sample of a heterogeneous material by specifying the volume fractions of a number of components to be combined in a mixture, the overall manner in which they may be mixed together and some technique to insure bonding between the mixed components. The exact geometric arrangement of the mixture is left unspecified. The samples produced according to this general overall (macroscopic) prescription comprise an ensemble that forms a basis for a statistical description. Since the overall prescription was the same for all the samples they have something in common that distinguishes this set of samples from a set produced according to a different set of overall rules.

The ensemble may be crudely characterized statistically by specifying only quantities like the mean value and standard deviation of the elastic or electric constants. In order to present a complete statistical description of the material, however, requires a knowledge of the joint probability density function

(5-49) $P_n[a(\mathbf{x}_1), a(\mathbf{x}_2), \ldots, a(\mathbf{x}_n); b(\mathbf{x}_1), b(\mathbf{x}_2), \ldots, b(\mathbf{x}_n); \ldots;$

$$g(\mathbf{x}_1), g(\mathbf{x}_2), \ldots, g(\mathbf{x}_n)]$$

in the limit as $n \to \infty$ where $a, b, \ldots, g$ are the elastic or electric properties which characterize the medium (see Sections 2.1.4 and 2.2.5). For example, for the elastic properties we might have $a = \mu$ (the shear modulus) and $b = \lambda$ (Lamé's constant); for the electric properties $a = \epsilon$ (the permittivity).

The function $P_n(\lim_{n \to \infty})$ contains an enormous amount of information and yields in the limit a probability density functional which gives the probability of a particular realization of the variation of the constants. It is rarely ever attainable in practice but anything short of knowledge of this functional gives only approximate statistical information about the ensemble. In practice we must usually settle for low-order correlation functions of the form

$$\overline{a(\mathbf{x}_1)a(\mathbf{x}_2)}$$

$$\overline{a(\mathbf{x}_1)b(\mathbf{x}_2)}$$

$$\overline{a(\mathbf{x}_1)a(\mathbf{x}_2)a(\mathbf{x}_3)}$$

$$\overline{a(\mathbf{x}_1)a(\mathbf{x}_2)b(\mathbf{x}_3)}$$

Very few measurements have been made on even these two-point and three-point moments. In fact, the only measurements with which we are familiar are currently in progress.

Theoretically the situation is not much better but we will attempt to present some information that is available. We will follow parts of the paper by Firsch (1965) and refer the reader to this paper for a more complete treatment. The heterogeneous medium that has received the most attention is the two-phase medium. This medium may be constructed, for example, by placing inclusions of one material in the matrix of another or by taking fine powders of two different metals, mixing them together and compressing the mixture in a mold to form a large solid sample.

The two-phase medium may be conveniently characterized by what may be termed a matter phase covering a region of space D_1 with volume fraction ϕ and a void phase covering a region of space D_0 with volume fraction $1 - \phi$. We then define a function $E(\mathbf{r})$ with the following properties:

$$E(\mathbf{r}) = 1 \quad \text{if} \quad \mathbf{r} \subset D_1$$

$$= 0 \quad \text{if} \quad \mathbf{r} \subset D_0$$

For convenience theoretically, and generally as an acceptable physical hypothesis, we assume that the material is statistically homogeneous and isotropic.

It is useful to describe the two-phase materials in terms of the probability functions

(5-50)
$$P_{\epsilon_1 \epsilon_2 \epsilon_3 \cdots \epsilon_n}(\mathbf{r}_1, \mathbf{r}_2, \ldots, \mathbf{r}_n)$$

$$\epsilon_i = 1 \quad \text{if} \quad \mathbf{r}_i \subset D_1$$

$$= 0 \quad \text{if} \quad \mathbf{r}_i \subset D_0$$

defined as the probability that at $\mathbf{r}_1$, $E(\mathbf{r}_1) = \epsilon_1$, and at $\mathbf{r}_2$, $E(\mathbf{r}_2) = \epsilon_2$, and, ..., and at $\mathbf{r}_n$, $E(\mathbf{r}_n) = \epsilon_n$. For example, $P_{010}(\mathbf{r}_1, \mathbf{r}_2, \mathbf{r}_3)$ is the probability that there is a matter phase at $\mathbf{r}_2$ and void phases at $\mathbf{r}_1$ and $\mathbf{r}_3$. We note also that since a point must be in either D_1 or D_0 then

(5-51) $P_{\epsilon_1 \cdots \epsilon_{k-1} 0}(\mathbf{r}_1, \ldots, \mathbf{r}_{k-1}, \mathbf{r}_k) + P_{\epsilon_1 \cdots \epsilon_{k-1} 1}(\mathbf{r}_1, \ldots, \mathbf{r}_{k-1}, \mathbf{r}_k)$

$$= P_{\epsilon_1 \cdots \epsilon_{k-1}}(\mathbf{r}_1, \ldots, \mathbf{r}_{k-1})$$

and

$$P_1(\mathbf{r}_1) + P_0(\mathbf{r}_1) = 1$$

The mean value of $E(\mathbf{r})$ may be computed from the equation

(5-52)
$$\gamma_1(\mathbf{r}) \equiv \overline{E(\mathbf{r})} = \sum_{\epsilon=0}^{1} P_\epsilon(\mathbf{r}) E(\mathbf{r})$$

$$= P_1(\mathbf{r})$$

since $E(\mathbf{r}) = 0$ when $\epsilon = 0$.

Similarly

(5-53) $\gamma_2(\mathbf{r}_1, \mathbf{r}_2) \equiv \overline{E(\mathbf{r}_1)E(\mathbf{r}_2)} = \displaystyle\sum_{\epsilon_2=0}^{1} \sum_{\epsilon_1=0}^{1} P_{\epsilon_1\epsilon_2}(\mathbf{r}_1, \mathbf{r}_2)E(\mathbf{r}_1)E(\mathbf{r}_2)$

$\qquad\qquad\qquad = P_{11}(\mathbf{r}_1, \mathbf{r}_2)$

since again when ϵ_1 or $\epsilon_2 = 0$, correspondingly, $E(\mathbf{r}_1)$ or $E(\mathbf{r}_2) = 0$.
In general we have thus

(5-54) $\gamma_n(\mathbf{r}_1, \ldots, \mathbf{r}_n) \equiv \overline{E(\mathbf{r}_1) \cdots E(\mathbf{r}_n)} = P_{1\cdots1}(\mathbf{r}_1, \ldots, \mathbf{r}_n)$

It is useful to note that the $P_{\epsilon_1\cdots\epsilon_n}$ may be expressed in general as a
linear function of the $\gamma_j(r_1, \ldots, r_j), j \leqslant n$. For example, we have the
following two-point relations ($\gamma_1 = $ constant)

(5-55) $P_{01}(\mathbf{r}_1, \mathbf{r}_2) = \gamma_1 - \gamma_2(\mathbf{r}_1, \mathbf{r}_2)$

(5-56) $P_{10}(\mathbf{r}_1, \mathbf{r}_2) = \gamma_1 - \gamma_2(\mathbf{r}_1, \mathbf{r}_2)$

(5-57) $P_{00}(\mathbf{r}_1, \mathbf{r}_2) = 1 - 2\gamma_1 + \gamma_2(\mathbf{r}_1, \mathbf{r}_2)$

These relations may be derived using Eq. 5-51. For example,
letting $k - 1 = 1$, we have

(5-58) $P_{10}(\mathbf{r}_1, \mathbf{r}_2) + P_{11}(\mathbf{r}_1, \mathbf{r}_2) = P_1(\mathbf{r}_1)$

Since we have assumed the random media to be statistically homogeneous, all the correlation functions depend only upon relative
positions rather than absolute position. Thus

$$\gamma_1(\mathbf{r}_1) = \gamma = \text{a constant}$$
$$\gamma_2(\mathbf{r}_1, \mathbf{r}_2) = \gamma_2(\mathbf{r}_{12})$$

where

$$\mathbf{r}_{12} = (\mathbf{r}_2 - \mathbf{r}_1)$$

and in general

$$\gamma_n(\mathbf{r}_1, \mathbf{r}_2, \ldots, \mathbf{r}_n) = \gamma_n(\mathbf{r}_{12}, \mathbf{r}_{13}, \ldots, \mathbf{r}_{1n})$$

where

$$\mathbf{r}_{1j} = \mathbf{r}_j - \mathbf{r}_1$$

Since the media have also been assumed to be isotropic

$$\gamma_2(\mathbf{r}_{12}) = \gamma_2(|\mathbf{r}_{12}|)$$
$$\gamma_3(\mathbf{r}_{12}, \mathbf{r}_{13}) = \gamma_3(|\mathbf{r}_{12}|, |\mathbf{r}_{13}|, \mathbf{r}_{12} \cdot \mathbf{r}_{13})$$

with similar simplifications for higher-order moments.

In general γ_2, γ_3, and all higher moments are independent of each other. In the particular case when $\gamma_1 = \frac{1}{2}$ and it is impossible to distinguish the geometry of one phase from the other it is possible to determine γ_{2n+1} from γ_{2n}; i.e., it is possible to determine the odd moment from the preceding even moment. It is not possible to determine γ_{2n+2} from γ_{2n}, these moments remain independent. The reason that this is possible results from relations like

$$P_{11\cdots 1}(\mathbf{r}_1, \mathbf{r}_2, \ldots, \mathbf{r}_n) = P_{00\cdots 0}(\mathbf{r}_1, \mathbf{r}_2, \ldots, \mathbf{r}_n)$$

and

$$P_{11\cdots 10}(\mathbf{r}_1, \mathbf{r}_2, \ldots, \mathbf{r}_n) = P_{00\cdots 01}(\mathbf{r}_1, \mathbf{r}_2, \ldots, \mathbf{r}_n)$$

We derive here the relationship between γ_3 and the γ_2's.

Consider a sample space composed of eight events 111, 110, 101, 100, 011, 010, 001, 000 that may be interpreted, respectively, as the events: matter phase at $\mathbf{r}_1$, $\mathbf{r}_2$, $\mathbf{r}_3$(111), matter phase at $\mathbf{r}_1$, $\mathbf{r}_2$, void phase at $\mathbf{r}_3$(110) and so on. The probability of a matter phase at $\mathbf{r}_1$, $P_1(\mathbf{r}_1)$, is

$$(5\text{-}59) \quad P_1(\mathbf{r}_1) = P_{111}(\mathbf{r}_1, \mathbf{r}_2, \mathbf{r}_3) + P_{110}(\mathbf{r}_1, \mathbf{r}_2, \mathbf{r}_3)$$
$$+ P_{101}(\mathbf{r}_1, \mathbf{r}_2, \mathbf{r}_3) + P_{100}(\mathbf{r}_1, \mathbf{r}_2, \mathbf{r}_3)$$

Similarly, the probability of a void phase at $\mathbf{r}_1$ is

$$(5\text{-}60) \quad P_0(\mathbf{r}_1) = P_{011}(\mathbf{r}_1, \mathbf{r}_2, \mathbf{r}_3) + P_{010}(\mathbf{r}_1, \mathbf{r}_2, \mathbf{r}_3)$$
$$+ P_{001}(\mathbf{r}_1, \mathbf{r}_2, \mathbf{r}_3) + P_{000}(\mathbf{r}_1, \mathbf{r}_2, \mathbf{r}_3)$$

The probability of a matter phase at both $\mathbf{r}_1$ and $\mathbf{r}_2$ is

$$(5\text{-}61) \qquad P_{11}(\mathbf{r}_1, \mathbf{r}_2) = P_{111}(\mathbf{r}_1, \mathbf{r}_2, \mathbf{r}_3) + P_{110}(\mathbf{r}_1, \mathbf{r}_2, \mathbf{r}_3)$$

with similar expressions for P_{10}, P_{01}, and P_{00}.

From these expressions we find the lengthy expression

$$(5\text{-}62) \quad P_1(\mathbf{r}_1) + P_1(\mathbf{r}_2) + P_1(\mathbf{r}_3) - P_{11}(\mathbf{r}_1, \mathbf{r}_2) - P_{11}(\mathbf{r}_1, \mathbf{r}_3) - P_{11}(\mathbf{r}_2, \mathbf{r}_3)$$
$$= P_{111}(\mathbf{r}_1, \mathbf{r}_2, \mathbf{r}_3) + P_{110}(\mathbf{r}_1, \mathbf{r}_2, \mathbf{r}_3) + P_{101}(\mathbf{r}_1, \mathbf{r}_2, \mathbf{r}_3)$$
$$+ P_{100}(\mathbf{r}_1, \mathbf{r}_2, \mathbf{r}_3) + P_{111}(\mathbf{r}_1, \mathbf{r}_2, \mathbf{r}_3) + P_{110}(\mathbf{r}_1, \mathbf{r}_2, \mathbf{r}_3)$$
$$+ P_{011}(\mathbf{r}_1, \mathbf{r}_2, \mathbf{r}_3) + P_{010}(\mathbf{r}_1, \mathbf{r}_2, \mathbf{r}_3) + P_{111}(\mathbf{r}_1, \mathbf{r}_2, \mathbf{r}_3)$$
$$+ P_{101}(\mathbf{r}_1, \mathbf{r}_2, \mathbf{r}_3) + P_{011}(\mathbf{r}_1, \mathbf{r}_2, \mathbf{r}_3) + P_{001}(\mathbf{r}_1, \mathbf{r}_2, \mathbf{r}_3)$$
$$- P_{111}(\mathbf{r}_1, \mathbf{r}_2, \mathbf{r}_3) - P_{110}(\mathbf{r}_1, \mathbf{r}_2, \mathbf{r}_3) - P_{111}(\mathbf{r}_1, \mathbf{r}_2, \mathbf{r}_3)$$
$$- P_{101}(\mathbf{r}_1, \mathbf{r}_2, \mathbf{r}_3) - P_{111}(\mathbf{r}_1, \mathbf{r}_2, \mathbf{r}_3) - P_{011}(\mathbf{r}_1, \mathbf{r}_2, \mathbf{r}_3)$$

which simplifies to

(5-63) $P_1(\mathbf{r}_1) + P_1(\mathbf{r}_2) + P_1(\mathbf{r}_3) - P_{11}(\mathbf{r}_1, \mathbf{r}_2) - P_{11}(\mathbf{r}_1, \mathbf{r}_3) - P_{11}(\mathbf{r}_2, \mathbf{r}_3)$

$$= 1 - P_{111}(\mathbf{r}_1, \mathbf{r}_2, \mathbf{r}_3) - P_{000}(\mathbf{r}_1, \mathbf{r}_2, \mathbf{r}_3)$$

upon noting the identity

$$P_{111} + P_{101} + P_{110} + P_{100} + P_{011} + P_{010} + P_{001} + P_{000} = 1$$

Since

$$P_{111}(\mathbf{r}_1, \mathbf{r}_2, \mathbf{r}_3) = P_{000}(\mathbf{r}_1, \mathbf{r}_2, \mathbf{r}_3)$$

and

$$P_1(\mathbf{r}_1) = P_1(\mathbf{r}_2) = P_1(\mathbf{r}_3) = \tfrac{1}{2}$$

we have

(5-64) $P_{111}(\mathbf{r}_1, \mathbf{r}_2, \mathbf{r}_3) = \tfrac{1}{2}[P_{11}(\mathbf{r}_1, \mathbf{r}_2) + P_{11}(\mathbf{r}_1, \mathbf{r}_3) + P_{11}(\mathbf{r}_2, \mathbf{r}_3) - \tfrac{1}{2}]$

or in terms of the correlation functions

(5-65) $\gamma_3(\mathbf{r}_1, \mathbf{r}_2, \mathbf{r}_3) = \tfrac{1}{2}[\gamma_2(\mathbf{r}_1, \mathbf{r}_2) + \gamma_2(\mathbf{r}_1, \mathbf{r}_3) + \gamma_2(\mathbf{r}_2, \mathbf{r}_3) - \tfrac{1}{2}]$

The correlation functions γ_2 and γ_3 can often be determined even for nonsymmetric media if the geometry is assumed to have some simple form. For example, we may derive the correlation functions for a material that is constructed in the following manner (see Frisch, 1965; Gilbert, 1962): points are distributed at random in a volume such that the probability of finding a point in an infinitesimal volume ΔV is proportional to ΔV and such that the position of any point is independent of the position of the other points. This may be termed a Poisson pattern and the points are called Poisson points. Next each point is made a matter point or a void point with a probability $P_1(\mathbf{r})$ or $1 - P_1(\mathbf{r})$, respectively. Since the medium is to be homogeneous, $P_1(\mathbf{r})$ is chosen to be a constant γ. An arbitrary point in space is denoted as a matter point or a void point depending upon whether or not the Poisson point closest to it is a matter or void point, respectively. An example of a two-dimensional region so defined is given in Fig. 5-5. The square points are matter Poisson points and the triangular points are void Poisson points.

In order to use this model to determine the correlation functions we must determine the probability that there is a Poisson point in a region V. Discussions of this calculation in one dimension are given

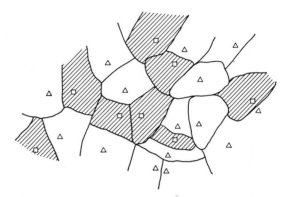

Fig. 5-5. Two-phase medium determined from a Poisson pattern.

in many texts (see, for example, Davenport and Root, 1958, or Feller, 1950). The extension to higher dimensions is immediate. Following the notation in Davenport and Root (1958), the probability $P(1, \Delta V)$ that there is one Poisson point in a small volume ΔV is

$$(5\text{-}66) \qquad\qquad P(1, \Delta V) = \lambda \Delta V$$

That is, the probability is proportional to ΔV. We also have the relation

$$(5\text{-}67) \qquad\qquad P(0, \Delta V) + P(1, \Delta V) = 1$$

where $P(0, \Delta V)$ is the probability that there are no Poisson points in ΔV.

Invoking the independence hypothesis

$$(5\text{-}68) \qquad\qquad P(0, V + \Delta V) = P(0, V)P(0, \Delta V)$$

we then find from Eqs. 5-66, 5-67, and 5-68

$$(5\text{-}69) \qquad\qquad \frac{P(0, V + \Delta V) - P(0, V)}{\Delta V} = -\lambda P(0, V)$$

and in the limit $\Delta V \to 0$

$$(5\text{-}70) \qquad\qquad \frac{dP(0, V)}{dV} = -\lambda P(0, V)$$

The solution of Eq. 5-70 is

$$(5\text{-}71) \qquad\qquad P(0, V) = e^{-\lambda V}$$

By similar arguments we can find the probability that there are j Poisson points in V.

We will now derive an expression for $\gamma_2(\mathbf{r}_{12})$. Similar reasoning can be used to find $\gamma_3(\mathbf{r}_{12}, \mathbf{r}_{13})$. The result will be given in terms of a quadrature as shown in the paper by Gilbert (1962). A numerical calculation is given in the paper by Frisch (1965).

Equation 5-53 allows us to interpret $\gamma_2(|\mathbf{r}_{12}|)$ as the probability that the two points connected by the vector $\mathbf{r}_{12}$ are both in the matter phase. Let us define $P_p(|\mathbf{r}_{12}|)$ as the probability that the two points have the same nearest Poisson point. $\gamma_2(|\mathbf{r}_{12}|)$ and $P_p(|\mathbf{r}_{12}|)$ are connected by the following relation:

(5-72) $$\gamma_2(|\mathbf{r}_{12}|) = \gamma^2(1 - P_p(|\mathbf{r}_{12}|)) + \gamma P_p(|\mathbf{r}_{12}|)$$

This may be seen by considering the two alternatives: (*1*) the two points have the same nearest Poisson point, and (*2*) the two points have different nearest Poisson points. The probability of statement (*1*) is, by the definition just given, P_p and the probability of the statement (*2*) is $1 - P_p$. The probability that both points are both in the matter phase is the sum of the probability that they are both in the matter phase if they have the same Poisson point and the probability that they are both in the matter phase if they do not have the same Poisson point. The probability that they are both in the matter phase if they have the same Poisson point is γP_p since by construction if one point is in the matter phase the other is also. The probability that both points are in the matter phase if they do not have the same Poisson point is $\gamma\gamma(1 - P_p)$ since the phases of the two points are not related.

The problem thus reduces to calculating $P_p(|\mathbf{r}_{12}|)$. To do this consider the point at the origin. The probability of its nearest Poisson point being at position R, θ, ϕ, P_R, is

(5-73) $$P_R = \lambda \exp\left[-\lambda \tfrac{4}{3}\pi R^3\right]R^2 \sin\theta \, dR \, d\theta \, d\phi$$

where θ is measured from the axis along $\mathbf{r}_{12}$. This follows from the fact that P_R is equal to the probability of there being no Poisson points within the sphere R multiplied by the probability that there is a Poisson point in the volume $\Delta V = R^2 \sin\theta d \, Rd \, \theta \, d\phi$. This Poisson point is also the nearest Poisson point to the other point at $\mathbf{r}_{12}$ only if there is no Poisson point in the volume $V(r, R, \theta, \phi)$ defined as the volume of a sphere of radius $r = |\mathbf{R} - \mathbf{r}_{12}|$ surrounding the point at $\mathbf{r}_{12}$ minus the volume of the portion of space formed from the intersection of this sphere and a sphere of radius R surrounding the point at the origin. The probability of this being true P_r is given by the expression

(5-74) $P_r = e^{-\lambda V(r,R,\theta,\phi)}$

$P_p(|r_{12}|)$ is then simply given as the integral over all points (R, θ, ϕ) of the product $P_R P_r$. That is,

(5-75)

$$P_p(|r_{12}|) = \int_0^\infty \int_0^\pi \int_0^{2\pi} \lambda \exp \left[-\lambda(\tfrac{4}{3}\pi R^3 + V(r, R, \theta, \phi))\right] R \sin \theta \, dR \, d\theta \, d\phi$$

This triple integral may be reduced to a double integral by a different choice of angles. (See Gilbert, 1962.) We note that $\tfrac{4}{3}\pi R^3 + V(r, R, \theta, \phi)$ is the union of two spheres, one centered at the origin and one centered at the point (r, θ, ϕ).

Weissberg and Prager (1962) have derived expressions for two- and three-point correlation functions for spheres imbedded in a random manner in a matrix. The arguments they use are similar to arguments presented above and we refer the reader to this paper. Since the matter and void phases are not symmetrical in this type of medium there is no simple relation between the two- and three-point correlation function. For ease of calculation, however, they explore an approximate relation that exists between the two- and three-point correlation functions.

5.3. Definition of Effective Constants

In the introduction we discussed the definition and calculation of effective constants in a manner that we hope appealed to the reader's physical intuition. In this section we shall give a more precise definition using ensemble averages. We shall consider the definition of both electrostatic and elastic effective constants. The definition of the electrostatic constants is equivalent to the definition of effective heat conduction, electrical conduction, diffusion, or magnetostatic constants with a change of notation. In the elastic case we restrict the discussion to media that are locally isotropic. We shall consider the locally nonisotropic case, however, for the electrostatic case.

We define effective constants only for a medium that (I) may be approximated by an infinite medium that is statistically homogeneous and isotropic, and (2) is subjected to a constant average electric field on an average linear displacement field. Effective constants can be defined locally in the presence of more complex average fields but this work is currently in the research stage and much more work must be done. (See Beran, 1965c.) As we stated in the introduction, these effective constants are also intended to be appropriate when the average field varies slowly in distances that are large compared to distances over which the medium constants undergo considerable variation, or perhaps more precisely when distances are large compared to a characteristic distance for which the two-point correlation function is effectively zero. Our derivation, however, will consider only the ideal case.

In the electrostatic case we consider two vectors. We treat the electric vector $E_i(\mathbf{x})$ and the displacement vector $D_i(\mathbf{x})$. Locally we consider that they are related by the tensor relation

$$(5\text{-}76) \qquad D_i(\mathbf{x}) = \epsilon_{ij}(\mathbf{x})E_j(\mathbf{x})$$

If $\epsilon_{ij}(\mathbf{x}) = \epsilon(\mathbf{x})\delta_{ij}$, the medium is locally isotropic; if the tensor contains off-diagonal terms, then the medium is locally nonisotropic. (An example of a nonisotropic heterogeneous medium would be a polycrystal wherein the permittivities along the principal axes are unequal in each crystal.) In the language of heat conductivity, for example, we would have the relation

$$(5\text{-}77) \qquad q_i(\mathbf{x}) = k_{ij}(\mathbf{x})T_{,j}(\mathbf{x})$$

where $q_i(\mathbf{x})$ is the heat flux vector, $k_{ij}(\mathbf{x})$ is the heat conductivity tensor, and $T_{,j}(\mathbf{x})$ is the temperature gradient in the x_j direction.

We set as the only condition the demand that the average electric field $\overline{E_i(\mathbf{x})}$ be a constant. Since the permittivity field $\epsilon_{ij}(\mathbf{x})$ is statistically homogeneous and isotropic, no point in the medium is in any way differentiated from any other point and hence $\overline{D_i(\mathbf{x})}$ is also a constant. An expression for $\overline{D_i(\mathbf{x})}$ is obtained by averaging both sides of Eq. 5-76. We find

$$(5\text{-}78) \qquad \overline{D_i(\mathbf{x})} = \overline{\epsilon_{ij}(\mathbf{x})E_j(\mathbf{x})}$$

The purpose of effective constants is to replace a basically heterogeneous material by an equivalent homogeneous material for the purpose of discussing the behavior of average fields. Thus we seek a relation between $D_i(\mathbf{x})$ and $\epsilon_i(\mathbf{x})$ of the form

(5-79)
$$\overline{D_i(\mathbf{x})} = \epsilon^* \overline{E_i(\mathbf{x})}$$

where ϵ^* is termed the effective permittivity. We note that since the $\epsilon_{ij}(\mathbf{x})$ field is statistically homogeneous and isotropic, ϵ^* is a simple constant scalar function, not a tensor. The local anisotropy is averaged out. For a statistically homogeneous and isotropic permittivity field we could *not* have a relationship of the form

$$\overline{D_i(\mathbf{x})} = \epsilon_{ij}^* \overline{E_j(\mathbf{x})}$$

where the off-diagonal terms of ϵ_{ij}^* were not equal to zero. Since $\overline{E_i(\mathbf{x})}$ is in some fixed direction, for example, the $i = 3$ direction, on the basis of this information it is equally plausible for $\overline{D_i(\mathbf{x})}$ to lie in any direction in the plane perpendicular to the fixed direction. Hence, we must take $\overline{D_1(\mathbf{x})} = \overline{D_2(\mathbf{x})} = 0$.

Combining Eqs. 5-78 and 5-79 we have

(5-80)
$$\epsilon^* = \frac{\overline{\epsilon_{3j}(\mathbf{x})E_j(\mathbf{x})}}{\overline{E_3(\mathbf{x})}} = \bar{\epsilon} + \frac{\overline{\epsilon_{3j}{}'(\mathbf{x})E_j{}'(\mathbf{x})}}{\overline{E_3(\mathbf{x})}}$$

where for convenience we have set the average field in the "three" directions and noted that $\epsilon_{33} = \epsilon$.

We also may deduce from the fact that

$$\overline{D_1(\mathbf{x})} = \overline{D_2(\mathbf{x})} = 0$$

the results

$$\overline{\epsilon_{1j}{}'(\mathbf{x})E_j{}'(\mathbf{x})} = \overline{\epsilon_{2j}{}'(\mathbf{x})E_j{}'(\mathbf{x})} = 0$$

In the elastic case we consider two tensors: the stress tensor $\tau_{ij}(\mathbf{x})$ and the strain tensor $\epsilon_{ij}(\mathbf{x})$. We also consider the displacement vector $u_i(\mathbf{x})$. The relationship between $\epsilon_{ij}(\mathbf{x})$ and $u_i(\mathbf{x})$ is taken to be

(5-81)
$$e_{ij}(\mathbf{x}) = \frac{1}{2}\left[\frac{\partial u_i(\mathbf{x})}{\partial x_j} + \frac{\partial u_j(\mathbf{x})}{\partial x_i}\right]$$

For a locally isotropic medium the relationship between $\tau_{ij}(\mathbf{x})$ and $\epsilon_{ij}(\mathbf{x})$ is

(5-82)
$$\tau_{ij}(\mathbf{x}) = \lambda(\mathbf{x})e_{ll}(\mathbf{x})\delta_{ij} + 2\mu(\mathbf{x})e_{ij}(\mathbf{x})$$

where $\lambda(\mathbf{x})$ is Lamé's constant and $\mu(\mathbf{x})$ is the shear modulus. $\lambda(\mathbf{x})$ and $\mu(\mathbf{x})$ are related to the bulk modulus $k(\mathbf{x})$ by the relation

$$k(\mathbf{x}) = \lambda(\mathbf{x}) + \tfrac{2}{3}\mu(\mathbf{x})$$

As a basic condition we require that $\overline{u_i(\mathbf{x})}$ be of the form (where α_{ij} is not identically zero)

$$(5\text{-}83) \qquad \overline{u_i(\mathbf{x})} = \alpha_{ij}x_j$$

This yields a constant average strain field

$$(5\text{-}84) \qquad \overline{e_{ij}(\mathbf{x})} = \alpha_{ij}$$

Since the statistical distribution of the elastic constants is assumed to be homogeneous no point in space is to be preferred over any other point in space and $\overline{\tau_{ij}(\mathbf{x})}$ is also a constant. The expression for $\overline{\tau_{ij}(\mathbf{x})}$ is found by averaging Eq. 5-82. We have then

$$(5\text{-}85) \qquad \overline{\tau_{ij}(\mathbf{x})} = \overline{\lambda(\mathbf{x})e_{ll}(\mathbf{x})\delta_{ij}} + \overline{2\mu(\mathbf{x})e_{ij}(\mathbf{x})}$$

If we wish to replace our basic heterogeneous material by an equivalent homogeneous material that is locally isotropic, we seek a relation between $\tau_{ij}(\mathbf{x})$ and $e_{ij}(\mathbf{x})$ of the form

$$(5\text{-}86) \qquad \overline{\tau_{ij}(\mathbf{x})} = \lambda^*\overline{e_{ll}(\mathbf{x})}\delta_{ij} + 2\mu^*\overline{e_{ij}(\mathbf{x})}$$

where λ^* and μ^* are effective constants that must be obtained from a comparison of Eqs. 5-85 and 5-86.

In order to see the relation between Eqs. 5-85 and 5-86 let us first write

$$\tau_{ij}(\mathbf{x}) = \overline{\tau_{ij}(\mathbf{x})} + \tau_{ij}'(\mathbf{x})$$

$$e_{ij}(\mathbf{x}) = \overline{e_{ij}(\mathbf{x})} + e_{ij}'(\mathbf{x})$$

$$\lambda(\mathbf{x}) = \overline{\lambda(\mathbf{x})} + \lambda'(\mathbf{x})$$

$$\mu(\mathbf{x}) = \overline{\mu(\mathbf{x})} + \mu'(\mathbf{x})$$

where the primed quantities have zero mean value. Introducing these expressions into Eq. 5-85 yields

$$(5\text{-}87) \qquad \overline{\tau_{ij}} = [\overline{\lambda}\overline{e_{ll}} + \overline{\lambda'e'_{ll}}]\delta_{ij} + 2\overline{\mu}\overline{e_{ij}} + 2\overline{\mu'e'_{ij}}$$

where all the barred quantities are independent of $\mathbf{x}$.

Since the equations of elasticity are linear and $\overline{e_{ij}}$ is a constant tensor, we may write in general

(5-88) $e_{ij}'(\mathbf{x}) = C_{ijmn}'(\mathbf{x})\overline{e_{mn}}$

where the $C_{ijmn}'(\mathbf{x})$ are random functions of $\mathbf{x}$ determined by the equations of motion. Substituting Eq. 5-88 into Eq. 5-87 yields

(5-89) $\overline{\tau_{ij}} = [\bar{\lambda}\,\overline{e_{ll}} + \overline{\lambda'C_{llmn}'\,\overline{e_{mn}}}]\,\delta_{ij} + 2\bar{\mu}\overline{e_{ij}} + 2\mu'\overline{C_{ijmn}'\,\overline{e_{mn}}}$

Eq. 5-89 may be written in the form

(5-90) $\overline{\tau_{ij}} = [\bar{\lambda}\,\delta_{ij}\,\delta_{mn} + \overline{\lambda'C_{llmn}'}\,\delta_{ij} + 2\bar{\mu}\delta_{im}\,\delta_{jn} + \overline{2\mu'C_{ijmn}'}]\overline{e_{mn}}$

$$= C^*{}_{ijmn}\overline{e_{mn}}$$

Since the material properties are statistically homogeneous and isotropic and since $\overline{\tau_{ij}}$ and $\overline{e_{mn}}$ are average quantities, C_{ijmn}^* must be an isotropic tensor. Hence

(5-91) $C_{ijmn}^* = A^*\delta_{ij}\delta_{mn} + B^*\delta_{im}\delta_{jn} + C^*\delta_{in}\delta_{jm}$

and thus we are led to Eq. 5-86:

(5-86) $\overline{\tau_{ij}} = \lambda^*\overline{e_{ll}\,\delta_{ij}} + 2\mu^*\overline{e_{ij}}$

where $\lambda^* = A^*$ and $2\mu^* = B^* + C^*$.

Comparing Eqs. 5-86 and Eq. 5-87, we find

(5-92) $\lambda^* = \bar{\lambda} + \dfrac{\overline{\lambda'e_{ll}'}}{\overline{e_{ll}}}$

$$\mu^* = \bar{\mu} + \dfrac{\overline{\mu'e_{ij}'}}{\overline{e_{ij}}} \qquad \text{(no summation over } i \text{ and } j\text{)}$$

if $\overline{e_{ll}}$ and $\overline{e_{ij}}$ are not equal to zero.

We pointed out in Section 5.1.4 that ϵ^*, λ^*, and μ^* may also be defined by energy relations. Thus we may also write

(5-93) $\tfrac{1}{2}\epsilon^*\bar{E}_3{}^2 = \tfrac{1}{2}\overline{\epsilon E_i E_i} = \tfrac{1}{2}\overline{D_i E_i} = \tfrac{1}{2}\bar{D}_3\bar{E}_3 + \tfrac{1}{2}\overline{D_i'E_i'}$

and

(5-94) $\tfrac{1}{2}\lambda^*\overline{e_{ll}}\,\overline{e_{ij}}\,\delta_{ij} + \tfrac{1}{2}\,2\mu^*\overline{e_{ij}}\,\overline{e_{ij}} = \tfrac{1}{2}\overline{\lambda e_{ll}e_{ij}}\,\delta_{ij} + \tfrac{1}{2}\,2\overline{\mu e_{ij}e_{ij}}$

$$= \tfrac{1}{2}\overline{\tau_{ij}e_{ij}}$$

$$= \tfrac{1}{2}\overline{\tau_{ij}}\,\overline{e_{ij}} + \tfrac{1}{2}\overline{\tau_{ij}'e_{ij}'}$$

These definitions are equivalent to those given in Eq. 5-79 and Eq. 5-86, since

$$\overline{E_i' D_i'} = 0$$

and

$$\overline{e_{ij}' \tau_{ij}'} = 0$$

To show that these relations are correct, we assume an ergodic-type hypothesis and show that the volume average of these quantities approaches zero as $V \to \infty$.

For example

$$(5\text{-}95) \quad \overline{E_i' D_i'} = \overline{\frac{\partial \phi'}{\partial x_i} D_i'} = \lim_{V \to \infty} \frac{1}{V} \int_V \frac{\partial \phi'}{\partial x_i} D_i' \, d\mathbf{x}$$

$$= \lim_{V \to \infty} \frac{1}{V} \int_V \phi' [\text{div } \mathbf{D}'] \, d\mathbf{x} + \lim_{V \to \infty} \frac{1}{V} \int_V \nabla \cdot (\phi' \mathbf{D}') \, d\mathbf{x}$$

$$= \lim_{V \to \infty} \frac{1}{V} \int_S \phi' [\mathbf{D}' \cdot \mathbf{n}] \, dS$$

since div $\mathbf{D}' = 0$. Assuming that the average quantity

$$\frac{1}{S} \int_S \phi' [\mathbf{D}' \cdot \mathbf{n}] \, dS$$

is bounded as $V \to \infty$, we find

$$\lim_{V \to \infty} \frac{1}{V} \int_S \phi' [\mathbf{D}' \cdot \mathbf{n}] \, dS = \lim_{V \to \infty} \frac{S}{V} \frac{1}{S} \int_S \phi' [\mathbf{D}' \cdot \mathbf{n}] \, dS = 0$$

since $(S/V) \to 0$ as $V \to \infty$. The elasticity proof proceeds similarly.

5.4. Statistical Moment Equations

In Chapter 3 we discussed the nature of a complete formulation of the statistical problem. A complete solution to the statistical problem for heterogeneous media entails a knowledge of the functional $P[E_i(\mathbf{x}), \epsilon_{lm}(\mathbf{x})]$ in the electrostatic case and $P[u_i(\mathbf{x}), \lambda(\mathbf{x}), \mu(\mathbf{x})]$ in the elastic case.

$$P[E_i(\mathbf{x}), \epsilon_{lm}(\mathbf{x})] \, dE_1(\mathbf{x}) \cdots dE_3(\mathbf{x}) \, d\epsilon_{11}(\mathbf{x}) \cdots d\epsilon_{33}(\mathbf{x})$$

is defined as the probability of the realization of the particular joint field $[E_i(\mathbf{x}), \epsilon_{lm}(\mathbf{x})]$. There is a similar definition for $P[u_i(\mathbf{x}), \lambda(\mathbf{x}), \mu(\mathbf{x})]$. Equations can be derived which govern the characteristic functional (the generalized Fourier transform of P) and in principle the solution of this equation with appropriate boundary conditions provides the complete solution to the statistical problem.

The equations governing the characteristic functionals have so far proved too difficult to solve and so approximate solutions have been sought by considering the statistical moment equations. The complete infinite hierarchy of statistical moment equations is equivalent to the equation governing the characteristic functional and is similarly intractable. To proceed we must make some assumption which reduces the infinite hierarchy of equations to a finite set with which we may cope. In the theory of heterogeneous media the only cutoff procedure that has received detailed attention is the perturbation technique. As of the writing of this book no other assumptions (as, for example, the cumulant neglect hypothesis) have been considered although there is no reason why attempts should not be made. See, however, Bourret (1962).

We shall now outline the derivation of the hierarchy of statistical moment equations for the electrostatic case with a specific form of tensor permittivity and the elastic case assuming materials with local isotropy. We shall restrict ourselves to materials that are statistically homogeneous and isotropic. We shall then apply perturbation theory to derive a set of soluble equations and conclude with a few solutions that have been obtained.

5.4.1. The Electrostatic Case

The governing equations for the electrostatic problem with tensor permittivity ϵ_{ij} are

(5-96)
$$\frac{\partial}{\partial x_i} D_i(\mathbf{x}) = 0$$

$$D_i(\mathbf{x}) = \epsilon_{ij}(\mathbf{x})E_j(\mathbf{x})$$

(5-97)
$$\delta_{ijk}\frac{\partial}{\partial x_j} E_k(\mathbf{x}) = 0$$

In the following development of the statistical moment equations we shall follow the procedure presented by Molyneux (1964).

$\epsilon_{ij}(\mathbf{x})$ is a symmetric tensor. We denote the values of $\epsilon_{ij}(\mathbf{x})$ along the principal axes at $\mathbf{x}$, by $\epsilon_{(i)}(\mathbf{x})$; $(i) = 1, 2, 3$. In terms of the principal axes we write $\tilde{\epsilon}_{ij}(\mathbf{x}) = \epsilon_{(i)}(\mathbf{x})\delta_{ij}$; (i) indicates no summation on i. The unit vectors along the fixed-reference axis are denoted by n_i and the unit vectors along the local principal axes are denoted by $\mathbf{v}_i(\mathbf{x})$. The principal axes at a point are specified by the tensor functions $a_{ij}(\mathbf{x})$ which in turn are defined as

$$(5\text{-}98) \qquad a_{ij}(\mathbf{x}) = \mathbf{v}_i(\mathbf{x}) \cdot \mathbf{n}_j$$

where $a_{ij}a_{ik} = a_{ji}a_{ki} = \delta_{jk}$.

$\epsilon_{ij}(\mathbf{x})$ and $\tilde{\epsilon}_{ij}(\mathbf{x})$ are related by the expression

$$(5\text{-}99) \qquad \begin{aligned} \epsilon_{ij}(\mathbf{x}) &= a_{ki}(\mathbf{x})a_{mj}(\mathbf{x})\tilde{\epsilon}_{km}(\mathbf{x}) \\ &= a_{ki}(\mathbf{x})a_{kj}(\mathbf{x})\epsilon_{(k)}(\mathbf{x}) \end{aligned}$$

We have distinguished $a_{ij}(\mathbf{x})$ and $\epsilon_{(k)}(\mathbf{x})$ since they both may vary. In the subsequent development we shall, for simplicity, consider the special case in which $\epsilon_{(k)}(\mathbf{x})$ is independent of $\mathbf{x}$. When $\epsilon_{(k)}(\mathbf{x})$ is independent of $\mathbf{x}$, the average value of $\epsilon_{ij}(\mathbf{x})$ is given by

$$(5\text{-}100) \qquad \overline{\epsilon_{ij}} = \overline{a_{ki}(\mathbf{x})a_{kj}(\mathbf{x})}\epsilon_{(k)}$$

Since we assume that the media are statistically homogeneous and isotropic, $\overline{a_{ki}(\mathbf{x})a_{kj}(\mathbf{x})}\epsilon_{(k)}$ must be independent of $\mathbf{x}$ and proportional to δ_{ij}. It may be shown that

$$(5\text{-}101) \qquad \overline{a_{(k)i}(\mathbf{x})a_{(k)j}(\mathbf{x})} = \tfrac{1}{3}\delta_{ij}$$

Thus we have

$$(5\text{-}102) \qquad \begin{aligned} \overline{\epsilon_{ij}} &= \tfrac{1}{3}(\epsilon_1 + \epsilon_2 + \epsilon_3)\delta_{ij} \\ &= \bar{\epsilon}\delta_{ij} \end{aligned}$$

We shall later need an expression for $\overline{\epsilon_{ij}\epsilon_{kl}}$. Direct calculation shows

$$(5\text{-}103) \qquad \begin{aligned} \overline{\epsilon_{ij}\epsilon_{kl}} &= \tfrac{1}{15}(\epsilon_1{}^2 + \epsilon_2{}^2 + \epsilon_3{}^2)[\delta_{ij}\delta_{kl} + \delta_{il}\delta_{jk} + \delta_{ik}\delta_{jl}] \\ &\quad + 2(\epsilon_1\epsilon_2 + \epsilon_1\epsilon_3 + \epsilon_2\epsilon_3)[\tfrac{2}{15}\delta_{ij}\delta_{kl} - \tfrac{1}{30}(\delta_{il}\delta_{jk} + \delta_{ik}\delta_{jl})] \end{aligned}$$

For convenience we now write the permittivity tensor in the form

$$(5\text{-}104) \qquad \epsilon_{ij}(\mathbf{x}) = \overline{\epsilon_{ij}} + \epsilon_{ij}'(\mathbf{x}) = \bar{\epsilon}\delta_{ij} + \epsilon_{ij}'(\mathbf{x})$$

where $\bar{\epsilon} = \frac{1}{3}(\epsilon_1 + \epsilon_2 + \epsilon_3)$. We also write the principal values $\epsilon_{(i)}$ in the form

$$(5\text{-}105) \qquad\qquad \epsilon_{(i)} = \bar{\epsilon} + \Delta\epsilon_{(i)}$$

We then find

$$(5\text{-}106) \quad \epsilon_{ij}'(\mathbf{x}) = a_{ki}(\mathbf{x})a_{kj}(\mathbf{x})\Delta\epsilon_{(k)} - \frac{1}{3}(\Delta\epsilon_1 + \Delta\epsilon_2 + \Delta\epsilon_3)\delta_{ij}$$

In the perturbation analysis we shall have most need for the two-point correlation function

$$C_{ijkl}(\mathbf{x}_1, \mathbf{x}_2) = \overline{\epsilon_{ij}'(\mathbf{x}_1)\epsilon_{kl}'(\mathbf{x}_2)}$$

In terms of the functions $a_{ij}(\mathbf{x})$ we find

$$(5\text{-}107) \quad C_{ijkl}(\mathbf{x}_1, \mathbf{x}_2) = \overline{a_{pi}(\mathbf{x}_1)a_{pj}(\mathbf{x}_1)a_{qk}(\mathbf{x}_2)a_{ql}(\mathbf{x}_2)}$$
$$\cdot \Delta\epsilon_{(p)}\Delta\epsilon_{(q)} - \frac{1}{9}(\Delta\theta_1)^2\delta_{ij}\delta_{kl}$$

where $\Delta\theta_1 = \Delta\epsilon_1 + \Delta\epsilon_2 + \Delta\epsilon_3$.

When $\mathbf{x}_1 = \mathbf{x}_2$, the function reduces to

$$(5\text{-}108) \quad C_{ijkl}(\mathbf{x}_1, \mathbf{x}_1) = -\frac{2}{45}(\Delta\theta_1{}^2 - 3\Delta\theta_2)\delta_{ij}\delta_{kl}$$
$$+ \frac{3}{45}(\Delta\theta_1{}^2 - 3\Delta\theta_2)[\delta_{il}\delta_{jk} + \delta_{ik}\delta_{jl}]$$

where

$$\Delta\theta_2 \equiv \Delta\epsilon_1\Delta\epsilon_2 + \Delta\epsilon_1\Delta\epsilon_3 + \Delta\epsilon_2\Delta\epsilon_3$$

The function $C_{ijkl}(\mathbf{x}_1, \mathbf{x}_2)$ is assumed to be homogeneous and thus we have

$$(5\text{-}109) \qquad\qquad C_{ijkl}(\mathbf{x}_1, \mathbf{x}_2) = C_{ijkl}(\mathbf{r})$$

where $\mathbf{r} = \mathbf{x}_2 - \mathbf{x}_1$.

Furthermore, since the tensor $\epsilon_{ij}'(\mathbf{x})$ is symmetric then $C_{ijkl}(\mathbf{r})$ has the following properties

$$(5\text{-}110) \qquad C_{ijkl}(\mathbf{r}) = C_{jikl}(\mathbf{r}) = C_{ijlk}(\mathbf{r}) = C_{klij}(-\mathbf{r})$$

Since $C_{ijkl}(\mathbf{r})$ is an isotropic tensor it has the form (see Batchelor, 1953)

$$(5\text{-}111) \quad C_{ijkl}(\mathbf{r}) = P(r)r_ir_jr_kr_l + Q(r)r_ir_j\delta_{kl} + R(r)r_jr_k\delta_{li}$$
$$+ Q'(r)r_kr_l\delta_{ij} + R'(r)r_ir_i\delta_{jk} + R''(r)r_ir_k\delta_{jl}$$
$$+ R'''(r)r_jr_l\delta_{ik} + S(r)\delta_{ij}\delta_{kl} + T(r)\delta_{ik}\delta_{jl}$$
$$+ T'(r)\delta_{il}\delta_{jk}$$

where the functions $P(r)$, $Q(r)$, $Q'(r)$, $R(r)$, ... are even scalar functions of r. (Primes do *not* denote derivatives here.)

The conditions given in Eq. 5-110 demand that

(5-112) $$Q(r) = Q'(r)$$

$$R(r) = R'(r) = R''(r) = R'''(r)$$

$$T(r) = T'(r)$$

When $\epsilon_{(i)}(\mathbf{x})$ is independent of $\mathbf{x}$, as we take it to be here, then $\varepsilon_{ii}' = 0$ and we have the condition

(5-113) $$C_{iikl}(\mathbf{r}) = C_{ijll}(\mathbf{r}) = 0$$

In this case we have the additional restraints

(5-114) $$r^2P + 3Q + 4R = 0$$

(5-115) $$r^2Q + 3S + 2T = 0$$

In general we have five independent scalars characterizing the two-point correlation tensor $C_{ijkl}(\mathbf{r})$. When $\epsilon_{(i)}(\mathbf{x})$ is independent of $\mathbf{x}$ we need only three independent scalar functions to characterize $C_{ijkl}(\mathbf{r})$. Similar analyses may be made for the higher-order correlation tensors but the algebra is very involved and to this writer's knowledge no one has as yet taken on the task of analyzing the character of these functions.

We now write the basic equations 5-96 and 5-97 in terms of average and fluctuating components. We write $\epsilon_{ij}(\mathbf{x})$ in the form given by Eq. 5-104 and write for $E_i(\mathbf{x})$

(5-116) $$E_i(\mathbf{x}) = \overline{E_i(\mathbf{x})} + E_i'(\mathbf{x})$$

This yields for the basic equations

(5-117)

$$\bar{\epsilon}\frac{\partial \overline{E_i(\mathbf{x})}}{\partial x_i} + \bar{\epsilon}\frac{\partial E_i'(\mathbf{x})}{\partial x_i} + \frac{\partial}{\partial x_i}\overline{\epsilon_{ij}'(\mathbf{x})E_j(\mathbf{x})} + \frac{\partial}{\partial x_i}\epsilon_{ij}'(\mathbf{x})E_j'(\mathbf{x}) = 0$$

(5-118) $$\delta_{ijk}\frac{\partial \overline{E_k(\mathbf{x})}}{\partial x_j} + \delta_{ijk}\frac{\partial E_k'(\mathbf{x})}{\partial x_j} = 0$$

In order to determine a hierarchy of moment equations we write Eqs. 5-117 and 5-118 explicitly in terms of the independent variable $\mathbf{x}_1$.

We then proceed exactly as we did in Chapter 3 and multiply these equations sequentially by a set of functions such as

$$1$$
$$\epsilon_{kl}{}'(\mathbf{x}_2)$$
$$E_j{}'(\mathbf{x}_2)$$
$$\epsilon_{kl}{}'(\mathbf{x}_2)\epsilon_{pq}{}'(\mathbf{x}_3)$$
$$\epsilon_{kl}{}'(\mathbf{x}_2)E_p{}'(\mathbf{x}_3)$$
$$E_p{}'(\mathbf{x}_2)E_q{}'(\mathbf{x}_3)$$
$$\cdot$$
$$\cdot$$
$$\cdot$$

and then take the ensemble average.
This yields here

(5-119a) $\qquad \bar{\epsilon}\dfrac{\partial \overline{E_i(\mathbf{x}_1)}}{\partial x_{1i}} + \dfrac{\partial}{\partial x_{1i}}\overline{\epsilon_{ij}{}'(\mathbf{x}_1)E_j{}'(\mathbf{x}_1)} = 0$

(5-119b) $\bar{\epsilon}\dfrac{\partial}{\partial x_{1i}}\overline{E_i{}'(\mathbf{x}_1)\epsilon_{kl}{}'(\mathbf{x}_2)} + \dfrac{\partial}{\partial x_{1i}}\overline{\epsilon_{ij}{}'(\mathbf{x}_1)\epsilon_{kl}{}'(\mathbf{x}_2)E_j(\mathbf{x}_1)}$

$$+ \dfrac{\partial}{\partial x_{1i}}\overline{\epsilon_{ij}{}'(\mathbf{x}_1)\epsilon_{kl}{}'(\mathbf{x}_2)E_j{}'(\mathbf{x}_1)} = 0$$

(5-119c) $\bar{\epsilon}\dfrac{\partial}{\partial x_{1i}}\overline{E_i{}'(\mathbf{x}_1)E_q{}'(\mathbf{x}_2)} + \dfrac{\partial}{\partial x_{1i}}\overline{[\epsilon_{ij}{}'(\mathbf{x}_1)E_q{}'(\mathbf{x}_2)\,\overline{E_j(\mathbf{x}_1)}}]$

$$+ \dfrac{\partial}{\partial x_{1i}}\overline{\epsilon_{ij}{}'(\mathbf{x}_1)E_j{}'(\mathbf{x}_1)E_q{}'(\mathbf{x}_2)} = 0$$

(5-119d) $\bar{\epsilon}\dfrac{\partial \overline{E_i(\mathbf{x}_1)}}{\partial x_{1i}}\overline{\epsilon_{kl}{}'(\mathbf{x}_2)\epsilon_{pq}{}'(\mathbf{x}_3)} + \bar{\epsilon}\dfrac{\partial}{\partial x_i}\overline{E_i{}'(\mathbf{x}_1)\epsilon_{kl}(\mathbf{x}_2)\epsilon_{pq}(\mathbf{x}_3)}$

$$+ \dfrac{\partial}{\partial x_{1i}}\overline{\epsilon_{ij}{}'(\mathbf{x}_1)\epsilon_{kl}{}'(\mathbf{x}_2)\epsilon_{pq}{}'(\mathbf{x}_3)\,\overline{E_j(\mathbf{x}_1)}}$$

$$+ \dfrac{\partial}{\partial x_{1i}}\overline{\epsilon_{ij}{}'(\mathbf{x}_1)\epsilon_{kl}{}'(\mathbf{x}_2)\epsilon_{pq}{}'(\mathbf{x}_3)E_j{}'(\mathbf{x}_1)} = 0$$

$$\cdot$$
$$\cdot$$
$$\cdot$$

(5-120a) $$\delta_{ijk}\frac{\partial}{\partial x_{1j}}\overline{E_k(\mathbf{x_1})} = 0$$

(5-120b) $$\delta_{ijk}\frac{\partial}{\partial x_{1j}}\overline{E_k'(\mathbf{x_1})\epsilon_{mn}'(\mathbf{x_2})} = 0$$

(5-120c) $$\delta_{ijk}\frac{\partial}{\partial x_{1j}}\overline{E_k'(\mathbf{x_1})E_n'(\mathbf{x_2})} = 0$$

(5-120d) $$\delta_{ijk}\frac{\partial}{\partial x_{1j}}\overline{E_k'(\mathbf{x_1})\epsilon_{mn}'(\mathbf{x_2})\epsilon_{pq}'(\mathbf{x_3})} = 0$$

.

.

.

Unless the entire infinite sequence of equations is considered, we cannot solve for the dependent variables. Any finite set of equations is indeterminate.

Consider the set Eqs. 5-119a, 5-120a. In this case the unknown functions are

$$\overline{E_k(\mathbf{x_1})} \quad \text{and} \quad \overline{\epsilon_{ij}'(\mathbf{x_1})E_j'(\mathbf{x_1})}$$

and it is only possible to determine $\overline{E_k(\mathbf{x_1})}$ in terms of $\overline{\epsilon_{ij}'(\mathbf{x_1})E_j'(\mathbf{x_1})}$ (and, of course, the value of $\overline{E_k(\mathbf{x_1})}$ on some surface S). The set Eqs. 5-119a,b, 5-120a,b is no more satisfactory than the set Eqs. 5-119a, 5-120a. Here the unknown functions are

$$\overline{E_k(\mathbf{x_1})}, \overline{\epsilon_{ij}'(\mathbf{x_1})E_j'(\mathbf{x_2})} \quad \text{and} \quad \overline{\epsilon_{ij}'(\mathbf{x_1})\epsilon_{kl}'(\mathbf{x_2})E_j'(\mathbf{x_1})}$$

and it is only possible to determine $\overline{E_k(\mathbf{x_1})}$ and $\overline{\epsilon_{ij}'(\mathbf{x_1})E_j'(\mathbf{x_1})}$ in terms of $\overline{\epsilon_{ij}'(\mathbf{x_1})\epsilon_{kl}'(\mathbf{x_2})E_j'(\mathbf{x_1})}$. The function $\overline{\epsilon_{ij}'(\mathbf{x_1})\epsilon_{kl}'(\mathbf{x_2})}$ is assumed to be known.

The difficulty appears for any finite set of equations which is chosen. In order to arrive at a determinate set of equations some method of approximation must be introduced. The method we wish to consider here is a perturbation procedure which rests on the assumption that

(5-121) $$\frac{|\epsilon_{ij}'^n|}{(\bar\epsilon_{ll})^n} \ll 1 \quad (\text{all } n, \bar\epsilon_{ll} \neq 0)$$

We assume that $E_j'(\mathbf{x})$ may be written in the form

(5-122) $E_j'(\mathbf{x}) = E_j^{(1)}(\mathbf{x}) + E_j^{(2)}(\mathbf{x}) + E_j^{(3)}(\mathbf{x}) + \cdots +$

where $E_j^{(1)}(\mathbf{x})$ is of order

$$(\epsilon_{ij}'/\epsilon_{ll})E_k(\mathbf{x})$$

and $E_j^{(2)}(\mathbf{x})$ is of order

$$[(\epsilon_{ij}')^2/(\epsilon_{ll})^2]E_k(\mathbf{x})$$

and so on. Similarly, we write

(5-123) $\overline{E_j(\mathbf{x})} = \overline{E_j(\mathbf{x})}^{(0)} + \overline{E_j(\mathbf{x})}^{(1)} + \overline{E_j(\mathbf{x})}^{(2)} + \cdots$

where $\overline{E_j(\mathbf{x})}^{(n)}$ is the same order as $E_j^{(n)}(\mathbf{x})$.

In order to find the determinate set of equations we substitute Eqs. 5-122 and 5-123 into the set Eqs. 5-119, 5-120 and combine terms of like order of magnitude. For Eqs. 5-119 and 5-120a we have

(5-124a) $\bar{\epsilon}\dfrac{\partial \overline{E_i(\mathbf{x_1})}^{(0)}}{\partial x_{1i}} + \bar{\epsilon}\dfrac{\partial \overline{E_i(\mathbf{x_1})}^{(1)}}{\partial x_{1i}} + \bar{\epsilon}\dfrac{\partial \overline{E_i(\mathbf{x_1})}^{(2)}}{\partial x_{1i}}$

$\quad + \dfrac{\partial}{\partial x_{1i}}\overline{\epsilon_{ij}'(\mathbf{x_1})E_j^{(1)}(\mathbf{x_1})} + \dfrac{\partial}{\partial x_{1i}}\overline{\epsilon_{ij}'(\mathbf{x_1})E_j^{(2)}(\mathbf{x_1})} + \cdots = 0$

(5-124b) $\delta_{ijk}\dfrac{\partial}{\partial x_{1j}}\overline{E_k(\mathbf{x_1})}^{(0)} + \delta_{ijk}\dfrac{\partial}{\partial x_{1j}}\overline{E_k(\mathbf{x_1})}^{(1)}$

$\qquad\qquad\qquad + \delta_{ijk}\dfrac{\partial}{\partial x_{1j}}\overline{E_k(\mathbf{x_1})}^{(2)} + \cdots = 0$

Comparing terms of the same order of magnitude we, find

(5-125a) $\dfrac{\partial \overline{E_i(\mathbf{x_1})}^{(0)}}{\partial x_{1i}} = 0$

(5-125b) $\delta_{ijk}\dfrac{\partial}{\partial x_{1j}}\overline{E_k(\mathbf{x_1})}^{(0)} = 0$

(5-126a) $\bar{\epsilon}\dfrac{\partial \overline{E_i(\mathbf{x_1})}^{(2)}}{\partial x_{1i}} + \dfrac{\partial}{\partial x_{1i}}\overline{\epsilon_{ij}'(\mathbf{x_1})E_j^{(1)}(\mathbf{x_1})} = 0$

(5-126b) $\delta_{ijk}\dfrac{\partial}{\partial x_{1j}}\overline{E_k(\mathbf{x_1})}^{(2)} = 0$

$[\overline{E_i(\mathbf{x_1})}^{(1)} = 0].$

Equations 5-125a and 5-125b [together with boundary conditions for $\overline{E_i(\mathbf{x}_1)}^{(0)}$] determine $\overline{E_i(\mathbf{x}_1)}^{(0)}$. These equations are normally used to determine the electric field in a medium where $\epsilon_{ij}(\mathbf{x}) = \text{const } \delta_{ij}$. Since we assume the perturbation about this field to be small, we expect that as a first approximation it may be neglected and we would recover the homogeneous equations. To get the first-order nonzero correction to $\overline{E_i(\mathbf{x}_1)}$, $\overline{E_i(\mathbf{x}_1)}^{(2)}$, we refer to Eqs. 5-126a and 5-126b. In Eq. 5-126a we find the additional term $\overline{\epsilon_{ij}'(\mathbf{x}_1)E_j^{(1)}(\mathbf{x}_1)}$. In order to find a determinate set of equations for

$$\overline{\epsilon_{ij}(\mathbf{x}_1)E_j^{(1)}(\mathbf{x}_1)}$$

we must use a second set of Eqs. 5-119b, 5-120b. To lowest order these equations yield

(5-127a)

$$\bar{\epsilon}\frac{\partial}{\partial x_{1i}}\overline{E_i^{(1)}(\mathbf{x}_1)\epsilon_{kl}'(\mathbf{x}_2)} + \frac{\partial}{\partial x_{1i}}\overline{\epsilon_{ij}'(\mathbf{x}_1)\epsilon_{kl}'(\mathbf{x}_2)E_j(\mathbf{x}_1)}^{(0)} = 0$$

(5-127b) $$\delta_{ijk}\frac{\partial}{\partial \mathbf{x}_{ij}}\overline{E_k^{(1)}(\mathbf{x}_1)\varepsilon_{mn}'(\mathbf{x}_2)} = 0$$

Since $\overline{\epsilon_{ij}'(\mathbf{x}_1)\epsilon_{kl}'(\mathbf{x}_2)}$ is given and $\overline{E_i(\mathbf{x}_1)}^{(0)}$ has been found, we may find $\overline{E_i^{(1)}(\mathbf{x}_1)\epsilon_{kl}'(\mathbf{x}_2)}$ from this set of equations. Using this value of $\overline{E_i^{(1)}(\mathbf{x}_1)\epsilon_{kl}'(\mathbf{x}_2)}$ in Eq. 5-126a we may find $\overline{E_i(\mathbf{x}_1)}^{(2)}$.

Proceeding in a similar manner it is clear that we may also find the statistical quantities

$$\overline{E_i(\mathbf{x}_1)} = \sum_{j=0}^{\infty}\overline{E_i(\mathbf{x}_1)}^{(j)}$$

$$\overline{E_i'(\mathbf{x}_1)\epsilon_{jk}'(\mathbf{x}_1)} = \sum_{j=0}^{\infty}\overline{E_i^{(j)}(\mathbf{x}_1)\epsilon_{jk}'(\mathbf{x}_1)}$$

$$\overline{E_i'(\mathbf{x}_1)E_k'(\mathbf{x}_2)} = \sum_{j=0}^{\infty}\sum_{l=0}^{\infty}\overline{E_i^{(j)}(\mathbf{x}_1)E_k^{(l)}(\mathbf{x}_2)}$$

.

.

.

to any accuracy we desire (assuming convergence of the series).

Very little work has been done with inhomogeneous fields (see, however, Beran, 1965c). Even though we can find a determinate set of equations, the resultant set is difficult to handle except for the simplest geometries. The case for which $\overline{E_i(\mathbf{x}_1)} = $ constant, however, has received much more attention since this set of equations provides us with a way of finding the effective constants of statistically homogeneous and isotropic media. The basic set of equations is much simpler when $\overline{E_i(\mathbf{x})}$ is not a function of $\mathbf{x}$ since Eq. 5-123 is replaced by the single-term expression

(5-128) $$\overline{E_j(\mathbf{x})} = \bar{E}_j = \text{const}$$

or for convenience since the direction of $\mathbf{E}$ is arbitrary

(5-129) $$\overline{E_j(\mathbf{x})} = \bar{E}_3 \delta_{3j}$$

The set of equations 5-124 are now identically satisfied and the lowest-order set of equations is given by Eqs. 5-127a and 5-127b with $\overline{E_j(\mathbf{x}_1)}^{(0)} = \bar{E}_3 \delta_{3j}$. Thus we have

(5-130a) $$\bar{\epsilon}\, \frac{\partial}{\partial x_{1i}} \overline{\bar{E}_i^{(1)}(\mathbf{x}_1)\epsilon_{kl}'(\mathbf{x}_2)} + E_3 \frac{\partial}{\partial x_{1i}} \overline{\epsilon_{i3}'(\mathbf{x}_1)\epsilon_{kl}'(\mathbf{x}_2)} = 0$$

(5-130b) $$\delta_{ijk} \frac{\partial}{\partial x_{1j}} \overline{E_k^{(1)}(\mathbf{x}_1)\epsilon_{mn}'(\mathbf{x}_2)} = 0$$

The next order of equations can also be easily obtained but we shall not need them here.

These equations have been solved for two cases of interest.

CASE 1. $\epsilon_{(i)}$ has three distinct values independent of $\mathbf{x}$.

CASE 2. $\epsilon_{ij}(\mathbf{x}) = \epsilon_{(i)}(\mathbf{x})\, \delta_{ij}$, where $\epsilon_1(\mathbf{x}) = \epsilon_2(\mathbf{x}) = \epsilon_3(\mathbf{x})$. The first case is intended to represent a polycrystal. Here it is supposed that the principal values of ϵ_{ij} are constant but the orientation of each crystal with respect to some fixed axis varies. (That is $a_{ij}(\mathbf{x}) = \mathbf{v}_i(\mathbf{x})\cdot \mathbf{n}_j$.) The second case is simply the case of a scalar permittivity that varies with position. For this case the governing moment equations have been derived in Chapter 3 (Eqs. 3-91 and 3-92). We will first consider Case 1 following the development given by Molyneux (1964). We shall also consider here the function $\overline{E_i^{(1)}(\mathbf{x}_1)E_j^{(1)}(\mathbf{x}_2)}$.

5.4.1.1. Tensor Permittivity When $\epsilon_{(i)}$ Is Independent of x. To simplify the notation we write

$$L_{ijk}(\mathbf{x}_1, \mathbf{x}_2) = \overline{E_i^{(1)}(\mathbf{x}_1)\epsilon_{jk}'(\mathbf{x}_2)}$$

$$\mathscr{E}_{ij}(\mathbf{x}_1, \mathbf{x}_2) = \overline{E_i^{(1)}(\mathbf{x}_1)E_j^{(1)}(\mathbf{x}_2)}$$

As we stated in the foregoing, we assume the statistics of the $\epsilon_{ij}(\mathbf{x})$ field to be homogeneous and isotropic. Since $\overline{E_j(\mathbf{x})} = \bar{E}_j\delta_{3j}$, $L_{ijk}(\mathbf{x}_1, \mathbf{x}_2)$ and $\mathscr{E}_{ij}(\mathbf{x}_1, \mathbf{x}_2)$ are statistically homogeneous and we may write

$$L_{ijk}(\mathbf{x}_1, \mathbf{x}_2) = L_{ijk}(\mathbf{r})$$

$$\mathscr{E}_{ij}(\mathbf{x}_1, \mathbf{x}_2) = \mathscr{E}_{ij}(\mathbf{r})$$

where $\mathbf{r} = \mathbf{x}_2 - \mathbf{x}_1$. We will discuss the symmetry properties of L_{ijk} and $\mathscr{E}_{ij}$ shortly.

In terms of $\mathbf{r}$ Eqs. 5-130a and 5-130b become

(5-131a) $$\frac{\partial}{\partial r_i} L_{ikl}(\mathbf{r}) = -\frac{\bar{E}_3}{\bar{\epsilon}} \frac{\partial}{\partial r_i} C_{i3kl}(\mathbf{r})$$

(5-131b) $$\delta_{ijk} \frac{\partial}{\partial r_j} L_{kpq}(\mathbf{r}) = 0$$

Using the procedures just outlined, we may also find equations governing $\mathscr{E}_{ij}(\mathbf{r})$. They are

(5-132a) $$\frac{\partial}{\partial r_i} \mathscr{E}_{ij}(\mathbf{r}) = -\frac{\bar{E}_3}{\bar{\epsilon}} \frac{\partial}{\partial r_i} L_{ji3}(-\mathbf{r})$$

(5-132b) $$\delta_{ijk} \frac{\partial}{\partial r_j} \mathscr{E}_{km}(\mathbf{r}) = 0$$

Since the $\epsilon_{ij}(\mathbf{x})$ field is statistically isotropic and $\overline{E_j(\mathbf{x})} = \bar{E}_3\delta_{3j}$, all statistical quantities must be symmetric with respect to the r_3 axis. $L_{ijk}(\mathbf{r})$ and $\mathscr{E}_{ij}(\mathbf{r})$ are thus axially symmetric tensors and have the following forms (see Batchelor, 1953).

(5-133) $$L_{ikl}(\mathbf{r}) = Ar_ir_kr_l + B\delta_{i3}\delta_{k3}\delta_{l3} + Cr_i\delta_{kl} + D[r_k\delta_{il} + r_l\delta_{ik}]$$
$$+ E\delta_{i3}\delta_{kl} + F(\delta_{k3}\delta_{il} + \delta_{l3}\delta_{ik}) + G(r_ir_k\delta_{l3} + r_ir_l\delta_{k3})$$
$$+ Hr_kr_l\delta_{i3} + Ir_i\delta_{k3}\delta_{l3} + J(r_k\delta_{i3}\delta_{l3} + r_l\delta_{i3}\delta_{k3})$$

(5-134) $$\mathscr{E}_{ij}(\mathbf{r}) = M_1r_ir_j + M_2\delta_{i3}\delta_{j3} + M_3\delta_{ij} + M_4r_i\delta_{j3} + M_5r_j\delta_{i3}$$

where $A, B, C, \ldots, J$ and $M_1, \ldots, M_5$ are scalar functions of r and r_3.*

The solution of the equations governing the scalar functions is straightforward but tedious. We present here only an outline of the solution. In addition to the equations determined by substituting Eq. 5-133 into Eqs. 5-131a, 5-131b, 5-132a, and 5-132b we note that $L_{ikk}(\mathbf{r}) = 0$ (since $\epsilon_{kk}' = 0$) giving the conditions

$$(5\text{-}135) \qquad Ar^2 + 3C + 2D + 2r_3G + I = 0$$

$$(5\text{-}136) \qquad B + 3E + 2F + Hr^2 + 2r_3J = 0$$

Solutions are then obtained by assuming the forms

$$A(r, r_3) = r_3 a_0(r) + a_1(r)$$

$$\cdot$$
$$\cdot$$
$$\cdot$$

$$J(r, r_3) = r_3 j_0(r) + j_1(r)$$

$$M_1(r, r_3) = r_3^2 m_1^{(0)}(r) + r_3 m_1^{(1)}(r) + m_1^{(2)}(r)$$

$$\cdot$$
$$\cdot$$
$$\cdot$$

$$M_5(r, r_3) = r_3^2 m_5^{(0)}(r) + r_3 m_5^{(1)}(r) + m_5^{(2)}(r)$$

After solving for the new functions, (many terms of which are equal to zero), we find

$$(5\text{-}137) \quad L_{ijk}(r) = r_3 a_0(r) r_i r_j r_k + r_3 c_0(r) r_i \, \delta_{jk} + r_3 \, d_0(r)[r_j \, \delta_{ik} + r_k \, \delta_{ij}]$$

$$+ \, e_1(r) \, \delta_{i3} \, \delta_{jk} + f_1(r)[\delta_{j3} \, \delta_{ik} + \delta_{k3} \, \delta_{ij}]$$

$$+ \, g_1(r)[r_i r_j \, \delta_{k3} + r_i r_k \, \delta_{j3}] + d_0(r) r_j r_k \, \delta_{i3}$$

$$(5\text{-}138) \quad \mathscr{E}_{ij}(r) = [r_3^2 m_1^{(0)}(r) + m_1^{(2)}(r)] r_i r_j + 2 r_3 m_3^{(0)}(r)[r_i \, \delta_{j3} + r_j \, \delta_{i3}]$$

$$+ [r_3^2 m_3^{(0)}(r) + m_3^{(2)}(r)] \, \delta_{ij} + m_2^{(2)}(r) \, \delta_{i3} \, \delta_{j3}$$

* Note that E defined in Eq. 5-133 is unrelated to E_i.

In Eq. 5-137 we have

$$a_0(r) = -\frac{2}{3}\frac{\bar{E}_3}{\bar{\epsilon}}\left[\frac{r^2P + R}{r^2}\right] + \frac{2\bar{E}_3}{\bar{\epsilon}}\frac{1}{r^9}\int_0^r \eta^6 u(\eta)\,d\eta$$

$$d_0(r) = -\frac{2}{7}\frac{\bar{E}_3}{\bar{\epsilon}}\left[\frac{1}{r^7}\int_0^r \eta^6 u(\eta)\,d\eta - 2\int_r^\infty \eta P(\eta)\,d\eta\right]$$

$$c_0(r) = -\frac{2}{7}\frac{\bar{E}_3}{\bar{\epsilon}}\left[\frac{1}{r^7}\int_0^r \eta^6 u(\eta)\,d\eta + \frac{4}{5}\int_r^\infty \eta P(\eta)\,d\eta\right]$$

$$-\frac{2}{5}\frac{\bar{E}_3}{\bar{\epsilon}}\frac{1}{r^5}\int_0^r v(\eta)\,d\eta + \frac{2}{9}\frac{\bar{E}_3}{\bar{\epsilon}}[r^2P + 4R + \frac{2}{r^2}T]$$

$$g_1(r) = -\frac{2}{7}\frac{\bar{E}_3}{\bar{\epsilon}}\left[\frac{1}{r^7}\int_0^r \eta^6 u(\eta)\,d\eta + \frac{4}{5}\int_r^\infty \eta P(\eta)\,d\eta\right]$$

$$+\frac{3}{5}\frac{\bar{E}_3}{\bar{\epsilon}}\frac{1}{r^5}\int_0^r v(\eta)\,d\eta - \frac{\bar{E}_3}{\bar{\epsilon}}\left[R + \frac{1}{r^2}T\right]$$

$$e_1(r) = \frac{2}{15}\frac{\bar{E}_3}{\bar{\epsilon}}\left[\frac{1}{r^3}\int_0^r v(\eta)\,d\eta - \int_r^\infty \eta u(\eta)\,d\eta\right] - \frac{1}{5}r^2 d_0(r)$$

$$f_1(r) = -\frac{\bar{E}_3}{5\bar{\epsilon}}\left[\frac{1}{r^3}\int_0^r v(\eta)\,d\eta - \int_r^\infty \eta u(\eta)\,d\eta\right] - \frac{1}{5}r^2 d_0(r)$$

where

$$u(r) = R(r) - Q(r)$$

$$v(r) = r^4[2R(r) - Q(r)] + 5r^2 T(r)$$

In Eq. 5-138 we have

$$m_1^{(0)}(r) = \frac{\bar{E}_3}{\bar{\epsilon}} \left[\frac{7}{r^9} \int_0^r \eta^6 p(\eta)\, d\eta - \frac{p(\eta)}{r^2} \right]$$

$$m_3^{(0)}(r) = - \frac{\bar{E}_3}{\bar{\epsilon}} \frac{1}{r^7} \int_0^r \eta^6 p(\eta)\, d\eta$$

$$m_1^{(2)}(r) = m_3^{(0)}(r) + \frac{\bar{E}_3}{\bar{\epsilon} r^5} \int_0^r [p(\eta) - q(\eta)] \eta^4\, d\eta$$

$$m_2^{(2)}(r) = \frac{2}{5} \frac{\bar{E}_3}{\bar{\epsilon}} \left[\frac{1}{r^5} \int_0^r \eta^6 p(\eta)\, d\eta + \int_r^\infty \eta p(\eta)\, d\eta \right]$$

$$m_3^{(2)}(r) = \frac{\bar{E}_3}{5\bar{\epsilon}} \left[\frac{1}{r^5} \int_0^r \eta^6 p(\eta)\, d\eta + \int_r^\infty \eta p(\eta)\, d\eta \right]$$

$$- \frac{\bar{E}_3}{3\bar{\epsilon}} \left[\frac{1}{r^3} \int_0^r [p(\eta) - q(\eta)] \eta^4\, d\eta + \int_r^\infty [p(\eta) - q(\eta)] \eta\, d\eta \right]$$

where

$$p(r) = r \frac{d}{dr} d_0(r) + 5\, d_0(r) + c_0(r) + g_1(r)$$

$$q(r) = r \frac{d}{dr} g_1(r) + 5 g_1(r) + c_0(r) + g_1(r)$$

It is interesting to note that if the functions $T(r)$ and $S(r)$ (see Eq. 5-111; these functions appear in the isotropic form of $\overline{\epsilon_{ij}'(x) \epsilon_{kl}'(x + r)}$) decay as r^{-n} as $r \to \infty$ then $Q(r)$ and $R(r)$ will decay as $r^{-(n+2)}$ and $P(r)$ will decay as $r^{-(n+4)}$. In this case $\mathscr{E}_{ij}(\mathbf{r})$ and $L_{ijk}(\mathbf{r})$ will decay as r^{-n} if $n \leqslant 3$ and as r^{-3} if $n > 3$. If the decay of $T(r)$ and $S(r)$ is faster than r^{-n} then $\mathscr{E}_{ij}(\mathbf{r})$ and $L_{ijk}(\mathbf{r})$ will decay as r^{-3}.

The expression for $\mathscr{E}_{ij}(0)$ is

$$\mathscr{E}_{ij}(0) = m_3^{(2)}(0)\, \delta_{ij} + m_2^{(2)}(0)\, \delta_{i3}\, \delta_{j3}$$

From this expression we find for the sum of the mean square deviations of the electric field, $\mathcal{E}_{ii}(0) = \overline{E_i'E_i'}$, the value

(5-139) $\quad \mathcal{E}_{ii}(0) = \dfrac{\bar{E}_3^{\,2}}{\bar{\epsilon}^2} \left[\dfrac{10}{9} T(0) - \dfrac{2}{3} \int_0^r \eta[R(\eta) - Q(\eta)]\, d\eta \right]$

In general then the mean square derivation depends upon the shape of the correlation function. Virtually nothing is known about the integral

$$\int_0^r \eta[R(\eta) - Q(\eta)]\, d\eta$$

and in the variational treatment of Hashin and Shtrikman (1963) they have assumed this integral to be equal to zero. We shall return to this point in the concluding sections of this chapter when we discuss the use of variational principals for determining bounds on the effective constants. If this integral is equal to zero then we have

(5-140) $\quad \mathcal{E}_{ii}(0) = \dfrac{2}{27} \dfrac{\bar{E}_3^{\,2}}{\bar{\epsilon}^2}$

$\times \left[(\Delta\epsilon_1 + \Delta\epsilon_2 + \Delta\epsilon_3)^2 - 3(\Delta\epsilon_1 \Delta\epsilon_2 + \Delta\epsilon_1 \Delta\epsilon_3 + \Delta\epsilon_2 \Delta\epsilon_3) \right]$

From Eq. 5-80 we find for the effective constant ϵ^*

(5-141) $\quad \epsilon^* = \dfrac{\overline{\epsilon_{3j}(\mathbf{x})E_j(\mathbf{x})}}{\bar{E}_3} = \bar{\epsilon} + \dfrac{L_{j3j}(0)}{\bar{E}_3}$

$= \bar{\epsilon}\, \dfrac{2}{27} \left[(\Delta\epsilon_1 + \Delta\epsilon_2 + \Delta\epsilon_3)^2 - 3(\Delta\epsilon_1 \Delta\epsilon_2 + \Delta\epsilon_1 \Delta\epsilon_3 + \Delta\epsilon_2 \Delta\epsilon_3) \right]$

$+ \dfrac{2}{3\bar{\epsilon}} \int_0^\infty r[R(r) - Q(r)]\, dr$

Thus unless the integral expression is equal to zero, we find that ϵ^* like $\mathcal{E}_{ii}(0)$ depends upon the shape of the correlation function. If this integral is equal to zero ϵ^* agrees with the limiting expression that one may find from the very general bounds derived by Hashin and Shtrikman (1963).

230   Statistical Continuum Theories

5.4.1.2. Scalar Permittivity.   We consider here the scalar permittivity field $\epsilon_{ij}(\mathbf{x}) = \epsilon(\mathbf{x})\delta_{ij}$. In this case (following Beran and Molyneux, 1963) the governing equations for

$$L_i(\mathbf{x}_1, \mathbf{x}_2) = L_i(\mathbf{r}) = \overline{E_i^{(1)}(\mathbf{x}_1)\epsilon'(\mathbf{x}_2)}$$

and

$$\mathscr{E}_{ij}(\mathbf{x}_1, \mathbf{x}_2) = \mathscr{E}_{ij}(\mathbf{r}) = \overline{E_i^{(1)}(\mathbf{x}_1)E_j^{(1)}(\mathbf{x}_2)}$$

are

(5-142a) $$\frac{\partial}{\partial r_i} L_i(\mathbf{r}) = -\frac{\bar{E}_3}{\bar{\epsilon}} \frac{\partial}{\partial r_3} C_0(r)$$

(5-142b) $$\delta_{ijk} \frac{\partial}{\partial r_j} L_k(\mathbf{r}) = 0$$

(5-143a) $$\frac{\partial}{\partial r_i} \mathscr{E}_{ij}(\mathbf{r}) = -\frac{\bar{E}_3}{\bar{\epsilon}} \frac{\partial}{\partial r_3} L_j(-\mathbf{r})$$

(5-143b) $$\delta_{ijk} \frac{\partial}{\partial r_j} \mathscr{E}_{km}(\mathbf{r}) = 0$$

We remember that we have assumed $\overline{E_j(\mathbf{x})} = \bar{E}_3 \delta_{3j}$. $C_0(r)$ is defined as the two-point correlation function

$$\overline{\epsilon'(\mathbf{x}_1)\epsilon'(\mathbf{x}_2)}$$

The functions $L_i(\mathbf{r})$ and $\mathscr{E}_{ij}(\mathbf{r})$ are axially symmetric and may be written in the form

(5-144) $$L_i(\mathbf{r}) = A(r, r_3)r_i + B(r, r_3)\delta_{i3}$$

(5-145) $$\mathscr{E}_{ij}(\mathbf{r}) = G(r, r_3)r_i r_j + F(r, r_3)\,\delta_{i3}\,\delta_{j3} + C(r, r_3)\,\delta_{ij}$$
$$+ D(r, r_3)r_i\,\delta_{j3} + E(r, r_3)r_j\,\delta_{i3}*$$

Proceeding in exactly the way as we did in the previous section, we find solutions of the form

(5-146) $$A(r, r_3) = g(r)r_3$$
$$B(r, r_3) = B(r)$$

---

* Note that E defined in this equation is unrelated to E_i.

for $L_i(\mathbf{r})$, where

(5-147)
$$g(r) = -\frac{\bar{E}_3}{\bar{\epsilon}r^5} \int_0^r r'^3 \frac{dC_0(r')}{dr'} \, dr'$$

$$B(r) = -\frac{1}{3}\frac{\bar{E}_3}{\bar{\epsilon}} C_0(r) + \frac{\bar{E}_3}{3\bar{\epsilon}}\frac{1}{r^3} \int_0^r r'^3 \frac{dC_0(r')}{dr'} \, dr'$$

and for $\mathscr{E}_{ij}(\mathbf{r})$

(5-148)
$$G(r, r_3) = r_3^2 h(r) + k(r)$$
$$C(r, r_3) = r_3^2 m(r) + n(r)$$
$$D(r, r_3) = r_3 \, d(r)$$
$$E(r, r_3) = r_3 e(r)$$
$$F(r, r_3) = f(r)$$

where

(5-149)

$$h(r) = -\frac{\bar{E}_3}{\bar{\epsilon}}\frac{1}{r^9} \int_0^r r' \frac{dg'}{dr'} \, dr'$$

$$m(r) = \frac{d(r)}{2} = k(r) = \frac{e(r)}{2} = -\frac{\bar{E}_3}{\bar{\epsilon}}\frac{1}{r^7} \int_0^r r'^6 g(r') \, dr'$$

$$n(r) = \frac{f(r)}{2} = \frac{1}{5}\frac{\bar{E}_3}{\bar{\epsilon}}\left[\frac{1}{r^5} \int_0^r r'^6 g(r') \, dr' - \int_0^r r' g(r') \, dr'\right] + \frac{1}{15}\frac{\bar{E}_3}{\bar{\epsilon}^2} C_0(0)$$

The properties of $L_i(\mathbf{r})$ and $\mathscr{E}_{ij}(\mathbf{r})$ as $r \to \infty$ are similar to their tensor permittivity analogs. If $C_0(r)$ behaves as $1/r^n$, then $L_i(\mathbf{r})$ and $\mathscr{E}_{ij}(\mathbf{r})$ decay as $1/r^n$ ($n < 3$) and $1/r^3$ ($n \geqslant 3$) as $r \to \infty$. If $C_0(r)$ decays faster than $1/r^n$ (all n), then $L_i(\mathbf{r})$ and $\mathscr{E}_{ij}(\mathbf{r})$ decay as $1/r^3$ as $r \to \infty$. The mean square values of

$$\overline{E_{(j)}^{(1)}(\mathbf{x}_1) E_{(j)}^{(1)}(\mathbf{x}_1)}$$

$\mathscr{E}_{11}(0)$, $\mathscr{E}_{22}(0)$ and $\mathscr{E}_{33}(0)$ are calculated to be

$$(5\text{-}150) \qquad \mathscr{E}_{11}(0) = \mathscr{E}_{22}(0) = \frac{1}{15} \frac{\bar{E}_3^{\,2}}{\bar{\epsilon}^2} \overline{\epsilon'^2}$$

$$\mathscr{E}_{33}(0) = \frac{1}{5} \frac{\bar{E}_3^{\,2}}{\bar{\epsilon}^2} \overline{\epsilon'^2}$$

The effective constant ϵ^* is found to have the value

$$(5\text{-}151) \qquad \epsilon^* = \bar{\epsilon} - \frac{1}{3} \frac{\overline{\epsilon'^2}}{\bar{\epsilon}}$$

Here ϵ^* is independent of the shape of the correlation function $C_0(r)$ but depends only upon the value $C_0(0) = \overline{\epsilon'^2}$.

The results in this section may also be derived by considering the equations governing the Fourier transforms of the moments (see Section 3.2.3). These calculations have not been given in the literature but the procedure is straightforward.

5.4.1.3. The Second-Order Perturbation Calculation for Scalar Permittivity.

When we assume that $\overline{E_j(\mathbf{x})} = \bar{E}_3 \delta_{3j}$ we may solve the second-order perturbation equation for a scalar permittivity field that is statistically homogeneous and isotropic. This calculation was made by Molyneux (1964). The governing equations may be found from Eqs. 5-119 and 5-120 by using the form for $E_j'(\mathbf{x})$ that is given in Eq. 5-122. Since $\overline{E_i(x)}$ is taken to be a constant, Eq. 5-123 reduces to

$$\overline{E_j(\mathbf{x})} = \overline{E_j(\mathbf{x})}^{(0)}$$

The appropriate equations for $L^{(2)}(\mathbf{x}_1, \mathbf{x}_2) = \overline{E^{(2)}(\mathbf{x}_1)\epsilon'(\mathbf{x}_2)}$ are

$$(5\text{-}152a) \qquad \frac{\partial}{\partial x_{1i}} L_i^{(2)}(\mathbf{x}_1, \mathbf{x}_2) = -\frac{1}{\bar{\epsilon}} \frac{\partial}{\partial x_{1i}} \overline{E_i^{(1)}(\mathbf{x}_1)\epsilon'(\mathbf{x}_1)\epsilon'(\mathbf{x}_2)}$$

$$(5\text{-}152b) \qquad \frac{\partial}{\partial x_{1i}} \overline{E_i^{(1)}(\mathbf{x}_1)\epsilon'(\mathbf{x}_2)\epsilon'(\mathbf{x}_3)} = -\frac{\bar{E}_3}{\bar{\epsilon}} \frac{\partial}{\partial x_{13}} \overline{\epsilon'(\mathbf{x}_1)\epsilon'(\mathbf{x}_2)\epsilon'(\mathbf{x}_3)}$$

$$(5\text{-}152c) \qquad \delta_{ijk} \frac{\partial}{\partial x_{1j}} L_k^{(2)}(\mathbf{x}_1, \mathbf{x}_2) = 0$$

The expression for $\overline{E_i'(\mathbf{x}_1)E_j'(\mathbf{x}_2)}$ is

$$(5\text{-}153) \qquad \overline{E_i'(\mathbf{x}_1)E_j'(\mathbf{x}_2)} = \sum_{p=1}^{\infty} \sum_{q=1}^{\infty} \overline{E_i^{(p)}(\mathbf{x}_1)E_j^{(q)}(\mathbf{x}_2)}$$

Thus to second order we find

(5-154) $\overline{E_i'(\mathbf{x}_1)E_j'(\mathbf{x}_2)} = \overline{E_i^{(1)}(\mathbf{x}_1)E_j^{(1)}(\mathbf{x}_2)}$

$+ \overline{[E_i^{(1)}(\mathbf{x}_1)E_j^{(2)}(\mathbf{x}_2)} + \overline{E_i^{(2)}(\mathbf{x}_1)E_j^{(1)}(\mathbf{x}_2)]}$

We therefore must find equations governing

$$\mathscr{E}_{ij}^{(1,2)}(\mathbf{x}_1, \mathbf{x}_2) = \overline{E_i^{(1)}(\mathbf{x}_1)E_j^{(2)}(\mathbf{x}_2)}$$

We note that

$$\mathscr{E}_{ij}^{(1,2)}(\mathbf{x}_1, \mathbf{x}_2) = \mathscr{E}_{ji}^{(2,1)}(\mathbf{x}_2, \mathbf{x}_1)$$

The equations governing $\mathscr{E}_{ij}^{(1,2)}(\mathbf{x}_1, \mathbf{x}_2)$ are

(5-155a) $\bar{\epsilon}\dfrac{\partial}{\partial x_{1i}}\mathscr{E}_{ij}^{(1,2)}(\mathbf{x}_1, \mathbf{x}_2) + \bar{E}_3\dfrac{\partial}{\partial x_{13}}L_j(\mathbf{x}_2, \mathbf{x}_1) = 0$

(5-155b) $\delta_{ijk}\dfrac{\partial}{\partial x_{1j}}\mathscr{E}_{ki}^{(1,2)}(\mathbf{x}_1, \mathbf{x}_2) = 0$

Equations 5-152a–c and 5-155a,b constitute a set of equations that may be solved for $L_i^{(2)}(\mathbf{x}_1, \mathbf{x}_2) = L_i^{(2)}(\mathbf{r})$ and $\mathscr{E}_{ij}^{(1,2)}(\mathbf{x}_1, \mathbf{x}_2) = \mathscr{E}_{ij}^{(1,2)}(\mathbf{r})$ in terms of $\overline{\epsilon'(\mathbf{x}_1)\epsilon'(\mathbf{x}_2)\epsilon'(\mathbf{x}_3)} = C_1(\mathbf{x}_1, \mathbf{x}_2, \mathbf{x}_3) = C_1(\mathbf{\rho}, \mathbf{r})$ where $\mathbf{\rho} = \mathbf{x}_2 - \mathbf{x}_1$ and $\mathbf{r} = \mathbf{x}_3 - \mathbf{x}_1$. We will shortly introduce $\cos\theta \equiv u \equiv \mathbf{\rho}\cdot\mathbf{r}/|\mathbf{\rho}|\,|\mathbf{r}|$. The details of obtaining the solutions are given in Molyneux (1964). The method of solution is similar to that given in the preceding sections except that Molyneux found it convenient to first obtain an integral solution for $\overline{E_i^{(1)}(\mathbf{x}_1)\epsilon'(\mathbf{x}_2)\epsilon'(\mathbf{x}_3)}$ in terms of $C_1(\mathbf{\rho}, \mathbf{r})$. The final expression for $L_i^{(2)}(\mathbf{r})$ is

(5-156) $L_i^{(2)}(\mathbf{r}) = [r_3\,d_0(r)]r_i + e_i(r)\,\delta_{i3}$

where

$$d_0(r) = -\frac{1}{\bar{\epsilon}}\frac{1}{r^5}\int_0^r\left(x^3\frac{dJ(x)}{dx} + 2x^2[J(x) - I(x)]\right)dx$$

$$e_1(r) = -\frac{1}{3\bar{\epsilon}}J(r) + \frac{2}{3\bar{\epsilon}}\int_r^\infty\frac{1}{x}[J(x) - I(x)]\,dx$$

$$+ \frac{1}{3\bar{\epsilon}}\frac{1}{r^3}\int_0^r\left\{\left[x^3\frac{dJ(x)}{dx} + 2x^2(J(x) - I(x))\right]\right\}dx$$

and

$$I(r) = \frac{\bar{E}_3}{4\bar{\epsilon}} \int\limits_0^\infty \int\limits_{-1}^1 \left[(1 - u^2) \frac{\partial C_1}{\partial \rho} - u(1 - u^2) \frac{1}{\rho} \frac{\partial C_1}{\partial u} \right] d\rho \, du$$

$$J(r) = \frac{\bar{E}_3}{2\bar{\epsilon}} \int\limits_0^\infty \int\limits_{-1}^1 \left[(u^2) \frac{\partial C_1}{\partial \rho} + u(1 - u^2) \frac{1}{\rho} \frac{\partial C_1}{\partial u} \right] d\rho \, du$$

$$u = \left(\frac{\boldsymbol{\rho} \cdot \mathbf{r}}{|\boldsymbol{\rho}| \, |\mathbf{r}|} \right)$$

The final expression for $\mathscr{E}_{ij}^{(1,2)}(r)$ is

(5-157) $\mathscr{E}_{ij}^{(1,2)}(r) = [r_3^2 f_1^{(0)}(r) + f_3^{(0)}(r)] r_i r_j$

$$+ 2f_3^{(2)}(r) \, \delta_{i3} \, \delta_{j3} + [r_3^2 f_3^{(0)}(r) + f_3^{(2)}(r)] \, \delta_{ij}$$

$$+ 2r_3 f_3^{(0)}(r)[r_i \, \delta_{j3} + r_j \, \delta_{i3}]$$

where

$$f_1^{(0)}(r) = \frac{\bar{E}_3}{\bar{\epsilon}} \left[\frac{7}{r^9} \int\limits_0^r x^6 \, d_o(x) \, dx - \frac{d_o(r)}{r^2} \right]$$

$$f_3^{(0)}(r) = - \frac{\bar{E}_3}{\bar{\epsilon}} \frac{1}{r^7} \int\limits_0^r x^6 \, d_o(x) \, dx$$

$$f_3^{(2)}(r) = \frac{1}{5} \frac{\bar{E}_3}{\bar{\epsilon}} \left[\frac{1}{r^5} \int\limits_0^r x^6 \, d_o(x) \, dx + \int\limits_r^\infty x d_o(x) \, dx \right]$$

From these expressions one may determine that $L_j^{(2)}(r)$ and $\mathscr{E}_{ij}^{(1,2)}(r)$ have the same asymptotic character when $r \to \infty$ as $L_j(r)$ and $\mathscr{E}_{ij}(r)$. The expressions for the mean square values $\overline{E_1'^2}$, $\overline{E_2'^2}$, and $\overline{E_3'^2}$ to second order are now

(5-158) $\overline{E_1'^2} = \overline{E_2'^2} = \frac{1}{3} \overline{E_3'^2} = \frac{1}{15} \bar{E}_3^2 \frac{\overline{\epsilon'^2}}{\bar{\epsilon}^2} - \frac{2}{45} \bar{E}_3^2 \frac{\overline{\epsilon'^3}}{\bar{\epsilon}^3}$

$$+ \frac{1}{5} \frac{\bar{E}_3^2}{\bar{\epsilon}^3} \int\limits_0^\infty dr \int\limits_0^\infty \int\limits_{-1}^1 \frac{u(u^2 - 1)}{\rho r} \frac{\partial C_1(\rho, r, u)}{\partial u} \, du \, d\rho$$

This integral may be evaluated if the third-order correlation function $C_1(\rho, r, u)$ is known. It also may be evaluated for a symmetric two-phase material in terms of two-point correlation functions since then we may use Eq. 5-65. In this particular case we find that $C_1(\rho, r, u) = 0$ and thus

(5-159)
$$\overline{{E_1'}^2} = \overline{{E_2'}^2} = \tfrac{1}{3}\overline{{E_3'}^2} = \tfrac{1}{15}\bar{E}_3{}^2 \frac{\overline{\epsilon'^2}}{\bar{\epsilon}^2}$$

This result is the same as that given in Eq. 5-150 which was obtained by first-order perturbation theory.

The effective constant ϵ^* is also found in terms of this integral. We have

(5-160) $\epsilon^* = \bar{\epsilon} - \dfrac{1}{3}\dfrac{\overline{\epsilon'^2}}{\bar{\epsilon}} + \dfrac{1}{9}\dfrac{\overline{\epsilon'^3}}{\bar{\epsilon}^2}$

$$- \frac{1}{2}\frac{1}{\bar{\epsilon}^2}\int_0^\infty dr \int_0^\infty \int_{-1}^1 \frac{u(u^2 - 1)}{\rho r}\frac{\partial C_1(\rho, r, u)}{\partial u}\,d\rho\,du$$

Thus if either ϵ^* or the mean square value of $\epsilon'(\mathbf{x})$ is known to second order we find the other from the relation (here $\overline{E'^2} = \overline{{E_1'}^2} + \overline{{E_2'}^2} + \overline{{E_3'}^2}$)

(5-161)
$$\overline{E'^2} = \bar{E}_3{}^2\left[2\left(1 - \frac{\epsilon^*}{\bar{\epsilon}}\right) - \frac{1}{3}\frac{\overline{\epsilon'^2}}{\bar{\epsilon}^2}\right]$$

To first order the equation corresponding to 5-161 is

(5-162)
$$\overline{E'^2} = \bar{E}_3{}^2\left(1 - \frac{\epsilon^*}{\bar{\epsilon}}\right)$$

It is a reasonable conjecture that to any order there exists an algebraic relationship among $\overline{E'^2}$, ϵ^*, and the quantities $\overline{\epsilon'^n}$. If this is the case it is worthwhile to pursue the perturbation solutions a few more steps in the hope of establishing the nature of the relationship to all orders. It is rather easy to measure ϵ^* and $\overline{\epsilon'^n}$ and it would be desirable to establish the magnitude of $\overline{E'^2}$ from measurements such as these.

5.4.2. The Elastic Case

The determination of the hierarchy of equations for an elastic material subject to a displacement boundary condition proceeds in the same manner as for the electrostatic case. As we mentioned in the foregoing we shall restrict ourselves here to materials that are locally isotropic and statistically homogeneous and isotropic. We shall present a development similar to that given by Molyneux and Beran (1965).

The local stress–strain relation will be taken to be of the form

(5-163) $$\tau_{ij}(\mathbf{x}) = \lambda(\mathbf{x})e_{ll}(\mathbf{x})\delta_{ij} + 2\mu(\mathbf{x})e_{ij}(\mathbf{x})$$

where the joint statistics of the $\lambda(\mathbf{x})$ and $\mu(\mathbf{x})$ fields are assumed to be homogeneous and isotropic. The equilibrium equation is

(5-164) $$\frac{\partial}{\partial x_j}\tau_{ij}(\mathbf{x}) = 0$$

and using both the relation

(5-165) $$e_{ij}(\mathbf{x}) = \frac{1}{2}\left(\frac{\partial u_i(\mathbf{x})}{\partial x_j} + \frac{\partial u_j(\mathbf{x})}{\partial x_i}\right)$$

and Eq. 5-163, we find for the equation governing the displacement $u_i(\mathbf{x})$

(5-166) $$\mu(\mathbf{x})\,\nabla^2 u_i(\mathbf{x}) + [\lambda(\mathbf{x}) + \mu(\mathbf{x})]\frac{\partial}{\partial x_i}\frac{\partial u_j(\mathbf{x})}{\partial x_j} + \frac{\partial \lambda(\mathbf{x})}{\partial x_i}\frac{\partial u_j(\mathbf{x})}{\partial x_j}$$

$$+ \frac{\partial \mu(\mathbf{x})}{\partial x_j}\left[\frac{\partial u_i(\mathbf{x})}{\partial x_j} + \frac{\partial u_j(\mathbf{x})}{\partial x_i}\right] = 0$$

In analogy to what we have done previously we write

$$\mu(\mathbf{x}) = \bar{\mu} + \mu'(\mathbf{x})$$

$$\lambda(\mathbf{x}) = \bar{\lambda} + \lambda'(\mathbf{x})$$

$$u'(\mathbf{x}) = \overline{u_i(\mathbf{x})} + u_i'(\mathbf{x})$$

We assume now that $\overline{\mu'(\mathbf{x})^n}/\bar{\mu}^n$ and $\overline{\lambda'(\mathbf{x})^n}/\bar{\lambda}^n$ are $\ll 1$ for all n and for convenience we suppose that μ' and λ' are of the same order. We now write $u_i(\mathbf{x})$ and $u_i'(\mathbf{x})$ in the form of a perturbation series

(5-167)
$$\overline{u_i(\mathbf{x})} = \overline{u_i(\mathbf{x})}^{(0)} + \overline{u_i(\mathbf{x})}^{(1)} + \overline{u_i(\mathbf{x})}^{(2)} + \cdots$$

$$u_i'(\mathbf{x}) = u_i^{(1)}(\mathbf{x}) + u_i^{(2)}(\mathbf{x}) + u_i^{(3)}(\mathbf{x}) + \cdots$$

where the terms with the (j) superscript are of order $(\lambda'/\bar{\lambda})^j$.

In order to derive a hierarchy of statistical moment equations we write Eq. 5-166 explicitly in terms of the independent variable $\mathbf{x}_1$, multiply this equation by the sequence

$$1$$
$$\lambda'(\mathbf{x}_2)$$
$$\mu'(\mathbf{x}_2)$$
$$u_i'(\mathbf{x}_2)$$
$$\lambda'(\mathbf{x}_2)\lambda'(\mathbf{x}_3)$$
$$\lambda'(\mathbf{x}_2)\mu'(\mathbf{x}_3)$$
$$\mu'(\mathbf{x}_2)\mu'(\mathbf{x}_3)$$
$$u_i'(\mathbf{x}_2)\lambda'(\mathbf{x}_3)$$
$$u_i'(\mathbf{x}_2)\mu'(\mathbf{x}_3)$$
$$u_i'(\mathbf{x}_2)u_j'(\mathbf{x}_3)$$
$$\cdot$$
$$\cdot$$
$$\cdot$$

and average. We then equate terms of like magnitude in each equation.

We considered this type of matching procedure exhaustively in the previous section and nothing is gained by giving essentially the same arguments again. Instead we will turn immediately to the equations that we find to lowest order if we let $\overline{u_i(\mathbf{x})} = \overline{\alpha_{ij}x_j}$ where the $\overline{\alpha_{ij}}$ are independent of position and are symmetric. To lowest order the dependent variables are

$$P_i(\mathbf{x}_1, \mathbf{x}_2) = \overline{u_i^{(1)}(\mathbf{x}_1)\lambda'(\mathbf{x}_2)}$$

$$Q_i(\mathbf{x}_1, \mathbf{x}_2) = \overline{u_i^{(1)}(\mathbf{x}_1)\mu'(\mathbf{x}_2)}$$

$$R_{ij}(\mathbf{x}_1, \mathbf{x}_2) = \overline{u_i^{(1)}(\mathbf{x}_1)u_j^{(1)}(\mathbf{x}_2)}$$

The equations governing these functions are

(5-168a) $\bar{\mu} \nabla_1^2 P_i(\mathbf{x}_1, \mathbf{x}_2) + (\bar{\lambda} + \bar{\mu}) \dfrac{\partial}{\partial x_{1i}} \dfrac{\partial}{\partial x_{1j}} P_j(\mathbf{x}_1, \mathbf{x}_2)$

$$= -\left[\dfrac{\partial}{\partial x_{1i}} \overline{\lambda'(\mathbf{x}_1)\lambda'(\mathbf{x}_2)}\right]\overline{\alpha_{ll}} - \left[\dfrac{\partial}{\partial x_{1j}} \overline{\mu'(\mathbf{x}_1)\lambda'(\mathbf{x}_2)}\right]2\overline{\alpha_{ij}}$$

(5-168b) $\bar{\mu} \nabla_1^2 Q_i(\mathbf{x}_1, \mathbf{x}_2) + (\bar{\lambda} + \bar{\mu}) \dfrac{\partial}{\partial x_{1i}} \dfrac{\partial}{\partial x_{1j}} Q_j(\mathbf{x}_1, \mathbf{x}_2)$

$$= -\left[\dfrac{\partial}{\partial x_{1i}} \overline{\lambda'(\mathbf{x}_1)\mu'(\mathbf{x}_2)}\right]\overline{\alpha_{ll}} - \left[\dfrac{\partial}{\partial x_{1j}} \overline{\mu'(\mathbf{x}_1)\mu'(\mathbf{x}_2)}\right]2\overline{\alpha_{ij}}$$

(5-168c) $\bar{\mu} \nabla_1^2 R_{ik}(\mathbf{x}_1, \mathbf{x}_2) + (\bar{\lambda} + \bar{\mu}) \dfrac{\partial}{\partial x_{1i}} \dfrac{\partial}{\partial x_{1j}} R_{jk}(\mathbf{x}_1, \mathbf{x}_2)$

$$= -\left[\dfrac{\partial}{\partial x_{1i}} P_k(\mathbf{x}_2, \mathbf{x}_1)\right]\overline{\alpha_{ll}} - \left[\dfrac{\partial}{\partial x_{1j}} Q_k(\mathbf{x}_2, \mathbf{x}_1)\right]2\overline{\alpha_{ij}}$$

The known functions from the point of view of this development are (in normalized form)

(5-169) $$A(\mathbf{x}_1, \mathbf{x}_2) = A(\mathbf{r}) = \dfrac{\overline{\lambda'(\mathbf{x}_1)\lambda'(\mathbf{x}_2)}}{\overline{\lambda'^2}}$$

$$B(\mathbf{x}_1, \mathbf{x}_2) = B(\mathbf{r}) = \dfrac{\overline{\lambda'(\mathbf{x}_1)\mu'(\mathbf{x}_2)}}{\overline{\lambda'\mu'}}$$

$$C(\mathbf{x}_1, \mathbf{x}_2) = C(\mathbf{r}) = \dfrac{\overline{\mu'(\mathbf{x}_1)\mu'(\mathbf{x}_2)}}{\overline{\mu'^2}}$$

The solution of these equations for arbitrary values of $\overline{\alpha_{ij}}$ allows us to determine quantities like the effective elastic constants and values of the mean square value of stress and strain. Since discussions of the elastic properties of a medium are more often about stress and strain rather than displacement, the equations given in Beran and Molyneux (1965) were cast in terms of the quantities

$$P_{ik}(\mathbf{x}_1, \mathbf{x}_2) = \overline{e_{ik}'(\mathbf{x}_1)\lambda'(\mathbf{x}_2)}$$

$$Q_{ik}(\mathbf{x}_1, \mathbf{x}_2) = \overline{e_{ik}'(\mathbf{x}_1)\mu'(\mathbf{x}_2)}$$

$(e_{ik}' = e_{ik}^{(i)}$ to this order).

The relation between these quantities and the P_i and Q_i are obtained simply by differentiation. We have

(5-170) $\qquad P_{ik}(\mathbf{x}_1, \mathbf{x}_2) = \dfrac{1}{2}\left[\dfrac{\partial P_i(\mathbf{x}_1, \mathbf{x}_2)}{\partial x_{1k}} + \dfrac{\partial P_k(\mathbf{x}_1, \mathbf{x}_2)}{\partial x_{1i}}\right]$

$\qquad\qquad Q_{ik}(\mathbf{x}_1, \mathbf{x}_2) = \dfrac{1}{2}\left[\dfrac{\partial Q_i(\mathbf{x}_1, \mathbf{x}_2)}{\partial x_{1k}} + \dfrac{\partial Q_k(\mathbf{x}_1, \mathbf{x}_2)}{\partial x_{1i}}\right]$

Lastly, we note that since the $u_i'(\mathbf{x})$ field is homogeneous

$$R_{ij}(\mathbf{x}_1, \mathbf{x}_2) = R_{ij}(\mathbf{r})$$
$$P_{ij}(\mathbf{x}_1, \mathbf{x}_2) = P_{ij}(\mathbf{r})$$
$$Q_{ij}(\mathbf{x}_1, \mathbf{x}_2) = Q_{ij}(\mathbf{r})$$
$$P_i(\mathbf{x}_1, \mathbf{x}_2) = P_i(\mathbf{r})$$
$$Q_i(\mathbf{x}_1, \mathbf{x}_2) = Q_i(\mathbf{r})$$

The set of equations governing R_{ij}, P_{ij}, and Q_{ij} were solved by Beran and Molyneux (1965) for the special case

(5-171) $\qquad\qquad \overline{u_i(\mathbf{x})} = -\beta x_i$

which may be shown to correspond to hydrostatic pressure. Other cases may be worked out if we care to perform the tedious calculations, but to the writer's knowledge no one has yet made explicit calculations. It should be noted, however, that determination of the effective constants may be done very simply from equations like 5-168 if they are cast in terms of the Fourier transformed quantities (see Section 3.2.3).

We find here, for example, that

(5-172) $\qquad R_{ij}(\mathbf{r}) = F(r)r_i r_j - \left[\displaystyle\int_r^\infty \eta F(\eta)\, d\eta\right]\delta_{ij}$

where

$$F(r) = \dfrac{9\beta^2 \overline{k'^2}}{2(\bar\lambda + 2\bar\mu)^2}\left[\dfrac{1}{r^5}\int_0^r \eta^4 D(\eta)\, d\eta - \dfrac{1}{r^3}\int_0^r \eta^2 D(\eta)\, d\eta\right]$$

$$\overline{k'^2}D(r) = \overline{k'(\mathbf{x})k'(\mathbf{x} + \mathbf{r})} = \overline{\lambda'^2}A(r) + \tfrac{4}{3}\overline{\lambda'\mu'}B(r) + \tfrac{4}{9}\overline{\mu'^2}C(r)$$

$k(\mathbf{x})$ is the bulk modulus; $k(\mathbf{x}) = \lambda(\mathbf{x}) + \tfrac{2}{3}\mu(\mathbf{x})$.

$R_{ij}(\mathbf{r})$ has the same properties as $r \to \infty$ as the electrostatic functions. If $D(r)$ decays faster than r^{-3}, $R_{ij}(\mathbf{r})$ decays as r^{-3} as $r \to \infty$. If $D(r)$ decays as r^{-m} ($m \leqslant 3$), $R_{ij}(\mathbf{r})$ decays as r^{-m}.

From this calculation the effective bulk modulus may be found. We find

(5-173)
$$k^* = \bar{k} - \frac{\overline{k'^2}}{\bar{\lambda} + 2\bar{\mu}}$$

From this calculation k^* is the only effective constant that can be found. Expressions for the mean square values of e_{ij}' and τ_{ij}' are

(5-174)
$$\overline{e_{11}'^2} = \overline{e_{22}'^2} = \overline{e_{33}'^2} = \frac{1}{5}\frac{(3\beta)^2}{(\bar{\lambda} + 2\bar{\mu})^2}\overline{k'^2}$$

$$\overline{e_{12}'^2} = \overline{e_{13}'^2} = \overline{e_{23}'^2} = \frac{1}{3}\overline{e_{11}'^2}$$

$$\overline{\tau_{11}'^2} = \overline{\tau_{22}'^2} = \overline{\tau_{33}'^2} = \frac{32}{15}\bar{\mu}^2\frac{(3\beta)^2}{(\bar{\lambda} + 2\bar{\mu})^2}\overline{k'^2}$$

$$\overline{\tau_{12}'^2} = \overline{\tau_{13}'^2} = \overline{\tau_{23}'^2} = \frac{1}{8}\overline{\tau_{11}'^2}$$

It is interesting to note that under hydrostatic pressure the off-diagonal mean square strain values are one third the diagonal mean square strain values and that the stress-tensor ratio is 1 to 8. It is, of course, no surprise to find off-diagonal values for these tensors, but it is not something we ordinarily think about. When the perturbation of $k'(\mathbf{x})$ about the mean is not small, considerable shear will develop within a medium that is under hydrostatic pressure; and it is perhaps worthwhile to attempt to extend the perturbation procedure to try to find a general relationship between k^* and $\overline{\tau_{ij}'^2}$ along the lines discussed in the material below Eqs. 5-161 and 5-162.

5.5. Variational Procedures

As we have repeatedly emphasized, the effective constants of a heterogeneous material are extremely important quantities. The perturbation procedures we have developed only allow us to calculate these quantities if the deviations from the mean are small. Considerable effort has thus gone into the problem of bounding the effective constants when the deviations are large. The procedure for bounding these quantities has been to use variational principles. We have outlined the mathematics of this bounding procedure in Section 3.4. Now we wish to restate the results and give bounds that depend upon higher-order correlation functions. We shall restrict our discussion to the electrostatic case (mostly assuming a scalar permittivity), although everything we say may be extended to the elastic problem. We shall discuss first the utility of the standard variational principle and then the more sophisticated forms studied by Brown, Hashin, and Shtrikman.

5.5.1. The Standard Variational Principles

In Section 3.4 we established the following variational principles for a material with scalar permittivity:

PRINCIPLE A.   The integral

$$(5\text{-}175) \qquad U = \frac{1}{2V} \int_V \epsilon E_i E_i \, d\mathbf{x}$$

subject to the subsidiary condition

$$(5\text{-}176) \qquad \delta_{ijk} \frac{\partial}{\partial x_j} E_k = 0$$

is stationary and a minimum for

$$(5\text{-}177) \qquad \frac{\partial}{\partial x_i} \epsilon E_i = 0$$

In Eq. 5-175, V is the volume and, although not mentioned here, S is a surface enclosing the volume. Equation 5-176 implies that $E_i = \partial\phi/\partial x_i$, where ϕ is a scalar field; as a boundary condition we impose the requirement that $\delta\phi(S) = 0$.

PRINCIPLE B.   The integral

$$(5\text{-}178) \qquad U = \frac{1}{2V} \int_V \frac{D_i D_i}{\epsilon} \, d\mathbf{x}$$

subject to the subsidiary condition

(5-179) $\dfrac{\partial}{\partial x_i} D_i = 0$

is stationary and is a minimum for

(5-180) $\delta_{ijk} \dfrac{\partial}{\partial x_j} \dfrac{D_k}{\epsilon} = 0$

Equation 5-179 implies that $D_i = \delta_{ijk}(\partial/\partial x_j\, A_k)$ where A_k is a vector field; as a boundary condition we impose the requirement that $\delta A_i(S) = 0$.

These variational principles were then considered in the limit $V \to \infty$ for statistically homogeneous fields by invoking an ergodic hypothesis. In this limit we set

(5-181) $U = \overline{\epsilon E_i E_i}$

(5-182) $U = \dfrac{\overline{D_i D_i}}{\epsilon}$

We considered the only conditions on admissible fields, E_{iA} or D_{iA}, [beyond, of course, that $E_{iA} = \partial \phi_A/\partial x_i$ or $D_{iA} = \delta_{ijk}\,\partial/\partial x_j\, A_k$] to be that $\overline{E_{iA}} = \overline{E_i}$ or $\overline{D_{iA}} = \overline{D_i}$, where $\overline{E_i}$ and $\overline{D_i}$ are the correct average values.

In Section 3.4 we showed that since

(5-183) $U = \epsilon^* \overline{E_i E_i} = \overline{\epsilon E_i E_i} \leqslant \overline{\epsilon E_{iA} E_{iA}}$

and

(5-184) $U = \dfrac{1}{\epsilon^*} \overline{D_i D_i} = \dfrac{\overline{D_i D_i}}{\epsilon} \leqslant \dfrac{\overline{D_{iA} D_{iA}}}{\epsilon}$

by simply taking, in Principle A,

$$E_{iA} = \overline{E_i}$$

and, in Principle B,

$$A_{iA} = \overline{D_i}$$

we could show that

(5-185) $\dfrac{1}{\overline{1/\epsilon}} \leqslant \epsilon^* \leqslant \bar{\epsilon}$

In this section we wish to show how these bounds may be improved by making use of the perturbation series for E_i that we developed in the last section. Following a development given by Beran (1965), we shall also outline the analysis for Principle B.

As we did in Eq. 5-122, we write

$$(5\text{-}186) \quad E_i(\mathbf{x}) = \bar{E}_i \, \delta_{i3} + E_i^{(1)}(\mathbf{x}) + E_i^{(2)}(\mathbf{x}) + \cdots + E_i^{(n)}(\mathbf{x}) + \cdots$$

and note (but do not prove) that we expect, if this series were introduced into Eq. 5-183, that $\overline{\epsilon E_i E_i}$ would converge to $\epsilon^* \overline{E_i} \, \overline{E_i}$. As an admissible solution we assume the form

$$(5\text{-}187) \quad {}_N E_{iA}(\mathbf{x}) = \bar{E}_i \, \delta_{i3} + \lambda_1 E_i^{(1)}(\mathbf{x}) + \lambda_2 E_i^{(2)}(\mathbf{x}) + \cdots + \lambda_N E_i^{(N)}(\mathbf{x})$$

where the λ_j are to be chosen to minimize the upper bound and $\lambda_0 = 1$. With this expression it is clear that this bound cannot be worse than that given by Eq. 5-185, since we may always choose $\lambda_1 = \lambda_2 = \cdots = \lambda_N = 0$. When $N = 0$, we of course find the upper bound of Eq. 5-185.

If Eq. 5-187 is substituted into Eq. 5-183, we find for $N > 2$

$$(5\text{-}188) \quad \epsilon^* \bar{E}_3^{\,2} \leqslant \bar{\epsilon} \bar{E}_3^{\,2} + \bar{\epsilon} \lambda_1^{\,2} \overline{E_i^{(1)} E_i^{(1)}} + 2 \lambda_1 \bar{E}_3 \overline{\epsilon' E_3^{(1)}}$$

$$+ \lambda_1^{\,2} \overline{\epsilon' E_i^{(1)} E_i^{(1)}} + 2 \bar{E}_3 \lambda_2 \overline{\epsilon' E_3^{(2)}}$$

$$+ 2 \bar{\epsilon} \lambda_1 \lambda_2 \overline{E_i^{(1)} E_i^{(2)}} + \text{higher-order terms}$$

These quantities may be calculated by the methods used in Section 5.4. Reference to this section will give explicit formulas for the quantities through second order. We found there, for example

$$(5\text{-}189) \qquad \overline{E_i^{(1)} E_i^{(1)}} = \tfrac{1}{3}(\bar{E}_3)^2 \frac{\overline{\epsilon'^2}}{\bar{\epsilon}^2}$$

$$\overline{2 \epsilon' E_3^{(1)}} = -\tfrac{2}{3}(\bar{E}_3) \frac{\overline{\epsilon'^2}}{\bar{\epsilon}}$$

For the third-order term we calculate similarly†

$$(5\text{-}190) \quad \overline{\epsilon' E_i^{(1)} E_i^{(1)}}$$

$$= \bar{E}_3^{\,2} I = \bar{E}_3^{\,2} \left[\frac{1}{16\pi^2 \bar{\epsilon}^2} \int\limits_{V'} \int\limits_{V''} \frac{\partial^2}{\partial r_3 \, \partial s_3} \overline{[\epsilon'(0) \epsilon'(\mathbf{r}) \epsilon'(\mathbf{s})]} \frac{r_i s_i}{r^3 s^3} \, d\mathbf{r} \, d\mathbf{s} \right]$$

† This integral may be related to the integral in Eq. 5-160.

An explicit calculation may be made for the case $N = 1$. We find, after choosing the value of λ_1 that minimizes the right-hand side of Eq. 5-188,

(5-191)
$$\epsilon^* \leqslant \bar{\epsilon}\,\frac{(1/3)(\overline{\epsilon'^2}/\bar{\epsilon})}{[1 + (3\bar{\epsilon}I/\overline{\epsilon'^2})]}$$

It may be shown (see Beran and Molyneux, 1966) that this bound and the lower bound that is given in Eq. 5-193 are equal to, or lie within, the bounds given in Eq. 5-185.

In a very similar manner we can derive a lower bound for ϵ^*. We use as a trial function

(5-192) $$_N D_i(\mathbf{x}) = \bar{D}_3\,\delta_{i3} + \mu_i D_i^{(1)}(\mathbf{x}) + \mu_2 D_i^{(2)}(\mathbf{x}) + \cdots + \mu_N D_i^{(N)}(\mathbf{x})$$

The perturbation procedure can be worked out exactly as in the $E_i(\mathbf{x})$ case (some of the details are given in Beran, 1965). We find, finally, using $_1 D_i(\mathbf{x})$

(5-193)
$$\epsilon^* \geqslant \frac{1}{\dfrac{\bar{I}}{\bar{\epsilon}} - \dfrac{[(4/3)(\overline{\epsilon'/\epsilon})]^2 1/4\bar{\epsilon}^2}{[1/3\bar{\epsilon}^2[\overline{\epsilon'^2}/\epsilon] + K]}}$$

where

$$K = \frac{1}{16\pi^2\bar{\epsilon}^2}\int\limits_{V'}\int\limits_{V''} \frac{\partial^2}{\partial r_3\,\partial s_3}\,\overline{\frac{\epsilon'(\mathbf{r})\epsilon'(\mathbf{s})}{\epsilon(0)}}\,\frac{r_i s_i}{r^3 s^3}\,d\mathbf{r}\,d\mathbf{s}$$

ϵ^* is thus bounded by a knowledge of the two correlation functions

$$\overline{\epsilon'(0)\epsilon'(\boldsymbol{\rho})\epsilon'(\mathbf{r})}\qquad \text{and}\qquad \overline{\frac{\epsilon'(\boldsymbol{\rho})\epsilon'(\mathbf{r})}{\epsilon(0)}}$$

At the present time not too much is known about three-point correlation functions for real materials but there is no barrier to obtaining this information, from either a theoretical or an experimental approach. Theoretically, models like the Poisson point model may be used to calculate three-point correlation functions for material geometries that may be so characterized. Experimentally, it is possible, for example, to measure three-point correlation functions from photographs of two-phase materials in which the phases may be distinguished optically.

We can, for example, evaluate the bounds for the special case of a symmetric two-phase material. In this case, we get the relations

$$\overline{\epsilon'(\mathbf{x})\epsilon'(\mathbf{x}')\epsilon'(\mathbf{x}'')} = 0$$

and

$$\frac{\overline{\epsilon'(\mathbf{x})\epsilon'(\mathbf{x}')}}{\epsilon(0)} = \frac{\bar{\epsilon}}{\epsilon_1\epsilon_2}\overline{\epsilon'(\mathbf{x})\epsilon'(\mathbf{x}')}$$

where ϵ_1 and ϵ_2 are the permittivity values in the two phases. These results may be derived using the analyses given in Section 5.2.

The final result of using these relations in Eqs. 5-192 and 5-193 is

$$(5\text{-}194) \qquad \left(\frac{6\alpha^2 + 6\alpha}{\alpha^2 + 10\alpha + 1}\right)\frac{1}{\alpha^{1/2}} \leqslant \frac{\epsilon^*}{\sqrt{\epsilon_1\epsilon_2}} \leqslant \left(\frac{2\alpha^2 + 8\alpha + 2}{6 + 6\alpha}\right)\alpha^{-1/2}$$

where $\alpha = \epsilon_2/\epsilon_1$, $\epsilon_2 > \epsilon_1$.

An evaluation of this formula is given in Table 5-1 (see Beran and Molyneux, 1966). Also given in this table are the results obtained by Hashin and Shtrikman (1962), Brown (1965), and by using Eq. 5-185. The Hashin and Shtrikman results are derived from Eq. 5-200. We shall not give a derivation of Brown's bound but only mention his method of approach in Section 5.5.2.3. The formula is given in Eq. 5-220. In terms of α, Eq. 5-185 becomes

$$(5\text{-}195) \qquad \frac{2\alpha^{1/2}}{(1 + \alpha)} \leqslant \frac{\epsilon^*}{\sqrt{\epsilon_1\epsilon_2}} \leqslant \tfrac{1}{2}(1 + \alpha^{-1})\alpha^{1/2}$$

TABLE 5-1

Tabulation of Bounds for Symmetric Two-Phase Media
(Reproduced from Berin and Molyneux, 1966, Table 1)

α	Beran (1965) Eq. 51-94		Hashin and Shtrikman (1962) Eq. 5-200		Brown (1965) Eq. 5-220		Eq. 5-195	
	$\dfrac{\epsilon_L^*}{\sqrt{\epsilon_1\epsilon_2}}$	$\dfrac{\epsilon_u^*}{\sqrt{\epsilon_1\epsilon_2}}$	$\dfrac{\epsilon_L^*}{\sqrt{\epsilon_1\epsilon_2}}$	$\dfrac{\epsilon_u^*}{\sqrt{\epsilon_1\epsilon_2}}$	$\dfrac{\epsilon_L^*}{\sqrt{\epsilon_1\epsilon_2}}$	$\dfrac{\epsilon_u^*}{\sqrt{\epsilon_1\epsilon_2}}$	$\dfrac{\epsilon_L^*}{\sqrt{\epsilon_1\epsilon_2}}$	$\dfrac{\epsilon_u^*}{\sqrt{\epsilon_1\epsilon_2}}$
1	1	1	1	1	1	1	1	1
2	1.02	1.02	1.01	1.02	1.01	1.02	0.943	1.06
5	1.06	1.15	0.985	1 20	0 995	1.15	0.744	1.35
10	1.04	1.35	0.889	1.49	0.930	1.37	0.575	1.74
20	0.940	1.71	0.735	1.95	0.810	1.75	0.425	2.35
50	0.720	2.50	0.520	2.83	0.590	2.58	0.277	3.60
$\alpha \to \infty$	$6\alpha^{-1/2}$	$0.333\alpha^{1/2}$	$4\alpha^{-1/2}$	$0.4\alpha^{1/2}$	$4.75\alpha^{-1/2}$	$0.348\alpha^{1/2}$	$2\alpha^{-1/2}$	$0.5\alpha^{1/2}$

Similar calculations may be made in the elastic case. The elastic problem is treated by Beran and Molyneux (1966).

Miller (1967) has recently considered the evaluation of I and K using a cell model to represent a class of random two-phase materials. The material volume is assumed to be completely covered by non-overlapping cells. A cell is the volume within a mathematically closed surface such that the material property ϵ_i is constant within the cell. Two adjacent cells may or may not be of the same material. He further assumes that (1) the cell distribution is statistically homogeneous and isotropic and (2) the material property ϵ_i of a cell is statistically independent of the material property of an adjacent cell. Subject to these assumptions Miller finds

$$\overline{\epsilon'(0)\epsilon'(r)\epsilon'(s)} = \epsilon_2'^3 \left(v_2 g_2(0, \mathbf{r}, \mathbf{s}) - \frac{v_2^3}{(1 - v_2)^2} g_1(0, \mathbf{r}, \mathbf{s}) \right)$$

$$\frac{\overline{\epsilon'(\mathbf{r})\epsilon'(\mathbf{s})}}{\epsilon(0)} = \frac{\epsilon_2'^2}{\epsilon_2} \frac{v_2}{(1 - v_2)}$$

$$\times [(\alpha - 1)(v_2^2 g_1(0, \mathbf{r}, \mathbf{s}) - (1 - v_2)^2 g_2(0, \mathbf{r}, \mathbf{s}))$$

$$+ (v_2(1 - \alpha) + \alpha)((1 - v_2) f_2(\mathbf{r}, \mathbf{s}) + f_1(\mathbf{r}, \mathbf{s}))]$$

where $g_i(0, \mathbf{r}, \mathbf{s})$ is the probability of a triangle $(0, \mathbf{r}, \mathbf{s})$ having all three vertices in a single cell of property ϵ_i given that one of the points is in the cell, $f_i(\mathbf{s}, \mathbf{r})$ is the probability of a line segment $(\mathbf{r}, \mathbf{s})$ having both ends in a single cell of material property ϵ_i given that one of the points is in the cell, and $\epsilon_i' = \epsilon_i - \bar{\epsilon}$. If these expressions are substituted in Eqs. 5-191 and 5-193, we find finally

$$(5\text{-}196) \qquad \frac{\epsilon^*}{(\epsilon_1 \epsilon_2)^{1/2}} \leqslant \frac{1}{\alpha^{1/2}}$$

$$\times \left[1 + v_2(\alpha - 1) - \frac{(1/3)v_2(1 - v_2)(\alpha - 1)^2}{1 + (\alpha - 1)(v_2 + 3[(1 - v_2)^2 G_2 - v_2^2 G_1])} \right]$$

$$(5\text{-}197)$$

$$\frac{\epsilon^*}{(\epsilon_1 \epsilon_2)^{1/2}} \geqslant \frac{\alpha^{1/2}}{[\alpha - v_2(\alpha - 1)] - \dfrac{(4/3)(1 - \alpha)^2(1 - v_2)v_2}{1 + \alpha + 3(\alpha - 1)(v_2^2 G_1 - (1 - v_2)^2 G_2)}}$$

where

$$G_i = \frac{1}{16\pi^2} \int\limits_{V} \int\limits_{V'} \frac{\partial^2 g_i(0, \mathbf{r}, \mathbf{s})}{\partial r_3 \, \partial s_3} \frac{r_j s_j}{r^3 s^3} \, d\mathbf{r} \, d\mathbf{s}$$

Thus for this model Miller finds that the bounds on ϵ^* depend on only two numbers, G_1 and G_2. Next he shows that by requiring the lower bound to be $< \infty$ and the upper bound to be > 0 that G_1 and G_2 must both lie between $\frac{1}{9}$ and $\frac{1}{3}$. For all values of G the bounds lie within the Hashin-Shtrikman bounds (Eq. 5-200). No combinations of G, however, yield the bounds themselves.

If v_1 or v_2 is $\ll 1$ then one material may be considered to be an inclusion in the matrix of the other. In this case the cell shape may be taken to be the same as the inclusion shape. It may be shown that for spherical inclusions $G = \frac{1}{9}$ and for disk inclusions $G = \frac{1}{3}$.

Miller (1967) has plotted Eqs. 5-196 and 5-197 for various combinations of G_1 and G_2 and the results may be found in his thesis. He also shows the improvement one obtains over the Hashin-Shtrikman bounds if G_1 and G_2 are known. Over most of the range of v_1 and v_2 the improvement is of the same order as that shown in Table 5-1 (when $G_1 = G_2$ and $v_1 = v_2$, Eqs. 5-196 and 5-197 reduce to Eq. 5-194). Miller also treats the elastic problem and presents similar results for the bulk modulus.

5.5.2. Brown, Hashin, Shtrikman-Type Variational Principles

The standard variational principles are valid for any permittivity and elastic-constant fields. The value of the constants may be confined to a finite range as in a two-phase material, or they may have a finite probability of taking on all finite values. When, however, the value of the constants are confined to a finite range, for example, $\epsilon_1 \leqslant \epsilon \leqslant \epsilon_2$, it is desirable when bounding the effective constant ϵ^* to have a principle which specifically takes this additional information into account. The variational principles developed by Brown, Hashin, and Shtrikman serve this purpose, and the bounds derived for ϵ^* are much better than those derived using the standard principles if only volume fractions are taken into account.

5.5.2.1. The Scalar Problem. In Section 3.4 we derived the basic form of these generalized variational principles.† In this section we shall restate the principle for the scalar permittivity case and refer specifically to the symmetric two-phase material and to some experimental results. We shall discuss the application of this principle to the tensor permittivity problem and stress some of the limitations inherent in its use. We shall conclude with a very brief outline of some recent work by Brown (1965) in which he generalizes these principles to allow for the dependence of the effective permittivity on higher-order correlation functions.

In Section 3.3 we established the following principle:

PRINCIPLE C. The integral

$$U_T = \frac{1}{2V} \int_V \left[\epsilon_o \mathbf{E}_o \cdot \mathbf{E}_o - \frac{\mathbf{T} \cdot \mathbf{T}}{\epsilon - \epsilon_o} + 2\mathbf{T} \cdot \mathbf{E}_o + \mathbf{T} \cdot \mathbf{E}' \right] d\mathbf{x}$$

subject to the conditions

$$\epsilon_o \operatorname{div} \mathbf{E}' + \operatorname{div} \mathbf{T} = 0$$

and $\phi'(S) = 0$, is stationary for

$$\mathbf{T} = [\epsilon - \epsilon_o]\mathbf{E}$$

Here

$$\mathbf{E}' = \mathbf{E} - \mathbf{E}_o$$
$$\phi' = \phi - \phi_o$$

and the subscript o denotes a reference medium with constant permittivity ϵ_o, subject to a constant electric field $\mathbf{E}_o$. On using this theorem it was shown in Section 3.4 that

(5-198)

$$\epsilon_{\min} + \frac{A_{\min}}{1 - (1/3)(A_{\min}/\epsilon_{\min})} \leqslant \epsilon^* \leqslant \epsilon_{\max} + \frac{A_{\max}}{1 - (1/3)(A_{\max}/\epsilon_{\max})}$$

where

$$A_{\max \atop \min} = \frac{1}{V} \int \frac{d\mathbf{x}}{(1/(\epsilon - \epsilon_{\max \atop \min})) + (1/3\epsilon_{\max \atop \min})}.$$

† See also Hashin (1967) for a discussion of a method for generating this type of variational principle.

For the case of a two-phase material, $\epsilon = \epsilon_1$ with volume fraction v_1, $\epsilon = \epsilon_2$ with volume fraction v_2. Taking $\epsilon_2 > \epsilon_1$, we have

$$(5\text{-}199) \quad \epsilon_1 + \frac{v_2}{1/(\epsilon_2 - \epsilon_1) + (v_1/3\epsilon_1)} \leqslant \epsilon^* \leqslant \epsilon_2 + \frac{v_1}{1/(\epsilon_1 - \epsilon_2) + (v_2/3\epsilon_2)}$$

As we pointed out in the introduction, these bounds are the best possible bounds for a two-phase material in which no information other than volume fractions is given. This was shown to be true by Hashin and Shtrikman (1962) by calculating ϵ^* for a material composed of composite spheres of all sizes. When the outer part of the sphere is composed of material with permittivity ϵ_2, ϵ^* is equal to the upper bound. When the outer part of the spheres is composed of material with permittivity, ϵ_1, ϵ^* is equal to the lower bound. No model has as yet been constructed to show that Eq. 5-198 yields the best bound for an n-phase material.

In terms of $\alpha = \epsilon_2/\epsilon_1$, we may write Eq. 5-199 in the following form.

$$(5\text{-}200) \quad \left[\frac{4\alpha + 2}{5 + \alpha}\right]\frac{1}{\alpha^{1/2}} \leqslant \frac{\epsilon^*}{\sqrt{\epsilon_1 \epsilon_2}} \leqslant \left[\frac{2\alpha + 4}{5\alpha + 1}\right]\alpha^{1/2}$$

This formula is tabulated in Table 5-1 and compared with the results obtained by Beran (1966) and Brown (1960) for a symmetric two-phase media. The reason the Beran and Brown bounds are more stringent than those obtained by Hashin and Shtrikman is that the former sets take into account more information than just volume fractions. As we have seen, the assumption of a symmetric medium gives information about three-point correlation functions.

The bounds given in Eq. 5-200 have been confirmed by experiments reported in Landauer (1952) and De Loor (1956). Landauer collected the results of experiments on electrical conductivity made by many investigators. (The references are given in his paper.) Here ϵ is replaced by the conductivity σ. Figure 5-6 has been reproduced as a sample from the article by Hashin and Shtrikman (1962), Fig. 1-*b*. Additional information has been added to this figure. (Note that $1/\sigma^*$ rather than σ^* is plotted as the ordinate.) Experimental data has also confirmed the bounds derived in the theory of elasticity. We refer the reader to Hashin and Shtrikman (1963b) for appropriate references and to a more recent article by Umekawa and Sherby (1966).

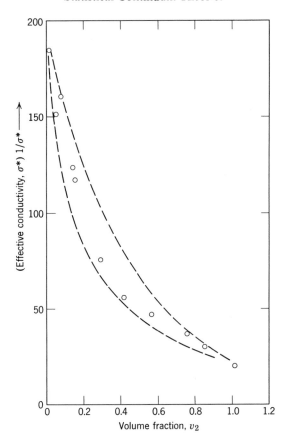

Fig. 5-6. Conductivity bounds: Mg_2Pb–Pb mixture. (From Hashin and Shtrikman, 1962.)

5.5.2.2. The Tensor Problem. In much the same way, we may determine bounds for materials with tensor permittivity in which the principal values are independent of **x**. An example of such a material is a polycrystal; Hashin and Shtrikman (1963a) have determined the conductivity of polycrystals in this manner. We shall outline their development using the language of the permittivity problem, following Molyneux (1964). Our purpose here is to show that application of this technique to problems that are more complicated than the scalar case may introduce hidden assumptions which imply a restriction on the internal geometry of the polycrystal.

We define the quantities $T_i(\mathbf{x})$ and $k_{ij}(\mathbf{x})$ by the following relations:

(5-201) $$T_i(\mathbf{x}) = D_i(\mathbf{x}) - \epsilon_o E_i(\mathbf{x})$$

(5-202) $$k_{ij}(\mathbf{x})[\epsilon_{jk}(\mathbf{x}) - \epsilon_o \delta_{jk}] = \delta_{ik}$$

$k_{ij}(\mathbf{x})$ can be expressed in terms of the $a_{ij}(\mathbf{x})$ (see Eq. 5-98). We have

(5-203) $$k_{ij}(\mathbf{x}) = \frac{1}{\epsilon_p - \epsilon_o} a_{pi}(\mathbf{x}) a_{pj}(\mathbf{x})$$

The form of the variational problem appropriate to this problem is

$$U = \frac{1}{2V} \int_V [\epsilon_o E_3{}^2 - k_{ij} T_i T_j - 2T_i \bar{E}_i - T_i E_i'] \, d\mathbf{x}$$

subject to the subsidiary condition

$$\epsilon_o \frac{\partial E_i'}{\partial x_i} + \frac{\partial T_i}{\partial x_i} = 0$$

and is stationary for

$$T_i = (\epsilon_{ij} - \epsilon_o \delta_{ij}) E_j$$

This principle may be established in the same way as the scalar principle was established in Section 3.4. It can be shown that U is a maximum when $\epsilon_o < \epsilon_1$ and a minimum when $\epsilon_o > \epsilon_3$ where $\epsilon_3 > \epsilon_1$. For convenience of manipulation, we will assume an ergodic hypothesis and replace the volume average for U by the ensemble average in the limit $V \rightarrow \infty$.

(5-204) $$U = \tfrac{1}{2}\epsilon_o \mathbf{E}_3{}^2 - \tfrac{1}{2}[k_{ij}\overline{T_i T_j} - 2\bar{T}_i \bar{E}_i - \overline{T_i E_i'}]$$

To make use of the principle, we expand $T_i'(\mathbf{x})$ in a Fourier expansion, set $E_i = \partial \phi'/\partial x_i$, and expand $\phi'(\mathbf{x})$ in a Fourier expansion. We emphasized in Chapters 2 and 3 that since these Fourier expansions do not exist in the limit $V \rightarrow \infty$, it is necessary to exercise some case in how we take limits. We have done this previously, and to avoid a lengthy discussion, we shall simply write the results in terms of $\Phi_{ij}(\mathbf{k})$, the Fourier transform of $\overline{T_i'(\mathbf{x})T_j'(\mathbf{x}+\mathbf{r})}$. We find

(5-205) $$U = \tfrac{1}{2}\epsilon_o \bar{E}_3{}^2 - \frac{1}{2}\left[\overline{k_{ij}T_iT_j} - 2\bar{T}_i\bar{E}_i + \int \frac{k_i k_j}{\epsilon_o k_l k_l}\Phi_{ij}(\mathbf{k})\,d\mathbf{k}\right]$$

This variational principle is useful if the integral over **k** may be written as $\overline{T_i'T_i'}$ multiplied by a constant. In this case, U may be made stationary by an appropriate choice of T_i', for fixed $\bar{T}_i$. The development is similar to the scalar development given in Chapter 3.

Now $\Phi_{ij}(\mathbf{k})$ is an axisymmetric tensor of the form

$$(5\text{-}206) \quad \Phi_{ij}(\mathbf{k}) = A(k, k_3)k_ik_j + B(k, k_3)\delta_{i3}\delta_{j3} + C(k, k_3)\delta_{ij}$$
$$+ D(k, k_3)k_i\delta_{j3} + F(k, k_3)k_j\delta_{i3}$$

Manipulation then shows that

$$(5\text{-}207) \quad \overline{T_iE_i'} = -\int_{\mathbf{k}} \frac{k_ik_k}{\epsilon_o k_l k_l} \Phi_{ij}(\mathbf{k})\,d\mathbf{k}$$

$$= -\frac{1}{\epsilon_o}\int_{\mathbf{k}} \left[k^2A + \frac{k_3^2 B}{k^2} + C + k_3(D + F) \right] d\mathbf{k}$$

and

$$(5\text{-}208) \qquad \overline{T_i'T_i'} = \int_{\mathbf{k}} [k^2A + B + 3C + k_3(D + F)]\,d\mathbf{k}$$

If we choose $A = D = F = 0$, B, and C arbitrary, we find

$$(5\text{-}209) \qquad\qquad \overline{T_iE_i'} = -\frac{1}{3\epsilon_o}\overline{T_i'T_i'}$$

which is the result found by Hashin and Shtrikman (1963).

Equation 5-209 may then be substituted into Eq. 5-204 and U maximized for fixed $\bar{T}_i$. The result is

$$(5\text{-}210) \qquad\qquad T_k = [\bar{T}_i + 3\epsilon_o\bar{E}_3\delta_{i3}][\overline{P_{ki}} + P_{ki}']$$

where P_{ij} is defined by the relation

$$P_{kj}[3\epsilon_o k_{ij} + \delta_{ij}] = \delta_{ik}$$
$$P_{ij}' = P_{ij} - Q\delta_{ij}$$

and

$$Q_0 = \frac{1}{3}\sum_{j=1}^{3} \frac{\epsilon_j - \epsilon_o}{\epsilon_j + 2\epsilon_o}$$

Averaging Eq. 5-210, we find that $\bar{T}_k$ must satisfy the relation

(5-211)
$$\bar{T}_k = \left[\frac{3\epsilon_o Q_o \bar{E}_3}{1 - Q_o}\right]\delta_{k3}$$

From the above expressions U is now given by

(5-212)
$$U = \frac{\epsilon^* \bar{E}_3^{\,2}}{2} = \frac{\epsilon_o \bar{E}_3^{\,2}}{2}\left[1 + \frac{2Q_o}{1 - Q_o}\right]$$

If we set $\epsilon_0 = \epsilon_1$, we derive a lower bound for ϵ^*, and if we set $\epsilon_o = \epsilon_3$, we find an upper bound for ϵ^*. Thus

(5-213)

$$\epsilon_1\left[1 + \frac{2Q_o(\epsilon_o = \epsilon_1)}{1 - Q_o(\epsilon_o = \epsilon_1)}\right] \leqslant \epsilon^* \leqslant \epsilon_3\left[1 + \frac{2Q_o(\epsilon_o = \epsilon_3)}{1 - Q_o(\epsilon_o = \epsilon_3)}\right]$$

In the limit of small perturbations, the bounds coincide, yielding Eq. 5-141 in which the integral term is set equal to zero. The absence of the integral term in this derivation is connected with the assumptions on $\Phi_{ij}(\mathbf{k})$ required to obtain Eq. 5-209. From Eq. 5-210 we find

(5-214) $$\overline{T_i'(\mathbf{x})T_j'(\mathbf{x} + \mathbf{r})} = \left[\frac{3\epsilon_o \bar{E}_3}{1 - Q}\right]^2\overline{P_{i3}'(\mathbf{x})P_{j3}'(\mathbf{x} + \mathbf{r})}$$

and from the definition of $P_{ij}(\mathbf{x})$

(5-215) $$P_{ij}(\mathbf{x}) = \left[\frac{\epsilon_q - \epsilon_o}{\epsilon_q + 2\epsilon_o}\right]a_{qi}(\mathbf{x})a_{qj}(\mathbf{x})$$

Denoting the Fourier transform of $\overline{P_{ij}(\mathbf{x})P_{lm}(\mathbf{x} + \mathbf{r})}$,

$$\Psi_{ijlm}(\mathbf{k})$$

the transform of Eq. 5-214 thus gives

(5-216) $$\Phi_{ij}(\mathbf{k}) = \left[\frac{3\epsilon_o \bar{E}_3}{1 - Q_o}\right]^2\Psi_{i3j3}(\mathbf{k})$$

From Eq. 5-215, $\Psi_{i3j3}(\mathbf{r})$ may be determined in terms of the spectrum of the $a_{ij}(\mathbf{x})$.

Since the spectrum associated with the $a_{ij}(\mathbf{x})$ is fixed, $\Phi_{ij}(\mathbf{k})$ must be compatible with this choice. In the scalar case compatibility is assured by the choice

$$\Phi_{ij}(\mathbf{k}) = \delta_{i3}\,\delta_{j3}B(k)$$

since

$$\overline{T_i'(\mathbf{x})T_j'(\mathbf{x}+\mathbf{r})} = f(r)\delta_{i3}\,\delta_{j3}$$

This follows from Eqs. 3-187 and 3-190. In the foregoing case we are not so fortunate in our choice. In order to see the nature of the difficulty, consider this calculation in the limit of small perturbations. In this case,

$$(5\text{-}217) \qquad \overline{P_{ij}(\mathbf{x})P_{kl}(\mathbf{x}+\mathbf{r})} \approx \frac{9\epsilon_o^{\,2}}{(\epsilon - 2\epsilon_o)^4}\,\overline{\epsilon_{ij}'(\mathbf{x})\epsilon_{kl}'(\mathbf{x}+\mathbf{r})}$$

and hence

$$(5\text{-}218) \qquad \overline{T_i'(\mathbf{x})T_j'(\mathbf{x}+\mathbf{r})} = \text{const} \times C_{i3j3}(\mathbf{r})$$

where $C_{ijlm}(\mathbf{r})$ is the two-point correlation function

$$\overline{\epsilon_{ij}'(\mathbf{x})\epsilon_{lm}'(\mathbf{x}+\mathbf{r})}$$

described earlier. Equation 5-111 gives a general expression for C_{ijlm}, and eventually it was shown there that C_{ijlm} depended on three scalar functions $P(r)$, $Q(r)$, and $R(r)$. Manipulation shows that if Eq. 5-218 is used to calculate the sum

$$\overline{T_i'E_i'} + \frac{1}{3\epsilon_o}\,\overline{T_i'T_i'}$$

which we have assumed to equal zero (see Eq. 5-209), we find instead that

$$(5\text{-}219) \qquad \overline{T_i'E_i'} + \frac{1}{3\epsilon_o}\,\overline{T_i'T_i'} = \text{const} \times \int_0^\infty r[R(r) - Q(r)]\,dr$$

Thus our assumption is only valid if the integral is equal to zero. This integral is exactly the term that appears in Eq. 5-141 and is the cause of the discrepancy between Eq. 5-141 and the small fluctuation limit of Eq. 5-213. At this time, not enough is known about the geometry to state whether or not the assumption $R(r) = Q(r)$ (or the less stringent assumption $\int_0^\infty r[R(r) - Q(r)]\, dr = 0$) is reasonable in most polycrystals. It appears that this integral is zero if the shape of each crystal is independent of the directions of the major and minor axis, but it is a matter that requires further attention. Experimental evidence up to the present, however (see Hashin & Shtrikman, 1963a), supports the view that the term is not important in the materials studied.

No one has yet determined whether or not the condition

$$\int_0^\infty r[R(r) - Q(r)]\, dr = 0$$

determined from a perturbation analysis is the only condition required to satisfy Eq. 5-218 in general. This, too, requires further investigation.

The Hashin, Shtrikman, Brown-type variational principles have also been used successfully in the study of elastic materials. We refer the reader to Hashin and Shtrikman (1963).

5.5.2.3. The Addition of Correlation Information in the Scalar Problem. Brown (1965) has shown how correlation information may be included in the foregoing type of variational principles, but in order to accomplish this he had to generalize the principles somewhat. His generalization consists essentially of writing the electrostatic energy in terms of $\mathbf{T}$, $\mathbf{E}$, and $\mathbf{E}_o$ in a manner similar to that given above but now allowing $\mathbf{T}$ and $\mathbf{E}$ to vary independently. To use the principle, one must assume some simple forms for $\mathbf{T}$ and $\mathbf{E}$ that are capable of bringing in the geometrical effects.

For a two-phase material Brown has set up a sequence of trial functions that allow correlation functions up to any order to be included in a specific calculation. For example, to include correlation effects up to the third order in an upper bound calculation, he sets

$$\mathbf{E} = f\mathbf{E}_o$$
$$\mathbf{T} = a\phi\mathbf{k} + b\phi(\mathbf{E}_o + \tfrac{1}{3}\phi\mathbf{k})$$

where $\mathbf{k}$ is a unit vector in the direction of $\mathbf{E}_o$, a, b, and f are adjustable parameters to be maximized and ϕ is a function that is unity in one phase and zero in the other. To lowest order, the results reduce to those of Hashin and Shtrikman presented above.

256 Statistical Continuum Theories

He explicitly calculates bounds for the two-phase material for the case in which the geometry of the phases is indistinguishable. This case was discussed in Section 5.1, and it was noted that in this case the third-order correlation function could be obtained in terms of the second-order functions. We refer the reader to Brown (1965) for the explicit calculation. A comparison of the results with the results of Hashin and Shtrikman (1962) and Beran (1966) is given in Table 5-1. The formula that Brown obtained is

$$(5\text{-}220) \quad \left[\frac{19\alpha^2 + 19\alpha - 2}{4\alpha^2 + 31\alpha + 1} \right] \frac{1}{\alpha^{1/2}} \leqslant \frac{\epsilon^*}{\sqrt{\epsilon_1 \epsilon_2}} \leqslant \left[\frac{8\alpha^2 + 26\alpha + 2}{23\alpha^2 + 14\alpha - 1} \right] \alpha^{1/2}$$

CHAPTER 6

Flow Through Porous Media

6.1. Introduction

Flow through porous media presents a statistical problem that is somewhat different from the problems considered previously in this book. Until now the geometrical boundary condition was never statistical in nature. In the theory of partial coherence, although we specified the statistics of the electric field over a surface, the surface geometry was the same for all members of the ensemble. In the theory of heterogeneous materials, we introduced the statistical information by considering some material constant, such as the permittivity, to be a statistical variable; even in two-phase materials we never explicitly considered the irregular boundary between phases. In considering flow through a medium such as sand, however, the sand geometry is usually considered more explicitly. There is no very natural way to introduce the irregular geometry directly into the governing partial differential equations and, for the most part, the statistical theories we present in this chapter will reflect this difficulty.

We shall now restrict ourselves to a consideration of a specific, well-defined problem—the problem of steady laminar flow under a uniform average pressure gradient through statistically homogeneous and isotropic media. We shall consider only those media that can properly be described from a statistical point of view. As we shall point out, regularly arranged, porous media may yield results strikingly different from those obtained in a medium such as beach sand. We shall assume that the fluid flow is described by the incompressible Navier-Stokes equations and that the flow is not turbulent. For the most part, we shall assume further that the flow is slow enough to neglect the inertial terms in the Navier-Stokes equations.

In this introduction we shall briefly discuss the properties of the porous media geometry and then state the basic quantities that may be determined. We shall discuss permeability and Darcy's law, the concept of velocity dispersion, and dispersion of soluble matter. In the next section we shall present statistical theories that attempt to treat these problems. Most of the statistical treatment given in this chapter will concern the dispersion problem. Unfortunately, very little has been done to determine the permeability using an explicitly statistical approach.

Flow through porous media is treated in books by Carman (1956), Collins (1961), and Scheidegger (1960); the reader is referred to these books for a treatment of the many different problems that arise in flow through porous media. As stated, we shall restrict ourselves to a specific, well-defined problem. (We neglect compressibility, thermal effects, adsorption effects, and so on.) In order to avoid duplication of Scheidegger's sections on statistical models for dispersion, we shall present a development given by Beran (1955). The connection between flow through porous media and Taylor's work (Taylor, 1953) on the dispersion of soluble matter in tube flows will also be emphasized.

6.1.1. A Description of Porous Media

The porous media that we wish to study in this chapter have properties similar to beach sand. We require that there be no simple analytic expression to describe the internal geometry of the media and that it be possible for a fluid to flow through any portion of the media (the pores must be connected). If we take a cross section of a sample of a porous medium, we expect a configuration somewhat like that shown in Fig. 6-1a. Both the solid geometry and associated pore geometry can be conveniently described here only from a statistical point of view. We do not wish to consider arrangements such as are shown in Fig. 6-1b. Although a two-dimensional figure such as 6-1a does not show whether or not the pores are connected, we shall consider only those media for which the pores are connected.

It is extremely difficult, practically, to characterize a porous medium. We must, moreover, characterize both the void and matter geometry, since, in general, they may have little in common. It is theoretically possible to do this, however, in the same manner as was outlined in Section 5.2. We have here a two-phase medium composed of a material phase and a void phase. The material is completely characterized by the

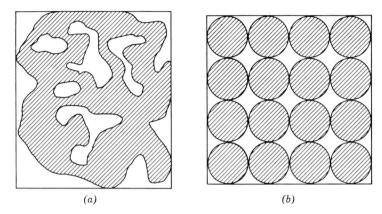

(a) (b)

Fig. 6-1. Geometry of various media (solid material cross hatched).

function (see Eq. 5-50)

(6-1)
$$P_{\epsilon_1 \epsilon_2 \epsilon_3 \cdots \epsilon_n}(\mathbf{r}_1, \mathbf{r}_2, \mathbf{r}_3, \ldots, \mathbf{r}_n)$$

$\epsilon_i = 1$ if $\mathbf{r}_i$ is in a material phase

$\epsilon_i = 0$ if $\mathbf{r}_i$ is in a void phase

This function gives the probability that $\epsilon = \epsilon_1$ at point $\mathbf{r}_1$, and $\epsilon = \epsilon_2$ at point $\mathbf{r}_2$, and, ..., and $\epsilon = \epsilon_n$ at point $\mathbf{r}_n$. For example, $P_{010}(\mathbf{r}_1, \mathbf{r}_2, \mathbf{r}_3)$ is the probability that there are voids at $\mathbf{r}_1$ and $\mathbf{r}_3$ and that there is material at $\mathbf{r}_2$. For statistically homogeneous media, $P_{\epsilon_1 \epsilon_2 \cdots \epsilon_n}$ depends upon the $n - 1$ vector differences, $\mathbf{r}_2 - \mathbf{r}_1, \mathbf{r}_3 - \mathbf{r}_1, \ldots, \mathbf{r}_n - \mathbf{r}_1$.

As we might suspect, very little is known about the foregoing function beyond one or two points. The function $P_0(\mathbf{r}_1)$ is the probability of finding a void at $\mathbf{r}_1$. For the statistically homogeneous media we consider here, this is simply the probability of finding a void at any point and hence is the familiar "porosity."

The function $P_{00}(\mathbf{r}_1, \mathbf{r}_2)$ is the probability of a void both at $\mathbf{r}_1$ and at $\mathbf{r}_2$. Again, since we assume the media are statistically homogeneous, the function depends only upon $\mathbf{r}_2 - \mathbf{r}_1 = \boldsymbol{\rho}$. Furthermore, since we also assume that the media are isotropic, P_{00} depends only upon $\rho \equiv |\boldsymbol{\rho}|$. Knowledge of the function $P_{00}(\rho)$ or rather the function $P_{00}'(\rho) = P_{00}(\rho) - P_0 P_0$, which approaches zero as ρ approaches infinity, gives us information about the pore-size distribution. For example, we may define a characteristic pore dimension l_P by the relation

$$(6\text{-}2) \qquad l_P = \int_0^\infty P_{00}'(\rho)\, d\rho$$

Similarly, the function $P_{11}'(\rho) = P_{11}(\rho) - P_1 P_1$ may be used to gain information about the size distribution of the matter phase. Unfortunately, it may be shown that $P_{11}'(\rho) = P_{00}'(\rho)$, and hence the function $P_{\epsilon_1 \epsilon_2}(\rho)$ alone does not provide a measure for distinguishing between pore and matter geometry. It provides information only about the overall geometry and would be useful only if the pore and matter geometry were very similar.

Knowledge of higher-order functions $P_{\epsilon_1 \epsilon_2 \cdots \epsilon_n}$, will eventually serve to distinguish between the void and matter geometry. It is difficult to measure these functions, however, and this theoretical structure has not yet proved to be of much value, practically, beyond the function P_0.

A statistical measure that goes somewhat beyond P_0 and is more discriminating than $P_{00}'(\rho)$ may be determined by taking a two-dimensional cross section of a porous medium, drawing lines at random in this plane, and determining the probability density of line segment lengths β which remain wholly in either the void or matter phases. The two functions denoted by $P_V(\beta)$ and $P_M(\beta)$ may be quite different, unlike the functions $P_{11}'(\rho)$ and $P_{00}'(\rho)$ which are the same. A characteristic pore dimension may be obtained from the relation

$$(6\text{-}3) \qquad l_P' = \int_0^\infty \beta P_V(\beta)\, d\beta$$

A characteristic grain dimension may be similarly found.

A statistical measure of the same kind but of a more three-dimensional nature, which we term, $P_V'(\delta)$, may be described as follows (see Scheidegger, 1960): For every point in the void, let δ be the diameter of the largest sphere that can be constructed about the point such that the sphere remains within the void. $P_V'(\delta)\, d\delta$ is the probability that the sphere diameter lies between δ and $\delta + d\delta$ for any void point chosen at random. From $P_V'(\delta)$, we may define a characteristic pore dimension l_P'', as

(6-4) $$l_P'' = \int_0^\infty \delta P_V'(\delta) \, d\delta$$

We may also define a function $P_M'(\delta)$, by performing the same type of measurements in the matter phase. Again, unlike the two functions $P_{11}'(\rho)$ and $P_{00}'(\rho)$, $P_V'(\delta)$ and $P_M'(\delta)$ may be quite different.

Not many measurements of this kind have been made. (See Scheidegger, 1960, for a discussion of what has typically been done.) Frequent reference to a characteristic pore diameter is made in the literature, but most often no very detailed measurements of the foregoing type have been performed to determine it. A precise quantity that has received somewhat more attention is the length S^{-1} defined as

(6-5) $$S^{-1} = \frac{\text{bulk volume}}{\text{internal area}}$$

This length appears in hydraulic-radius type theories and will be discussed in more detail later.

The details of measurement of quantities such as P_0 and S^{-1} may be found in Scheidegger (1960). Numerous references to the literature may also be found there. In order to obtain the more detailed statistical information we would like, we need only to obtain a photograph of a planar cross section of the porous medium. From this section, the porosity may be easily obtained, and the functions $P_V(\beta)$, $P_M(\beta)$, and $P_{00}'(\rho)$ may be measured in a very straightforward manner. The measurements of the latter functions from a photograph are tedious, but once a satisfactory picture of ample size is obtained, the measurements may be made by relatively untrained people. From this type of picture, we may also obtain the functions $P_{\epsilon_1\epsilon_2\epsilon_3}(\mathbf{r}_1, \mathbf{r}_2, \mathbf{r}_3)$ which depend upon $|\mathbf{r}_2 - \mathbf{r}_1|$, $|\mathbf{r}_3 - \mathbf{r}_1|$ and $(\mathbf{r}_2 - \mathbf{r}_1) \cdot (\mathbf{r}_3 - \mathbf{r}_1)$ (i.e., the configuration of a triangle). Even S^{-1} may be obtained from a picture such as this (see Kendall and Moran, 1963). Although the difficulty of making such cross-sectional photographs should not be underemphasized, this writer believes it is worth considerable effort. The need for measurements of functions like $P_V(\beta)$ and even $P_{\epsilon_1\epsilon_2\epsilon_3}$ is beginning to be recognized in studies of heterogeneous media; theoretical developments indicate that they would also be useful in scientific studies of flow through porous media.

6.1.2. Darcy's Law

One of the most important problems in flow through porous media is the determination of the average flow rate for a given pressure gradient. The problem is illustrated in Fig. 6-2.

We consider ideally a porous medium filling all space. There is an average pressure gradient $\partial \bar{p}/\partial z$ in the z direction; and as a result of

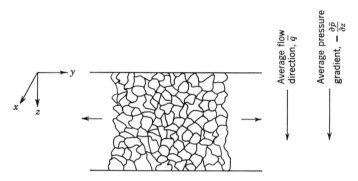

Fig. 6-2. Flow through a porous medium under a pressure gradient.

the gradient, there is an average volume flow rate per unit area, $\bar{q}$. We suppose that there is no average flow in the x and y directions. The problem is to determine $\bar{q}$ from $\partial \bar{p}/\partial z$, the fluid viscosity, and a knowledge of the properties of the porous medium. For simplicity we assume the porous medium is statistically homogeneous and isotropic, has interconnected pores, and the flow is very slow and steady.

In practice, the foregoing ideal case may be approximated by filling a tube with a porous medium like sand and allowing a fluid like water to percolate through the tube under the influence of gravity. It is only necessary that the tube length and tube diameter both be very much larger than both characteristic grain and pore dimensions (using any reasonable definitions). In this manner it is possible to establish experimentally the following relationship, termed Darcy's law:

$$(6\text{-}6) \qquad\qquad \bar{q} = -\frac{k}{\mu}\,\mathrm{grad}\,\bar{p}$$

where μ is the viscosity of the fluid (units: gram/cm-sec) and k is a constant of the porous medium that is independent of $\bar{q}$ and grad $\bar{p}$. k is called the permeability and has the dimensions of cm^2.

A linear integral relation governing $\bar{q}$ and grad $\bar{p}$ follows from the steady state Navier-Stokes equations

$$(6\text{-}7) \qquad (\mathbf{v} \cdot \nabla)\mathbf{v} = -\frac{1}{\rho}\,\text{grad}\,p + \nu\,\nabla^2\mathbf{v}$$

if the inertia terms on the left-hand side of the equation are neglected. Equation 6-6 may be inferred from this linear relation using dimensional reasoning since $\bar{q}$ can only depend on grad p and μ for fixed geometry. Recently Poreh and Elata (1966) gave a proof of Eq. 6-6 using the Lorentz reciprocal relation associated with the Navier-Stokes equations in the absence of inertia terms. Unfortunately, the writer became aware of their proof when this book was in press and their proof could not be included here.

Practically, k is insensitive to the displacement of a few or, in fact, many grains, and the question arises as to how dependent k is upon geometry. Unfortunately, we can really say very little and thus will confine our discussion to a few remarks. It is known that k is very dependent upon the porosity of the medium. Porosity, however, is the crudest of geometrical properties, and it would be quite remarkable if this quantity were the only geometric property on which the permeability is dependent. For example, a simple argument shows that, indeed, this is improbable, since porosity and interconnectedness of the pores may be taken as independent properties of a medium. In the limiting case of *no* interconnectedness, the permeability is zero independent of the porosity; and it is easy to conceive of gradually improving the inter-connectedness (keeping the porosity constant) until some maximum value of permeability is obtained.*

It seems that in order to gain a better understanding of the permeability of porous media, functions such as $P_{00}'(\rho)$, $P_V(\beta)$, or $P_V'(\delta)$ must at least be observed in more detail. Porosity and an additional length or two are not sufficient to determine the permeability. This is indicated

---

* Even though we stated that in this section we would consider only porous media that have interconnected pores and that are statistically isotropic, we do discuss models in which these conditions are not met. The consideration of the limit of non-interconnected pores is intended to show that some statistical parameters are insensitive to this restriction. Nonisotropic nonrandom models are treated since they often provide clues to effects common to many types of porous media.

by the crude argument previously given and the almost endless number of phenomenological and empirical formulas that appear in the literature. Unfortunately, little more than this can really be said at the present time. There is now little understanding of the probability functions cited in the foregoing. The sensitivity of k to the shape of these functions is not known.

Despite the fact that porosity and even an additional length are not adequate for a real understanding of the permeability, it would be

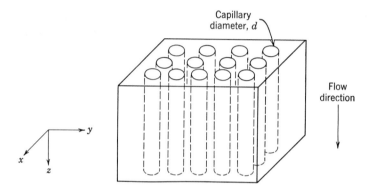

Fig. 6-3. Capillary model of a porous medium.

improper to dismiss the many studies that seek to incorporate them in an expression for the permeability. These certainly allow us to make order-of-magnitude estimates of the permeability. It is only important to realize that they have very serious limitations. In order to show the utility of these developments, we shall now consider some simple capillary type models.

The simplest way in which we could describe a porous medium for the purposes of estimating the permeability is to assume that it may be approximated by a solid medium, permeated by a number of straight circular capillaries of equal diameter d (see Fig. 6-3). To analyze such a model, it is assumed that the flow progresses through each capillary under a pressure gradient $\partial \bar{p}/\partial z$. An effective k may be determined for each tube and, taking account of the porosity (i.e., essentially the knowledge that there are a number of capillaries of area $\pi d^2/4$ per unit area in the x-y plane), the permeability of the medium may be derived.

In a single, circular tube the relation between q and $\partial\bar{p}/\partial z$ is

(6-8)
$$q_c = -\frac{d^2}{32\mu}\frac{\partial\bar{p}}{\partial z}$$

The permeability for this tube k_c is thus

(6-9)
$$k_c = \frac{d^2}{32}$$

In order to find the permeability for the medium, we assume that a fraction P of the area is covered by capillaries. This fraction P is to be identified with the porosity. Then for the medium

(6-10)
$$\bar{q} = -\frac{P d^2}{32\mu}\frac{\partial\bar{p}}{\partial z}$$

and

(6-11)
$$k = \frac{P d^2}{32}$$

For purposes of generalization this formula could be written in terms of S^{-1}. Here

(6-12)
$$S^{-1} = (\pi\ d^2/4)L/P\pi\ dL = \frac{d}{4P}$$

Thus

(6-13)
$$k = \frac{P^3[S^{-1}]^2}{2}$$

The straight circular-tube model may be generalized in two ways. The shapes of the tubes may be made arbitrary, and the tubes may be made curved in the direction of flow. The form of Eq. 6-13 may be readily generalized to include these effects.

Equation 6-13 was written in terms of S^{-1} rather than d in the hope that this form has some universal validity. The length

$$m = \frac{\text{cross-sectional area normal to flow}}{\text{wetted perimeter}}$$

is called the hydraulic radius and has proved useful in pipe studies in the past. For capillaries, m may be expressed in the following manner:

(6-14) $$m = \frac{\text{volume filled with fluid}}{\text{internal area}} = S^{-1}P$$

We may write for Eq. 6-13

(6-15) $$k = \frac{Pm^2}{2}$$

and in general we may write for noncircular pipes

(6-16) $$k = \frac{Pm^2}{c_0}$$

Equation 6-16 is termed a Kozeny equation (see Kozeny, 1927).

This form is useful if m varies with capillary shapes; but c_0 is rather insensitive to the shape. Carman (1956) gives a list of values of c_0 for various capillary shapes. For most shapes c_0 varies between 1.5 and 2.5. (For an equilateral triangle c_0 is 1.67; for an ellipse with a semiaxis ratio of 10 c_0 is 2.45.) The variation of c_0 is thus not too great; but on the other hand, workers in the field have had considerable difficulty in choosing an appropriate average value.

The effect of pipe curvature essentially lengthens the pipe from a length L to a new length L_F. Since the pressure gradient must now push the fluid through a length L_F instead of L, the flow equation

(6-17) $$\bar{q} = -\frac{k}{\mu}\frac{\partial \bar{p}}{\partial z} = -\frac{k}{\mu}\frac{\Delta p}{L}$$

may be replaced by

(6-18) $$\bar{q} = -\frac{k}{\mu}\frac{\Delta p}{L_F} = -\frac{k}{\mu}\frac{L}{L_F}\frac{\Delta p}{L} = -\frac{k}{\mu}\frac{L}{L_F}\frac{\partial \bar{p}}{\partial z}$$

Incorporating the L/L_F factor into the permeability, we have now, in place of Eq. 6-16

(6-19) $$k = \frac{Pm^2}{c_0}\frac{L}{L_F} = \frac{P^3(S^{-1})^2}{c_0}\frac{L}{L_F}$$

The ratio L_F/L is termed the tortuosity T.

There have been various modifications of Eq. 6-19; the reader is referred to Carman (1956) and Scheidegger (1960) for a discussion of the many forms given. It is very difficult to determine experimentally the validity of Eq. 6-19 for real porous media, since the factors c_0 and L/L_F have no clearly prescribed measurement procedure associated with them. S^{-1} also is unspecified if we restrict ourselves to capillaries, but here we may make an assumption that takes us from the capillary model to the real porous media. We may assume that Eq. 6-19 may be applied to a real porous medium wherein

$$S^{-1} = \frac{\text{bulk volume}}{\text{internal area}}$$

the internal area thus being the one measured for the real porous medium.

In view of the impreciseness of c_0 and T, the writer has difficulty in understanding how Eq. 6-19 may be verified experimentally—except to determine the dependence of k on P for very similar packings. (See, however, Carman, 1956, for a somewhat different point of view.) It does seem reasonable that Eq. 6-19 can be used to estimate k. P may be measured and S^{-1} may be measured; c_0 probably lies most often between 1.5 and 2.5, and T probably lies most often between 1 and $\sqrt{2}$.

More recently there have been attempts to modify Eq. 6-19 by introducing statistical ideas into the shape and connection of the pores. We cite articles by Childs and Collis-George (1950), Marshall (1957), Wylie and Gardner (1958a,b). In the next section on statistical theories we shall present the theory given by Childs and Collis-George (1950) as an example, so that the reader may see the type of approach that is followed. The statistical ideas introduced are not applied directly to a differential equation as we have hitherto done, but the development requires a knowledge of a function like $P_V(\beta)$ or $P_V'(\delta)$.

In closing this subsection we should note that Darcy's linear law is probably correct only if the inertia terms in the Navier-Stokes equations can be neglected. It is not enough that the flow be nonturbulent; in addition the flow must be very slow. Just how slow the flow must be is not known, but it is expected that if the Reynolds number is much less than one, using any reasonable definition of pore diameter, the inertia terms may be neglected. (See Scheidegger, 1960, for a further discussion of this point.) We should not be deceived by the solution for flow through straight capillaries where the inertia terms are identically zero. When the tubes are curved as they certainly are in any realistic model of a porous medium, then the inertia terms are present, and they may be neglected only if the flow is very slow.

6.1.3. Dispersion

On referring to Fig. 6-2, suppose that at time $t = 0$ we introduced a molecular tracer into the fluid in the form of a slug lying between $z = 0$ and $z = \Delta h$, where Δh is much greater than both characteristic pore and grain dimensions. We assume that the concentration of the tracer is a constant C_0 between $z = 0$ and $z = \Delta h$ for all x and y. We also assume that the tracer does not affect the fluid properties in any way. We denote the average fluid velocity in the flow direction by $\bar{v}$ $(P\bar{v} = \bar{q})$. We now ask what the concentration of the tracer C is for arbitrary time t. If detailed measurements of C are made, we will find that C depends upon x, y, z, and t [i.e., we have $C(x, y, z, t)$]. If, however, we take a local average of $C(x, y, z, t)$ of the form

$$(6\text{-}20) \quad \tilde{C}(z, t) = \frac{1}{8\, \Delta x\, \Delta y\, \Delta z} \int_{z-\Delta z}^{z+\Delta z} \int_{y-\Delta y}^{y+\Delta y} \int_{x-\Delta x}^{x+\Delta x} C(x', y', z', t)\, dx'\, dy'\, dz'$$

where Δx, Δy, and Δz are all much greater than both characteristic pore and grain dimensions but are much less than a characteristic variation σ of $\tilde{C}(z, t)$, we find a function dependent only upon z and t.*

The first thing we note is that at time t the tracer is not confined to a slug positioned between $z = \bar{v}t$ and $z = \bar{v}t + \Delta h$. There has been dispersion, and although the maximum concentration $\tilde{C}_M$ will ideally occur at $z = \bar{v}t + (\Delta h/2)$, $\tilde{C}(z, t)$ will have nonzero values for $z < \bar{v}t$ and $z > \bar{v}t + \Delta h$. For large t (this will be defined more precisely later) the concentration assumes the normal form pictured in Fig. 6-4.

The reason why the slug does not remain a slug is fairly clear if we focus our attention on a single tracer molecule. Beginning in the neighborhood of $z = 0$, this particle travels with a variable macroscopic

---

* The condition that $\Delta x/\sigma$ and $\Delta y/\sigma$ and $\Delta z/\sigma \ll 1$ is apparently circular. It can be performed operationally, however, by choosing Δx, calculating $\tilde{C}(z, t)$, and seeing if it is consistent.

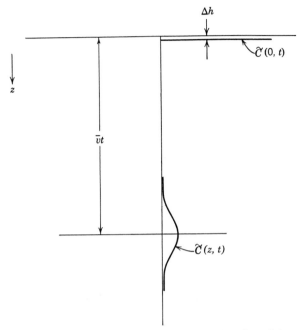

Fig. 6-4. Concentration distribution as a function of time.

fluid velocity. As it wends its way through the porous medium, the fluid velocity with which the molecule travels, $\mathbf{v}(t)$, changes in a random manner.* Sometimes it goes slowly, sometimes it is traveling very fast. A typical plot of the z component of fluid velocity might look like that pictured in Fig. 6-5.

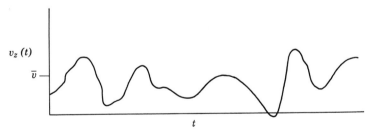

Fig. 6-5. z Component of fluid velocity of tracer molecule vs. time.

---

* It is important to emphasize that $\mathbf{v}(t)$ is the fluid velocity with which the given molecule travels at time t. It is to be distinguished from the velocity $\mathbf{v}(\mathbf{x})$, which is the fluid velocity at a given point $\mathbf{x}$ in the fluid.

For any given time t, its z coordinate $Z(t)$ is given by

(6-21) $$Z(t) = \int_0^t v_z(t') \, dt'$$

where $Z(t)$ is also a random function. For the concentration to remain in slug form, we must have for all t, $Z(t) = \bar{v}t$. Since $v_z(t)$ and hence $Z(t)$ are random functions, this is not true, and the molecule may have a z position at time t such that $Z(t) < \bar{v}t$ or $Z(t) > \bar{v}t$. The argument given for one molecule, of course, applies to all molecules, and hence the distribution shown in Fig. 6-4 is not unreasonable.

Molecular diffusion does not affect the qualitative aspects of the picture given. Molecular diffusion just shifts the tracer molecules from one macroscopic fluid element to another; hence the molecule's position as a function of time will be somewhat different than if molecular diffusion were negligible and it stayed with its original element. In either case, v_z will be random, and the molecule's position will still be represented by a random function $Z(t)$. In the remainder of this introduction, we shall neglect explicit mention of molecular diffusion. We shall consider these effects later in the chapter.

The fact that we consider porous media that have random geometries of course is responsible for the random character of the velocity fields. If the porous medium were composed of spheres such as are shown in Fig. 6-1b, the fluid velocity pattern of a tracer molecule (neglecting molecular diffusion) would not be random but, periodic. At large t, $Z(t)$ would again not be confined to the region $\bar{v}t < z < \bar{v}t + \Delta h$, but $\tilde{C}(z, t)$ would look quite different from the distribution pictured in Fig. 6-4. The characteristic spread of $\tilde{C}(z, t)$ would depend on time in a different way. To see this difference, let us first consider a rough derivation of $\tilde{C}(z, t)$ for large times in the case of a random porous medium. [We follow the arguments given by Beran (1955,1957). A similar discussion is given in Scheidegger (1960) summarizing his earlier papers.]

We first note that if the tracer molecule is situated in the neighborhood of $z = 0$ at time $t = 0$ (its x-y coordinate unspecified), then it may be assumed at large values of t that the probability of the molecule being at $z = z$ at time t, denoted $P(z, t)$, is identical to a constant *times* the function $\tilde{C}(z, t)$ if we neglect the small initial spread Δh. This is a type of ergodic theorem in which one assumes that any molecule passes through all possible velocities a large number of *times*, and hence its probable distribution is identical to the actual distribution of a large number of molecules.*

At successive instants, δt, $2\,\delta t$, ..., $n\,\delta t$, the molecule has successive fluid velocities in the z direction, $v_{z1}, v_{z2}, \ldots, v_{zn}$. The z coordinate of the particle is thus

$$(6\text{-}22) \qquad Z(t) = \sum_{j=1}^{n} v_{zj}\,\delta t$$

in the limit $n \to \infty$, $\delta t \to 0$ taken in such a manner that $n\,\delta t \to t$. We write $Z(t)$ in the discrete form, since mathematically it is easier to treat in that form. Associated with v_{zj} is a probability distribution $P(v_{zj})\,dv_{zj}$ defined as the probability that the molecule has a fluid velocity between v_z and $v_z + dv_z$ at time $j\,\delta t$. The probability of the molecule having a given fluid velocity is independent of time, however, and $P(v_{zj})\,dv_{zj}$ may be replaced by $P(v_z)\,dv_z$.

$P(z, t)\,dz$ is thus the probability that a random variable $Z(t)$ has a value between z and $z + dz$ at time t. Here $Z(t)$ is the sum of a large number of random variables, all with the same probability distribution; and if the v_{zj} are all independent it is well known that under quite general conditions $P(z, t)$ would have the gaussian form

$$(6\text{-}23) \qquad P(z, t) = \frac{1}{\sqrt{2\pi}\sigma(t)} \exp\left[-\frac{(z - \bar{z})^2}{2\sigma(t)^2} \right]$$

In the foregoing case the v_{zj} are, of course, not independent, since they represent the fluid velocity of the molecule at successive instants $j\,\delta t$, $(j + 1)\,\delta t, \ldots, (j + l)\,\delta t$. However, the correlation between the fluid velocity of the molecule at time $j\,\delta t$, and the fluid velocity at $(j + l)\,\delta t$ becomes less as l increases. For l large enough the correlation may be taken to be zero. Physically this means that after the molecule has moved several characteristic pore or grain dimensions, its fluid velocity is uncorrelated with the fluid velocity it had originally. If the correlation is taken to be zero for two points separated by $l\,\delta t$, it may be shown that $P(z, t)$ still is gaussianly distributed. Although the appropriate central limit theorem has not been proved to this writer's knowledge in the continuous case, it is a reasonable assumption to

* This assumption will be discussed further in the concluding section of the chapter.

suppose that Eq. 6-23 holds in the limit $l\,\delta t \to \tau_v$, $n\,\delta t \to t$, where τ_v is a characteristic correlation time associated with the molecule's fluid velocity and where $\tau_v/t \ll 1$.

The fact that $P(z, t)$ is gaussianly distributed depends upon the fact that $v_z(t)$ may be considered to be a random function of time. (See Fig. 6-5.) The correlation function $R'(\tau)$ associated with $v_z(t) - \bar{v}$ is defined as

$$(6\text{-}24) \qquad R'(\tau) = \lim_{T \to \infty} \frac{1}{T} \int_{0}^{T} [v_z(t + \tau) - \bar{v}][v_z(t) - \bar{v}]\, dt$$

We assume that $R'(\tau) \to 0$ as $\tau \to \infty$ and that a characteristic decay time is τ_v.

A gaussian distribution is determined completely by the standard deviation $\sigma(t)$ where

$$(6\text{-}25) \qquad \sigma^2(t) = \int_{-\infty}^{\infty} [z - \bar{z}(t)]^2 P(z, t)\, dz$$

$\sigma^2(t)$ may also be derived more directly as

$$(6\text{-}26) \qquad \sigma^2(t) = (Z(t) - \overline{Z(t)})^2$$

where the bar denotes an ensemble average. From Eq. 6-26 and the definition

$$Z(t) = \int_{0}^{t} v_z(t)\, dt$$

we may show (see Section 6.3.2) that

$$(6\text{-}27) \qquad \sigma^2(t) = 2t \int_{0}^{\infty} R'(\tau)\, d\tau$$

if $t \gg \tau_v$ and the time and ensemble average definition of $R'(\tau)$ may be equated. The important fact to notice here is that

$$(6\text{-}28) \qquad \sigma(t) = \alpha t^{1/2}$$

(where α is a constant) just as in the familiar random-walk problem.

Let us now consider the configuration shown in Fig. 6-1*b*. If we plot the fluid velocity record of a number of molecules chosen at random, we notice that the average fluid velocity of the molecule depends upon its initial position, since the record contains a strong periodic component associated with the periodicity of the placement of the material spheres. Moreover, since the molecule's fluid velocity record depends upon its initial position, we cannot invoke an ergodic hypothesis; $\tilde{C}(z, t)$ is clearly not proportional to $P(z, t)$. Instead P depends upon x_0 and y_0, the initial x and y coordinates of the molecule. In place of $P(z, t)$, we must write $P(z, t; x_0, y_0)$; we have the relation

$$(6\text{-}29) \qquad \tilde{C}(z, t) = \text{const} \lim_{\substack{X \to \infty \\ Y \to \infty}} \frac{1}{4XY} \int_{-Y}^{Y} \int_{-X}^{X} P(z, t, x_0, y_0)\, dx_0\, dy_0$$

The fact that the average fluid velocity of the molecule depends upon the initial conditions means that some molecules will always proceed more slowly through the porous medium than others. Some will proceed with average velocity $\bar{v}_1$, others with average velocity $\bar{v}_2$, and so on. After a time t, molecules 1 and 2 will be separated in the z direction by a distance of magnitude $(\bar{v}_1 - \bar{v}_2)t$.

Since, in this case the separation of position for two molecules is proportional to t, the implication is that the standard deviation $\sigma(t)$, associated with $\tilde{C}(z, t)$, is also proportional to t. We now have

$$(6\text{-}30) \qquad \sigma^2(t) = \left(\int_{-\infty}^{\infty} \tilde{C}(z, t)\, dz \right)^{-1} \int_{-\infty}^{\infty} [z - \bar{z}(t)]^2 \tilde{C}(z, t)\, dz$$

$$= \beta^2 t^2$$

(where β is a constant) in contrast to Eq. 6-28. The dispersive properties of the configurations given in Figs. 6-1*a* and 6-1*b* are thus radically different.

It is important to realize that Eq. 6-30 holds true only in the limit of zero molecular diffusion. If the molecule is allowed to change at random from any fluid streamline to any other, the behavior of σ will eventually assume the form given in Eq. 6-28 although α will be changed. Since, physically, molecular diffusion is always finite, it is really a question of how long on the average the tracer molecule remains in the porous medium. We have taken infinite porous media; but if we are to neglect the effects of molecule diffusion, we must, strictly speaking, consider media of finite length.

As long as the medium may be considered to be random, $\tilde{C}(z, t)$ and $P(z, t)$ will differ only by a normalization constant. When $t \to \infty$, $P(z, t)$ is gaussianly distributed, and to characterize completely the distribution, we only require a knowledge of $\bar{v}$ and $\sigma(t)$. $\sigma(t)$ is given by Eq. 6-27. Thus if $\bar{v}$ and $R(\tau)$ are known, $P(z, t)$ is completely determined. $R(\tau)$ is termed a Lagrangian correlation function. Unfortunately, there has been virtually no success in relating $R(\tau)$ to the statistical parameters of the porous media geometry.

It might be expected that there is some connection between $\int_0^\infty R(\tau) \, d\tau$ and the permeability k since both quantities depend upon the velocity distribution. Some connection between these quantities is implied in the work of Scheidegger (1954), but the independent variables, upon which k and $\int_0^\infty R(\tau) \, d\tau$ are found to depend, are too vague to warrant making comparisons. In the following sections k and $R(\tau)$ will be discussed separately with no attempt made to provide a theory which predicts both parameters.

6.2. Statistical Approaches to the Determination of the Permeability

In this section we shall present three statistical approaches that have been used in an attempt to derive expressions for the permeability. The first approach (Childs and Collis-George, 1950) is essentially a statistical theory aimed at deriving a more appropriate Kozeny-type equation using the basic capillary idea. As we mentioned previously, this is not at all like the statistical approaches used in the other chapters; but since the porous medium problem is so intractable to conventional statistical approaches, we have included it here. The second approach is more in keeping with the statistical ideas emphasized in this book. Here again, however, no attempt is made to derive the permeability from the governing partial differential equation, but rather a random-walk type approach is used. As the reader will note, this type of approach is not particularly satisfying for the permeability problem. It is much more appropriate for studying the dispersion problem. The third approach developed by Prager (1961) is a variational calculation and has many similarities to work done in heterogeneous media.

We pointed out in the introduction that there is no very natural way to introduce the irregular geometry directly into the governing partial differential equations. It may be possible to do this by introducing a function $g(\mathbf{x})$ with the properties*

(6-31) $g(\mathbf{x}) = 1$ for points in the fluid

   $g(\mathbf{x}) = 0$ for points in the solid portion of the media

Prager (1961) has introduced this function into his variational calculation, but to our knowledge no one has introduced $g(\mathbf{x})$ into the governing equations and formulated either a hierarchy of moment equations or a functional equation.

We may state here that the solution of the complete statistical problem requires a knowledge of the functional $P[u_i(\mathbf{x}), p(\mathbf{x})]$ that is obtained from knowledge of both $\partial \bar{p}/\partial x_i$ and the function

$$P_{\epsilon_1 \cdots \epsilon_n}(\mathbf{x}_1, \ldots, \mathbf{x}_n)$$

in the limit $n \to \infty$. We do not now have, however, an equation governing $P[u_i(\mathbf{x}), p(\mathbf{x})]$ with

$$\underset{\lim n \to \infty}{P_{\epsilon_1 \cdots \epsilon_n}(\mathbf{x}_1, \ldots, \mathbf{x}_n)}$$

as a boundary condition. We have included this chapter on flow through porous media in the expectation that eventually the techniques used in the other statistical continuum theories will be systematically applied to this area. Prager's work is perhaps a first step in this direction.

6.2.1. Random Capillary Model

Childs and Collis-George (1950) derive an expression for the permeability assuming a statistical distribution of pore sizes. Whereas we follow their discussion in the main, we emphasize different aspects of their development and make comments with which they might not agree. Consider two planes in a porous medium taken perpendicular to the mean flow direction and separated by some

---

* $g(\mathbf{x}) = 1 - \epsilon(\mathbf{x})$ if we identify points in the void phase with points in the fluid. For clarity, it seemed useful to have separate symbols.

distance h. In each plane Childs and Collis-George define a function $f(r)$, where $f(r)$ is the fraction of pores in the total volume with "radius" between r and $r + dr$. (Since the "radius" of a pore with arbitrary shape is undefined, the function $f(r)$ is somewhat vague, but presumably either of the precisely defined functions $P_V'(\delta)$ or $P_V(\beta)$ could be renormalized and substituted for $f(r)$. Childs and Collis-George determine $f(r)$ experimentally from moisture content measurements, and they seem to have a function proportional to $P_V'(\delta)$ in mind.)

The fraction of pores that have a "radius" between ρ and $\rho + d\rho$ in one plane and between σ and $\sigma + d\sigma$ in the second plane is taken to be proportional to

$$f(\rho)\, d\rho f(\sigma)\, d\sigma$$

In other words, h is chosen large enough for the pore "radius" in one plane to be independent of the pore "radius" in the other plane. It is also assumed that the pore sequence is direct; the effects of several linked pores between the planes are neglected.

In order to determine the contribution of the permeability of a particular sequence, we must estimate the effect of "radius" on the resistance to the flow. The relation between the average volume flow rate per unit area and the pressure gradient in a single, circular tube is given by Eq. 6-8

$$(6\text{-}8) \qquad\qquad q_c = -\frac{d^2}{32\mu}\frac{\partial \bar{p}}{\partial z}$$

and the permeability for a single tube is thus

$$(6\text{-}9) \qquad\qquad k_c = \frac{d^2}{32}$$

Childs and Collis-George assume this type of dependence on pore "diameter"* holds for a sequence when $\rho \to \sigma$ if d is identified with the smaller pore "diameter." For the contribution to k from the sequence $\rho \to \sigma$, denoted by δk, they write

$$(6\text{-}32) \qquad\qquad \delta k = M\sigma^2 f(\sigma) f(\rho)\, d\sigma\, d\rho$$

where $\sigma < \rho$. M is taken to be a universal constant that is to be determined experimentally. The total permeability may then be

_____
* The pore "diameter" is twice the pore "radius."

written

(6-33)
$$k = M \iint\limits_{\substack{\text{all } \sigma \\ \text{all } \rho}} \beta^2 f(\sigma) f(\rho) \, d\sigma \, d\rho$$

(where β is the smaller of σ, ρ). For practical application this may be replaced by the summation

(6-34)
$$k = (\Delta r)^2 M \sum_{\rho=0}^{R} \sum_{\sigma=0}^{R} \beta^2 f(\sigma) f(\rho)$$

(where β is the smaller of σ, ρ). Here Δr is a "radius" change for which $f(r)$ does not change appreciably, and R is the maximum pore size that need be considered.

Childs and Collis-George use moisture-content measurements to determine $f(r)$. The constant M is then determined by comparing the value of k that is derived in terms of M from Eq. 6-34 with the measured values of k that are a function of moisture content. For the particular porous media they studied, the foregoing authors show results that are significantly better than those obtained by the Kozeny equation as they interpret it. (See Carman, 1956, p. 51, for some further brief remarks on their interpretation of the Kozeny equation.)

The Childs and Collis-George development is an application of simple statistical concepts. Whether or not it captures the essence of the problem can only be decided by experiment. Although the literature contains very many experiments, unfortunately very few beyond the Childs and Collis-George experiments contain the function $f(r)$ which is necessary for the verification. The writer feels that Eq. 6-33 certainly has as much physical merit as the Kozeny equation, and, in fact, in a sense it is much more satisfactory, since it contains only one universal constant M. Once M is determined for any porous medium, k is uniquely determined from $f(r)$ for any other porous medium. The formula gives either a correct result or an incorrect result; there can be no further adjustments. Of course, if the results do not check with experiments for many classes of porous media, and if it is sought to make M a variable depending on some classification of porous media, then the formula loses much of its utility.

Whereas $f(r)$ can presumably be determined by moisture content, there seems to be no reason to do this in a study for which the sole aim is the determination of permeability. Although qualitative arguments are made to assure the reader that the procedure is sound; this writer feels very uncomfortable about blanket statements which tell how the largest pores will behave when the moisture content is changed. The argument leading to Eq. 6-33 does not really depend critically on the way in which $f(r)$ is determined; it seems that it might be much more satisfactory to check Eq. 6-33, using either of the precisely defined functions, $P_V(\beta)$ or $P_V'(\delta)$.

6.2.2. Random-Walk Type Theory

In the first part of this section we follow the development given by Scheidegger (1954). Scheidegger considers the path of a particle of fluid (essentially a geometric point in the fluid continuum) as it passes through the porous medium. He divides the time t into discrete intervals, $0, \tau, 2\tau, \ldots, j\tau, \ldots, n\tau$ ($n\tau = t$) and supposes that in the time interval $j\tau - (j - 1)\tau$, the particle undergoes a displacement ξ_j. The particle velocity in the interval is thus taken to be $v_j = \xi_j/\tau$. He assumes for convenience that the particle displacement ξ_j is uncorrelated with the particle displacement ξ_k ($k \neq j$) but the introduction of correlation does not change the essential results of the argument when t is very much larger than the characteristic correlation time. The effect of correlation in dispersion problems will be discussed in detail in Section 6.3.

For very slow flows the basic relation connecting fluid velocity v and local pressure p is

(6-35) $$\nabla^2 v = \frac{1}{\mu} \nabla p$$

where

$$\nabla^2 p = 0$$

A solution of this equation may be given formally in terms of a Green's function $G(x, x')$ satisfying the equation

(6-36) $$\nabla^2 G(x, x') = \delta(x - x')$$

and the boundary condition $G(x, x_S) = 0$ where x_S is a point on the surface of the solid phase of the porous medium. We have

$$(6\text{-}37) \qquad \mathbf{v}(\mathbf{x}) = \int_{V_F'} \frac{1}{\mu} \nabla' p(\mathbf{x}') G(\mathbf{x}, \mathbf{x}') \, d\mathbf{x}'$$

(where V_F' indicates all points in the fluid only; $\mathbf{x}$ is also a point in the fluid). We see that $\mathbf{v}(\mathbf{x})$ depends upon the values of $\nabla p(\mathbf{x})$ over all space.

In a simplified theory the nonlocal relationship between $\mathbf{v}(\mathbf{x})$ and $\nabla p(\mathbf{x})$ is not usually taken into account. Instead, a local relationship between $v_i(\mathbf{x})$ and $\partial p(\mathbf{x})/\partial x_k$ is often postulated. We can write either

$$(6\text{-}38) \qquad v_i(\mathbf{x}) = \frac{1}{\mu} b_{ik}'(\mathbf{x}) \frac{\partial p(\mathbf{x})}{\partial x_k}$$

or

$$(6\text{-}39) \qquad v_i(\mathbf{x}) = \frac{1}{\mu} b_{ik}(\mathbf{x}) \frac{\partial \bar{p}}{\partial x_k}$$

In Eq. 6-39, $\partial \bar{p}/\partial x_k$ is the average pressure gradient. If this gradient is in the z direction, we can write

$$(6\text{-}40) \qquad v_i(\mathbf{x}) = \frac{1}{\mu} b_{i3}(\mathbf{x}) \frac{\partial \bar{p}}{\partial z}$$

Flow in directions other than the z direction occurs because of the irregular boundaries. It appears somewhat inconsistent to neglect pressure fluctuations in the x and y directions and still have flow in those directions, but essentially the pressure fluctuation effect is incorporated into the $b_{i3}(\mathbf{x})$ functions. In the random-walk model Scheidegger writes

$$(6\text{-}41) \qquad \frac{|\xi(\mathbf{x})|}{\tau} = \frac{B(\mathbf{x})}{\mu} \frac{\partial \bar{p}}{\partial z} \cos [\theta(\mathbf{x})]$$

where $\theta(\mathbf{x})$ is the angle between ξ and the z direction. $B(\mathbf{x})$ is a function that depends upon the shape and size of the pores at every point. Thus he lets

$$(6\text{-}42) \qquad b_{33}(\mathbf{x}) = -B(\mathbf{x}) \cos [\theta(\mathbf{x})] \cos [\theta(\mathbf{x})]$$

The assumption here is that the pressure in the $\boldsymbol{\xi}$ direction is always proportional to $(\partial \bar{p}/\partial z) \cos \theta$, the component of the mean pressure in that direction.

The step from Eq. 6-37 to Eq. 6-38 or 6-39 is a significant one, and Scheidegger gives no justification for it beyond the statement (Scheidegger, 1956) that Eq. 6-39 is appropriate for narrow-channel flow. To the extent that porous media can be described by capillary models, presumably this is adequate, but the reader must keep this limitation in mind.

In order to arrive at a relation similar to Darcy's law, the component of $\boldsymbol{\xi}(\mathbf{x})$ in the average flow direction in Eq. 6-41 is next averaged over an ensemble of porous media. Since the geometry in each sample of the ensemble is different, averaging $|\boldsymbol{\xi}(\mathbf{x})|$ at a particular point $\mathbf{x}$ will often place one within the solid portion of the medium. We avoid this difficulty here by simply averaging over only those members of the ensemble where $\mathbf{x}$ is a point in the fluid. The component of $\boldsymbol{\xi}$ in the average flow direction is $|\boldsymbol{\xi}| \cos \theta \equiv -\xi_z$, and hence averaging Eq. 6-41 yields

$$(6\text{-}43) \qquad \bar{v}_z \equiv \frac{\bar{\xi}_z}{\tau} = -\frac{1}{\mu} \frac{\partial \bar{p}}{\partial z} \overline{B(\mathbf{x}) \cos^2 [\theta(\mathbf{x})]}$$

If $B(\mathbf{x})$ and $\theta(\mathbf{x})$ are taken to be independent, as Scheidegger assumes, we have

$$(6\text{-}44) \qquad \bar{v}_z = -\frac{1}{\mu} \frac{\partial \bar{p}}{\partial z} \bar{B} \overline{\cos^2 \theta}$$

Both $\overline{B(\mathbf{x}) \cos^2 [\theta(\mathbf{x})]}$ and the expressions $\overline{B(\mathbf{x})}$ and $\overline{\cos^2 [\theta(\mathbf{x})]}$ are independent of $\mathbf{x}$ as a result of the homogeneity assumption. The $\mathbf{x}$ argument has thus been omitted in Eq. 6-44.

There is little that can be said about the independence assumption for $B(\mathbf{x})$ and $\cos [\theta(\mathbf{x})]$. It is not clear what $B(\mathbf{x})$ really represents beyond the vague statement that it depends upon the shape and size of the pores. The reason for making the assumption is to put Eq. 6-44 into a form that may be compared more easily to the Kozeny equation, since $\overline{\cos^2 \theta}$ may be identified with the reciprocal of the square of the tortuosity.

Comparison of Eq. 6-44 with Darcy's law shows

$$k = P \bar{B} \overline{\cos^2 \theta}$$

The porosity factor P arises from the fact that $\bar{v}_z$ is the average fluid velocity. The average volume flow rate per unit area is $P\bar{v}_z$.

Using similar arguments Scheidegger derives expressions for the dispersion coefficient D. The reader is referred to Scheidegger (1956) or (1960) for a discussion of this approach and to Scheidegger (1965) for a discussion of generalizations of this approach. In Section 6.3 we shall discuss the determination of D following the approach given by Beran (1955,1957).

To conclude this present section, we should like to point out how, under certain assumptions Eq. 6-37 may be used to convert the determination of the permeability to a simpler problem than is required by consideration of the flow equations. If we average Eq. 6-37 over an ensemble, we have

$$(6\text{-}45) \qquad \overline{v_z(\mathbf{x})}\bigg|_{\mathbf{x}=\text{fluid point}} = \int_{V_{F'}} \overline{\frac{1}{\mu} \frac{\partial p(\mathbf{x}')}{dz'} G(\mathbf{x}, \mathbf{x}')} \, d\mathbf{x}'$$

In Eq. 6-1 we should prefer to integrate over V' rather than $V_{F'}$. Similarly, we should like to consider $\mathbf{x}$ any point, not just a fluid point. We may accomplish these aims by introducing the function $g(\mathbf{x})$, defined to be "one" in the fluid region and zero in the solid region. Thus

$$(6\text{-}46) \qquad \overline{g(\mathbf{x})v_z(\mathbf{x})} = \int_V \overline{\frac{1}{\mu} g(\mathbf{x})g(\mathbf{x}') \frac{\partial p(\mathbf{x}')}{\partial z'} G(\mathbf{x}, \bar{x}')} \, d\mathbf{x}$$

where $\mathbf{x}$ and $\mathbf{x}'$ are any points in the fluid-solid volume V.

Next we note that

$$(6\text{-}47) \qquad \overline{g(\mathbf{x})v_z(\mathbf{x})} = \overline{g(\mathbf{x})} \, \bar{v}_z$$

where $\bar{v}_z$ is the average fluid velocity. Writing

$$(6\text{-}48) \qquad G_F(\mathbf{x}, \mathbf{x}') = \frac{\overline{g(\mathbf{x})g(\mathbf{x}')G(\mathbf{x}, \mathbf{x}')}}{\overline{g(\mathbf{x})}}$$

Eq. 6-46 becomes

$$(6\text{-}49) \qquad \bar{v}_z = \int_V \overline{\frac{1}{\mu} \frac{\partial p(\mathbf{x}')}{\partial z'} G_F(\mathbf{x}, \mathbf{x}')} \, d\mathbf{x}$$

In general the local pressure gradients $\partial p/\partial z'(\mathbf{x}')$ and the function $G_F(x, \mathbf{x}')$ are correlated. If we assume this correlation is weak and may be neglected or that fluctuations in $\partial p(\mathbf{x}')/\partial z'$ are small, then Eq. 6-49 becomes

$$(6\text{-}50) \qquad \bar{v}_z = -\left[-\int_{V'} \overline{G_F(\mathbf{x}, \mathbf{x}')}\, dx \right] \frac{1}{\mu} \frac{\partial \bar{p}}{\partial z}$$

We thus find Darcy's law, where now the permeability is

$$(6\text{-}51) \qquad k = -P \int_V \overline{G_F(\mathbf{x}, \mathbf{x}')}\, d\mathbf{x}'$$

No real justification can be generally given for the assumption of small pressure gradient fluctuations. The assumption of small pressure gradient fluctuations would be appropriate if a narrow-channel capillary model were appropriate, but this is an undesirable model to rely upon for general results. Rather it is felt that since $G(\mathbf{x}, \mathbf{x}')$ and $\partial p(\mathbf{x}')/\partial z'$ arise from the solution of different type boundary value problems, perhaps the correlation between them is small.

$p(\mathbf{x})$ satisfies the harmonic equation $\nabla^2 p = 0$, and pressure gradient fluctuations must be present within the fluid to reflect the fact that the flow is deflected by the solid boundaries. $G_F(\mathbf{x}, \mathbf{x}')$ results from the solution of the equation

$$(6\text{-}52) \qquad \nabla^2 G(\mathbf{x}, \mathbf{x}') = \delta(\mathbf{x} - \mathbf{x}')$$

subject to the boundary condition $G(\mathbf{x}, \mathbf{x}_S) = 0$, where $\mathbf{x}_S$ is a point on the solid boundary. The solution of Eq. 6-52 may be interpreted in terms of a diffusion problem. Suppose that a delta function source of some concentration is placed at $\mathbf{x}'$ and that as it diffuses from $\mathbf{x}'$ to a point $\mathbf{x}$, it will be absorbed if it comes in contact with a solid boundary. $G(\mathbf{x}, \mathbf{x}')$ is proportional to the probability that this diffusing particle, initially at $\mathbf{x}'$, reaches $\mathbf{x}$ before it is absorbed.

Both $\partial p(\mathbf{x}')/\partial z'$ and $G(\mathbf{x}, \mathbf{x}')$ depend upon the solid boundaries in the neighborhood of $\mathbf{x}'$. $G(\mathbf{x}, \mathbf{x}')$ depends upon two points, however, and $\partial p(\mathbf{x}')/\partial z'$ depends upon only one. Thus, whereas one portion of solid boundary may greatly influence $\partial p(\mathbf{x}')/\partial z'$, a different portion of solid boundary may affect $G(\mathbf{x}, \mathbf{x}')$ more. Furthermore, proximity of $\mathbf{x}'$ to a boundary need not introduce a fluctuation in $\partial p(\mathbf{x}')/\partial z'$; but it certainly will affect $G(\mathbf{x}, \mathbf{x}')$. The expectation is that even though arguments may also be given to show that $\partial p(\mathbf{x}')/\partial z'$ and $G(\mathbf{x}, \mathbf{x}')$ are correlated in certain instances, counter arguments such as those given in the foregoing indicate that on the average the overall correlation will be weak.

If we accept the foregoing argument, the permeability determination is reduced to the diffusion problem described above. We must find $\overline{G_F(\mathbf{x}, \mathbf{x}')}$ which is dependent on $|\mathbf{x} - \mathbf{x}'|$ and is interpreted as being proportional to the probability of a diffusing particle reaching a distance $|\mathbf{x} - \mathbf{x}'|$ from its initial position (where the initial position is random) before being absorbed. In fact, even less information than that is required since only the integral of $\overline{G_F(\mathbf{x}, \mathbf{x}')}$ is desired.

6.2.3. Variational Approach for Bounding the Magnitude of the Permeability

Prager (1961) and Weissberg and Prager (1962) have found an upper bound for the permeability by using variational techniques similar to those outlined in the previous chapter. Although we shall follow their development in this section, we shall make some additional comments. Prager (1961) begins with the following variational theorem for deriving the Navier-Stokes equation for very slow flows (i.e., neglecting the inertial terms as we have usually done in this chapter). Let

$$(6\text{-}53) \qquad \mathscr{E} = \frac{1}{2\mu} \int_{\substack{\text{over all} \\ \text{fluid}}} \sigma_{ij}(\mathbf{x})\sigma_{ij}(\mathbf{x})\, d\mathbf{x}$$

subject to subsidiary conditions on the stress deviation tensor σ_{ij} of the form

$$(6\text{-}54a) \qquad\qquad \sigma_{ij} = \sigma_{ji}$$

$$(6\text{-}54b) \qquad\qquad \sigma_{ll} = 0$$

$$(6\text{-}54c) \qquad\qquad \sigma_{ij,j} = p_{,i}$$

Then $\mathscr{E}$ is stationary for

$$(6\text{-}55) \qquad\qquad \sigma_{ij} = \mu\left[\frac{\partial v_i}{\partial x_j} + \frac{\partial v_j}{\partial x_i}\right]$$

284 Statistical Continuum Theories

where v_i is to be identified with the fluid velocity. The variation must be taken such that the admissible solution always satisfies the same tractions as the true solution on the solid surfaces.

It is easy to show that Eq. 6-55 is sufficient for the stationarity of $\mathscr{E}$. The proof of the necessity of Eq. 6-55 is very difficult, but it has been established. This theorem is discussed in terms of elasticity theory in Courant and Hilbert (1953), to which we refer the reader for a discussion of the principle.

In order to make the problem tractable, Prager assumes an infinite medium and treats the problem for an ensemble point of view. He thus replaces Eq. 6-53 by

$$(6\text{-}56) \qquad \mathscr{E} = \overline{\frac{1}{2\mu} g(\mathbf{x})\sigma_{ij}(\mathbf{x})\sigma_{ij}(\mathbf{x})}$$

where $g(\mathbf{x})$ is a function that is "one" in the fluid region and "zero" in the solid region. $\bar{g}$ is equal to the porosity. The bar denotes an ensemble average. An ergodic hypothesis is assumed to allow the expressions in Eqs. 6-53 and 6-56 to be equated.

As we mentioned previously, the variational principle is solved for a given specification of tractions on the solid surface in any member of the ensemble. It is, of course, impossible to find admissible trial functions that have this complicated specification, and in fact in an ensemble approach, it is somewhat meaningless, since the geometry changes from ensemble sample to sample. Instead, Prager states that this specification may be replaced in the ensemble approach by the specification of the mean pressure gradient

$$(6\text{-}57) \qquad -\gamma_i = \frac{\overline{g(\partial p/\partial x_i)}}{\bar{g}} = \frac{\overline{g\sigma_{ij,j}}}{\bar{g}}$$

Also, since the medium as a whole is not sheared, there is no net shear at any point, and

$$(6\text{-}58) \qquad \overline{g\sigma_{ij}} = 0$$

A similar type assumption was made in our study of electric fields in heterogeneous materials where we replaced the specification of electric potential on the medium surface by the average electric field. There, however, the surface was exterior to the entire medium under consideration; here it is internal to the medium. In the heterogeneous material case the statistical variable appears directly in the governing equation; here it appears directly in the boundary condition. No proof is given by Prager that the variational principle subject to Eqs. 6-57 and 6-58 is derivable from the variational principle that was initially cited for a single system. It seems reasonable to this writer that the conditions given in Eqs. 6-57 and 6-58 may be sufficient in an ensemble formulation, but Prager does not supply a proof of the form given in the dielectric case. We will thus assume with Prager that any admissible function need satisfy only Eqs. 6-54a and b, Eq. 6-57, and Eq. 6-58.

Before proceeding to a choice of the trial function, let us first define the permeability in terms of $\mathscr{E}$ and γ_i. We have

$$(6\text{-}59) \qquad\qquad \mathscr{E} = -\gamma_i \overline{q}_i$$

where $\overline{q}_i$ has the dimensions of a velocity $(\text{cm}^3 \ \text{sec}^{-1})/\text{cm}^2$. From the definition of permeability (Eq. 6-6)

$$(6\text{-}60) \qquad\qquad \overline{q}_i = -\frac{k}{\mu}\gamma_i$$

From Eqs. 6-59 and 6-60 we find

$$(6\text{-}61) \qquad\qquad \mathscr{E} = \frac{k}{\mu}\gamma_i\gamma_i$$

From Eq. 6-56 we note next that

$$(6\text{-}62) \qquad\qquad k = \frac{1}{\gamma_i\gamma_i}\frac{1}{2}\overline{g\sigma_{ij}\sigma_{ij}}$$

Now $\mathscr{E}$ is a minimum for the true solution and thus

$$(6\text{-}63) \qquad\qquad k \leqslant \frac{1}{\gamma_i\gamma_i}\frac{1}{2}\overline{g\sigma_{ijA}\sigma_{ijA}}$$

where σ_{ijA} is an admissible function.

There is no way yet known to develop σ_{ijA} by the perturbation procedures similar to those given in Chapter 5. In his development Prager assumes a trial function of the form

$$(6\text{-}64) \qquad\qquad \sigma_{ijA}(\mathbf{x}) = \int\limits_{\text{all } \mathbf{w}} A_{ij}(\mathbf{w})g(\mathbf{x}+\mathbf{w})\,d\mathbf{w}$$

where $A_{ij}(\mathbf{w})$ will be some regular function rather than a stochastic function.

From the conditions of σ_{ij} and Eq. 6-64, we have the following conditions on A_{ij}:

(6-65) $A_{ij}(\mathbf{w}) = A_{ji}(\mathbf{w})$

(6-66) $A_{ii}(\mathbf{w}) = 0$

(6-67) $\epsilon_{mik}A_{ij,jk} = 0$

(6-68) $\int A_{ij}(\mathbf{w}) \frac{\partial S(\mathbf{w})}{\partial w_j} \, d\mathbf{w} = -\gamma_i \bar{g}$

(6-69) $\int A_{ij}(\mathbf{w})S(\mathbf{w}) \, d\mathbf{w} = 0$

where $S(\mathbf{w}) \equiv \overline{g(\mathbf{x})g(\mathbf{x} + \mathbf{w})}$.

From Eq. 6-64 we find for $\overline{g\sigma_{ijA}\sigma_{ijA}}$ the expression

(6-70) $\overline{g\sigma_{ijA}\sigma_{ijA}} = \int\int A_{ij}(\mathbf{w})g(\mathbf{x} + \mathbf{w})A_{ij}(\mathbf{p})g(\mathbf{x} + \mathbf{p})g(\mathbf{x}) \, d\mathbf{w} \, d\mathbf{p}$

Interchanging orders of integration and averaging yields

(6-71) $\overline{g\sigma_{ijA}\sigma_{ijA}} = \int\int A_{ij}(\mathbf{w})A_{ij}(\mathbf{p})G(\mathbf{w}, \mathbf{p}) \, d\mathbf{w} \, d\mathbf{p}$

where

$$G(\mathbf{w}, \mathbf{p}) \equiv \overline{g(\mathbf{x} + \mathbf{w})g(\mathbf{x} + \mathbf{p})g(\mathbf{x})}$$

Finally, we then find the following expression for the upper bound on k

(6-72) $k \leqslant \frac{1}{2}(\bar{g})^2 \dfrac{\int\int A_{ij}(\mathbf{w})A_{ij}(\mathbf{p})G(\mathbf{w}, \mathbf{p}) \, d\mathbf{w} \, d\mathbf{p}}{\left[\int A_{ij}(\mathbf{w})(\partial S(\mathbf{w})/\partial w_j) \, d\mathbf{w}\right]\left[\int A_{ik}(\mathbf{w})(\partial S(\mathbf{w})/\partial w_k) \, d\mathbf{w}\right]}$

where $A_{ij}(\mathbf{w})$ satisfies Eqs. 6-65 through 6-69.

We consider only isotropic homogeneous media so that $S(\mathbf{w})$ is equal to $S(|\mathbf{w}|)$ and $G(\mathbf{w}, \mathbf{p})$ depends only upon $|\mathbf{w}|$, $|\mathbf{p}|$, and $\mathbf{w} \cdot \mathbf{p}$. A form of $A_{ij}(\mathbf{w})$ which is invariant with respect to coordinate rotation, depends linearly upo.1 γ_i, and vanishes as $\gamma_i \to 0$ (see Eq. 6-68) is the following

(6-73) $A_{ij}(\mathbf{w}) = a(w)(\gamma_i w_j + \gamma_j w_i) + b(w)\gamma_k w_k w_i w_j + c(w)\gamma_k w_k \delta_{ij}$

$$(w = |\mathbf{w}|)$$

Since $S(\mathbf{w}) = S(w)$, Eq. 6-69 is satisfied by any choice of a, b, and c in Eq. 6-73. The other conditions of A_{ij} yield the restrictions

(6-74) $2a + w^2 b + 3c = 0$

(6-75) $w^4 \dfrac{da}{dw} = w^5 b + \text{const}$

(6-76) $\dfrac{4\pi}{3} \displaystyle\int_0^\infty [4a + w^2 b + c]w^3 \dfrac{dS}{dw}\, dw = -\bar{g}$

Prager points out that we could maximize the choice of a, b, and c, and he outlines the procedure. As he also remarks, however, it is much simpler to choose a convenient set of a, b, and c, for it is not clear how much is to be gained by finding the best a, b, and c, since even the best choice is not an exact solution. A particularly simple choice is to take

(6-77) $a(w) = \dfrac{1}{w^3}$

$$b(w) = 0$$

$$c(w) = -\dfrac{2}{3}\dfrac{1}{w^3}$$

Prager then shows that Eq. 6-72 reduces to

(6-78) $k \leqslant \dfrac{9}{10} \displaystyle\int_0^\infty \int_0^\infty G^{(1)}(w, p)\, dw\, dp \bigg/ [1 - \bar{g}]^2$

where

$$G^{(1)}(w, w') = \dfrac{1}{2}\int_{-1}^{1} u\, G(w, p, u)\, du$$

and

$$u \equiv \mathbf{w} \cdot \mathbf{p}$$

Calculation of the upper bound for k thus depends upon the knowledge of $G(w, p, u)$.

We pointed out earlier in the chapter and also in Chapter 5 that information about $G(w, p, u)$ is difficult to obtain and, to avoid having to find it, Prager (1961) notes that

(6-79) $$\mathscr{E} < \frac{1}{2\mu} \overline{\sigma_{ij}\sigma_{ij}}$$

since $g \leqslant 1$. He then finds

(6-80) $$k < \frac{9}{10} \frac{\int\limits_0^\infty [S(w) - \bar{g}^2]w\,dw}{[1 - \bar{g}]^2}$$

The integral function may be easily found from a photograph of a cross section of a sample of a porous medium and an upper bound for k may be calculated.

In the hope of obtaining a better result, Weissberg and Prager (1962) approximate the function $G(w, p, r)$, where $r = |\mathbf{w} - \mathbf{p}|$, in the following manner:

(6-81) $$G(w, p, r) \approx \frac{S(w')S(w'')}{\bar{g}}$$

where w' and w'' are the smallest and next to smallest lengths of w, p, and r. This approximation gives the correct behavior for G when $r = 0$ and p and $r = \infty$, and Weissberg and Prager feel (without more than intuitive justification) that it probably holds reasonably well for intermediate values of these distances. Since they then make some calculations and give results for dilute beds of spheres, we refer the reader to their paper. The reader will note that using Eq. 6-81 and Eq. 6-78 results in only an approximate rather than a rigorous bound. Using Eq. 6-81 may well give a better bound than that given by Eq. 6-80, but the bound given in Eq. 6-80 is rigorous whereas the bound obtained using Eq. 6-31 depends upon the correctness of Eq. 6-81.

6.3. Statistical Dispersion Theories

In the introduction we outlined the way in which statistical ideas may be used in predicting the dispersion of a tracer that is carried by a fluid flowing through a porous medium. We shall now discuss this problem in detail following the analysis given in Beran (1955). The motivation for approach grew out of studying an analysis of a problem on dispersion in pipe flow given by Taylor (1953). We shall thus begin this section by studying the pipe-flow problem. After developing a formulation to treat the pipe-flow problem, we shall then apply it to the porous medium case. We shall conclude the section with some comments on a paper by Saffman (1959) in which he discusses the importance of molecular diffusion in dispersion problems.

6.3.1. Dispersion in Pipe Flow

The pipe-flow problem analyzed by Taylor (1953) was the following: Consider a viscous fluid flowing through an infinite circular pipe of radius a. (Let r and θ be the coordinates in a cross section perpendicular to the flow direction, and let z be the axis along the flow direction.) We suppose the flow to be nonturbulent, and hence the velocity v is of the form (only the z component is nonzero)

$$(6\text{-}82) \qquad v(r) = v_{m0}\left(1 - \frac{r^2}{a^2}\right)$$

At the point $z = 0$ and at time $t = 0$, a slug of soluble matter with concentration $C(z)$ of the following form is introduced into the fluid:

$$(6\text{-}83) \qquad C(z) = C_0 \qquad 0 \leqslant z \leqslant Z \qquad Z \ll a$$
$$= 0 \qquad z < 0, z > Z$$

C_0 is a constant independent of r. We assume that the introduction of the soluble matter does not influence the fluid flow field. We again have in mind something like a radioactive tracer. The tracer is to be dispersed by both fluid convection and molecular diffusion. The quantity we wish to determine in this problem is the average quantity $C_m(z, t)$ which is defined as

$$(6\text{-}84) \qquad C_m(z, t) \equiv \frac{1}{\pi a^2} \int_0^a \int_0^{2\pi} C(r, \theta, z, t) r \, dr \, d\theta$$

Taylor (1953) solved this problem for large t by considering an approximation to the governing equation

(6-85)
$$\frac{\partial C}{\partial t} = D \nabla^2 C - \mathbf{v} \cdot \nabla C$$

He solved the problem for small t by neglecting molecular diffusion. We wish to consider here a different method of solution that allows us to determine the moments of $C_m(z, t)$ which are defined as

(6-86)
$$\overline{z^n(t)} = \frac{1}{C_0 Z} \int\limits_{-\infty}^{\infty} C_m(z, t) z^n \, dz$$

for all t. Our main concern will be the explicit determination of the second moment

(6-87)
$$\sigma^2(t) \equiv \overline{z^2(t)} - [\overline{z(t)}]^2$$

For large values of time we shall see that $C_m(z, t)$ has a gaussian distribution and that only $\sigma^2(t)$ is required to determine $C_m(z, t)$ completely. An approach to determining moments of $C_m(z, t)$ may also be found in a paper by Aris (1956).

Instead of focusing attention on the function $C(z, t)$, we shall consider the probability function $P(z, z_0, t)$; this function is defined as the probability that a tracer molecule initially ($t = 0$) at z_0 will be found at position z at time t. In this problem the molecule is initially at the approximate position $z_0 = 0$; and $P(z, z_0, t)$ is simply proportional to $C(z, t)$, subject to the boundary condition given in Eq. 6-83. In order to find $P(z, z_0, t) \, dz$, let us find the probable position of the molecule at times $0, \delta t, \dots, n \, \delta t$. Eventually we shall let $n \to \infty$, $\delta t \to 0$ in a manner such that $n \, \delta t \to t$.

The tracer molecule changes its position by convection and molecular diffusion. At time $t = j \, \delta t$, we denote the molecule's z position by z_j. During the time interval from $j \, \delta t$ to $(j + 1) \, \delta t$, we suppose the z component of the fluid velocity of the molecule is v_j. In this interval the molecule changes its position by convection, an increment $v_j \, \delta t$. During this interval we denote its change in z position resulting from molecular diffusion by d_j. At time $t = n \, \delta t$ the molecule is thus at position

(6-88)
$$z_n = \sum_{j=0}^{n-1} (v_j \, \delta t + d_j)$$

wherein we will eventually let $n \to \infty$, $\delta t \to 0$ such that $n \, \delta t \to t$.

The method of approach will be to solve for the probability distribution of z_n, using the expression in the summation. We shall consider here only those cases for which the sum

$$\sum_{j=0}^{n-1} d_j$$

may be calculated independently of the fluid velocity distribution. In the pipe flow problem this is clear since the fluid velocity is only in the z direction, and the molecular diffusion proceeds as if the fluid were stationary. This is not to say, of course, that the sum

$$\sum_{j=0}^{n-1} v_j \, \delta t$$

is independent of molecular diffusion, for the effect of molecular diffusion on the sum is the key to determining $P(z, z_0, t)$ for large t.

Ultimately we shall be concerned with determining the mean probability distribution

(6-89) $$P_m(z, t) = \frac{1}{\pi a^2} \int_0^a \int_0^{2\pi} P(r, \theta, z, z_0) r \, dr \, d\theta$$

Subject to the foregoing assumption $P_m(z, t)$ may be calculated by determining the contribution to $P_m(z, t)$ resulting from the sums

$$\sum_{j=0}^{n-1} v_j \, \delta t \quad \text{and} \quad \sum_{j=0}^{n-1} d_j$$

independently. On denoting the contribution to $P_m(z, t)$ from the v_j sum $P_{mv}(z, t)$ and the contribution from the d_j sum $P_{md}(z, t)$, $P_m(z, t)$ is given by

(6-90) $$P_m(z, t) = \int_{-\infty}^{\infty} P_{mv}(z', t) P_{md}(z - z', t) \, dz'$$

$P_{md}(x', t)$ is simply given by the expression

(6-91) $$P_{md}(z, t) = \frac{1}{\sqrt{2\pi Dt}} \exp\left[-z^2/2Dt\right]$$

and thus our main concern will be to find $P_{mv}(z, t)$. The moments of $P_m(z, t)$ may be determined from the moments of $P_{mv}(z, t)$ and $P_{ma}(z, t)$, since Eq. 6-90 is a convolution integral and the characteristic function of $P_m(z, t)$ is in the form of a product. In order to avoid undue algebraic complications, however, we shall only calculate the moments of $P_{mv}(z, t)$ in detail.

To study $P_{mv}(z, t)$ we first find the characteristic function associated with the sum

$$\sum_{j=0}^{n} v_j \equiv I$$

(δt may be neglected for the time being, since it is independent of j.) Denote $W(v_0, v_1, \ldots, v_n) \, dv_0 \, dv_1 \cdots dv_n$ to signify the probability that the velocity (z component) of the molecule lies between v_0 and $v_0 + dv_0$ at time $t = 0$, between v_1 and $v_1 + dv_1$ at time $t = \delta t, \ldots$, and between v_n and $v_n + dv_n$ at time $t = n \, \delta t$.* $P(I) \, dI$, the probability that I lies between I and $I + dI$ at time $t = n \, \delta t$, may be determined from $W(v_0, v_1, \ldots, v_n) \, dv_0 \, dv_1 \cdots dv_n$ by making a change of variables from the set $v_0, v_1, \ldots, v_n$ to the set $I, v_1' = v_1, v_2', \ldots, v_n' = v_n$ and integrating over $v_1', v_2', \ldots, v_n'$. For our purposes it will be more convenient to determine the characteristic function of I, $M_I(\xi)$, which is defined by the transform relation

(6-92)
$$M_I(\xi) = \int_{-\infty}^{\infty} e^{i\xi I} P(I) \, dI$$

From $M_I(\xi)$ the moments of $P(I)$ may be obtained by differentiation (see Section 2.1.5.2). From the definition given in Eq. 6-92 and with a manipulation of the relationship between $P(I)$ and $W(v_0, v_1, \ldots, v_n)$, we may find

(6-93)
$$M_I(\xi) = \int_{-\infty}^{\infty} \cdots \int \exp\left\{ i\xi \left[\sum_{j=0}^{n} v_j \right] \right\} W(v_0, v_1, \ldots, v_n) \, dv_0 \, dv_1, \ldots dv_n$$

* Note that W is the probability density associated with a given molecular *velocity at many times*. This is to be differentiated from the probability density associated with the *velocity at many points in the fluid*.

The mth-order moment of $P(I)$, $\overline{I^n}$, may be determined from the derivative relation (see Eq. 2-14)

(6-94) $$\overline{I^n} \equiv \int_{-\infty}^{\infty} P(I)I^n \, dI = (-i)^n \frac{d^n M_I(\xi)}{d\xi^n}\bigg|_{\xi=0}$$

For example, the mean value of I is

(6-95) $$\overline{I} = -i \frac{dM_I(\xi)}{d\xi}\bigg|_{\xi=0}$$

and the mean square value of I is

(6-96) $$\overline{I^2} = (-i)^2 \frac{d^2 M_I(\xi)}{d\xi^2}\bigg|_{\xi=0}$$

If the δt is reinserted into the formulation and the limit

$$n \, \delta t \rightarrow t$$
$$n \rightarrow \infty$$
$$\delta t \rightarrow 0$$

is taken, we have

(6-97) $$\overline{I} \, \delta t \rightarrow \overline{z}$$
$$\overline{I^2} \, \delta t^2 \rightarrow \overline{z^2}$$

If we perform the differentiation indicated in Eq. 6-94, we have from Eq. 6-93

(6-98) $$\overline{I^r} = \int_{-\infty}^{\infty} \cdots \int \sum_{l=0}^{n} \cdots \sum_{l+r=0}^{n} v_l \cdots v_{l+r} W(v_0, v_1, \ldots v_n) \, dv_0 \, dv_1, \ldots dv_n$$
$$\underset{n \text{ fold}}{}$$

By definition

$$W(v_0, \ldots, v_{k-1}, v_{k+1}, \ldots, v_n) = \int_{-\infty}^{\infty} W(v_0, \ldots, v_{k-1}, v_k, v_{k+1}, \ldots, v_n) \, dv_k$$

and hence

(6-99) $$\overline{I^r} = \int_{-\infty}^{\infty} \cdots \int \sum_{l=0}^{n} \cdots \sum_{l+r=0}^{n} v_l \cdots v_{l+r} W(v_l \ldots, v_{l+r}) \, dv \cdots dv_{l+r}$$
$$\underset{r \text{ fold}}{}$$

in particular

(6-100)
$$\bar{I} = \int_{-\infty}^{\infty} \sum_{l=0}^{n} v_l W(v_l) \, dv_l$$

(6-101)
$$\overline{I^2} = \int_{-\infty}^{\infty} \int \sum_{k=0}^{n} \sum_{l=0}^{n} v_k v_l W(v_k, v_l) \, dv_k \, dv_l$$

The probability of the molecule having a particular velocity v is independent of time, and Eq. 6-100 may be simplified to

(6-102)
$$\bar{I} = n\bar{v}$$

where $\bar{v}$ is the mean velocity of the molecule:

(6-103)
$$\bar{v} = \int_{-\infty}^{\infty} v_l W(v_l) \, dv_l$$

The double sum in Eq. 6-101 does not simplify so readily for small n, and we will discuss Eq. 6-101 when taking the limit ($\delta t \to 0$, $n \to \infty$, $n \, \delta t \to t$). From Eq. 6-99 we see that in order to determine $\overline{I^r}$ we require a knowledge of $W(v_0, \ldots, v_r)$. Since, in general, determination of $W(v_0, \ldots, v_r)$ can be very complicated, we will restrict ourselves here to the determination of $W(v_j)$ and $W(v_k, v_l)$ for the pipe flow problem. In addition, for long times we can show that $P(I)$ will be gaussian, and hence only $\bar{I}$ and $\overline{I^2}$ are then required.

$W(v_j) \, dv_j$ is related to $W(r_j) \, dr_j$, the probability that at time t_j the molecule has a position between r_j and $r_j + dr_j$. The relationship between v and r is given by Eq. 6-82. Thus we find

(6-104)
$$W(v_j) \, dv_j = W(r_j(v_j)) \left| \frac{dr_j}{dv_j} \right| dv_j$$

$$= \frac{2\pi r}{\pi a^2} \left(\frac{a^2}{2r} \right) \frac{dv_j}{v_{m0}}$$

$$= \frac{1}{v_{m0}} \, dv_j$$

since the molecule has equal probability of being anywhere in the pipe cross section.

Similarly, $W(v_k, v_l)$ is related to $W(r_k, r_l)$. In this case, however, it is convenient to write for $W(r_k, r_l)$, the conditional form

$$W(r_k, r_l) = W(r_k)W(r_k/r_l)$$

where $W(r_k/r_l)$ is defined as the probability that the position of the molecule is between r_l and $r_l + dr_l$ at time $l\,\delta t$, if it were between r_k and $r_k + dr_k$ at time $k\,\delta t$. Then in terms of $W(r_k/r_l)$, we have

$$(6\text{-}105) \qquad W(v_k, v_l)\,dv_k\,dv_l = W(r_k)W(r_k/r_l)\frac{a^4}{4r^2 v_{m0}{}^2}\,dv_k\,dv_l$$

Again $W(r_k) = 2r/a^2$ and Eq. 6-105 becomes

$$(6\text{-}106) \qquad W(v_k, v_l)\,dv_k\,dv_l = \left[\frac{a^2}{2r}W(r_k/r_l)\right]\frac{dv_k\,dv_l}{v_{m0}{}^2}$$

In the pipe problem, $W(r_k/r_l)$ may be explicitly evaluated by solving the diffusion equation within a pipe cross section. That is, $W(r_k/r_l)$ satisfies the equation

$$(6\text{-}107) \qquad \frac{\partial W(r_k/r_l)}{\partial t} = D\left[\frac{\partial^2}{\partial r^2} + \frac{1}{r}\frac{\partial}{\partial r}\right]W(r_k/r_l)$$

with boundary conditions

$$\frac{\partial W(r_k/r_l)}{\partial r} = 0 \qquad r = a$$

$$W(r_k/r_l) = \frac{\delta(r - r_k)}{4\pi r^2} \qquad (k = l)$$

The reason for this is that the radial movement of a tracer molecule is independent of its axial convective velocity. Thus, in order to calculate the radial position the tracer molecule has at time t—if it were at $r = r_0$ at time $t = 0$—we need only consider its diffusion in a radial direction. (The angular dependence within a plane perpendicular to z is averaged out before writing Eq. 6-107. Actually the basic diffusion equation is

$$\frac{\partial W(r_k, \theta_k/r_l, \theta_l)}{\partial t} = D\,\nabla_{r,\theta}^2 W(r_k, \theta_k/r_l, \theta_l)$$

but the equation is averaged over θ_k. This averaging is useful, since the condition $\partial W(r_k/r_l)/\partial r = 0$, $r = a$, is independent of θ_l.)

For the pipe problem we find

(6-108) $W(r_k/r_l) = \dfrac{2r}{a^2} \displaystyle\sum_{i=1}^{\infty} \dfrac{J_0(\xi_i r_k)J_0(\xi_i r_l) \exp\left[-\xi_i^2 D\, \delta t(l-k)\right]}{[J_0(\xi_i a)]^2}$

where the ξ_i are determined from the equation

(6-109) $J_1(a\xi) = 0$

J_0 and J_1 are the zero and first-order Bessel functions, respectively.

Equations 6-108 and 6-106 may be substituted into Eq. 6-101 and an expression is obtained for $\overline{I^2}$. Similar calculations could be made to find $\overline{I^n}$ through the use of a sequence of conditional probabilities.

$\bar{z}$ and $\overline{z^2}$ follow from Eq. 6-97 upon letting $\delta t \rightarrow 0$, $n \rightarrow \infty$, $n\, \delta t \rightarrow t$. From Eqs. 6 102 and 6-103 we find

(6-110) $\bar{z} = t\bar{v} = t\displaystyle\int_{-\infty}^{\infty} v_l W(v_l)\, dv_l$

Since $W(v_l) = 1/v_m$ in the pipe flow problem,

(6-111) $\bar{z} = \dfrac{v_m t}{2}$

The evaluation of z^2 from Eq. 6-101 by taking limits requires the replacement

$$\sum_{k=0}^{\infty}\sum_{l=0}^{\infty} \rightarrow \int_0^t \int_0^t dt'\, dt''$$

yielding

(6-112) $\overline{z^2} = \displaystyle\int_0^t \int_0^t$

$\times \left[\displaystyle\int_{-\infty}^{\infty} \int_{-\infty}^{\infty} v(t')v(t'')W(v(t'))W(v(t')/v(t''))\, dv(t')\, dv(t'') \right] dt'\, dt''$

(We assume the integrals may be interchanged.)

The double integral over $v(t')$ and $v(t'')$ is a correlation function and is usually denoted $R(t', t'')$. Thus*

(6-113)
$$\overline{z^2} = \int_0^t \int_0^t R(t', t'') \, dt' \, dt''$$

In terms of the variables $u(t) = v(t) - \bar{v}$, we find

(6-114)
$$\overline{z^2} - \overline{z}^2 = \int_0^t \int_0^t R'(t', t'') \, dt' \, dt''$$

where

$$R'(t', t'') = \int_{-\infty}^{\infty} \int u(t')u(t'')W(u(t'))W(u(t')/u(t'')) \, du(t') \, du(t'')$$

In our problem the initial radial position of the tracer molecule is simply proportional to a cross-sectional area element, and this is true for all time t. Thus $R(t', t'')$ can only depend upon $t'' - t'$. Changing to a coordinate system $s = t'' - t'$, $s' = t''$ and integrating over s', we have

(6-115)
$$\overline{z^2} = 2 \int_0^t R(s) \, ds \int_s^t ds'$$

$$= 2 \int_0^t R(s)(t - s) \, ds$$

In the limit $t \to \infty$, this equation becomes

(6-116)
$$\overline{z^2} = 2t \int_0^{\infty} R'(s) \, ds + \bar{v}^2 t^2$$

---

* Equation 6-110 and Eq. 6-113 may be derived immediately by averaging, or by squaring and then averaging the relation $z = \int_0^t v(t) \, dt$. We have chosen the foregoing method of derivation, since it allows us to establish the gaussian distribution for I and since it yields formula in terms of W directly.

The integral in Eq. 6-115 is evaluated using Eq. 6-108. Details may be found in Beran (1955), wherein a slightly different evaluation procedure is used. The result is

(6-117) $$\overline{z^2} - \overline{z}^2 = \sum_{i=1}^{\infty} \frac{32 v_{m0}^2}{a^4 \xi_i^4} \left\{ \frac{t}{\xi_i^2 D} + \frac{(\exp[-\xi_i^2 Dt] - 1))}{(\xi_i^2 D)^2} \right\}$$

In the limit $t \to 0$

(6-118) $$\overline{z^2} - \overline{z}^2 \to \frac{v_{m0}^2 t^2}{12} - \frac{2}{3} v_{m0}^2 \frac{Dt^3}{a^2}$$

In the limit $t \to \infty$

(6-119) $$\overline{z^2} - \overline{z}^2 \to \frac{2 v_{m0}^2 a^2}{192 D} t$$

The result in Eq. 6-119 was first obtained by Taylor (1953) by different arguments. The first term on the right-hand side of Eq. 6-118 was also first obtained by Taylor. The latter result is quite simple to obtain, however, since in the absence of molecular diffusion, the molecules at initial position r_0 always remain at that position. The probability of a molecule lying between r_0 and $r_0 + dr_0$ is $2\pi r_0/\pi a^2$; and since $v = v_{m0}[1 - (r^2/a^2)]$, the probability of a molecule at any r_0 having a velocity between v and $v + dv$ is simply $1/v_{m0}$. This means that $C(z, t)$ is uniformly distributed from 0 to $v_{m0} t$ and $\overline{z^2} - \overline{z}^2$ (essentially the normalized moment of inertia about the point $v_{m0} t/2$) is $v_{m0} t/12$.

The result given in Eq. 6-119 is, of course, very interesting. When t is very large, $\sigma \equiv \sqrt{\overline{z^2} - \overline{z}^2} = \text{const } t^{1/2}$; this implies a random-walk type behavior in the x direction. Physical reasoning indeed bears this out. A tracer molecule diffuses from point to point and in this random manner occupies all positions from $r = 0$ to $r = a$. As a consequence, the molecule attains all convective velocities between 0 and v_m. A plot of its convective velocity vs. time would appear as a random-time series; hence the variance σ^2 about the mean position $z_m = \bar{v}t$ would be proportional to t, not t^2. The only difference between the tracer molecule and a particle performing a simple random walk in the z direction (where the probability is $\frac{1}{2}$ to take a step Δz in the z direction; the probability is $\frac{1}{2}$ not to take a step every δt second) is that the successive steps of the tracer molecule are correlated whereas in the simple random-walk problem we usually assume no correlation. If the correlation goes essentially to zero in a finite time t_c, however, the overall behavior of the tracer molecule and the particle performing a simple random walk is the same, in both cases $\sigma \propto t^{1/2}$. In the foregoing problems, $W(r_{t'}/r_{t''})$ and $R(t'' - t')$ have a characteristic time of the order of a^2/D, which is roughly the time it takes for the tracer molecule to diffuse a pipe radius (see Eq. 6-108). For times much greater than a^2/D the tracer molecule behaves as though it were performing a simple random walk in the z direction. Only the constant in the relation $\sigma = \text{const } t^{1/2}$ is dependent on the correlation of successive velocities.

Since the tracer molecule essentially is performing a random walk in the z direction, for $n\delta t \gg a^2/D$ we expect $I(n)$ to be gaussianly distributed about its mean value. Hoeffing and Robbins (1948) have shown that $I(n)$ is gaussianly distributed about its mean value if the correlation between v_l and v_{l+r} is equal to zero for some value of r such that $n \gg r$ and the third-order moment of v_l exists. If we take $r \, \delta t$ of the order of several t_c, then we expect this theorem to hold here, since physically the correlation between the tracer molecule's successive convection velocities may be set equal to zero for such time separations. In the above problem the third-order moment of v_l exists, since $0 \leqslant v_l \leqslant v_{m0}$. It only remains then to assume that the same behavior is exhibited in the limit $(\delta t \to 0, n \to \infty, n\delta t \to t)$. For large times then

$$(6\text{-}120) \qquad P_{mv}(z, t) = \frac{1}{\sqrt{2\pi\sigma}} \exp\left[-\frac{(z - \bar{v}t)^2}{2\sigma}\right]$$

where $\bar{v} = v_{m0}/2$ and $\sigma^2 = (2v_{m0}^2 a^2/192D)t$.

In the next section we shall adapt the formulism just developed to the porous-media problem. Before concluding, however, we should like to point out, as an aside, that the foregoing procedure can be used to solve the dispersion problem for flow between parallel plates (Couette flow) and, more interestingly, to solve the dispersion problem between parallel plates when the concentrate is subject to gravitational effects. Beran (1955) treated this latter problem and obtained the standard deviation σ. In order to solve this problem, Eq. 6-107 is replaced by the equation

$$(6\text{-}121) \qquad \frac{\partial W(y_k/y_l)}{\partial t} - c\frac{\partial W(y_k/y_l)}{\partial y} = D\frac{\partial^2 W(y_k/y_l)}{\partial y^2}$$

where y is the coordinate perpendicular to the flow direction. c is the fluid velocity that the tracer molecules attain in the presence of a gravitational field acting in the negative y direction. As an example, we find that when $H \equiv ac/D \ll 1$ (where a is the separation between parallel plates) and $t \to \infty$

$$(6\text{-}122) \qquad \sigma^2 = t^2 v_{m0}{}^2 \left(1 - \frac{H}{6} \right)^2 \bigg/ 4 + \frac{8 v_m{}^2 a^2}{\pi^6 D} \left(1 + \frac{H}{4} \right) t$$

where v_{m0} is the maximum fluid velocity. Again as $t \to \infty$, the distribution is gaussian and σ^2 and $\bar{z}$ are all that are needed to define the distribution. We note that in this case

$$(6\text{-}123) \qquad \bar{z} = \frac{v_{m0}}{H} \left[1 - \frac{H}{e^H - 1} \right] t$$

and not

$$\bar{z} = \frac{v_{m0}}{2}$$

since the tracer molecules are more likely to have lower velocities than higher velocities; gravity tends to force the molecules to occupy low y positions.

6.3.2. Dispersion in Granular-Media Continuum Theory

In order to apply the foregoing formulism to the granular-medium problem, we imagine that at time $t = 0$ we choose a molecule at random and ask for the probability $P(z, t)\,dz$, that it shall have gone a distance z in the mean flow direction at time t. This is similar to asking whether or not the tracer molecule in the pipe problem has progressed a distance z in the mean flow direction. In a porous medium a tracer molecule will be constantly changing its fluid velocity in the z direction, since it will (1) be passing through a medium with irregular internal boundaries and (2) will change from streamline to streamline under the influence of molecular diffusion. As we have pointed out previously, $v_z(t)$ may be treated as a stationary random-time series if we consider very long times.

The sequence of Eqs. 6-92 through 6-101 applies to the porous-medium problem as well as to the pipe problem. In order to determine the distribution $P(z)$, we require, in general, a knowledge of the function $W(v_0, v_1, \ldots, v_n)$ (i.e., dropping the z subscript).

In the pipe problem the tracer molecule changed its fluid velocity because it diffused in a direction perpendicular to the mean flow direction; here we shall assume it changes its fluid velocity because of the irregularity of the solid internal boundaries and because of molecular diffusion. The only difference between the two problems is that $W(v_0, v_1, \ldots, v_n)$ must be calculated in a different manner. The formulism, however, is identical. We shall always assume in the porous-medium problem, however, that the effects of molecular diffusion alone, as represented in the sum $\sum_j d_j$ is negligible. This implies that $H = \bar{v}d/D \gg 1$ where d is some characteristic pore or grain dimension.

In addition, we shall only be concerned with large times in the porous medium problem. By large times we mean times in which a tracer molecule moving with the mean fluid velocity would have traversed distances very, very large compared to a characteristic pore or grain dimension. In this case, the analysis given in the pipe problem and outlined in the introduction shows that $P(z)$ is gaussianly distributed about the mean distance $z = \bar{v}t$, where $\bar{v}$ is the mean fluid velocity in the z direction. $P(z)$ has the form

$$(6\text{-}124) \qquad P(z, t) = \frac{1}{\sqrt{2\pi}\sigma(t)} \exp\left[-\frac{(z - \bar{v}t)^2}{2\sigma(t)^2} \right]$$

and to determine $P(z, t)$ it remains only to find σ. σ^2 is given by Eq. 6-114. We write here

$$(6\text{-}125) \qquad \sigma^2 = \overline{z^2} - \bar{z}^2 = \int_0^t \int_0^t R'(t', t'') \, dt' \, dt''$$

where

$$(6\text{-}126) \quad R'(t', t'') = \int\!\!\!\int_{-\infty}^{\infty} u(t')u(t'')W(u(t'))W(u(t')/u(t'')) \, du(t') \, du(t'')$$

$W(u(t')/u(t'')) \, du(t') \, du(t'')$ is the probability that a tracer molecule will have a fluctuating z component of fluid velocity between $u(t'')$ and $u(t'') + du(t'')$ at time t'' if it had a fluctuating z component of fluid velocity between $u(t')$ and $u(t') + du(t')$ at time t'.

For large times, $R'(t', t'')$ is stationary and depends only upon $t'' - t'$. In addition we expect that $R'(t'' - t')$ will approach zero as $t'' - t' \rightarrow \infty$. Thus $R'(t'' - t')$ in this porous-medium problem has the same general properties that it had in the pipe problem. In analogy to Eq. 6-116 we have here

(6-127) $$\sigma^2 = 2t \int_0^\infty R'(s)\, ds$$

where $R'(s) \equiv R'(t'' - t')$ is given by Eq. 6-126.

For convenience $R'(s)$ is often normalized. We write

(6-128) $$R'(s) = \sigma_v^2 \rho(s)$$

where $\sigma_v^2 = R'(0)$ is the variance of the velocity field. The integral $\int_0^\infty \rho(s)\, ds$ defines a characteristic time. It is perhaps easier to visualize a characteristic length. Thus we change to the variable

$$\eta = \frac{\bar{v}t}{d}$$

where d is a characteristic length. It may be any of the lengths, l_P, l_P' or l_P'', defined in the introduction. Equation 6-127 now becomes

(6-129) $$\sigma^2 = \frac{2t\sigma_v^2}{\bar{v}} L_L$$

where

$$L_L = d \int_0^\infty \rho(\eta)\, d\eta$$

L_L is of the order of the average length a tracer molecule must travel in the mean flow direction before the correlation drops significantly between the fluid velocity in the mean flow direction and the initial fluid velocity in the mean flow direction.

Both σ_v^2 and L_L are measurable, in principle, but the measurement would be exceptionally difficult. Since we consider only slow flows ($Re = \bar{v}d/\nu \ll 1$) and have set the condition $H \gg 1$, it is possible, however, to determine βd, where

(6-130) $$\beta = \alpha^2 \int_0^\infty \rho(\eta)\, d\eta$$

and

$$\alpha^2 = \frac{\sigma_v^{\,2}}{\bar{v}^2}$$

for one value of $\bar{v}$ and thus predict σ^2 for all values of $\bar{v}$ ($Re \ll 1$). The condition $H \gg 1$ allows us to neglect molecular diffusion; and for slow flows α is a constant, since the governing fluid flow equations are linear. Similarly, $\int_0^\infty \rho(\eta) \, d\eta$ is a constant. We may write Eq. 6-129 in the form

(6-131) $\sigma^2 = 2t\bar{v}\beta d$

For a fixed porous medium, βd may be determined by a single experiment, and the relation between σ^2 and $\bar{v}$ may be checked by varying $\bar{v}$.

We note here that Saffman (1959) disagrees with the conclusion that molecular diffusion may be neglected even when $H \gg 1$. He expects βd to depend on H even in this case. We will return to his arguments below after giving some experimental data in support of the independence of βd.

In a series of experiments reported in detail by Beran (1955), N. Matalas showed that in the flow of a radioactive tracer (barium–lanthanum-140—$D \sim 10^{-5}$ cm²/sec) in water through 20–30 Ottawa sand, the foregoing conclusions were confirmed. A 16-ft glass tube, 2.54 cm in diameter, was set vertically and filled with 20–30 Ottawa sand (average sand "diameter," 0.07 cm). Distilled water was forced through the column under gravity. The mean velocity of the fluid was varied in seven runs from 0.42 cm/sec to 0.028 cm/sec. $P(z, t)$ was found to have a gaussian shape, and Eq. 6-131 was verified. βd was found to have the value of about 1.1 cm. (The velocity of 0.42 cm/sec corresponds to a Reynolds number of somewhat over 2, and strictly speaking the theory should not hold there. Apparently, however, inertial effects at this Reynolds number were small.)

It is unfortunate that measurements do not allow us to distinguish between L_L and α. In these experiments it was found only that

(6-132) $L_L = \frac{d\beta}{\alpha^2} = \frac{1.1}{\alpha^2}$

Scheidegger (1960, Chapter X) points out that, in general, similar experiments confirm the fact that the function $P(z, t)$ has a gaussian distribution. He gives the reader a number of references to experiments. It must be realized, however, that unless the experiment is very carefully controlled, the results may be different. For example, in the early phases of the experiments previously outlined, the soluble matter was being absorbed by the sand in significant amounts, and the tail of the distribution obtained was appreciably different from the gaussian form. Only after this effect was eliminated were results obtained that were in agreement with theoretical predictions. Furthermore, the foregoing theory is true only when the soluble matter is present in infinitesimal traces and does not affect the fluid flow field of the basic fluid. Care must be taken when applying the foregoing theory to fluids with appreciable concentrations of soluble matter. The confirmation of the particular form given by

$$(6\text{-}131) \qquad\qquad \sigma^2 = 2t\bar{v}\beta d$$

under controlled conditions has not received much attention beyond the experiment mentioned. Most experiments have more practical ends in mind and do not dwell on confirming this very simple relation. Also no attempts known to the writer have been made to devise experiments to determine $\alpha = \sigma_v/\bar{v}$ or

$$L_L = d \int\limits_0^\infty \rho(p)\, dp$$

Ultimately α and L_L must be related to the statistical geometrical properties of the porous medium. As we have seen in the discussion of the permeability, such relations are very difficult to obtain theoretically, and it would be most desirable if experiments could provide a guide.

6.3.2.1. Effects of Molecular Diffusion. Saffman (1959), using a random network model to represent a porous medium, concluded that molecular diffusion was important in determining the value of the integral $\int_0^\infty R'(s)\, ds$ even when $H \gg 1$. Although his remarks were not phrased in this language, this is the essence of his conclusion. This writer feels some caution is required in applying results obtained by a network model to a real medium; but the physical effect which led to Saffman's conclusion can be discussed without reference to his model.

In this section we shall first discuss the difficulties that may be encountered if molecular diffusion is neglected. Subsequent to this we discuss the dependence of the integral

$$\int_0^\infty R'(s)\, ds$$

on D. Our conclusion will be that, in agreement with the assumptions made in this chapter,

$$\int_0^\infty R'(s)\, ds$$

is independent of D when $H \gg 1$. The arguments are somewhat subtle in nature, and it is recommended that the reader also read Saffman (1959,1960) to see his approach. This section was written with the assistance of A. Somoroff.

The basic difficulty of neglecting molecular diffusion may be illustrated by considering the pipe problem treated in Section 6.3.1 and, in the absence of molecular diffusion, by asking the following two questions:

1. What is the average position $\bar{z}$ of a tracer molecule after a time T?

2. What is the average time $\bar{t}$ that it takes a tracer molecule to travel a distance $(v_m/2)T$? ($v_m/2$ is here the average pipe velocity.)

In both cases the tracer molecule initially has an equal probability of being found anywhere in the pipe cross section, but since we neglect molecular diffusion, it may not change its streamline.

The answer to question *1* is the expected answer:

(6-133) $$\bar{z} = \frac{v_m}{2}\, T$$

Equation 6-133 may be derived by noting that the distance traveled by a molecule at radius r is

(6-134) $$z_r = \int_0^T v(r, t)\, dt = v(r) \int_0^T dt = v(r)T$$

Since the probability of the molecule being between r and $r + dr$,

$P(r)\, dr$, is $2\pi r\, dr/\pi a^2$ we find

$$(6\text{-}135) \qquad \bar{z} = \frac{1}{\pi a^2}\int_0^a z_r 2\pi r\, dr = \frac{T}{\pi a^2}\int_0^a 2\pi r\, dr\, v(r) = \frac{v_m}{2}\, T$$

The answer to question 2 is perhaps unexpected. We have for the time a molecule takes at radius r to travel a distance $v_m T/2$

$$(6\text{-}136) \qquad t_r = \int_0^{v_m T/2} \frac{dz}{v(r, z)} = \frac{v_m T}{2}\frac{1}{v(r)}$$

since $v(r, z)$ is independent of z. For a pipe the probability of having a velocity between v and $v + dv$ is dv_m/v_m. Thus

$$(6\text{-}137) \qquad \bar{t} = \int_0^{v_m} t_r \frac{dv}{v_m} = \frac{T}{2}\int_0^{v_m}\frac{dv}{v}$$

This yields finally

$$(6\text{-}138) \qquad \bar{t} = \frac{T}{2}\int_0^1 \frac{d\eta}{\eta}$$

which gives an infinite value for $\bar{t}$.

The slow velocities near the pipe boundary thus cause considerable difficulty if one is concerned with average transit times rather than average positions after a fixed time. Moreover, this is not a mathematically pathological result. Even if $D \neq 0$, we would find $\bar{t} \gg T$ if $a^2/D \gg T$.

If molecular diffusion is present and $T \gg a^2/D$, we arrive at a different result. We find in this case that

$$(6\text{-}139) \qquad \bar{t} = T$$

In order to see this we note that when $T \gg a^2/D$ the molecule has a high probability of diffusing across the pipe cross section many times in the course of its travel. Thus the molecule travels a distance $v_m T/2$, sometimes with low velocities and sometimes with high velocities. This is counter to the case of zero molecular diffusion in which each molecule travels with a single velocity.

In traveling a given distance a molecule will traverse most of this distance when traveling at higher velocities rather than at lower velocities if it spends an equal amount of time traveling with all velocities from 0 to v_m. This is so since the distance traveled in time Δt is $v \, \Delta t$. The time it takes for the molecule to travel a distance dz is

$$(6\text{-}140) \qquad\qquad dt = \frac{dz}{v(r, z)}$$

The average time it takes for the molecule to travel this distance is

$$(6\text{-}141) \quad d\bar{t} = \int_0^v P(v(r, z)) \, dv(r, z) \, dt = \int_0^m \frac{dz \, P(v(r, z)) \, dv(r, z)}{v(r, z)}$$

where $P(v(r, z)) \, dv(r, z)$ is the probability of the molecule having a velocity between $v(r, z)$ and $v(r, z) + dv(r, z)$ *when traveling a distance dz.*

We next note that the probability of the molecule having a velocity between $v(r, z)$ and $v(r, z) + dv(r, z)$ *when traveling a distance dz* is equal to the probability of the molecule having a velocity between $v(r, z)$ and $v(r, z) + dv(r, z)$ at position z multiplied by the fraction of the distance dz that would be traveled with this velocity if all velocities were equally probable. Thus

$$(6\text{-}142) \qquad\qquad P(v(r, z)) = \left[\frac{1}{v_m}\right]\left[\frac{v(r, z)}{v_m/2}\right]$$

Since we consider $T \gg a^2/D$, the probability of a molecule having a velocity between $v(r)$ and $v(r) + dv(r)$ is dv/v_m.

$$\frac{v(r, z)}{v_m/2} = \frac{v(r, z)}{\bar{v}}$$

is the fraction of the distance dz, traveled with velocity $v(r, z)$, if all velocities were equally probable. This yields

$$(6\text{-}143) \qquad\qquad d\bar{t} = \frac{dz}{v_m/2}$$

and

$$(6\text{-}144) \qquad\qquad \bar{t} = \int_0^{v_m T/2} \frac{dz}{v_m/2} = T$$

We thus arrive at the interesting result that when $T \gg a^2/D$, the presence of molecular diffusion has changed the value of $\bar{t}$ from infinity to T and the result is independent of the magnitude of D.

The difference between the case of finite molecular diffusion and zero molecular diffusion may thus be seen by considering the probability of the molecule having a velocity between v and $v + dv$ *when traveling any distance dz*. In the case of zero molecular diffusion this probability is dv/v_m since the molecule has an equal probability of traveling any distance dz, with all velocities between 0 and v_m. When molecular diffusion is present this probability is $[v/(v_m/2)](dv/v_m)$ since the molecule will now have a probability proportional to $v/(v_m/2)$ of traveling any distance dz. In this case the molecule may change streamlines and most of the distance it travels will be with the higher velocities. In the former case the molecule, probabilistically, travels the same proportion of any distance with low velocities as it does with high velocities.

We note that we are not saying here that the molecule will change its velocity during the travel of an infinitesimal distance dz. Rather, what we are saying is that in the course of its travel down the pipe the probability of the molecule traversing an arbitrary distance dz with velocity between v and $v + dv$ is porportional to $v/(v_m/2)$.

In order to apply this discussion to the porous-media problem we note that the important quantity to be determined therein is

$$t_c = \int_0^\infty R'(s)\, ds$$

t_c may be interpreted as the average time a molecule must travel before its velocity is uncorrelated with the velocity it had initially. In the porous-media problem we may assume that the velocity of the molecule is uncorrelated with its previous velocity after it has traversed several characteristic pore diameters. Thus t_c is the characteristic time required for a molecule to travel a distance of several characteristic pore diameters. Returning to our original question we may now phrase it as follows: Does the characteristic time it takes for the molecule to travel several characteristic pore diameters depend upon D when $H \gg 1$?

First let us note the sense in which we neglect molecular diffusion when we set the condition $H \gg 1$. We mean that when a molecule travels with the average velocity, significant molecular diffusion will not occur until it has traveled many characteristic pore diameters. It is unrealistic to suppose that molecular diffusion is so small that it plays no role at all in distances of the order z for which Eq. 6-124 is valid. For example, in the experiment cited in the foregoing $D \approx 10^{-5}$ cm²/sec, $d \approx 0.07$ cm, $v \approx 0.1$ cm/sec and the tube was 16 ft long. Thus $H \approx 700$; but in the time it took for an average molecule to traverse the 16 ft, approximately 5000 sec, it diffused a distance of 0.2 cm. In most cases of interest, molecular diffusion is strong enough to insure the condition that the velocity history of a molecule is essentially independent of the initial streamline with which is entered the porous medium.

This latter role of molecular diffusion is similar to the role of molecular diffusion in the pipe problem. There too we considered pipe lengths such that the velocity history of the molecule was independent of its initial position in the pipe cross section. As we shall now point out, molecular diffusion plays no role other than this when $H \gg 1$.

Let $d\bar{t}$ be the average time it takes a molecule in the porous medium to travel a distance dz. Just as in the pipe problem, we may write

(6-145)
$$ d\bar{t} = \int_0^v \frac{dz}{v(z)} P(v(z)) \, dv(z) $$

$$ = \int_0^{v_m} \frac{dz}{v(z)} P(v(z), z) \frac{v(z)}{\bar{v}} \, dv(z) $$

Here $P(v(z))$ is the probability of the molecule having a velocity between $v(z)$ and $v(z) + dv(z)$ when *traveling a distance dz* and $P(v(z), z)$ is the probability of molecule having a velocity between $v(z)$ and $v(z) + dv(z)$ at position z. Since

$$ \int_{-\infty}^{\infty} P(v(z), z) \, dv(z) = 1 $$

Eq. 6-145 yields

(6-146)
$$ d\bar{t} = \frac{dz}{\bar{v}} $$

From Eq. 6-146 we find

(6-147)
$$t_c = \int_0^{\gamma d} \frac{dz}{\bar{v}} = \gamma \frac{d}{\bar{v}}$$

where γd is the number of characteristic pore diameters that the molecule is required to travel before it looses significant correlation with its initial velocity. γ is assumed to be of order unity.

Molecular diffusion would only enter Eq. 6-147 through the constant γ. When $H \gg 1$, however, significant molecular diffusion does not occur in times of the order of $\gamma d/\bar{v}$ if γ is assumed to be of order unity. Thus we conclude t_c is independent of H.

CHAPTER 7

Turbulence

7.1. Introduction

The statistical theory of turbulence was the first of the continuum theories treated in this book that was studied in the literature from an explicitly statistical point of view. Modern statistical theories of turbulence began with the works of Taylor (1921, 1935, 1936) and von Kármán (1937a,b, 1938). The functional formulation was given by Hopf (1952). From the works of these persons it is easy to see how to give most other continuum theories an explicitly statistical formulation.

Most theoretical work using a statistical formulation has been done for spatially homogeneous or spatially homogeneous and isotropic turbulence. The practical problem that inspired the study of turbulence, that is, turbulent flow in pipes, is, however, neither spatially homogeneous nor isotropic. The change of emphasis from the pipe problem to the spatially homogeneous problem was brought about by recognition of the simplicities introduced into the mathematical formulation by the homogeneity assumption. In addition, it was found that spatially homogeneous turbulence could be studied experimentally by considering flow behind grids. Hence, a comparison between theory and experiment could be made for a real turbulent flow.

In this introduction we shall, however, begin historically by discussing turbulent flow in a pipe and refer to Reynolds' very basic work (Reynolds, 1901). Following this we shall discuss mixing length theories, which were intended primarily to determine the velocity profile in a pipe and which today provide much of the basis for practical work in hydraulics. (A useful early reference for mixing length theories is Goldstein, 1938. A consideration of these theories from a more modern viewpoint is given in Townsend, 1956, and Hinze, 1959.) Subsequent to the discussion of mixing length theories, we shall try to give some physical interpretation to statistical quantities similar to those we shall consider in detail in the next sections. In this discussion we shall also present some of the channel measurements of Laufer (1951). As we shall see in later sections, both the physical ideas and mathematical techniques developed in the pipe and channel studies have been used in the more idealized homogeneous and isotropic case. Despite our later theoretical emphases on the homogeneous and iso-tropic case, it was felt that stressing the pipe and channel problems in the introduction would provide a more intuitive understanding of turbulence than if we had considered turbulent flow through grids.

In the next section (Section 7.2) we shall review the statistical formulation that has already been given in Chapter 3. We shall begin with the formulation for turbulence with no symmetry properties and then give the governing equations for spatially homogeneous and isotropic turbulence. Here we refer the reader to Batchelor (1953). In Section 7.3 we shall consider the consequences that may be drawn from the governing equations both with and without some simple assumptions, and in particular we shall consider Kolmogorov's hypotheses (Kolmogorov, 1941), Heisenberg's theory (1948a), and the cumulant neglect hypothesis. Section 7.4 will deal with the more recent statistical formulations of turbulence given by Kraichnan (1957, 1958a,b, 1959, 1961, 1964a,b,c, 1965), Wyld (1961), Hopf (1952), Hopf and Titt (1953), Tatarski (1962), Edwards (1964), and Deissler (1965a).

7.1.1. Reynolds' Early Studies

⋅ The difference between laminar and turbulent flow in a pipe was recognized early, but apparently systematic studies aimed at a deep understanding of the phenomena involved began with Osborne Reynolds. In a series of papers beginning in 1883,* Reynolds discussed the conditions under which flow became turbulent, and he averaged the Navier-Stokes equations to obtain equations connecting mean values of the velocity field. Reynolds' work was both theoretical and experimental in nature, and his writing is unhurried and philosophical. Although all his important results are reported in modern books on fluid mechanics, it is worthwhile to read his original articles to under-stand more fully how he came upon the importance of the now-called

* We reference here Vol. II of his *Collected Papers* (Reynolds, 1901), in which all of the papers may be found.

Reynolds' number and how this led him to make his fundamental experiment, which we shall now describe.

Reynolds pointed out that the difference between laminar and turbulent flow was known in his time for two principal reasons. The first was the visible observation of free surface flow. Here one could see the distortion in the appearance of reflected objects when the flow was turbulent. He compares the reflecting properties of laminar flow to plate glass and the reflecting properties of the turbulent flow to sheet glass. The second reason was the observation that the resistance to flow in pipes was either proportional to the average flow velocity or roughly proportional to the square of the average flow velocity. The latter case was identified with eddying or turbulent motion.

It was known before Reynolds that small capillary tubes and slow average velocities produced fluid resistance in pipe flow that was proportional to velocity, while large tubes and high average velocities produced fluid resistance that was roughly proportional to the square of the velocity. Reynolds reasoned that since there was no such thing as absolute time or space recognized in mechanical theory at that time, these facts taken by themselves were insufficient to explain the reason why one sometimes obtained laminar flow and sometimes obtained turbulent flows. It was clear to him that some fluid parameter must be crucial in these experiments since the average velocity $\bar{u}$ and the average diameter D must be compared to some other characteristic parameter that had the dimension of length and velocity or some combination of both.

The obvious fluid parameter to consider was the viscosity, μ, or eliminating the mass dependence, the kinematic viscosity, $\nu \equiv \mu/\rho$, where ρ is the fluid density. ν has the dimensions of a diffusion coefficient, (length)^2/time. Reynolds was then led to conjecture that the dimensionless ratio $\bar{u}D/\nu$ might be the important parameter for determining whether or not the flow in a tube was laminar or turbulent.

Reynolds also sought to answer whether or not eddying came suddenly with a critical value of the parameter $\bar{u}D/\nu$ or was this appearance gradual. In order to investigate the entire problem, he undertook an experimental program in which he visually observed the behavior of dye injected into water flowing through glass tubes. His experimental arrangement is schematically shown in Fig. 7-1a and b.

Reynolds observed two distinct experimental situations. In one case, illustrated in Fig. 7-1a, the dye remained in the neighborhood

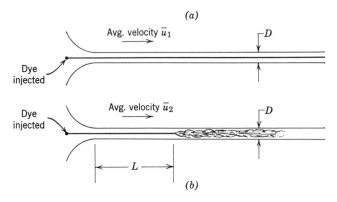

Fig. 7-1. Reynolds' experiment (see Reynolds, 1901, *Scientific Papers of Osborne Reynolds*, Vol. II, Cambridge Univ. Press, London, pp. 76–77).

of one parallel streamline as the flow progressed down the tube. (Molecular diffusion effects were evidently small in his experiments.) This corresponded to laminar flow. In the second case, illustrated in Fig. 7-1*b*, the dye suddenly, at some distance L from the entrance to the tube, ceased to follow a parallel streamline and in a short distance spread throughout the pipe cross section. This corresponded to turbulent flow. In his initial experiment he was careful to eliminate, as best he could, all disturbances in the water flowing into the tube.

From this experiment Reynolds showed that the flow changed from the laminar to the turbulent state when the parameter $\bar{u}D/\nu$, later called the Reynolds number Re exceeded a value of about 12,000. As he expected, this was the only parameter of importance. He also showed that the onset to turbulence was sudden. There was no range of Reynolds numbers in which the flow exhibited only small undulations. The flow was either laminar or beyond some distance L, fully turbulent.

Reynolds noted that the value Re $\approx$ 12,000 exceeded the value at which turbulence was noted by other investigators and that the value 12,000 was obtained only under very stable conditions of the incoming flow. If the water was disturbed when it entered the tube, turbulence would occur when Re $<$ 12,000. It occurred to him that although he had shown that turbulence depended upon only the Reynolds number, perhaps the value Re $=$ 12,000 was dependent upon conditions of the experiment. The next interesting thing to investigate would be the hypothesis that there was a minimum critical Reynolds number below which the pipe flow was always laminar, independent of the initial disturbance in the water entering the pipe.

The dye experiment described above was inadequate to use for studying the above question, since the dye would be spread about upon entering the pipe if initial disturbances were introduced into the water. To test the hypothesis Reynolds fell back upon the fact that the resistance to the flow was proportional to the average velocity in laminar flow and roughly proportional to the square of the average velocity in turbulent flow. He then performed a whole series of resistance experiments with initially disturbed water. He did indeed find a minimum critical Reynolds number, the value of which was approximately 2000. He also found in the course of his experiments that the resistance was proportional to $\bar{u}^{1.723}$, a dependence significantly different from the square law dependence usually assumed.

Reynolds' minimum value of approximately 2000 has been borne out by subsequent investigators. His upper value of approximately 12,000 was indeed dependent upon his experimental apparatus, and the value has been exceeded by a considerable degree in more recent times in very carefully controlled experiments.

At the time of Reynolds' experiments, Joule's 1850 discovery of the mechanical equivalent of heat was still a matter for active inquiry in the investigation of fluid motion. Reynolds considered the relations between the mean flow, turbulent fluctuations, and heat motion for turbulent flows. Prior to his investigations, the notions of mean velocity and relative velocity were already used in the kinetic theory of gases. The mean motion was taken to be the average motion of a group of molecules in some small volume δV, and the relative motion was defined as the motion of any of the molecules in δV relative to the mean motion. Reynolds realized that the concepts of mean and relative motion could be applied to turbulent flows. In this case, it was necessary to define three categories of motion, mean-mean motion, relative-mean motion, and heat motion (relative-relative motion). The mean-mean motion is the average motion of the fluid in a volume ΔV, where ΔV contains many turbulent eddies. We shall term this motion simply the mean motion from here on. The relative-mean velocity is the average motion of the molecules in a volume δV, where δV contains many molecules but is much smaller than the smallest eddy volumes present in the turbulent flow. The heat motion remains the motion of any molecule relative to the average group of molecules contained in δV.

The only quantities that appear in the Navier-Stokes equations are the mean velocity, which we denote $\bar{\mathbf{u}}$, and the relative mean velocity, which we denote $\mathbf{u}'$. $\mathbf{u} = \bar{\mathbf{u}} + \mathbf{u}'$ is the fluid velocity. Heat motion does not appear explicitly in the equations. Reynolds was the first person to derive the sets of equations governing both $\bar{\mathbf{u}}$ and $\mathbf{u}'$. These equations, now termed the Reynolds' equations, are found by simply averaging the Navier-Stokes equations in a manner similar to the procedure given in Chapter 3. The Navier-Stokes equations and the continuity equation are respectively

$$(7\text{-}1) \qquad \frac{\partial \mathbf{u}}{\partial t} + (\mathbf{u} \cdot \nabla)\mathbf{u} = \nu\,\nabla^2\mathbf{u} - \frac{1}{\rho}\,\nabla p$$

$$(7\text{-}2) \qquad \nabla \cdot \mathbf{u} = 0$$

The equations governing $\bar{\mathbf{u}}$ are

$$(7\text{-}3) \qquad \frac{\partial \bar{\mathbf{u}}}{\partial t} + (\bar{\mathbf{u}} \cdot \nabla)\bar{\mathbf{u}} + \overline{(\mathbf{u}' \cdot \nabla)\mathbf{u}'} = \nu\,\nabla^2\bar{\mathbf{u}} - \frac{1}{\rho}\,\nabla\bar{p}$$

$$(7\text{-}4) \qquad \nabla \cdot \bar{\mathbf{u}} = 0$$

where $p = \bar{p} + p'$. The equation for $\mathbf{u}'$ may be obtained by subtracting Eqs. 7-3 and 7-4 from Eqs. 7-1 and 7-2. (We note that Reynolds' definition of averaging is a local space average, while the averaging procedure followed in Chapter 3 and which will be used in the later sections of this chapter, is an ensemble average. We discussed the difficulties of local space averages in Chapter 5, and a reading of Reynolds' articles will show that he was quite aware of the problem involved and in fact paid very special attention to this question when comparing the characteristic small eddy sizes to characteristic distances over which molecular interaction occurs. For purposes of this descriptive introduction, however, we need not distinguish between local space and ensemble averaging.) Generally the root mean square value of $\mathbf{u}'$, $(\mathbf{u}' \cdot \mathbf{u}')^{1/2}$, is small compared to $|\bar{\mathbf{u}}|$, say of the order of 1 to 10%. See, for example, Fig. 7-4.

In addition to further probing the nature of viscous dissipation in fluid motion, Reynolds studied the equations governing $\bar{\mathbf{u}}$ and $\mathbf{u}'$ in an attempt to understand why there was a minimum Reynolds number below which the flow was not turbulent. He reasoned that energy flowed from the mean fluid motion to the turbulent motion and hence was dissipated by viscous action into heat. In a steady flow, if the flow was to be turbulent, the energy going into turbulent motion must equal the energy dissipated. Hence he derived an expression for the rate of change of the kinetic energy in the turbulent fluctuations and set the volume integral of this quantity equal to zero. The kinetic energy in turbulent fluctuations, $\bar{E}'$, is given by $\bar{E}' = \frac{1}{2}\rho \mathbf{u}' \cdot \mathbf{u}'$. Reynolds thus wrote

(7-5) $$\int \frac{D}{Dt} \bar{E}' \, d\mathbf{x} = 0$$

where $D/Dt = (\partial/\partial t) + \bar{\mathbf{u}} \cdot \nabla$ is the substantial derivative; i.e., it gives the rate of change of $\bar{E}'$ for a fluid element moving with the mean flow velocity.

The part of the expression, $D\bar{E}'/Dt$, corresponding to terms representing the inflow of energy from the mean flow is of the form

$$\overline{\rho u'^2} \frac{\partial \bar{u}}{\partial x}, \qquad \overline{\rho u'v'} \frac{\partial \bar{u}}{\partial y}$$

etc., where $\mathbf{u}$ has components (u, v, w). The part of the expression representing dissipation of energy by viscosity has terms of the form

$$2\mu \overline{\left[\frac{\partial u'}{\partial x}\right]^2}, \qquad 2\mu \overline{\left(\frac{\partial w'}{\partial y} + \frac{\partial v'}{\partial x}\right)^2}$$

On setting the order of magnitude of the terms $\overline{\rho u'v'}(\partial \bar{u}/\partial y)$ equal to the order of magnitude of the term $2\mu \overline{[\partial u'/\partial x]^2}$, Reynolds then reasoned that the Reynolds number must be greater than some critical value for turbulent flow to exist. He said essentially that the order of magnitude of $\overline{(\partial u'/\partial x)^2}$ would be

$$\overline{u'^2}/l_c^2$$

where l_c is a characteristic eddy size and the order of magnitude of $\overline{u'v'}$ would be $\overline{u'^2}$.* Thus equating production and dissipation terms yields

(7-6) $$\overline{u'v'} \frac{\partial \bar{u}}{\partial y} = O\left[\frac{\nu}{l_c^2} \overline{u'^2}\right]; \qquad \frac{\partial \bar{u}}{\partial y} = O\left[\frac{\nu}{l_c^2}\right]$$

* His terminology is different, but this is what he does in effect.

Taking pipe flow with $\bar{u}$ in the flow direction and y in a direction perpendicular to the flow direction, we estimate that $\partial \bar{u}/\partial y$ is of the order of $\bar{u}/D$, where D is the pipe diameter. Hence

$$(7\text{-}7) \qquad\qquad \frac{\bar{u}D}{\nu} = A\,\frac{D^2}{l_c^{\,2}}$$

where A is a constant of order of unity. If we allow l_c to approach infinity, $\mathrm{Re} = \bar{u}D/\nu \rightarrow 0$; we may have turbulence at any Reynolds number. l_c should be bounded by D, however, and hence turbulence can occur only at a finite Reynolds number.

This rough order of magnitude argument, of course, does not give the critical Reynolds number, and Reynolds pursued the matter in more quantitative fashion for flow between parallel plates. He treated this problem more explicitly as a stability problem by considering the ratio of the production to dissipation terms for various types of disturbances. This general method of attack through the integral equation was considered by a number of later workers, but this type of analysis only allows the determination of a minimum critical Reynolds number, since it does not rule out instabilities that are forbidden by the Navier-Stokes equations. The more quantitative approach is to study the problem of stability by considering the first-order perturbation of the Navier-Stokes equations. This method, which also has been studied for many years, is presented in modern form in books by Lin (1955) and Chandrasekhar (1961). We shall not consider the stability problem in this book, since the basic problem as it is usually treated is not really statistical at all. The underlying idea is to determine whether a specific periodic infinitesimal disturbance will grow or decay. The finite amplitude stability question would be more explicitly a statistical problem, but this has received little attention.

7.1.2. Concept of Eddy Viscosity and Mixing Lengths

The recognition that turbulence is associated with a different law of resistance than the linear law obtained for laminar flow leads naturally to the expectation that the mean flow properties of turbulent flow may be quite different than those found in laminar flow. One phenomenological way of taking this into account is to consider the concept of an additional viscosity of mechanical rather than intrinsic origin. In laminar flow we assume that the relation between stress and rate of strain for an incompressible fluid is of the form

$$(7\text{-}8) \qquad \tau_{ij} = -\delta_{ij}p + \nu\rho\left(\frac{\partial u_i}{\partial x_j} + \frac{\partial u_j}{\partial x_i}\right)$$

where τ_{ij} is the fluid stress tensor, p is the hydrostatic pressure, and ν is the kinematic viscosity. For turbulent flow it was suggested by a number of early workers [it appears that Boussinesq, 1877 was the first] that perhaps it would be appropriate to write, instead of Eq. 7-8, the relation

$$(7\text{-}9) \qquad \overline{\tau_{ij}} = -\delta_{ij}\bar{p} + \rho(\nu + \epsilon)\left[\frac{\partial \bar{u}_i}{\partial x_j} + \frac{\partial \bar{u}_j}{\partial x_i}\right]$$

where now the overbar indicates average quantities and ϵ is an additional viscosity termed the eddy viscosity.

ϵ is, of course, different in kind from ν. It results from the turbulent eddying, and there is no reason to suppose it will be the same in pipe turbulence as it would be in jet turbulence. In fact, in general, since we would guess that the eddy structure near the boundary of the pipe would probably be different than the eddy structure near the pipe center, we expect that ϵ would be a function of position within the pipe cross section. ϵ, however, is not simply an arbitrary function that may be so constituted to bring about agreement between theory and experiment; its introduction may be crudely justified on physical grounds by analogy to the gas kinetic derivation of viscosity.

Kinematic viscosity is derived by considering the amount of momentum transferred by fluid molecules from one portion of the fluid to another. (See, for example, Hirschfelder, Curtiss, and Bird, 1954.) Consider two parallel layers of fluid in, say, Couette flow. Referring to Fig. 7-2, we note that molecules are continually being interchanged between layers A and B as a result of the random kinetic motion of the

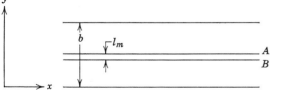
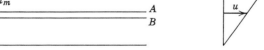

Fig. 7-2. Momentum transport in Couette flow.

molecules. If layers A and B are moving at different fluid velocities in the x direction (as they are in this flow), then transfer of molecules from B to A will tend to lower the fluid velocity of layer A, since the average fluid velocity of molecules leaving B is lower than the average fluid velocity of molecules in A. Similarly, molecules arriving in B from A tend to raise the fluid velocity of B.

Let us say that on the average a molecule travels a distance l_m before it collides with another molecule and that its average molecular speed in the y direction is $v_m{}'$. On the average we may say that if layers A and B are separated by a distance l_m, then the net rate of transfer per unit area of momentum from layer A to B is

$$(7\text{-}10) \qquad a(nmu_A v_m{}' - nmu_B v_m{}') = anmv_m{}'l_m \frac{d\bar{u}}{dy}$$

(If the mean flow does not have a linear velocity gradient, this relation is only approximate, but since $l_m \ll b$, the velocity may be considered linear over dimensions of the order of l_m.) The constant a is a numerical factor of the order of unity and accounts for the fact that the molecules are moving in all directions; n represents the number of molecules per unit volume, and m is the molecular mass. This transfer of momentum acts like a shearing force between the two layers, and thus we may write

$$(7\text{-}11) \qquad \tau_{xy} = anmv_m{}'l_m \frac{d\bar{u}}{dy}$$

where τ_{xy} is the shear in the x direction transmitted across a surface whose normal is along the y axis. Comparing Eq. 7-11 with Eq. 7-8 and noting that $\rho = nm$, we see that

$$(7\text{-}12) \qquad \nu = av_m{}'l_m$$

The argument for a physical interpretation of the eddy viscosity, ϵ, proceeds along similar lines. Instead of individual molecules, we focus our attention on small but macroscopic elements of fluid. In a turbulent fluid we imagine the overall fluid to be composed of small elements of fluid each of which possesses a different turbulent velocity. Let $\bar{v}'$ denote the root mean square value of the y component of turbulent velocity, i.e., $(\overline{v'^2})^{1/2}$. These small elements are imagined to travel about within the flow in a random manner in much the same way as the molecules did in the example just treated. We suppose that these elements may travel a distance l' before interacting with other fluid elements. We have in analogy to Eq. 7-12

(7-13) $\epsilon = a'l'\tilde{v}'$

In the kinetic theory used to determine ν, a and l are reasonably well defined quantities, and in fact a more sophisticated theory may be employed to determine ν quite accurately for gases. In turbulence theory a' and l' cannot be evaluated with any definiteness, and thus it is usual to absorb the a' into the length l' and write

(7-14) $\epsilon = l\tilde{v}'$

where $l = a'l'$.

From Eq. 7-14 it is easy to see that ϵ is, in general, a function of position. $\tilde{v}'$, the characteristic turbulent velocity, varies from zero on the pipe boundary to some finite value at the pipe center. Similarly, l, which must depend on eddy size, would be expected to be small near the pipe boundary and larger in the pipe interior. Some conjectures can be made about the manner in which ϵ varies, and this has been an active field for investigation for many years. The most basic work in this field was performed by Prandtl, von Kármán, and Taylor, and we refer the reader to Goldstein (1938) for many of the early references to their work and for a more detailed summary of their work than we shall give below.

In terms of the eddy viscosity, the equation of motion governing $\bar{u}(y)$, the average velocity of steady flow in a two-dimensional channel, is

(7-15) $\dfrac{1}{\rho}\dfrac{\partial \bar{p}}{\partial x} = \dfrac{\partial}{\partial y}\left\{[\epsilon(y) + \nu]\dfrac{\partial \bar{u}}{\partial y}\right\}$

x is in the flow direction, y is perpendicular to the flow direction, and all terms of the form $\partial/\partial x(\quad)$ have been set equal to zero with the exception of the mean pressure gradient. This equation implies immediately that the total shear (viscous and turbulent) is of the form

(7-16) $\tau_{xy} = \rho[\epsilon(y) + \nu]\dfrac{d\bar{u}}{dy}$

where τ_{xy} is a linear function of y.

In general, it is assumed in turbulent flow that except in the very immediate neighborhood of the channel boundaries, $\epsilon(y) \gg \nu$. In other words, it is assumed that the transfer of momentum from one fluid layer to another fluid layer takes place principally by macroscopic fluid transfer rather than by microscopic molecular transfer. Thus, over most of the channel, Eq. 7-16 is replaced by

(7-17) $$\tau_{xy} = \rho\epsilon(y)\frac{d\bar{u}}{dy}$$

or introducing Eq. 7-14

(7-18) $$\tau_{xy} = \rho l \tilde{v}' \frac{d\bar{u}}{dy}$$

In order to determine $\bar{u}$, we require two hypotheses, one to determine the form of $\tilde{v}'$ and the other to determine the form of l. To find $\tilde{v}'$, Prandtl reasoned that variations in velocity occurred at a layer at $y = y_0$ as a result of fluid traveling with the average velocity in a layer at $y = y_0 - y'$, moving to the layer $y = y_0$. Since the mean free path is l, then we should have roughly

(7-19) $$\tilde{v}' = l \left| \frac{d\bar{u}}{dy} \right|$$

and substituting Eq. 7-19 into Eq. 7-18

(7-20) $$\tau_{xy} = \rho l^2 \frac{d\bar{u}}{dy} \left| \frac{d\bar{u}}{dy} \right|$$

In order to find an expression for l, Prandtl simply assumed that l was proportional to y in the neighborhood of the walls of the channel. Thus he set

$$l = A'y$$

and found

(7-21) $$\tau_{xy} = \rho A'^2 y^2 \frac{d\bar{u}}{dy} \left| \frac{d\bar{u}}{dy} \right|$$

If $\partial\bar{p}/\partial x = 0$, Eq. 7-21 may be integrated and yields finally

(7-22) $$\bar{u} = \frac{\sqrt{\tau_0/\rho}}{A'} \log y + B'$$

where B' is a constant of integration.

This equation, hopefully valid near the wall, has the undesirable property that it is infinite at the wall. This equation is, however, not expected to be valid in the very immediate neighborhood of the wall, since here $\nu > \epsilon$, for $\tilde{v}'$ must be zero at the wall. von Kármán proposed a different form for l using a similarity hypothesis. He chose

$$(7\text{-}23) \qquad l = k \frac{\dfrac{d^2\bar{u}}{dy^2}}{\dfrac{d\bar{u}}{dy}}$$

which, in the absence of a mean pressure gradient, gives the same logarithmic form as Eq. 7-22. A nondimensionalized form of Eq. 7-22 with universal constants was given by von Kármán, and we shall discuss this form at more length later on (see Eq. 7-43).

7.1.3. Connection between Mixing Lengths, Eddy Viscosity, and a Cross-Correlation Function

We note that from the Reynolds stress equation, Eq. 7-3, we find for steady two-dimensional channel flow

$$(7\text{-}24) \qquad \frac{1}{\rho}\frac{\partial \bar{p}}{\partial x} = -\overline{(\mathbf{u}' \cdot \nabla)u'} + \nu \frac{\partial^2 \bar{u}}{\partial y^2}$$

Writing the components of $\mathbf{u}'$ as (u', v', w') and using the continuity equation

$$(7\text{-}25) \qquad \frac{\partial u'}{\partial x} + \frac{\partial v'}{\partial y} + \frac{\partial w'}{\partial z} = 0$$

we have

$$(7\text{-}26) \qquad \frac{1}{\rho}\frac{\partial \bar{p}}{\partial x} = \frac{d}{dy}\left[-\overline{u'v'} + \nu \frac{d\bar{u}}{dy}\right]$$

Comparing Eqs. 7-15 and 7-26, we see that

$$(7\text{-}27) \qquad \epsilon(y)\frac{d\bar{u}}{dy} = -\overline{u'v'}$$

Thus $\epsilon(y)$ is related to a statistical correlation function.

Substituting from Eqs. 7-14 and 7-19 into Eq. 7-27, we find that we have assumed

$$(7\text{-}28) \qquad \overline{u'v'} = -l^2 \frac{d\bar{u}}{dy} \left| \frac{d\bar{u}}{dy} \right|$$

This relation could, however, have been derived to the same rough order of approximation by considering $\overline{u'v'}$ alone. First, it is necessary to note that u' and v' are probably highly correlated in pipe flow. Consider the lower half of the channel. If v' is positive, then fluid from a layer close to the wall is moving toward the wall center. As it travels toward the channel center, it passes through layers moving faster, on the average, than the layer in which it originated. Thus u' tends to be negative. Conversely, if v' is negative, u' tends to be positive, and, therefore in general we expect here good (negative) correlation between u' and v'. We may write

$$(7\text{-}29) \qquad \overline{u'v'} = -\alpha^2 [\tilde{v}']^2$$

where α is a positive constant of somewhere near order unity assuming that $\tilde{u}'$ and $\tilde{v}'$ are of the same order. If now we invoke Eq. 7-19, are careful of signs, and absorb α into l, we arrive at Eq. 7-28.

The above arguments are certainly open to serious objection if viewed very carefully. Unlike molecules, macroscopic fluid "particles" do not travel a finite distance and then suddenly transfer a large portion of their excess momentum to adjacent "particles." Nevertheless, use of the type of ideas presented above has led to rough agreement with experiment (the presence of adjustable constants being a great help, of course), and it is interesting to discuss the ways in which these ideas fit in with the explicitly statistical formulation of turbulence.

First we note that Eq. 7-26 is a consequence of a rigorous theory No approximations have been made, and a knowledge of $\overline{u'v'}$ would certainly allow us to find $\bar{u}$. For example, intergating Eq. 7-26 we have

$$(7\text{-}30) \qquad \nu \frac{d\bar{u}}{dy} = \overline{u'v'} + \left[\frac{1}{\rho} \frac{\partial \bar{p}}{\partial x} \right] y + \frac{\tau_0}{\rho}$$

where τ_0/ρ is a constant of integration. τ_0 is to be identified with the wall stress. For a channel of width $2d$, with both walls stationary

$$(7\text{-}31) \qquad \nu \frac{d\bar{u}}{dy} \bigg|_d = \frac{1}{\rho} \frac{\partial \bar{p}}{\partial x} d + \frac{\tau_0}{\rho} = 0$$

by symmetry. Thus

(7-32) $$v \frac{d\bar{u}}{dy} = \overline{u'v'} + \frac{1}{\rho} \frac{\partial \bar{p}}{\partial x} (y - d)$$

and

(7-33) $$\bar{u}(y) = \frac{1}{v} \int_0^y \overline{u'v'} \, dy' + \frac{1}{\rho v} \frac{\partial \bar{p}}{\partial x} \left[\frac{y}{2} - yd \right]$$

noting that $\bar{u}(0) = 0$. $\partial \bar{p} / \partial x$ is assumed known. $\overline{u'v'}$ may be measured in gas flow using a hot-wire anemometer (see Hinze, 1959, for details of the type of measurement), and a number of measurements have been made in channels. If $\overline{u'v'}$ is known, Eq. 7-33 allows us to determine $\bar{u}(y)$.

The correlation function $\overline{u'v'}$ is a local quantity, but the discussion leading to Eq. 7-29 indicates that its value depends upon the flow field in the immediate neighborhood of the point at which we evaluate it. The arguments given there have no validity if a quantity like

(7-34) $$R_v(\Delta y) = \overline{v'(x, y, z)v'(x, y + \Delta y, z)}$$

did not have finite values when Δy was of the order of l. Consider the continuity equation

(7-35) $$\frac{\partial u'(\mathbf{x}_1)}{\partial x_1} + \frac{\partial v'(\mathbf{x}_1)}{\partial y_1} + \frac{\partial w'(\mathbf{x}_1)}{\partial z_1} = 0$$

Let us multiply this equation by $v'(\mathbf{x}_2)$ and average. We find

(7-36) $$\frac{\partial}{\partial x_1} \overline{u'(\mathbf{x}_1)v'(\mathbf{x}_2)} + \frac{\partial}{\partial y_1} \overline{v'(\mathbf{x}_1)v'(\mathbf{x}_2)} + \frac{\partial}{\partial z_1} \overline{w'(\mathbf{x}_1)v'(\mathbf{x}_2)} = 0$$

We note that these average quantities depend only upon $x_2 - x_1 = s$, y_1 and y_2, and $z_2 - z_1$. In terms of these variables, Eq. 7-36 becomes

(7-37) $$-\frac{\partial}{\partial s} \overline{u'(x_1, y_1, z_1)v'(x_1 + s, y_2, z_2)}$$

$$= -\frac{\partial}{\partial y_1} \overline{v'(x_1, y_1, z_1)v'(x_1 + s, y_2, z_2)}$$

$$-\frac{\partial}{\partial z_1} \overline{w'(x_1, y_1, z_1)v'(x_1 + s, y_2, z_2)}$$

Integrating Eq. 7-37 with respect to s from 0 to ∞ yields (assuming $\overline{u'(x_1, y_1, z_1)v'(x_1 + \infty, y_2, z_2)} = 0$)

$$(7\text{-}38) \quad -\overline{u'(x_1, y_1, z_1)v'(x_1, y_2, z_2)}$$

$$= \int_0^\infty \frac{\partial}{\partial y_1} \overline{[v'(x_1, y_1, z_1)v'(x_1 + s, y_2, z_2)]} \, ds$$

$$+ \int_0^\infty \frac{\partial}{\partial z_1} \overline{[w'(x_1, y_1, z_1)v'(x_1 + s, y_2, z_2)]} \, ds$$

If we now set $y_1 = y_2$, $z_1 = z_2$, we have (dropping explicit mention of the z coordinate)

$$(7\text{-}39) \quad \overline{u'v'} = -\int_0^\infty \left\{ \frac{\partial}{\partial y_1} \overline{[v'(x_1, y_1)v'(x_1 + s_1, y_2)]} \right\}_{y_1 = y_2} ds$$

since the second term is zero by symmetry.

It is important to notice that the correlation functions

$$\overline{v'(x_1, y_1)v'(x_1 + s, y_1 + \Delta y)}$$

and

$$\overline{v'(x_1, y_1)v'(x_1 + s, y_1 - \Delta y)}$$

are not equal. If they were, we would have

$$\left\{ \frac{\partial}{\partial y_1} \overline{[v'(x_1, y_1)v'(x_1 + s, y_2)]} \right\}_{y_1 = y_2} = 0$$

and $\overline{u'v'} = 0$.

A form for $\overline{u'v'}$ such as is given in Eq. 7-29 may be obtained if we write

$$(7\text{-}40) \quad \left\{ \frac{\partial}{\partial y_1} \overline{[v'(x_1, y_1)v'(x_1 + s, y_2)]} \right\}_{y_1 = y}$$

$$= \frac{1}{l_y(s)} \overline{v'(x_1, y_1)v'(x_1 + s, y_1)}$$

where $l_y(s)$ is proportional to some characteristic distance over which $\overline{v'(x_1, y_1)v'(x_1 + s, y_2)}$ varies. Equation 7-39 may then be written

(7-41)
$$\overline{u'v'} = -\int_0^\infty \frac{1}{l_y(s)}\,\overline{v'(x_1, y_1)v'(x_1 + s, y_1)}\,ds$$

Introducing, finally, a characteristic correlation distance, l_x, associated with $\overline{v'(x_1, y_1)v'(x_1 + s, y_1)}$ and taking some average value for $l_y(s)$, denoted by l_y, we have

(7-42)
$$\overline{u'v'} = -\alpha^2[\tilde{v}']^2$$

where $\alpha^2 = l_x/l_y$. l_x/l_y must be positive if $\overline{u'v'}$ is to be negative. This yields a form like Eq. 7-29.

The argument from the rigorous statistical relationship given by Eq. 7-39 to the useful but assumption-ridden relationship given in Eq. 7-42 is indeed tenuous. How much light the statistical formulism sheds on the validity of mixing length theory is probably a matter of personal taste. What the formulism does show, however, is how complex the actual flow configuration is and the number of mathematical simplifications that must be introduced to arrive at a mixing length theory. Unfortunately, the rigorous theory does not easily yield the physical picture of lumps of fluid exchanging momentum.

7.1.4. Experiments in Channel Flow

We want to mention now some of the modern experimental results obtained in turbulent flows in channels. We present here results obtained by Laufer (1951). Laufer obtained data for both the mean velocity $\bar{u}(y)$ and the moments $\tilde{u}'$, $\tilde{v}'$, $\tilde{w}'$, $\overline{u'v'}$. He also measured the spatial correlation functions

$$R_u(x) = \overline{u'(x_1, 0, 0)u'(x_2, 0, 0)}/[\tilde{u}']^2$$

$$R_u(y) = \overline{u'(0, y_1, 0)u'(0, y_2, 0)}/[\tilde{u}']^2$$

$$R_u(z) = \overline{u'(0, 0, z_1)u'(0, 0, z_2)}/[\tilde{u}']^2$$

The experiments were performed at three Reynolds numbers 12,300,

30,800, 61,000, where Re $= dU_0/\nu$. d is the channel half-width and U_0 is the maximum mean velocity.

The first thing to be noted is that $\bar{u}(y)$ follows the von Kármán logarithmic law

$$(7\text{-}43) \qquad \bar{u}(y) = A \left(\frac{\tau_0}{\rho}\right)^{1/2} \log \left[\frac{y(\tau_0/\rho)^{1/2}}{\nu}\right] + B$$

(Laufer found that $A = 6.9$ and $B = 5.5$) over the range

$$30 \leqslant \frac{y\sqrt{\tau_0/\rho}}{\nu} \leqslant 400$$

where the 400 is determined by the lowest Reynolds number. We may write

$$\frac{30}{R_\tau} \leqslant \frac{y}{d} \leqslant \frac{400}{R_\tau}$$

where

$$R_\tau = \sqrt{\frac{\tau_0}{\rho}} \frac{d}{\nu}$$

For $d = 2.5$ in., Re $= 12,300$, $R_\tau = 520$, this gives

$$0.06 \leqslant y/d \leqslant 0.8$$

This means that the logarithmic law holds over most of the channel except very near the wall and in the channel center. As we mentioned in the foregoing, we would hardly expect this law to hold very near the wall, since here $|\nu\, d\bar{u}/dy| > |\overline{u'v'}|$ and viscous effects dominate.

In Fig. 7-3 we have reproduced Laufer's data for $d = 2.5$ in. Re $= 12,300$. k is the correlation coefficient defined as

$$(7\text{-}44) \qquad\qquad k = \frac{\overline{u'v'}}{\bar{u}'\bar{v}'}$$

From Eq. 7-32 we find, using Eq. 7-31, that

$$(7\text{-}45) \qquad\qquad \overline{u'v'} = \nu \frac{d\bar{u}}{dy} - \frac{\tau_0}{\rho}\left(1 - \frac{y}{b}\right)$$

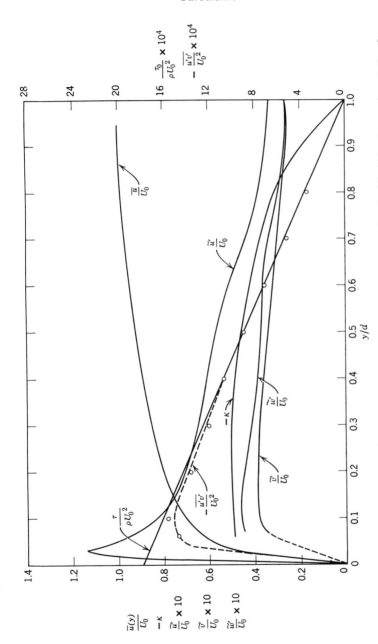

Fig. 7-3. Distribution of mean and fluctuating quantities. Re = 12,300. (Reproduced with slight changes in notation from Laufer, 1951, Fig. 16.)

Thus, in the region where $|u'v'| \gg v \, d\bar{u}/dy$ we expect that

$$(7\text{-}46) \qquad \overline{u'v'} \approx -\frac{\tau_0}{\rho}\left(1 - \frac{y}{b}\right)$$

This formula is verified experimentally from about $y/d = 0.05$ to $y/d = 1$. Below $y/d \approx 0.05$, viscous effects become important, and as noted previously the logarithmic law fails.

In our discussion of mixing length theories we had occasion to postulate a relation of the form (Eq. 7-29)

$$(7\text{-}29) \qquad \overline{u'v'} = -\alpha^2 [\tilde{v}']^2$$

where α was taken to be a constant roughly of the order of unity. We note from Fig. 7-3 that k lies between 0.3 and 0.5 over much of the channel width and that from $y/d = 0.1$ to 1, $\tilde{v}'/\tilde{u}'$ varies roughly from $\frac{1}{2}$ to $\frac{2}{3}$. Thus, since $\alpha = \sqrt{k}\,\sqrt{\tilde{u}'/\tilde{v}'}$, we find that α is indeed of the order of unity.

We thus see from Laufer's measurements of the statistical quantities that the crude assumptions made in mixing length theories have some validity when relating $\overline{u'v'}$ and $(\tilde{v}')^2$. It is interesting to next look at the validity of the relation

$$(7\text{-}47) \qquad \tilde{v}' = l\frac{d\bar{u}}{dy}$$

where l is some mixing length. If we write this equation in the

TABLE 7-1

Values of l (calculated roughly from Fig. 7-5)

y/d	l/d
0.1	0.03
0.3	0.09
0.5	0.13
0.7	0.16
0.9	0.26

nondimensional form

(7-48)
$$\frac{\tilde{v}'}{U_o} = \frac{l}{d}\frac{d\left(\dfrac{\bar{u}}{U_o}\right)}{d\left(\dfrac{y}{d}\right)}$$

l/d may be calculated from the curves given in Fig. 7-3. The results of a rough calculation are given in Table 7-1.

For this particular case we see that l is approximately proportional to y as Prandtl had assumed. In addition, since l/d is significantly less than 1, the concept of a mixing length has some meaning as a local property.

7.1.5. The Similarity Hypothesis

To conclude our discussion of channel flow, we want to make a few more remarks about the derivation of the von Kármán logarithmic law (Eq. 7-43) from the point of view of similarity. We follow here parts of Townsend (1956). In the fully turbulent region the following hypothesis may be made: For sufficiently high Reynolds numbers, $\text{Re} = dU_o/v$, the form of the velocity distribution is independent of Re. The form depends only upon y/d, the distance from the channel boundary. Thus we set

(7-49) $\bar{u}(y) = U_o + v_o f\left(\dfrac{y}{d}\right)$ $(f(1) = 0)$

where v_o is some suitable velocity scale.

In order to determine v_o, we note that the only important physical quantity in the fully turbulent region is the shear stress, and hence it is natural to set $v_o = \sqrt{\tau_o/\rho}$. This gives

(7-50) $\bar{u}(y) = U_o + \sqrt{\dfrac{\tau_o}{\rho}}\, f(y/d)$

Measurements show that in the region near the wall (but outside the layer where viscous effects dominate), called the constant stress layer, there is maximum production of turbulent energy. To see the meaning of this statement, we note that an energy equation is obtained from Eq. 7-1 by multiplying this equation by $\mathbf{u}'$ and averaging. We find for two-dimensional channel flow that

$$(7\text{-}51) \quad \overline{u'v'}\frac{d\bar{u}}{dy} + \frac{1}{2}\frac{\partial}{\partial y}\overline{(u'^2 + v'^2 + w'^2)v'}$$

$$= -\frac{1}{\rho}\frac{\overline{\partial p'v'}}{\partial y} - \nu\overline{\frac{\partial u_i'}{\partial x_l}\frac{\partial u_i'}{\partial x_l}} + \frac{1}{2}\nu\frac{\partial^2}{\partial y^2}\overline{[u'^2 + v'^2 + w'^2]}$$

The term $\overline{u'v'}(d\bar{u}/dy)$ may be interpreted as the turbulent energy production term; the second term on the left-hand side corresponds to the convection of the turbulent energy, $\frac{1}{2}[u'^2 + v'^2 + w'^2]$, by the turbulent field; the first term on the right side represents the energy change resulting from turbulent pressure gradients; the second term on the right-hand side represents conversion of turbulent energy into heat through viscous dissipation; the third term on the right-hand side represents the diffusion of turbulent energy through viscous action.

As Laufer's measurements bear out, the term $\overline{u'v'}(d\bar{u}/dy)$ is a maximum in the constant stress layer, and an integral of this term over y shows that most of the energy production occurs in this layer. Turbulent energy in the central channel region is transported to this region from the constant stress layer; it is not produced there in significant amounts. As Townsend (1956) points out, the velocity in the shear stress layer should be determined by the quantities y, τ_0/ρ, ν, and l_s, where l_s is the distance over which most of the energy production takes place. Using nondimensional variables, we may write

$$(7\text{-}52) \qquad \bar{u}(y) = \left(\frac{\tau_0}{\rho}\right)^{1/2} F\left(\frac{\tau_0^{1/2}y}{\nu}, \frac{y}{l_s}\right)$$

If now l_s is smaller than the "size" of the constant stress layer, then we expect F to be independent of y/l_s over some of the layer. Assuming $y \geq l_s$, we have

$$(7\text{-}53) \qquad \bar{u}(y) = \left[\frac{\tau_0}{\rho}\right]^{1/2} F\left(\frac{\tau_0^{1/2}y}{\nu}\right)$$

Lastly, we note that for high Reynolds numbers, the fully turbulent region (described by Eq. 7-50) overlaps the constant stress layer (described by Eq. 7-53), and hence both laws are applicable. The functional form of $\bar{u}(y)$ satisfying both Eq. 7-50 and Eq. 7-53 is the logarithmic form given in Eq. 7-43.

$$(7\text{-}43) \qquad \bar{u}(y) = A\left[\frac{\tau_0}{\rho}\right]^{1/2} \log\left[\frac{y(\tau_0/\rho)^{1/2}}{\nu}\right] + B$$

7.1.6. Further Remarks

The purpose of this introduction was to bring to the reader in qualitative fashion some of the intuitive ideas that have been used to understand turbulence. After Reynolds' work, there was a clear understanding that the Navier-Stokes equations, which presumably governed turbulent flow, could not easily be solved to yield even the mean velocity distribution in a channel when the flow was turbulent. Averaging the Navier-Stokes equations (Eq. 7-3) gives an equation for $\bar{u}(y)$, but in this equation we have undetermined quantities like $\overline{u'v'}$. The approach in the remainder of this chapter will be analogous to an attempt to find other equations governing $\overline{u'v'}$ and $\bar{u}(y)$ in the hope of eventually obtaining in some way a determinate set of equations to use in solving for $\bar{u}(y)$ and $\overline{u'v'}$. Earlier investigators chose a more pragmatic approach and tried to modify the Reynolds stress equations themselves by assuming a form of $\overline{u'v'}$. Depending upon how one chose to present it, this approach entailed introducing concepts like eddy viscosity or mixing length. In the later work it also entailed introducing concepts of similarity to allow one to postulate general functional forms for $\bar{u}(y)$ and indeed, $\overline{u'v'}$, in restricted portions of the flow field. The early investigations also provided us with the ideas of correlation between velocity components and, through the average energy equations, the ideas of turbulent energy transport from the energy source through to viscous dissipation.

The early investigators spent most of their effort studying practical problems like flow through pipes and channels, flow near walls, flow in jets, etc. These are all flows that are not homogeneous and most often not locally isotropic. After the explicitly statistical theory of turbulence was introduced, it became clear that considerable formal simplification may be introduced if the flow field is to be considered homogeneous and isotropic. An increasing amount of work was then begun to consider the turbulent flow behind grids, since this was a physical situation which more or less approximated the ideal conditions. As we shall see later, many of the older concepts were carried over to aid in understanding this problem.

The statistical theory of turbulence has been used in the study of nonhomogeneous and nonisotropic flow fields, but the most intensive theoretical work has been directed toward the study of homogeneous and isotropic turbulence. The rest of the chapter will reflect this emphasis. Despite this emphasis, however, which is designed to reflect work in this field, it is not clear to this writer that the symmetric problem is more tractable than the nonhomogeneous problem if we look at the overall set of equations. Cutting off the infinite hierarchy of statistical moment equations has proven to be a very difficult problem in the homogeneous case, and perhaps the perturbation approach that suggests itself in shear flow problems (see Deissler, 1965) may yet prove a more satisfactory way for the understanding of turbulence.

7.2. Derivation of Statistical Moment Equations

The statistical moment equations have been derived from the Navier-Stokes equations in Section 3.2.2.3. In that section two classes of moment equations were derived. In the first class, all correlations were defined with respect to different space-time points. For example, the second-order moment was defined as

$$\overline{u_i(\mathbf{x}_1, t_1)u_j(\mathbf{x}_2, t_2)}$$

where, in general, $\mathbf{x}_1 \neq \mathbf{x}_2$ and $t_1 \neq t_2$. In the second class of equations the correlation functions were defined with respect to different space points, but the same time was to be used at both points. For example, the two-point correlation function in this case was defined as

$$\overline{u_i(\mathbf{x}_1, t)u_j(\mathbf{x}_2, t)}$$

where, in general, $\mathbf{x}_1 \neq \mathbf{x}_2$.

The first class of equations is more general than the second class, but until recently most workers in the field of turbulence restricted their attention to the second class of equations. We shall thus, for the most part, discuss here only the second class of equations.* We note that this clear separation into two classes of equations occurs only if we seek to determine differential equations governing the correlation functions. If an integral formulation of the Navier-Stokes equations is attempted, no such clear distinction explicitly arises. In our later review of the modern work in turbulence theory, we shall see that often neither of these fundamental sets of moment equations is used explicitly as the starting point for the investigations.

In order to review the derivation of the moment equations for single-time correlation functions, we first write the Navier-Stokes equations and continuity equation with respect to two space points.

(7-54a)

$$\frac{\partial}{\partial t} u_i(\mathbf{x}_1, t) + \frac{\partial}{\partial x_{1j}} [u_j(\mathbf{x}_1, t) u_i(\mathbf{x}_1, t)] = \nu \nabla_1^2 u_i(\mathbf{x}_1, t) - \frac{\partial p(\mathbf{x}_1, t)}{\partial x_{1i}}$$

(7-54b)

$$\frac{\partial}{\partial x_{1j}} u_j(\mathbf{x}_1, t) = 0$$

(7-55a)

$$\frac{\partial}{\partial t} u_k(\mathbf{x}_2, t) + \frac{\partial}{\partial x_{2j}} [u_j(\mathbf{x}_2, t) u_k(\mathbf{x}_2, t)] = \nu \nabla_2^2 u_k(\mathbf{x}_2, t) - \frac{\partial p(\mathbf{x}_2, t)}{\partial x_{2k}}$$

(7-55b)

$$\frac{\partial}{\partial x_{2j}} u_j(\mathbf{x}_2, t) = 0$$

where for convenience ρ has been absorbed into p.

To find an equation for the two-point correlation, we multiply Eq. 7-54a by $u_k(\mathbf{x}_2, t)$ and Eq. 7-55a by $u_i(\mathbf{x}_1, t)$. We then add the two equations and take an ensemble average. The resulting equation is

(7-56) $$\frac{\partial}{\partial t} \overline{u_i(\mathbf{x}_1, t) u_k(\mathbf{x}_2, t)} + \frac{\partial}{\partial x_{1j}} \overline{u_j(\mathbf{x}_1, t) u_i(\mathbf{x}_1, t) u_k(\mathbf{x}_2, t)}$$

$$+ \frac{\partial}{\partial x_{2j}} \overline{u_j(\mathbf{x}_2, t) u_k(\mathbf{x}_2, t) u_i(\mathbf{x}_1, t)} = \nu \nabla_1^2 \overline{u_i(\mathbf{x}_1, t) u_k(\mathbf{x}_2, t)}$$

$$+ \nu \nabla_2^2 \overline{u_k(\mathbf{x}_2, t) u_i(\mathbf{x}_1, t)} - \frac{\partial}{\partial x_{1i}} \overline{p(\mathbf{x}_1, t) u_k(\mathbf{x}_2, t)}$$

$$- \frac{\partial}{\partial x_{2k}} \overline{p(\mathbf{x}_2, t) u_i(\mathbf{x}_1, t)}$$

* One may also define a Lagrangian correlation function (see Eq. 6-112). This is particularly useful in diffusion problems, but we shall not consider this type of function in this chapter.

From the divergence equation, Eq. 7-54b, we find after successive multiplication by $u_k(\mathbf{x}_2, t)$, $u_k(\mathbf{x}_2, t)u_l(\mathbf{x}_3, t)$, and $p(\mathbf{x}_2, t)$

(7-57a)
$$\frac{\partial}{\partial x_{1j}} \overline{u_j(\mathbf{x}_1, t)u_k(\mathbf{x}_2, t)} = 0$$

(7-57b)
$$\frac{\partial}{\partial x_{1j}} \overline{u_j(\mathbf{x}_1, t)u_k(\mathbf{x}_2, t)u_l(\mathbf{x}_3, t)} = 0$$

(7-57c)
$$\frac{\partial}{\partial x_{1j}} \overline{u_j(\mathbf{x}_1, t)p(\mathbf{x}_2, t)} = 0$$

As we have pointed out repeatedly, we note that Eqs. 7-56 and 7-57a, b, c are inadequate to determine $\overline{u_i(\mathbf{x}_1, t)u_j(\mathbf{x}_2, t)}$. The pressure term may be eliminated by use of the divergence condition, since the divergence of Eq. 7-54a or 7-55a yields

(7-58)
$$\nabla^2 p = -\frac{\partial^2 u_i u_j}{\partial x_i \, \partial x_j}$$

Third-order correlation functions like

$$\overline{u_j(\mathbf{x}_1, t)u_i(\mathbf{x}_1, t)u_k(\mathbf{x}_2, t)},$$

however, may not be removed unless some special assumption is made.

In an attempt to find a determinate set of equations, one may use Eqs. 7-54a and 7-55a and a third equation written in terms of $u_l(\mathbf{x}_3, t)$. The equation is found by multiplying Eq. 7-54a by $u_k(\mathbf{x}_2, t)u_l(\mathbf{x}_3, t)$, Eq. 7-55a by $u_i(\mathbf{x}_1, t)u_l(\mathbf{x}_3, t)$, the $u_l(\mathbf{x}_3, t)$ equation by $u_i(\mathbf{x}_1, t)u_k(\mathbf{x}_2, t)$; and then adding and averaging. This equation unfortunately will contain fourth-order correlation functions of the form

$$\overline{u_i(\mathbf{x}_1, t)u_j(\mathbf{x}_1, t)u_k(\mathbf{x}_3, t)u_l(\mathbf{x}_4, t)}$$

Proceeding similarly, however, an infinite hierarchy of equations may be found that hopefully represents the governing equations of a statistical theory of turbulence. This infinite hierarchy may be circumvented by considering the governing functional equation. Unfortunately, as we stressed in Chapter 3, this type of equation is very difficult to solve, and little progress has been made in this direction.

Most analyses, until very recently, have been carried out in terms of Eqs. 7-56 and 7-57, with some attempts to include the next set in the hierarchy. Various physical assumptions have been made in an attempt to glean useful results from these equations. These assumptions are introduced more easily if the conditions of homogeneity and isotropy are introduced. We shall now derive in turn the equations for homogeneous turbulence and then homogeneous and isotropic turbulence.

7.2.1. Homogeneous Turbulence

Homogeneous turbulence is characterized by the fact that all correlation functions depend only upon the difference of positions of the various points, not upon absolute position in space. Thus the two-point correlation $\overline{u_i(\mathbf{x}_1, t)u_k(\mathbf{x}_2, t)}$ function may be written in terms of the vector

$$\mathbf{r}_2 = \mathbf{x}_2 - \mathbf{x}_1$$

We write for homogeneous turbulence (suppressing the time argument)

(7-59) $$R_{ij}(\mathbf{r}_2) \equiv \overline{u_i(\mathbf{x}_1)u_j(\mathbf{x}_2)} = \overline{u_i(\mathbf{x}_1)u_j(\mathbf{x}_1 + \mathbf{r}_2)}$$

Similarly for the three-point correlation function we use the vectors

$$\mathbf{r}_2 = \mathbf{x}_2 - \mathbf{x}_1$$
$$\mathbf{r}_3 = \mathbf{x}_3 - \mathbf{x}_1$$

and write

(7-60) $$S_{ijk}(\mathbf{r}_2, \mathbf{r}_3) \equiv \overline{u_i(\mathbf{x}_1)u_j(\mathbf{x}_2)u_k(\mathbf{x}_3)} = \overline{u_i(\mathbf{x}_1)u_j(\mathbf{x}_1 + \mathbf{r}_2)u_k(\mathbf{x}_1 + \mathbf{r}_3)}$$

The pressure-velocity correlation function is written as

(7-61) $$P_j(\mathbf{r}_2) \equiv \overline{p(\mathbf{x}_1)u_j(\mathbf{x}_2)} = \overline{p(\mathbf{x}_1)u_j(\mathbf{x}_1 + \mathbf{r}_2)}$$

In terms of these functions, Eqs. 7-56 and 7-57 assume the form

(7-62a) $$\frac{\partial}{\partial t} R_{ik}(\mathbf{r}_2) - \frac{\partial}{\partial r_{2j}} S_{jik}(0, \mathbf{r}_2) + \frac{\partial}{\partial r_{2j}} S_{jki}(0, -\mathbf{r}_2)$$

$$= 2\nu \nabla_{\mathbf{r}_2}^2 R_{ik}(\mathbf{r}_2) + \frac{\partial}{\partial r_{2i}} P_k(\mathbf{r}_2) - \frac{\partial}{\partial r_{2k}} P_i(-\mathbf{r}_2)$$

(7-62b) $$\frac{\partial}{\partial r_{2j}} R_{jk}(\mathbf{r}_2) = 0$$

(7-62c) $$\frac{\partial}{\partial r_{2j}} S_{jkl}(\mathbf{r}_2, \mathbf{r}_3) = 0$$

(7-62d) $$\frac{\partial}{\partial r_{2j}} P_j(-\mathbf{r}_2) = 0$$

In this derivation we have used the fact that

$$\frac{\partial}{\partial x_1} = -\frac{\partial}{\partial r_2} = -\frac{\partial}{\partial x_2}$$

and let $x_3 = x_2$. We note that except in Eq. 7-62c the three-point moments used here are degenerate in the sense that S_{ijk} is not a function of r_2 and r_3 but only of r_2.

In the nonhomogeneous problem it is useful to write

(7-63) $u_i(x, t) = \overline{u_i(x, t)} + u'(x, t)$

$$p(x, t) = \overline{p(x, t)} + p'(x, t)$$

where $\overline{u_i'(x, t)} = \overline{p'(x, t)} = 0$. These expressions could be substituted into Eq. 7-56 to distinguish the mean flow from the turbulent fluctuations. For homogeneous turbulence $\overline{u_i(x, t)}$ and $\overline{p(x, t)}$ must be constants, and for convenience we set both quantities equal to zero. Thus in homogeneous turbulence, $u_i(x, t)$ and $p(x, t)$ are taken to be fluctuating quantities with zero mean value.

7.2.2. Homogeneous and Isotropic Turbulence

If the turbulence is isotropic in addition to being homogeneous, Eqs. 7-62a and b simplify even further, since the forms of $R_{ik}(r)$ and $S_{ijk}(0, r)$ are severely restricted in form. Batchelor (1953) has a fairly complete discussion about the forms of isotropic tensors, and we shall make only a few remarks here to show how the form of an isotropic tensor may be determined. The concept of isotropy was first discussed in detail by Taylor (1935), and the governing statistical equations for isotropic turbulence were given by von Kármán and Howarth (1938).

Consider the correlation between the vector $u_i(x)$ and the vector $u_j(x + r)$, (i.e., $R_{ij}(r)$). The geometry associated with this correlation is given in Fig. 7-4. λ and μ are unit vectors along $u(x)$ and $u(x + r)$, respectively. The correlation tensor $\overline{u_i(x)u_j(x + r)}$ is independent of x by the condition of homogeneity. Since the flow is isotropic, the scalar quantity $\overline{\lambda_i u_i(x)\mu_j u_j(x + r)}$ does not depend on the absolute orientation of the configuration pictured in Fig. 7-4. It depends only on the relative orientation. The relative orientation is specified by the

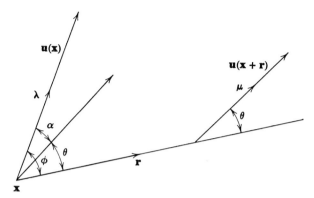

Fig. 7-4. Geometry for two-point correlation.

angles ϕ, θ, and α, or equivalently $\lambda_i r_i$, $\mu_i r_i$ and $\lambda_i \mu_i$. In addition, this quantity depends on $r_i r_i = r^2$. Thus we may write

(7-64) $\overline{\lambda_i u_i(\mathbf{x}) \mu_j u_j(\mathbf{x}+\mathbf{r})} = \lambda_i \mu_j R_{ij}(r) = A(\lambda_i r_i, \mu_i r_i, \lambda_i \mu_i, r^2)$

From the middle equality of Eq. 7-64 we note that $A(\lambda_i r_i, \mu_i r_i, \lambda_i \mu_i, r^2)$ depends linearly on λ_i and μ_i. This means that A must be composed of a sum of the two terms

$$\lambda_i r_i \mu_j r_j a(r)$$

$$\lambda_i \mu_j \delta_{ij} b(r)$$

where a and b are scalar functions of r. $R_{ij}(\mathbf{r})$ is then of the form

(7-65) $R_{ij}(\mathbf{r}) = F(r)r_i r_j + G(r)\delta_{ij}$

where F and G are scalar functions of r.

In a similar manner one may show that $S_{ijk}(\mathbf{r})$ is of the form

(7-66) $S_{ijk}(\mathbf{r}) = a_1(r)r_i r_j r_k + a_2(r)r_i \delta_{jk} + a_3(r)r_j \delta_{ik} + a_4(r)r_k \delta_{ij}$

where the a_i are scalar functions of r.

We will next substitute the isotropic forms for $R_{ij}(\mathbf{r})$ and $S_{ijk}(0, \mathbf{r})$ into Eqs. 7-62a–d. Considering the divergence condition first, we find using the form given in Eq. 7-65 that Eq. 7-62b becomes (setting $\mathbf{r}_2 = \mathbf{r}$)

(7-67) $r_i r_j \dfrac{\partial F}{\partial r_j} + F r_j \, \delta_{ij} + 3 F r_i + \dfrac{\partial G}{\partial r_j} \delta_{ij} = 0$

Noting that

$$\frac{\partial F(r)}{\partial r_j} = \frac{\partial F(r)}{\partial r}\frac{\partial r}{\partial r_j} = \frac{\partial F(r)}{\partial r}\frac{r_j}{r}$$

Eq. 7-67 simplifies to

(7-68) $$r_i\left[r\frac{dF}{dr} + 4F + \frac{1}{r}\frac{dG}{dr}\right] = 0$$

Since Eq. 7-68 must hold for arbitrary values of $\mathbf{r}$, we have finally

(7-69) $$r\frac{dF}{dr} + 4F + \frac{1}{r}\frac{dG}{dr} = 0$$

Similarly, if we have the form for $S_{ijk}(0, \mathbf{r}_2)$ given in Eq. 7-66, relations can be determined among the a_i. We note that $S_{ijk}(0, \mathbf{r}_2)$ is a special case of the three-point correlation function $S_{ijk}(\mathbf{r}_2, \mathbf{r}_3)$. If the next set of the infinite hierarchy of moment equations is to be considered, it would be necessary to have the isotropic form for $S_{ijk}(\mathbf{r}_2, \mathbf{r}_3)$ rather than $S_{ijk}(0, \mathbf{r}_2)$. In this section we shall only discuss $S_{ijk}(0, \mathbf{r}_2)$ and hence shall restrict ourselves to the two-point isotropic forms. The functions $S_{jik}(0, \mathbf{r}_2)$, $S_{jki}(-\mathbf{r}_2, \mathbf{r}_2)$, and $S_{jkl}(\mathbf{r}_2, \mathbf{r}_2)$ are all functions of only $\mathbf{r}_2$ and in the isotropic case simply related. They are all expressible in the form given in Eq. 7-66. For example

$$S_{jkl}(0, \mathbf{r}_2) = -S_{jkl}(0, -\mathbf{r}_2)$$
$$S_{jkl}(-\mathbf{r}_2, -\mathbf{r}_2) = S_{klj}(0, \mathbf{r}_2)$$

For simplicity of notation we shall drop the double argument and write

$$S_{jkl}(\mathbf{r}) \equiv S_{jkl}(0, \mathbf{r}) = \overline{u_j(\mathbf{x}_1)u_k(\mathbf{x}_1)u_l(\mathbf{x}_1 + \mathbf{r})}$$

S_{jkl} is symmetric in the j and k indices. Hence the general form for $S_{jkl}(\mathbf{r})$ is

(7-70) $$S_{jkl}(r) = A(r)r_jr_kr_l + B(r)[r_j\delta_{kl} + r_k\delta_{jl}] + C(r)r_l\delta_{jk}$$

Using the divergence condition, we find after some manipulation

(7-71)

$$\frac{\partial S_{jkl}}{\partial r_l} = \left(5A + r\frac{dA}{dr} + \frac{2}{r}\frac{dB}{dr}\right)r_jr_k + \left(2B + 3C + r\frac{dC}{dr}\right)\delta_{jk} = 0$$

Since this equation must be true for all values of **r**, we find the two conditions

(7-72)
$$5A + r\frac{dA}{dr} + \frac{2}{r}\frac{dB}{dr} = 0$$

(7-73)
$$2B + 3C + r\frac{dC}{dr} = 0$$

From Eq. 7-72 and Eq. 7-73 we then find (if $S_{jkr}(\mathbf{r})$ is to be finite at $r = 0$)

(7-74)
$$A = \frac{1}{r}\frac{C}{dr}$$

(7-75)
$$B = -\frac{3}{2}C - \frac{1}{2}r\frac{dC}{dr}$$

Thus, as in the case of $R_{ij}(\mathbf{r})$, the tensor $S_{ijk}(\mathbf{r})$ depends on only one scalar function. In a similar manner we may show that $P_i(\mathbf{r}) \equiv 0$, since its divergence is zero. In this case $P_i(\mathbf{r}) = D(r)r_i$ and since $\partial P_i(\mathbf{r})/\partial r_i = 0$, we find $D(r) = 0$ if we require that $P_i(\mathbf{r})$ be finite at $r = 0$.

In the literature it is common to find $R_{ij}(\mathbf{r})$ and $S_{ijk}(\mathbf{r})$ expressed in terms of longitudinal and lateral correlation functions rather than referring these tensors to an arbitrary Cartesian set of axes. Longitudinal and lateral correlation functions associated with $R_{ij}(\mathbf{r})$ are pictured in Fig. 7-5.

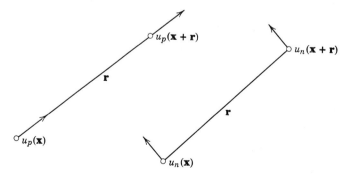

Fig. 7-5. Longitudinal and lateral velocity correlation functions. [See Batchelor (1953), *The Theory of Homogeneous Turbulence*, Cambridge Univ. Press, London, Fig. 3-1, p. 46.]

The longitudinal correlation function is written

(7-76) $$u^2 f(r) = \overline{u_p(\mathbf{x}) u_p(\mathbf{x} + \mathbf{r})}$$

where u^2 is the mean square turbulent velocity. ($u^2 \equiv \overline{u^2}$; the bar is usually dropped in the literature.)

The lateral velocity correlation function is written

(7-77) $$u^2 g(r) = \overline{u_n(\mathbf{x}) u_n(\mathbf{x} + \mathbf{r})}$$

These functions were introduced by von Kármán and Howarth (1938). It may be shown that

(7-78) $$u^2 f = r^2 F + G$$

and

(7-79) $$u^2 g = G$$

Thus

(7-80) $$R_{ij}(\mathbf{r}) = u^2 \left[\frac{(f - g)}{r^2} r_i r_j + g \delta_{ij} \right]$$

where

$$g = f + \frac{1}{2} r \frac{df}{dr}$$

The tensor $S_{jkl}(\mathbf{r})$ may be treated similarly. We define

(7-81) $$u^3 k(r) = \overline{u_p{}^2(\mathbf{x}) u_p(\mathbf{x} + \mathbf{r})}$$

$$u^3 h(r) = \overline{u_n{}^2(\mathbf{x}) u_p(\mathbf{x} + \mathbf{r})}$$

$$u^3 q(r) = \overline{u_p(\mathbf{x}) u_n(\mathbf{x}) u_n(\mathbf{x} + \mathbf{r})}$$

where $u^3 = [\overline{u^2}]^{3/2}$.

From these definitions we find

(7-82) $$S_{jkl}(r) = u^3 \left\{ \frac{[(k - r(dk/dr)]}{2r^3} r_j r_k r_l + \frac{[2k + r(dk/dr)]}{4r} \right.$$

$$\left. \times (r_j \delta_{kl} + r_k \delta_{jl}) - \frac{k}{2r} r_l \delta_{jk} \right\}$$

and

(7-83) $$k = -2h$$

(7-84) $$q = -h - \frac{r}{2}\frac{dh}{dr}$$

Equation 7-62a may be expressed in terms of only f and k. Equation 7-62a becomes

(7-85) $$\frac{\partial}{\partial t}u^2 f = u^3\left[\frac{\partial k}{\partial r} + \frac{4}{r}k\right] + 2vu^2\left[\frac{\partial^2 f}{\partial r^2} + \frac{4}{r}\frac{\partial f}{\partial r}\right]$$

This equation governs the change in $f(r)$ and $k(r)$ as a function of time. (It would perhaps be clearer to write $f(r, t)$ and $k(r, t)$. u^2 is independent of r but is a function of t.) Again we emphasize that Eq. 7-85 is not sufficient to determine $f(r)$. $k(r)$ is an unknown function. If the next set in the statistical moment hierarchy were derived, we would find an equation governing $k(r)$, but it would include another unknown function. One method of making Eq. 7-85 a determinate equation for $f(r)$ is to find a physical situation in which $k(r)$ may be neglected in this equation. For example, this term may be neglected for very weak turbulence, and this approximation will be discussed in a later section.

7.2.3. *Fourier Transform of $R_{ij}(\mathbf{x}_1, \mathbf{x}_2)$ and the Transformed Moment Equations*

In this chapter we have mentioned the term "eddy size" in a rather loose manner. "Eddy size" may be given a more precise definition by considering the spatial Fourier transform of the correlation function $R_{ij}(\mathbf{x}, \mathbf{r})$ with respect to $\mathbf{r}$. ($\mathbf{r} = \mathbf{x}_2 - \mathbf{x}_1$, and we drop the subscript on $\mathbf{x}_1$ for convenience.) Denoting this transform, $\Phi_{ij}(\mathbf{x}, \mathbf{k})$, we define it as

(7-86) $$\Phi_{ij}(\mathbf{x}, \mathbf{k}) = \frac{1}{(2\pi)^3}\iiint\limits_{-\infty}^{\infty} R_{ij}(\mathbf{x}, \mathbf{r})e^{-i\mathbf{k}\cdot\mathbf{r}}\,d\mathbf{r}$$

$\mathbf{k}$ space is termed wave number space. The inverse Fourier relation is

(7-87) $$R_{ij}(\mathbf{x}, \mathbf{r}) = \iiint\limits_{-\infty}^{\infty}\Phi_{ij}(\mathbf{x}, \mathbf{k})e^{-i\mathbf{k}\cdot\mathbf{r}}\,d\mathbf{k}$$

Since $R_{ij}(\mathbf{x}, \mathbf{r})$ is real, $\Phi_{ij}(\mathbf{x}, \mathbf{k})$ satisfies the relation

(7-88) $\Phi_{ij}(\mathbf{x}, \mathbf{k}) = \Phi_{ij}{}^*(\mathbf{x}, -\mathbf{k})$

(The asterisk denotes the complex conjugate.) $R_{ij}(\mathbf{x}, \mathbf{r})$ satisfies the continuity equation

(7-89) $\dfrac{\partial}{\partial r_j} R_{ij}(\mathbf{x}, \mathbf{r}) = 0$

Taking the Fourier transform of both sides of this equation yields

(7-90) $k_j \Phi_{ij}(\mathbf{x}, \mathbf{k}) = 0$

7.2.3.1. Qualitative Discussion of "Eddy Sizes."   An eddy is usually roughly thought of as a circulating region of fluid of some characteristic size. It may be isolated or it may occur closely connected with a number of other eddies. When we think of eddies as an aid in describing a turbulent flow, we have in mind the superposition of many eddies of varying size and orientation occurring more or less at random throughout the fluid. To represent this notion analytically, we consider the function Φ_{ij}. In a sense we shall now discuss, a scalar form of Φ_{ij} may be used to describe the superposition of many eddies of varying size and orientation.

Townsend (1956) in his introductory chapter gives the correlation function and spectrum associated with a few simple eddy distributions. For example, one may think of an isolated eddy as represented by the velocity field

(7-91) $u_1 = -\dfrac{\partial}{\partial x_2} \exp\left[-\tfrac{1}{2}\alpha^2 x^2\right] = \alpha_2{}^2 x_2 \exp\left[-\tfrac{1}{2}\alpha^2 x^2\right]$

$u_2 = \dfrac{\partial}{\partial x_1} \exp\left[-\tfrac{1}{2}\alpha^2 x^2\right] = -\alpha_1{}^2 x_1 \exp\left[-\tfrac{1}{2}\alpha^2 x^2\right]$

$u_3 = 0$

where $\alpha^2 x^2 = \alpha_1{}^2 x_1{}^2 + \alpha_2{}^2 x_2{}^2 + \alpha_3{}^2 x_3{}^2$. Here the circulation is taken in the x_1, x_2 plane. If isolated eddies are homogeneously superimposed at random with average separation between centers $\gg 1/\alpha_i$, then the correlation functions and spectra associated with the velocity field are, respectively

(7-92) $R_{11}(\mathbf{r}) = \tfrac{1}{2}A\alpha_2^2(1 - \tfrac{1}{2}\alpha_2^2 r_2^2)\exp[-\tfrac{1}{4}\alpha^2 r^2]$

$R_{22}(\mathbf{r}) = \tfrac{1}{2}A\alpha_1^2(1 - \tfrac{1}{2}\alpha_1^2 r_1^2)\exp[-\tfrac{1}{4}\alpha^2 r^2]$

$R_{12}(\mathbf{r}) = \tfrac{1}{4}A\alpha_1^2\alpha_2^2 r_1 r_2\exp[-\tfrac{1}{4}\alpha^2 r^2]$

$R_{13}(\mathbf{r}) = R_{23}(r) = R_{33}(r) = 0$

(where A is a constant and $\alpha^2 r^2 = \alpha_1^2 r_1^2 + \alpha_2^2 r_2^2 + \alpha_3^2 r_3^2$) and

(7-93) $\Phi_{11}(\mathbf{k}) = Ak_2^2 \exp - \left[\dfrac{k_1^2}{\alpha_1^2} + \dfrac{k_2^2}{\alpha_2^2} + \dfrac{k_3^2}{\alpha_3^2}\right]$

$\Phi_{22}(\mathbf{k}) = Ak_1^2 \exp - \left[\dfrac{k_1^2}{\alpha_1^2} + \dfrac{k_2^2}{\alpha_2^2} + \dfrac{k_3^2}{\alpha_3^2}\right]$

$\Phi_{12}(\mathbf{k}) = -Ak_1 k_2 \exp - \left[\dfrac{k_1^2}{\alpha_1^2} + \dfrac{k_2^2}{\alpha_2^2} + \dfrac{k_3^2}{\alpha_3^2}\right]$

$\Phi_{13}(\mathbf{k}) = \Phi_{23}(\mathbf{k}) = \Phi_{33}(\mathbf{k}) = 0.$

The form of the velocity field indicates that the eddy has a characteristic size in the ith direction of magnitude $1/\alpha_i$. This is reflected by a
similar characteristic length in the correlation functions. It is also
indicated by the fact that the Φ_{ij} have characteristic wave numbers
of order α_i.

In order to speak of "eddy size" it is useful to average over direction.
This is obtained by introducing spherical coordinates in $\mathbf{k}$ space and
integrating over the angle variables. We write

$$k_1 = k \sin\theta\cos\phi$$

$$k_2 = k \sin\theta\sin\phi$$

$$k_3 = k \cos\theta$$

and define the integrated spectrum Ψ_{ij} by the relation (for the homogeneous case)

(7-94) $\Psi_{ij}(k) = \displaystyle\int_0^\pi \int_0^{2\pi} k^2 \Phi_{ij}(k, \theta, \phi)\sin\theta\, d\phi\, d\theta$

Furthermore, it is convenient to consider only a scalar quantity rather than a tensor quantity. The most natural scalar to consider is the trace of Ψ_{ij}. Thus in speaking of "eddy sizes," we often confine our attention to the quantity

$$(7\text{-}95) \qquad \Psi_{ii}(k) = \int_0^\pi \int_0^{2\pi} k^2 \Phi_{ii}(k, \theta, \phi) \sin \theta \, d\phi \, d\theta$$

In this connection it is useful to note that

$$R_{ii}(0) = \overline{u_i(\mathbf{x})u_i(\mathbf{x})}$$

and thus the kinetic energy density $\frac{1}{2}\rho \, \overline{u_i(\mathbf{x})u_i(\mathbf{x})}$ is related to $\Psi_{ii}(k)$ through the relation

$$(7\text{-}96) \qquad \frac{1}{2}\rho \, \overline{u_i(\mathbf{x})u_i(\mathbf{x})} = \frac{1}{2}\rho \int_0^\infty \Psi_{ii}(k) \, dk$$

$\Psi_{ii}(k)$ is a complicated function of the α_i's. In the special case when $\alpha_1 = \alpha_2 = \alpha_3 = \alpha$, we have

$$(7\text{-}97) \qquad \Psi_{ii}(k) = 2\pi A k^4 \exp\left[-\frac{k^2}{\alpha^2} \right]$$

In this case, the characteristic eddy size is of order $1/\alpha$. In addition it is interesting to note that $\Psi_{ii}(k)$ has a maximum at

$$k = 2^{1/2}\alpha$$

and that the variance about $k = 2^{1/2}\alpha$, defined as

$$\sigma_k^2 = \left[\frac{1}{\displaystyle\int_0^\infty \Psi_{ii}(k) \, dk} \right] \int_0^\infty (k - 2^{1/2}\alpha)^2 \Psi_{ii}(k) \, dk$$

has a value of approximately $0.16\alpha^2$. Thus

$$\frac{\sigma_k}{2^{1/2}\alpha} \approx 0.28$$

indicating that the maximum at $k = 2^{1/2}\alpha$ is reasonably sharp. Thus not only is the characteristic wave number roughly α, but most of the wave numbers associated with $\Psi'_{ii}(k)$ lie in the vicinity of this wave number.

Usually we have no knowledge of the velocity field $\mathbf{u}$ and have only the functions R_{ij} and Φ_{ij} from which to estimate "eddy sizes." In analogy to the single size eddy superposition given in the foregoing, we look to the function $\Psi'_{ii}(k)$ to give us this information. It is not clear now, however, how to interpret the function $\Psi'_{ii}(k)$. In the previous example the superposition of eddies all of a single "size" gave a distribution for k that was nonzero for $0 < k < \infty$. We chose $1/\alpha$ as the characteristic size of the eddy, since α was approximately the value of the maximum (and also nearby mean) value of the wave number. If there are many different size eddies present, such a rough measure will not tell us anything about the distribution of "eddy size"; it will tell us only the average size of all the eddies. To circumvent this difficulty of interpretation, we note that in the above example not only did the maximum value of $\Psi'_{ii}(k)$ occur at $k \approx \alpha$ (actually $k = \sqrt{2}\alpha$) but that $\Psi'_{ii}(k)$ was concentrated near this value. For order of magnitude purposes, we may then neglect the spread in $\Psi'_{ii}(k)$ around $k = \alpha$ and say that when many different "eddy sizes" are present, the number of eddies with "size" equal to $1/k$ is simply proportional to $\Psi'_{ii}(k)$. If the eddies are anisotropic, this statement implies an average over three directions.

The reader should note that the foregoing interpretation is in no way essential for using the function Φ_{ij}. It is intended only to give a rough physical interpretation of "eddy size," since the term is so commonly employed. If the reader feels the interpretation too forced, he should feel free to discard it. Instead of "eddy size" distribution, one may consider the wave number distribution which is precisely defined analytically.

7.2.3.2. Transformed Moment Equations.

Equation 7-56 may be written in terms of the spatial Fourier transforms of $\overline{u_i(\mathbf{x}_1, t)u_j(\mathbf{x}_1 + \mathbf{r}, t)}$, $\overline{u_i(\mathbf{x}_1, t)p(\mathbf{x}_1 + \mathbf{r}, t)}$ and $\overline{u_j(\mathbf{x}_1, t)u_k(\mathbf{x}_1, t)u_i(\mathbf{x}_1 + \mathbf{r}, t)}$ taken with respect to the difference coordinate $\mathbf{r}$. Little attention has been paid in the literature to this very general transformed equation, and we shall here just consider the special cases of homogeneous and homogeneous-and-isotropic turbulence. For homogeneous turbulence we introduce the tensors

$$\Phi_{ij}(\mathbf{k}) = \frac{1}{(2\pi)^3} \int\!\!\!\int\!\!\!\int_{-\infty}^{\infty} R_{ij}(\mathbf{r})e^{-i\mathbf{k}\cdot\mathbf{r}}\,d\mathbf{r}$$

$$\Upsilon_{ijk}(\mathbf{k}) = \frac{1}{(2\pi)^3} \int\!\!\!\int\!\!\!\int_{-\infty}^{\infty} S_{ijk}(\mathbf{r})e^{-i\mathbf{k}\cdot\mathbf{r}}\,d\mathbf{r}$$

$$\Theta_i(\mathbf{k}) = \frac{1}{(2\pi)^3} \int\!\!\!\int\!\!\!\int_{-\infty}^{\infty} P_i(\mathbf{r})e^{-i\mathbf{k}\cdot\mathbf{r}}\,d\mathbf{r}$$

Taking the Fourier transform of both sides of Eqs. 7-62a–d, we find

(7-98a) $\quad \dfrac{\partial}{\partial t}\Phi_{ij}(\mathbf{k}) = ik_l[\Upsilon_{ilj}(\mathbf{k}) - \Upsilon_{jli}(-\mathbf{k})]$

$$+ i[k_i\Theta_j(\mathbf{k}) - k_j\Theta_i(-\mathbf{k})] - 2\nu k^2\Phi_{ij}(\mathbf{k})$$

(7-98b) $\qquad\qquad\qquad k_j\Phi_{ij}(\mathbf{k}) = 0$

(7-98c) $\qquad\qquad\qquad k_j\Upsilon_{ilj}(\mathbf{k}) = 0$

(7-98d) $\qquad\qquad\qquad k_j\Theta_j(\mathbf{k}) = 0$

In writing these equations we have used the same notation as Batchelor (1953). Care must be taken when taking the transforms of related quantities like $S_{jik}(0, \mathbf{r})$ and $S_{jik}(0, -\mathbf{r}_2)$ to make certain that the minus signs and subscripts are correct. In addition to the above functions, the following quantities are often defined:

$$T_{ij}(\mathbf{r}) = \frac{\partial}{\partial r_l}\left[\overline{u_i(\mathbf{x})u_l(\mathbf{x})u_j(\mathbf{x}+\mathbf{r})} - \overline{u_i(\mathbf{x})u_l(\mathbf{x}+\mathbf{r})u_j(\mathbf{x}+\mathbf{r})}\right]$$

$$\Gamma_{ij}(\mathbf{k}) = \frac{1}{(2\pi)^3} \int\!\!\!\int\!\!\!\int_{-\infty}^{\infty} T_{ij}(\mathbf{r})e^{-i\mathbf{k}\cdot\mathbf{r}}\,d\mathbf{r}$$

$$P_{ij}(\mathbf{r}) = \frac{\partial}{\partial r_i}\overline{p(\mathbf{x})u_j(\mathbf{x}+\mathbf{r})} - \frac{\partial}{\partial r_j}\overline{p(\mathbf{x}+\mathbf{r})u_i(\mathbf{x})}$$

$$\Pi_{ij}(\mathbf{k}) = \frac{1}{(2\pi)^3} \int\!\!\!\int\!\!\!\int_{-\infty}^{\infty} P_{ij}(\mathbf{r})e^{-i\mathbf{k}\cdot\mathbf{r}}\,d\mathbf{r}.$$

On using the functions $\Gamma_{ij}(\mathbf{k})$ and $\Pi_{ij}(\mathbf{k})$, Eq. 7-98a becomes

(7-99) $\qquad \dfrac{\partial \Phi_{ij}(\mathbf{k})}{\partial t} = \Gamma_{ij}(\mathbf{k}) + \Pi_{ij}(\mathbf{k}) - 2\nu k^2 \Phi_{ij}(\mathbf{k})$

The form of Eqs. 7-98a–d simplifies considerably in the isotropic case. The isotropic form of the tensors $\Phi_{ij}(\mathbf{k})$, $\Upsilon_{ijk}(\mathbf{k})$ and $\Theta_i(\mathbf{k})$ are obtained in the same manner as the corresponding transform tensors with argument $\mathbf{r}$. As Batchelor (1953) points out, since $\Phi_{ij}(\mathbf{k})$ and $\Upsilon_{ijk}(\mathbf{k})$ each depend upon only one scalar function, a simple way to find the governing equation in the isotropic case is to contract the indices in Eq. 7-99. We find

(7-100) $\qquad \dfrac{\partial}{\partial t} \Phi_{ii}(\mathbf{k}) = \Gamma_{ii}(\mathbf{k}) - 2\nu k^2 \Phi_{ii}(\mathbf{k})$

$\Pi_{ii}(\mathbf{k}) = 0$, since $P_{ii}(\mathbf{r}) = 0$ in this case.

$\Phi_{ij}(\mathbf{k})$ may be written in the form

(7-101) $\qquad \Phi_{ij}(\mathbf{k}) = \dfrac{E(k)}{4\pi k^4} [k^2 \delta_{ij} - k_i k_j]$

where $E(k) = \frac{1}{2}\Psi_{ii}(k)$ (see Eq. 7-94). This may be shown by writing $\Phi_{ij}(\mathbf{k})$ in isotropic form, invoking the divergence condition, contracting the indices and performing the integration in Eq. 7-94. $\Upsilon_{ijl}(\mathbf{k})$ may be written in the form (noting that $k_l \Upsilon_{ijl} = 0$ and $\Upsilon_{ijl} = \Upsilon_{jil}$)

(7-102) $\qquad \Upsilon_{ijl}(\mathbf{k}) = i\Upsilon(k)[k_i k_j k_l - \frac{1}{2}k^2 k_i \delta_{jl} - \frac{1}{2}k^2 k_j \delta_{il}]$

A relation between $\Upsilon(k)$ and $k(r)$ is given in Batchelor, but we shall omit it here. From Eq. 7-102 we find

(7-103) $\qquad \Gamma_{ii}(k) = 2k^4 \Upsilon(k)$

and hence we arrive at the commonly used equation

(7-104) $\qquad \dfrac{\partial}{\partial t} E(k) = 4\pi k^6 \Upsilon(k) - 2\nu k^2 E(k)$

Just as Eq. 7-85 is inadequate to determine $f(r)$, so too Eq. 7-104 is inadequate to determine $E(k)$. In the next sections we shall consider some of the approximations that have been made for $\Upsilon(k)$ in order to yield a determinate equation for $E(k)$.

7.3. Attempts at Solution of the Statistical Moment Equations

In order to solve the statistical moment equations, some assumption must be made to terminate the infinite hierarchy of equations. In this section we present some of the earlier attempts at termination. In the next section we shall discuss the more recent attempts that are being made. Except in our discussion of Deissler's work, we shall confine our attention to homogeneous turbulence, although as we shall mention, Kolmogorov's hypothesis applies in some cases to non-homogeneous turbulence.

7.3.1. Final Period of Decay and the Nature of $\Phi_{ij}(\mathbf{k}, t)$ Near $k_i = 0$

Perhaps the simplest assumption that may be made to terminate the hierarchy is to assume in Eq. 7-62a that the terms S_{ijk} and P_i may be neglected. This assumption was first used in studying the isotropic equations by von Kármán and Howarth (1938). It is appropriate for the last stages of decay of a turbulent field when the inertia forces and pressure fluctuations become negligible. In terms of the spectral tensor $\Phi_{ij}(\mathbf{k})$, the governing equations are now (see Eqs. 7-98a and 7-98b). (We reintroduce the t argument for clarity.)

$$(7\text{-}105) \qquad \frac{\partial}{\partial t}\,\Phi_{ij}(\mathbf{k}, t) = -2\nu k^2\Phi_{ij}(\mathbf{k}, t)$$

$$(7\text{-}106) \qquad\qquad k_j\Phi_{ij}(\mathbf{k}, t) = 0$$

The solution of Eq. 7-105 is simply

$$(7\text{-}107) \qquad \Phi_{ij}(\mathbf{k}, t) = \Phi_{ij}(\mathbf{k}, t_0)\,\exp\,[-2\nu k^2(t - t_0)]$$

where $\Phi_{ij}(\mathbf{k}, t_0)$ must be known at time $t = t_0$. $\Phi_{ij}(\mathbf{k}, t_0)$ must satisfy Eq. 7-106 and be positive definite. $R_{ij}(\mathbf{r}, t)$ may be obtained from Eq. 7-107 using the Fourier transform relation given in Eq. 7-87. From this equation we see that as a result of the exp $[-\nu k^2(t - t_0)]$ term, only small wave numbers are significant as $t - t_0 \rightarrow \infty$.

Batchelor (1953) pointed out that *if* $\Phi_{ij}(\mathbf{k}, t)$ may be considered analytic in the neighborhood of $k_i = 0$; i.e., if we may write

$$(7\text{-}108) \qquad \Phi_{ij}(\mathbf{k}, t) = c_{ij}(t) + k_l c_{ijl}(t) + k_l k_m c_{ijlm}(t) + 0(k^3)$$

the form of $\Phi_{ij}(\mathbf{k}, t)$ may be determined for small wave numbers. Then, noting that only small wave numbers are important as $t - t_0 \to \infty$, a simplified form for $\Phi_{ij}(\mathbf{k}, t)$ may be found in this limit.

In the discussion of the cumulant neglect hypothesis (see Sec. 7.3.5), we shall see that the analyticity of $\Phi_{ij}(\mathbf{k}, t)$ near $k_i = 0$ is brought into question. This stimulated analysis by Batchelor and Proudman (1956), and they showed that in general we should *not* expect $\Phi_{ij}(\mathbf{k}, t)$ to be analytic near $k_i = 0$, and hence Eq. 7-107 assumes no very simple form as $t - t_0 \to \infty$.

Using a rather involved analysis, Batchelor and Proudman (1956) were able, with suitable assumptions, to determine the nature of the singularity in the neighborhood of $k_i = 0$ and say something about the decay of $\overline{u^2}$ as $t - t_0 \to \infty$ (see also Lee, 1965). For this discussion we refer the reader to their paper. Of perhaps more interest is the reason for the nonanalytic character of $\Phi_{ij}(\mathbf{k}, t)$, and we shall now consider this point here following the reasoning given in their paper.

If we assume $\Phi_{ij}(\mathbf{k}, t)$ may be expanded in a Taylor series about $k_i = 0$, we find, upon expanding the exponential term in the definition

$$\Phi_{ij}(\mathbf{k}, t) = \frac{1}{(2\pi)^3} \iiint_{-\infty}^{\infty} R_{ij}(\mathbf{r}, t) e^{-i\mathbf{k}\cdot\mathbf{r}} \, d\mathbf{r}$$

the series

$$(7\text{-}109) \quad \Phi_{ij}(\mathbf{k}, t) = \frac{1}{(2\pi)^3} \iiint_{-\infty}^{\infty} R_{ij}(\mathbf{r}, t) \, d\mathbf{r}$$

$$- \frac{i}{(2\pi)^3} k_l \iiint_{-\infty}^{\infty} r_l R_{ij}(\mathbf{r}, t) \, d\mathbf{r}$$

$$- \frac{1}{(2\pi)^3} \frac{k_l k_m}{2} \iiint_{-\infty}^{\infty} r_l r_m R_{ij}(\mathbf{r}, t) \, d\mathbf{r} + 0(k^3)$$

If all integral moments of $R_{ij}(\mathbf{r}, t)$ exist and we assume the series converges, then $\Phi_{ij}(\mathbf{k}, t)$ is analytic near $k_i = 0$. The analyticity of $\Phi_{ij}(\mathbf{k}, t)$ thus depends upon the existence of the integral moments of $R_{ij}(\mathbf{r}, t)$.

In the final period of decay, we see from Eq. 7-107 that if $\Phi_{ij}(\mathbf{k}, t_0)$ is analytic near $k_i = 0$, $\Phi_{ij}(\mathbf{k}, t)$ is analytic in this region. Thus, if the turbulence is created in a manner such that when inertia and pressure forces are negligible $\Phi_{ij}(k, t_0)$ is analytic, it remains analytic. A simplified form may then be obtained for $\Phi_{ij}(\mathbf{k}, t)$ using Eq. 7-108, the divergence condition and the positive definiteness of $\Phi_{ij}(\mathbf{k}, t)$. (See Batchelor, 1953.) This, however, is not the problem in which we are usually interested. We are usually interested in the final period of decay as it evolves from a previous period in which inertial and pressure forces were not negligible. Thus, $\Phi_{ij}(\mathbf{k}, t_0)$ is not specified arbitrarily but has a form dependent on the previous history of the flow. This is generally the case when considering flow behind grids if the initial Reynolds number is moderately high.

In order to investigate the character of $\Phi_{ij}(\mathbf{k}, t_0)$, Batchelor and Proudman consider the form of $R_{ij}(\mathbf{r}, t_1)$ $(t_1 < t_0)$ as $r \to \infty$ when inertial and pressure forces are important. In particular, they consider the effect of the pressure fluctuations. The pressure fluctuations appear in Eq. 7-62a through the $P_k(\mathbf{r})$ terms. Taking the divergence of this equation, we find that $P_k(\mathbf{r})$ satisfies the equation

$$(7\text{-}110) \qquad \nabla^2 P_k(\mathbf{r}) = -\frac{\partial^2 S_{ijk}(0, \mathbf{r})}{\partial r_i\, \partial r_j}$$

Equation 7-110 is a Poisson equation and in infinite space has the solution

$$(7\text{-}111) \qquad P_k(\mathbf{r}) = \frac{1}{4\pi} \int_V \frac{\partial^2 S_{ijk}(0, \mathbf{r}')}{\partial r_i'\, \partial r_j'} \frac{dr'}{|\mathbf{r} - \mathbf{r}'|}$$

If we know nothing about the character of $S_{ijk}(0, \mathbf{r})$, we can say nothing about the character of $P_k(\mathbf{r})$. The interesting point of Eq. 7-111 is, however, that even if at some time t_1 $S_{ijk}(0, \mathbf{r})$ is such that all integral moments of this function exist, this is not true for the function $P_k(\mathbf{r})$. If all integral moments of $S_{ijk}(0, \mathbf{r})$ exist, we may expand the term

$$1/|\mathbf{r} - \mathbf{r}'|$$

in inverse powers of r and evaluate Eq. 7-111 term by term. Noting that $(\partial S_{ijl}/\partial r_i)(0, \mathbf{r}) = 0$, Batchelor and Proudman find for the leading term in the expansion

(7-112) $$P_j(\mathbf{r}) \sim -\frac{1}{4\pi} \frac{\partial^3}{\partial r_i r_k \, \partial r_l} \left(\frac{1}{r}\right) \int\limits_{V} S_{ikj}(0, -\mathbf{r}')r_l' \, d\mathbf{r}'$$

that is, $P_j(\mathbf{r})$ behaves as $1/r^4$ as $r \to \infty$.

If now Eq. 7-112 is introduced into Eq. 7-62a, we find that

$$\left. \frac{\partial R_{ij}(\mathbf{r}, t)}{\partial t} \right|_{t=t_1}$$

vanishes as $1/r^5$ as $r \to \infty$. Thus for $t > t_1$, $R_{ij}(\mathbf{r}, t) \sim 1/r^5$ as $r \to \infty$. (This depends, of course, on the fact that $R_{ij}(\mathbf{r}, t)$ approached zero at this rate or a faster rate for $t < t_1$. Batchelor and Proudman actually assume that all integral moments of $R_{ij}(\mathbf{r}, t)$ exist when $t < t_1$.) For this rate of decay, higher order integral moments of $R_{ij}(\mathbf{r}, t)$ will not exist, and from Eq. 7-109 we see that $\Phi_{ij}(\mathbf{k}, t)$ will not be analytic in the neighborhood of $k_i = 0$.

When the turbulence is isotropic, the above argument does not hold, since $P_i(\mathbf{r}) = 0$. Batchelor and Proudman have been unable to determine the order of decay in this case, although they point out that it is no larger than $1/r^6$. In addition, we note that the above analysis is predicted on the fact that at some time t_1, all integral moments of the velocity correlation tensors exist. The above analysis must thus be accepted with some reservations. It does, however, serve to show that under reasonable assumptions $\Phi_{ij}(\mathbf{k})$ is not analytic in the neighborhood of $k_i = 0$. As in Chapter 5 (see the discussions below Eqs. 5-138 and 5-149), we find that correlation functions do not necessarily decay exponentially and, in fact, may decay as $1/r^n$ ($r \to \infty$) where n is a moderately small integer. In both cases the result occurs because some correlation function is governed by a Poisson-type equation. It is clear that the decay of correlation functions as $r \to \infty$ must be carefully considered in any physical problem, and any a priori assumptions must be accepted with caution.

Finally we note that instead of neglecting the inertial and pressure terms in Eq. 7-99, we could allow them to remain but neglect the counterpart of these terms in the next equation in the hierarchy, that is, consider the first perturbation about the viscous solution. This set of equations would describe a state of what might be called moderately weak turbulence. For references to work of this kind, we refer the reader to a note by Deissler (1965b).

7.3.2. General Remarks

Before discussing possible approximations for $\Gamma_{ij}(\mathbf{k})$ and $\Pi_{ij}(\mathbf{k})$ in Eq. 7-99 (or their transforms in Eq. 7-62a), it is important to note the contributions to the tensor $\Phi_{ii}(\mathbf{k})$ that are made by inertia and pressure forces. We have

$$R_{ii}(\mathbf{r}) = \int\!\!\!\int\!\!\!\int_{-\infty}^{\infty} \Phi_{ii}(\mathbf{k}) e^{i\mathbf{k}\cdot\mathbf{r}}\, d\mathbf{k}$$

and setting $\mathbf{r} = 0$

$$R_{ii}(0) = \overline{u_i(\mathbf{x})u_i(\mathbf{x})} = \int\!\!\!\int\!\!\!\int_{-\infty}^{\infty} \Phi_{ii}(\mathbf{k})\, d\mathbf{k}$$

Thus $\Phi_{ii}(\mathbf{k})$ is the contribution to turbulent kinetic energy in the wave number range $\mathbf{k}$ to $\mathbf{k} + d\mathbf{k}$.

From Eq. 7-100 we see that since $\Pi_{ii}(\mathbf{k}) = 0$, pressure forces do not change the turbulent kinetic energy in any wave number range. It may serve to change the relative values of $\overline{u_1^2}$, $\overline{u_2^2}$, or $\overline{u_3^2}$, but it does not affect the sum $\overline{u_i u_i}$. The function $\Gamma_{ii}(\mathbf{k})$ does serve to change $\Phi_{ii}(\mathbf{k})$. Integration of Eq. 7-100 with respect to $\mathbf{k}$, however, shows that

$$(7\text{-}113) \qquad \frac{\partial}{\partial t} \int\!\!\!\int\!\!\!\int_{-\infty}^{\infty} \Phi_{ii}(\mathbf{k})\, d\mathbf{k} = \frac{\partial}{\partial t}\, \overline{u_i u_i} = -2\nu \int\!\!\!\int\!\!\!\int_{-\infty}^{\infty} k^2 \Phi_{ii}(\mathbf{k})\, d\mathbf{k}$$

since

$$\int\!\!\!\int\!\!\!\int_{-\infty}^{\infty} \Gamma_{ij}(\mathbf{k})\, d\mathbf{k} = T_{ij}(0) = 0$$

Note

$$T_{ij}(0) = \overline{u_i(\mathbf{x})u_l(\mathbf{x})\frac{\partial u_j(\mathbf{x})}{\partial x_l}} + \overline{\frac{\partial u_i(\mathbf{x})}{\partial x_l} u_j(\mathbf{x})u_l(\mathbf{x})}$$

$$= \frac{\partial}{\partial x_l}\, \overline{[u_i(x)u_j(x)u_l(x)]} = 0$$

This means, as indeed we would expect, that the total turbulent kinetic energy is in no way changed by inertia forces. They serve only to transfer the spectral resolution of the kinetic energy from one wave number range to the other. Only viscous effects diminish the total kinetic energy by conversion of this energy into heat.

The dissipative term

$$2\nu \int\!\!\!\int\!\!\!\int_{-\infty}^{\infty} k^2 \Phi_{ii}(\mathbf{k})\, d\mathbf{k}$$

is weighted in favor of large wave numbers through the presence of the k^2 factor. Thus most of the viscous dissipation is done by the small eddies. This is shown in the correlation equation by the presence of the ∇^2 operator; the rate of change of the rate of change of velocity with distance is greatest for the small eddies, and hence their contribution to the dissipative term $2\nu\nabla^2 R_{ii}(\mathbf{r})$ is greater for small eddies than for larger eddies of the same strength.

The physical picture that emerges from this analysis when the nonlinear terms are important is one of transfer of energy from large eddies to small eddies wherein it is dissipated. We could, of course, set up initial conditions so that energy flowed from small to large eddies; but normally in a physical problem, such as flow through a grid, the turbulent energy is fed from the mean flow into the largest eddies, and it is then transferred to the small eddies where it is dissipated. We also expect the energy distribution among eddies to be relatively smooth, there being no apparent reason for bunching in a narrow wave number range. Further, we might expect that as the energy is transferred from the large eddies to the small eddies, it would tend to lose any directionality that it might have had initially. It is reasonable to suppose that the small eddies should be isotropic. In the final period of decay when the nonlinear terms are negligible, the energy transfer ceases, and $\Phi_{ij}(\mathbf{k}, t)$ is governed by Eq. 7-107. Thus we see that eventually only the largest eddies contain significant amounts of energy.

7.3.3. Kolmogorov's Hypothesis

The physical ideas discussed in Section 7.3.2 helped Kolmogorov (1941) to find the form of the spectral function in a restricted range of

k. (Kolmogorov actually determined the form of the structure function $\overline{[u_i(\mathbf{x}, t) - u_i(\mathbf{x} + \mathbf{r}, t)][u_j(\mathbf{x}, t) - u_j(\mathbf{x} + \mathbf{r}, t)]}$ (see Tatarski, 1961), but we shall follow Batchelor (1953) and consider the spectral function.) Kolmogorov hypothesized that for very large Reynolds numbers the range of eddies that receive the turbulent energy should be well separated from the range of eddies where the dissipation occurs. (He loosely defined the Reynolds number as LU_c/ν where L is some characteristic length and U_c is some characteristic velocity. We could choose L as the characteristic size of the energy containing eddies and let $U_c = (\overline{u^2})^{1/2}$. He reasoned that if this is the case, all eddies with wave number substantially greater than the eddies directly receiving energy are isotropic and obey a similarity hypothesis wherein their distribution is a function only of the energy dissipation per unit time, $\bar{\epsilon}$, and the viscosity ν. (He did not distinguish between the very largest eddies and the somewhat smaller eddies which contain most of the energy, but it is not too important for his arguments. More properly, perhaps, we should consider all eddies with wave numbers substantially greater than the energy containing eddies.)

His assumption implies that the eddy-size distribution of small eddies does not depend on the particular character of the big eddies. It depends only on the energy fed through the big eddies into the turbulent field and on the viscosity which governs the size at which dissipation of energy will begin. It is implicit in his hypothesis that the characteristic times associated with the small eddies must be small compared to the characteristic times associated with the big eddies so that they can quickly adjust to any initial state.

If the small eddies are isotropic and of a universal character then $E(k, t)$ must have a universal form containing only the two parameters $\bar{\epsilon}$ and ν. We must have

$$(7\text{-}114) \qquad E(k) = AE_0(lk)$$

where E_0 is a nondimensional function of lk, l is some characteristic length, and A must have the dimensions of $E(k)$. A and l must be functions of $\bar{\epsilon}$ and ν. $\bar{\epsilon}$ has the units of energy/unit mass/unit time (ergs/gram sec = cm²/sec³) and ν has the units of velocity × length (cm²/sec). The quantity l may thus be defined as

$$l = \left[\frac{\nu^3}{\bar{\epsilon}}\right]^{1/4}$$

The units of $E(k)$ are (velocity)^2 × length (cm^3/sec^2). Hence

$$A = (\nu^5\bar\epsilon)^{1/4}$$

and finally

(7-115) $$E(k) = (\nu^5\bar\epsilon)^{1/4}E_0(lk)$$

Kolmogorov carried this procedure one step further by hypothesizing that there may be a range of eddy sizes small compared to the energy containing eddies but large compared to the eddy sizes where significant viscous dissipation occurs. In this case, $E(k)$ would depend only upon $\bar\epsilon$. If $E(k)$ depends only upon $\bar\epsilon$, then E_0 must be proportional to $\nu^{-5/4}$ and hence

(7-116) $$E(k) = (\nu^5\bar\epsilon)^{1/4}B(lk)^{-5/3}$$

$$= B\bar\epsilon^{2/3}k^{-5/3}$$

where B is an absolute constant.

Kolmogorov in his basic paper did not limit himself to homogeneous turbulence, and it is clear from the above remarks that the analyses hold as long as the small eddies are small compared to any characteristic distances arising in a nonhomogeneous problem. In fact, the Reynolds numbers needed for the applicability of Eq. 7-116 (not Eq. 7-115) are too high for most laboratory studies, and this result finds its greatest use in atmospheric and oceanic turbulence studies. Lumley and Panofsky (1964, Chapter 5) give a list of references in which the validity of the $k^{-5/3}$ spectrum is discussed for atmospheric turbulence. By and large, experiments seem to confirm the validity of this law, but there are some discrepancies. Just how closely experiments confirm the law requires considerable discussion, and the reader is referred to the review in Lumley and Panofsky (1964). Grant, Stewart, and Moilliet (1962) showed in a tidal channel study that Kolmogorov's spectrum was in close agreement with measured values.

It should be noted that Obukhoff (1962) and Kolmogorov (1962) have recently proposed modification of the basic ideas presented in the foregoing. Their modification is based on the idea that $\bar\epsilon$ is actually a statistical variable. For a discussion of this notion we refer the reader to their papers and to some similar but not equivalent remarks by Grant, Stewart, and Moilliet (1962).

7.3.4. Heisenberg's Theory

A number of investigators have made hypotheses in order to make Eq. 7-104 a determinate equation and find $E_0(lk)$ theoretically. They make some hypothesis which essentially allows one to express the term $4\pi k^6 \Upsilon(k)$ in terms of $E(k)$. Batchelor (1953) and Hinze (1959) discuss and reference a number of theories, but here we will only present the theory by Heisenberg (1948a). Which theory, if any, is correct is a matter of considerable discussion in the literature (see, for example, Reid, 1960), and it is only necessary to present one theory to show the nature of the assumptions. In presenting Heisenberg's theory we wish to make clear to the reader that there are actually two aspects to Heisenberg's theory. After his first paper which applies to eddies in the equilibrium range, Heisenberg (1948b) used the same type of ideas, in addition to a similarity hypothesis involving time, to consider the spectrum of the energy containing eddies. We consider here only his first paper. Actually his ideas are probably more appropriate for the energy containing eddies, but this latter case would require too lengthy a discussion, and the basic ideas we wish to discuss will be somewhat more transparent in the equilibrium case.

In order to make a suitable approximation for $F(k) \equiv 4\pi k^6 \Upsilon(k)$, we first integrate Eq. 7-104 from 0 to k and from k to ∞. We have

$$(7\text{-}117) \qquad \frac{\partial}{\partial t} \int_0^k E(k')\, dk' = \int_0^k F(k')\, dk' - 2\nu \int_0^k k'^2 E(k')\, dk'$$

and

$$(7\text{-}118) \qquad \frac{\partial}{\partial t} \int_k^\infty E(k')\, dk' = \int_k^\infty F(k')\, dk' - 2\nu \int_k^\infty k'^2 E(k')\, dk'$$

We choose k to lie below the equilibrium range but to contain all the energy containing eddies. We assume the eddies in the equilibrium state have a fixed amount of energy; the energy transferred from the big eddies being dissipated by viscosity. We thus set

$$\frac{\partial}{\partial t} \int_k^\infty E(k')\, dk' \approx 0$$

and

$$\frac{\partial}{\partial t} \int_0^k E(k') \, dk' = -\bar{\epsilon}$$

where again $\bar{\epsilon}$ is the rate of transfer of energy from the big eddies to the eddies in the equilibrium range. With these assumptions we find from Eq. 7-117

(7-119) $$-\bar{\epsilon} = \int_0^k F(k') \, dk' - 2\nu \int_0^k k'^2 E(k') \, dk'$$

The term $\int_0^k F(k') \, dk'$ denotes the net rate of transfer of energy to or from the wave number range 0 to k. Adding $\int_0^k F(k') \, dk'$ to both sides of Eq. 7-118 and noting that $\int_0^\infty F(k') \, dk' = 0$, we see that

(7-120) $$\int_0^k F(k') \, dk' = -2\nu \int_k^\infty k'^2 E(k') \, dk'$$

The righthand side is just the energy/unit mass/unit time that is dissipated by viscous action. Using the analogy with the transfer of energy to heat in laminar flow, Heisenberg introduces an eddy viscosity similar to the eddy viscosity considered in Section 7.1. He postulates

(7-121) $$\int_0^k F(k') \, dk' = -2\bar{\eta}(k) \int_0^k k'^2 E(k') \, dk'$$

so that Eq. 7-118 becomes

(7-122) $$-\bar{\epsilon} = -2\bar{\eta}(k) \int_0^k k'^2 E(k') \, dk' - 2\nu \int_0^k k'^2 E(k') \, dk'$$

$\bar{\eta}(k)$ is the physical equivalent of ν.

In the introduction we discussed some of the qualitative aspects of a kinematic viscosity. The dimensions of ν are

$$\text{length}^2/\text{time} = (\text{length}/\text{time})(\text{length}) = (\text{velocity})(\text{length})$$

From molecular considerations we found $\nu = a v_m' l_m$, where a is a constant of order unity, v_m' is an average molecular speed, and l_m is the molecular mean free path. Analogously we may write here the eddy viscosity in the form

$$\bar{\eta} = \sqrt{\overline{u^2}}\, l$$

where $[\overline{u^2}]^{1/2}$ is the root mean square turbulent velocity, and l is a characteristic eddy size. (We use $[\overline{u^2}]^{1/2}$ rather than the root mean square value of a particular velocity component since no preferred direction is indicated here.)

In the foregoing problem $\bar{\eta}(k)$ represents the integrated effect of those eddies that transport energy from the energy containing eddies to the smaller eddies. The eddies that transport energy away from the energy containing eddies are the small eddies. Thus $\bar{\eta}(k)$ may be written in the form

$$(7\text{-}123) \qquad \bar{\eta}(k) = \int_k^\infty \eta(k')\, dk' = \int_k^\infty \alpha u_{k'} l_{k'}\, dk'$$

where α is a constant of order unity. u_k is the characteristic velocity of an eddy with wave number, k, and l_k is its characteristic size. $\eta(k)$ is the eddy viscosity associated with a particular eddy. The characteristic size of an eddy of wave number k is $1/k$, and the characteristic velocity per unit wave number may be written as $\sqrt{E(k)/k}$. Thus we may write

$$(7\text{-}124) \qquad \bar{\eta}(k) = \alpha \int_k^\infty \sqrt{\frac{E(k')}{k'^3}}\, dk'$$

and

$$(7\text{-}125) \qquad \bar{\epsilon} = \left[2\alpha \int_k^\infty \sqrt{\frac{E(k')}{k'^3}}\, dk' + 2\nu \right] \int_0^k k'^2 E(k')\, dk'$$

The solution of this equation (see Chandrasekhar, 1949, and Hinze, 1959) is

$$(7\text{-}126) \qquad E(k) = \frac{C(\bar{\epsilon})^{2/3} k^{-5/3}}{\{1 + [8/3\alpha^2][k/k_d]^4\}^{4/3}}$$

where $k_d = [\bar{\epsilon}/\nu^3]^{1/4}$ and C is a constant.

When $k/k_d \ll 1$, Eq. 7-126 yields the Kolmogorov spectrum. When $k/k_d \gg 1$, we find

$$E(k) \approx k^{-7}$$

Reid (1960) compared Eq. 7-126 and other expressions derived by Kovaszny (1948) and Obukhoff (1941) with experiments of Stewart and Townsend (1951). Grant, Stewart, and Moilliet (1962) compared Eq. 7-126 and the Kovaszny theory with their tidal channel experiments. Equation 7-126 agrees with the experiments for values of k up to the neighborhood of $k \approx k_d$ but appears to diverge from experimental results for $k/k_d > 1$. Kovaszny's theory gives similar agreement with experiment.

The lack of agreement with experiment at large wave numbers should probably not be unexpected. The physical idea behind Heisenberg's postulate is applicable for calculating the spectrum of only the larger eddies. If k is very large (a small eddy), it is not too meaningful to speak of the even smaller eddies acting as an effective viscosity for energy transport to or from this eddy, for if $E(k)$ decreases monotonically in the large wave number range, much of the contribution to the integral

$$\int\limits_{k}^{\infty} \sqrt{\frac{E(k')}{k'^3}}\, dk'$$

will come from wave numbers near k. This violates the physical analogy to molecular viscosity where the two length scales are sharply separated. As we mentioned before, Heisenberg's type of analysis should apply to the energy carrying eddies if the formulism is modified to take into account the decay of these eddies. Heisenberg (1948b) has done this, and the reader is referred to his paper and the discussion in Batchelor (1953) and Hinze (1959).

7.3.5. Cumulant Neglect Hypothesis

In the previous section the first equation of the infinite hierarchy of moment equations governing isotropic turbulence was solved by expressing the third-order moment in terms of the second-order moment (actually the relationship was written in terms of the Fourier transforms of these moments). The relationship (Eqs. 7-121 and 7-124) was determined from very physical considerations, and it is not too applicable to other statistical continuum theories. In this section we shall present a procedure which at least formally may be applied to almost any statistical theory and may be used to terminate the hierarchy of equations at any order. This method, termed the cumulant neglect hypothesis (see Section 3.3.3), was applied to the turbulence problem by Proudman and Reid (1954) and Tatsumi (1957). They terminated the moment hierarchy by expressing the fourth-order moments in terms of the second-order moments. This method was introduced into turbulence theory by Millionshtchikov (1941a, b), but we shall base our discussion principally on this later work by Proudman and Reid (1954). The reader is also referred to Heisenberg (1948a), Chandrasekhar (1955), and Kraichnan (1957). Chandrasekhar considers the more general two-time correlation functions, and Kraichnan comments upon this work.

In the theory of heterogeneous media and in the theory of turbulence, third-order moments appear in the equations governing the second-order moments. Except in very special cases (small fluctuations in the heterogeneous case, final period of decay in the turbulent problem), these third-order terms cannot be neglected. Since third-order moments are zero for gaussian processes, it is clear that in general these physical problems cannot be represented exactly by gaussian probability density functions. It is a useful hypothesis, however, to assume that the cumulant (see Section 3.3.3) of a higher order moment may be approximately equal to zero. This type of assumption allows one to terminate the hierarchy of moment equations at any order by expressing the $(n + 1)$th-order moments (occurring in the equations governing the nth-order moments) in terms of moments of order n or less.

It is very difficult to tell *a priori* just how plausible is this type of assumption. Experiments (see Batchelor, 1953, Chapter 8; Frenkiel and Klebanoff, 1965) show that the one-point probability density function approximates the form of the gaussian distribution but that the two-point density function exhibits some deviation. Furthermore, it appears that if the two-point density function that is associated with only large eddies was calculated, it would be approximately gaussian; on the other hand, if this calculation were made for only small eddies, it would not be gaussian. It is not clear, however, how much light this throws on the validity of the calculations made on the assumption that the relationship between fourth-order moments and second-order moments is approximately gaussian (i.e., the result of the cumulant neglect hypothesis we shall shortly introduce). The only statement that can really be made is that the approximation might be good if it gives physically meaningful results.

The requirement that the cumulant neglect hypothesis should give physically meaningful results has proven to be a serious difficulty for the theory. It has been found that for certain initial conditions, the energy spectrum, which must be positive for all values of k, assumes negative values in the energy containing range. This has been confirmed by numerical calculation by Ogura (1963) for flows at moderate Reynolds numbers (at low Reynolds numbers the spectrum remains positive). (Similar results had been obtained when the approximation was introduced into the turbulent diffusion equations.) The initial conditions used by Ogura are not conditions that have been determined by experiment; they have rather been chosen for convenience. Thus the approximation may have validity for actual flows, but the outlook does not seem too promising, except perhaps for low Reynolds numbers. We have presented the theory here, since the approximation scheme may have merit in other statistical continuum theories and indeed perhaps in turbulence if a higher order cumulant is set equal to zero. We also wished the reader to be familiar with the approximation in a theory in which it has received considerable attention (as opposed to just stating a set of equations as we did in Section 3.3.3). In addition this type of development did have in turbulence theory the useful result of forcing investigators to rethink some basic conclusions hitherto accepted in the field, since they were at variance with results obtained with the cumulant neglect assumption. We refer here to Proudman and Reid's discussion of Loitsiansky's integral which we shall mention later (see also Section 7.3.1).

The cumulant neglect hypothesis can be made at any order, but the resulting equations are so complex for even the lowest-order moment equation for which the approximation is useful, that all work has so far been restricted to the simplest set of equations that are possible. The approximation is possible for nonhomogeneous turbulence, but we will restrict ourselves to homogeneous turbulence and, after the equations are derived, to homogeneous-and-isotropic turbulence.

The basic equation governing the second-order moment is Eq. 7-62a.

We repeat this equation here in the notation used by Proudman and Reid (1954).

$$(7\text{-}127) \quad \frac{\partial}{\partial t} R_{ij}(\mathbf{r}) = O_2 \left[\frac{\partial}{\partial r_m} R_{ijm}(\mathbf{r}, 0) + \frac{\partial}{\partial r_i} P_j(\mathbf{r}) + \nu \nabla^2 R_{ij}(\mathbf{r}) \right]$$

where O_2 is the operator such that

$$O_2 A_{ij}(\mathbf{r}) = A_{ij}(\mathbf{r}) + A_{ji}(-\mathbf{r})$$

Here

$$R_{ijk}(\mathbf{r}, \mathbf{r}') \equiv \overline{u_i(\mathbf{x}) u_j(\mathbf{x} + \mathbf{r}) u_k(\mathbf{x} + \mathbf{r}')}$$

$$\equiv S_{ijk}(\mathbf{r}, \mathbf{r}')$$

If we assumed here that $R_{ijm}(\mathbf{r}, O)$ should be determined by neglecting the third-order cumulant, we should be forced to set this term equal to zero. This, of course, is unsatisfactory, since except in the final period of decay the inertia term is quite important. To make use of the approximation we desire, we must find an additional equation governing $R_{ijk}(\mathbf{r}, \mathbf{r}')$ and a fourth-order moment. The derivation of such an equation is straightforward: One simply considers a third set of equations in addition to 7-54a,b and 7-55a,b written in terms of $u_j(\mathbf{x}_3)$.* Proudman and Reid (1954) find

$$(7\text{-}128) \quad \frac{\partial}{\partial t} R_{ijk}(\mathbf{r}, \mathbf{r}')$$

$$= O_3 \left[\left(\frac{\partial}{\partial r_m} + \frac{\partial}{\partial r_{m'}} \right) \overline{u_i(\mathbf{x}) u_m(\mathbf{x}) u_j(\mathbf{x} + \mathbf{r}) u_k(\mathbf{x} + \mathbf{r}')} \right.$$

$$+ \left(\frac{\partial}{\partial r_i} + \frac{\partial}{\partial r_{i'}} \right) P_{jk}(\mathbf{r}, \mathbf{r}')$$

$$\left. + \nu \left(\frac{\partial}{\partial r_m} + \frac{\partial}{\partial r_{m'}} \right) \left(\frac{\partial}{\partial r_m} + \frac{\partial}{\partial r_{m'}} \right) R_{ijk}(\mathbf{r}, \mathbf{r}') \right]$$

where O_3 is an operator such that

$$O_3 A_{ijk}(\mathbf{r}, \mathbf{r}') = A_{ijk}(\mathbf{r}, \mathbf{r}') + A_{jki}(\mathbf{r}' - \mathbf{r}, -\mathbf{r}) + A_{kij}(-\mathbf{r}', \mathbf{r} - \mathbf{r}')$$

---

* It should be noted that the cumulant neglect equations can be found directly from an expansion of the logarithm of the Hopf characteristic functional.

Here

$$P_{ij}(\mathbf{r}, \mathbf{r}') = \overline{p(\mathbf{x})u_i(\mathbf{x} + \mathbf{r})u_j(\mathbf{x} + \mathbf{r}')}$$

The cumulant neglect hypothesis is now made to simplify Eq. 7-128. The cumulant associated with fourth-order moment

$$\overline{u_i(\mathbf{x})u_m(\mathbf{x})u_j(\mathbf{x} + \mathbf{r})u_k(\mathbf{x} + \mathbf{r}')}$$

is assumed to be approximately zero, and this has the consequence that this moment has the form it would have if the statistics were gaussian. For gaussian statistics we would have

(7-129) $\overline{u_i(\mathbf{x})u_m(\mathbf{x})u_j(\mathbf{x} + \mathbf{r})u_k(\mathbf{x} + \mathbf{r}')}$

$$= [\overline{u_i(\mathbf{x})u_m(\mathbf{x})}][\overline{u_j(\mathbf{x} + \mathbf{r})u_k(\mathbf{x} + \mathbf{r}')}]$$

$$+ [\overline{u_i(\mathbf{x})u_j(\mathbf{x} + \mathbf{r})}][\overline{u_m(\mathbf{x})u_k(\mathbf{x} + \mathbf{r}')}]$$

$$+ [\overline{u_i(\mathbf{x})u_k(\mathbf{x} + \mathbf{r}')}][\overline{u_m(\mathbf{x})u_j(\mathbf{x} + \mathbf{r})}].$$

Thus with this assumption Eq. 7-128 becomes

(7-130) $\dfrac{\partial}{\partial t} R_{ijk}(\mathbf{r}, \mathbf{r}')$

$$= O_3 \left\{ \left(\frac{\partial}{\partial r_m} + \frac{\partial}{\partial r_m'} \right) (R_{ij}(\mathbf{r})R_{mk}(\mathbf{r}') + R_{ik}(\mathbf{r}')R_{mj}(\mathbf{r})) \right.$$

$$+ \left(\frac{\partial}{\partial r_i} + \frac{\partial}{\partial r_i'} \right) P_{jk}(\mathbf{r}, \mathbf{r}')$$

$$\left. + v \left(\frac{\partial}{\partial r_m} + \frac{\partial}{\partial r_m'} \right) \left(\frac{\partial}{\partial r_m} + \frac{\partial}{\partial r_m'} \right) R_{ijk}(\mathbf{r}, \mathbf{r}') \right\}$$

Equations 7-128 and 7-130, coupled with the fact that the divergences of $R_{ij}(\mathbf{r})$, $P_i(\mathbf{r})$, $R_{ijk}(\mathbf{r}, \mathbf{r}')$, and $P_{ij}(\mathbf{r}, \mathbf{r}')$ are zero, form a determinate set of equations for finding $R_{ij}(\mathbf{r})$ and $R_{ijk}(\mathbf{r}, \mathbf{r}')$ as a function of time. The boundary conditions needed to solve these equations are a knowledge of $R_{ij}(\mathbf{r})$ and $R_{ijk}(\mathbf{r}, \mathbf{r}')$ at some time, t_0. (The pressure correlations may be determined at time t_0 and in fact at all time from the vanishing divergence conditions.)

Equations 7-128 and 7-130 have not been handled analytically in their entirety, but Proudman and Reid (1954) and Tatsumi (1957) have obtained some results. Most results that have been found, however, have been principally in the wave number domain. As we mentioned previously, Ogura (1963) treated the wave number equations numerically and showed that for some initial conditions the energy spectrum assumed negative values. We now present the equations in the wave number domain as they were derived in Proudman and Reid (1954). They may be derived by Fourier-transforming the correlation equations. In Eqs. 7-131 and 7-132 the pressure terms have been eliminated. We find

$$(7\text{-}131) \quad \frac{\partial}{\partial t} \Phi_{ij}(\mathbf{k}) = O_2 \left\{ k_m \left(\delta_{ir} - \frac{k_i k_r}{k^2} \right) \int \Phi_{rjm}(\mathbf{k}, \mathbf{k}') \, d\mathbf{k}' - \nu k^2 \Phi_{ij}(\mathbf{k}) \right\}$$

$$(7\text{-}132) \quad \frac{\partial}{\partial t} \Phi_{ijk}(\mathbf{k}, \mathbf{k}') = \Omega_3 \left\{ -(k_m + k_m') \left[\delta_{ir} - \frac{(k_i + k_i')(k_r + k_r')}{(k_n + k_n')^2} \right] \right.$$

$$\times \left[\Phi_{rj}(\mathbf{k})\Phi_{mk}(\mathbf{k}') + \Phi_{rk}(\mathbf{k}')\Phi_{mj}(\mathbf{k}) \right] - \nu(k_n + k_n')^2 \Phi_{ijk}(\mathbf{k}, \mathbf{k}') \right\}$$

where

$$\Phi_{ijk}(\mathbf{k}, \mathbf{k}') = \frac{i}{(2\pi)^6} \iint R_{ijk}(\mathbf{r}, \mathbf{r}') \exp\left[-i(\mathbf{k} \cdot \mathbf{r} + \mathbf{k}' \cdot \mathbf{r}')\right] d\mathbf{r} \, d\mathbf{r}'$$

and Ω_3 is an operator such that

$$\Omega_3 A_{ijm}(\mathbf{k}, \mathbf{k}') = A_{ijm}(\mathbf{k}, \mathbf{k}') + A_{jmi}(\mathbf{k}', -\mathbf{k} - \mathbf{k}') + A_{mij}(-\mathbf{k} - \mathbf{k}', \mathbf{k})$$

Proudman and Reid (1954) specialized these equations to the isotropic case and drew some conclusions about the production of vorticity* and the distribution of energy transfer for a given set of initial conditions. Tatsumi (1957), also considering the isotropic case, compared the form of the three-point correlation function with that derived by Heisenberg (1948a), and he calculated the evolution of the energy spectrum in time for a number of initial conditions. The solutions he obtained are all nonnegative. Here we only wish to summarize the development of Proudman and Reid (1954) that led to the conclusion that Loitsiansky's integral was not invariant.

---

* See in this connection Betchov (1956). The vorticity result obtained by Proudman and Reid is inconsistent with exact inequalities derived by Betchov.

Loitsiansky's integral is given by (Batchelor, 1953)

(7-133) $$C = \frac{\overline{u^2}}{3\pi} \int_0^\infty r^4 f(r)\, dr$$

where C is related to the C_{ijlm} of Eq. 7-108 by the relation

(7-134) $$C_{ijlm} = \frac{C}{4\pi} (\delta_{ij}\, \delta_{lm} - \tfrac{1}{2} \delta_{il}\, \delta_{jm} - \tfrac{1}{2} \delta_{im}\, \delta_{jl})$$

valid for isotropic turbulence. Equation 7-133 follows from Eq. 7-134 and the fact that

(7-135) $$C_{ijlm} = \frac{1}{2} \frac{\partial^2 \Phi_{ij}(\mathbf{k})}{\partial k_l\, \partial k_m}\bigg|_{k_i=0}$$

Eq. 7-135 is based on the supposition that

$$\frac{\partial^2 \phi_{ik}(\mathbf{k})}{\partial k_l\, \partial k_m}\bigg|_{k_i=0}$$

exists. As we noted in Section 7.3.1, this is not generally true, but it is probably correct for the special case of isotropic turbulence.

We can study the variation of C when $k(r)$ may not be neglected by considering Eq. 7-85. If Eq. 7-85 is multiplied by r^4 and integrated from 0 to ∞, we find, assuming

$$r^4 \frac{\partial f}{\partial r}\bigg|_{r=\infty} = 0$$

that

(7-136) $$\frac{\partial C}{\partial t} = \text{const } r^4 k(r)\bigg|_{r=\infty}$$

Thus, if we assume $r^4 k(r)\big|_{r=\infty} = 0$, C is independent of time and Loitsiansky's integral is independent of time. This assumption had usually been made until the early 1950's.

Proudman and Reid (1954) were able to determine if $\partial C/\partial t = 0$ did indeed follow from the cumulant neglect hypothesis by examining the equation governing $T(k)$. We have

(7-137) $$T(k) \equiv 4\pi k^6 \Upsilon(k) = 4\pi k^2 k_m \int \Phi_{iim}(\mathbf{k}, \mathbf{k}')\, d\mathbf{k}'$$

(See Eq. 7-104.) The equation governing $T(k)$ is found from Eq. 7-132 in the isotropic case. Expanding this equation in powers of k, they found, neglecting viscous effects,

$$(7\text{-}138) \qquad \frac{\partial T(k)}{\partial t} = \frac{14}{15} k^4 \int_0^\infty \frac{E^2(k')}{k'^2} \, dk'$$

Since $E^2(k') > 0$, the integral must be greater than zero if there is to be any energy in the turbulent field at small wave numbers. This implies that $T(k)$ is no lower than order k^4 as $k \to 0$.

From the Fourier transform relation between $\Gamma_{ij}(k)$ and $T_{ij}(\mathbf{r})$, one can in the special case of isotropic turbulence establish that*

$$(7\text{-}139) \qquad T(k) = \text{const } k^4 [r^4 k(r)]_{r=\infty}$$

Thus Eqs. 7-138 and 7-139 are incompatible unless $r^4 k(r)|_{r=\infty} \neq 0$. From Eq. 7-136 we conclude that for the cumulant neglect hypothesis Loitsiansky's integral is not an invariant.

This result of Proudman and Reid forced a reconsideration of the entire notion that $k(r)$ decayed faster than $1/r^4$ as $r \to \infty$. The current feeling is that $r^4 k(r)|_{r=\infty} \neq 0$ and $k(r) \to 1/r^4$ as $r \to \infty$. For a discussion of this point the reader is referred to Batchelor and Proudman (1956). The slow decay of $k(r)$ also forced the reevaluation of the asymptotic properties of $R_{ij}(\mathbf{r})$ considered in Section 7.3.1. The lesson learned from this discussion is quite important, as we pointed out in Section 7.3.1. It is quite intuitive to imagine that correlation functions decay exponentially as $r \to \infty$ and that all moments of a correlation function $A(r)$ of the form

$$\int_0^\infty r^n A(r) \, dr$$

exist. From this analysis and from our discussion of the asymptotic behavior of correlation functions associated with heterogeneous media (see discussions below Eqs. 5-138 and 5-149), we see that this is often a very poor hypothesis. We also note that in the theory of partial coherence we often find correlation functions whose higher-order integral moments do not exist. See Eqs. 4-60 and 4-62.

---

* The reader must be careful to distinguish between the wave number and the function $k(r)$.

7.4. Recent Approaches

Beginning in the 1950s, a number of papers were published that depart from the formulisms we have so far presented in this chapter. We have in mind principally the work of Kraichnan and subsequent work that is related to his approach and the functional approach initiated by Hopf. We shall now discuss these works under the broad headings: (*1*) Kraichnan and related work, and (*2*) the functional approach. We shall consider the following papers: Kraichnan (1957, 1958a,b, 1959, 1961, 1964a–c, 1965a,b), Wyld (1961), Shut'ko (1965), Hopf (1952), Hopf and Titt (1953), Tatarski (1962), and Edwards (1964). To conclude the section, we shall also mention some work by Deissler (1965a) on nonhomogeneous turbulence and list some other recent papers that may be of interest to the reader. The formulation associated with all these more recent approaches is very formidable, and we shall try to stress the places in these developments in which the key assumptions are made. Only the broad outlines will be discussed but, in many cases, in enough detail so that the very dedicated reader can fill in the intermediate steps if he so desires.

7.4.1. Kraichnan and Related Work*

In this section we consider in detail the works of Kraichnan and Wyld. We also mention a paper by Shut'ko. In Kraichnan's work, we shall try as far as we are able to show the motivation for what he terms the direct-interaction approximation. In Wyld's work we shall see Kraichnan's direct-interaction equations result at a particular stage of a formal perturbation procedure. Shut'ko includes an additional term of the Wyld formulation beyond those necessary to yield the direct-interaction equations.

7.4.1.1. Kraichnan (1957, 1958a, b, 1959, 1961, 1964a–c, 1965a, b).
As the references show, Kraichnan's work has extended from the late 1950's to the present, and in this time Kraichnan has criticized and extended his original formulation. His latest work using Lagrangian

* The term related is meant here only in the sense that in all cases the direct-interaction equations are considered.

velocity fields is difficult to evaluate at this time, and we shall for the most part restrict our attention to his earlier formulations in which he uses the more conventional Eulerian fields. His most recent work is based on the ideas given in his earlier formulation, and it is important that these earlier ideas be presented before Kraichnan's later modification can be understood. His basic idea, which he has termed the direct-interaction approximation, is perhaps best presented in Kraichnan (1959).† We shall follow the development he gives there but shall also include our own comments, as well as those from other authors and those from his own later papers.

Basic Equations. In order to see the nature of Kraichnan's approximations, we write the Navier-Stokes equations in terms of the Fourier coefficients $u_i(\mathbf{k}, t)$ that are defined by the relation

$$(7\text{-}140) \qquad u_i(\mathbf{x}, t) = \sum_{\mathbf{k}} u_i(\mathbf{k}, t)e^{i\mathbf{k}\cdot\mathbf{x}}$$

For convenience Kraichnan assumes that the turbulent fluid is confined in a cubical box of side L and considers the limit $L \to \infty$. The boundary condition is periodicity of the function $u_i(\mathbf{x}, t)$. In order to simplify the notation we shall often suppress the t argument and write instead of $u_i(\mathbf{k}, t)$, $u_i(\mathbf{k})$. To indicate a different time, t', we write $u_i'(\mathbf{k})$. We note that since $u_i(\mathbf{x}, t)$ is real, we must have

$$u_i(-\mathbf{k}) = u_i^*(\mathbf{k})$$

If the form for $u_i(\mathbf{x}, t)$ given in Eq. 7-140 is substituted into the Navier-Stokes equations and the coefficients of the terms $e^{i\mathbf{x}\cdot\mathbf{k}}$ set equal to zero, we find after eliminating the pressure term

$$(7\text{-}141) \qquad \left(\frac{\partial}{\partial t} + \nu k^2\right)u_i(\mathbf{k}) = -\frac{i}{2}\beta_{ijm}(\mathbf{k}) \sum_{\mathbf{k}'+\mathbf{k}''=\mathbf{k}} u_j(\mathbf{k}')u_m(\mathbf{k}'')$$

where

$$\beta_{ijm}(\mathbf{k}) = k_m\alpha_{ij}(\mathbf{k}) + k_j\alpha_{im}(\mathbf{k})$$

$$\alpha_{ij}(\mathbf{k}) = \delta_{ij} - \frac{k_ik_j}{k^2}$$

† The reader is also referred to Kadomtsev (1965) for a somewhat different approach.

In order to eliminate the pressure term, use has been made of the divergence condition that takes the following form in $\mathbf{k}$ space

(7-142) $k_i u_i(\mathbf{k}) = 0$

The entire development will be for homogeneous turbulence in which the mean velocity is zero. For homogeneous turbulence the condition that

$$\overline{u_i(\mathbf{x}_1, t_1)u_j(\mathbf{x}_2, t_2) \cdots u_p(\mathbf{x}_n, t_n)}$$

depends only on $\mathbf{x}_2 - \mathbf{x}_1$, $\mathbf{x}_3 - \mathbf{x}_1, \ldots$, and $\mathbf{x}_n - \mathbf{x}_1$ becomes in $\mathbf{k}$ space the requirement that

$$\overline{u_i(\mathbf{k}_1, t_1)u_j(\mathbf{k}_2, t_2) \cdots u_p(\mathbf{k}_n, t_n)}$$

is nonzero only if $\mathbf{k}_1 + \mathbf{k}_2 + \cdots + \mathbf{k}_n = 0$.

In his work Kraichnan introduces an impulse response function. If at time $t = t_0$ an infinitesimal solenoidal force term $\delta\xi_j(\mathbf{k}, t)$ is introduced on the righthand side of Eq. 7-141, then the contribution that this term makes to $u_i(\mathbf{k}, t)$, denoted by $\delta u_i(\mathbf{k}, t)$, may be written formally as

(7-143) $$\delta u_i(\mathbf{k}, t) = \int_{t_0}^{t} \zeta_{ij}(\mathbf{k}; t, t') \, \delta\xi_j(\mathbf{k}, t') \, dt'$$

$\zeta_{ij}(\mathbf{k}; t, t')$ is termed the impulse response function. In general, since Eq. 7-141 is nonlinear, $\zeta_{ij}(\mathbf{k}; t, t')$ contains within it the effect of the nonlinear terms throughout the interval t_0 to t and depends upon t and t', not simply $t - t'$. $\zeta_{ij}(\mathbf{k}; t, t')$ is essentially a functional of $u_i(\mathbf{k}, t)$ and is thus different in kind from the impulse response functions usually encountered in linear systems.

We mentioned earlier that one may consider correlation functions of the form

$$\overline{u_i(\mathbf{x}_1, t)u_j(\mathbf{x}_2, t)}$$

or of the form

$$\overline{u_i(\mathbf{x}_1, t_1)u_j(\mathbf{x}_2, t_2)}$$

In our previous discussion in this chapter we have confined ourselves to the first form; but Kraichnan's equations are in terms of the more general form. In addition, the equations are written in $\mathbf{k}$ space so that actually the function

$$\overline{u_i(\mathbf{k}_1, t_1)u_j(\mathbf{k}_2, t_2)}$$

is considered.

From the condition of spatial homogeneity, we have the condition that $\mathbf{k}_1 + \mathbf{k}_2 = 0$ for a two-point moment. Thus we require equations for the moment

$$\overline{u_i(-\mathbf{k}_2, t_1)u_j(\mathbf{k}_2, t_2)}$$

Such an equation may be found in the manner described in Chapter 3 by multiplying Eq. 7-141 (written with $\mathbf{k}_2$ and t_2 as independent variables) by $u_n(-\mathbf{k}_2, t_1)$ and taking an ensemble average. Since two times are used, the function $u_n(-\mathbf{k}_2, t_1)$ may be taken inside the $\partial/\partial t_2$ differentiation. We then find, dropping the subscript 2 and replacing t_1 by t' [remember $u_n'(\mathbf{k}) \equiv u_n(\mathbf{k}, t')$],

(7-144)

$$\left(\frac{\partial}{\partial t} + \nu k^2\right)\overline{u_n'(-\mathbf{k})u_i(\mathbf{k})} = -\frac{i}{2}\beta_{ijm}(\mathbf{k})\sum_{\mathbf{k'}+\mathbf{k''}=\mathbf{k}}\overline{u_n'(-\mathbf{k})u_j(\mathbf{k'})u_m(\mathbf{k''})}$$

Just as in the spatial formulation, the equation for $\overline{u_n'(-\mathbf{k})u_i(\mathbf{k})}$ is indeterminate since it contains terms of the form

$$\overline{u_n'(-\mathbf{k})u_j(\mathbf{k'})u_m(\mathbf{k''})}$$

We shall now outline the approximation procedure Kraichnan uses to find a determinate equation for $\overline{u_n'(-\mathbf{k})u_i(\mathbf{k})}$. In his development he expresses the third-order moment in terms of $\overline{u_n'(-\mathbf{k})u_i(\mathbf{k})}$ and $\overline{\zeta_{ij}(\mathbf{k}; t, t')}$ and then finds an additional equation governing $\overline{\zeta_{ij}(\mathbf{k}; t, t')}$ that contains only two-point moments.

Approximate Form for Third-Order Moment. Consider the third-order moment

(7-145) $S_{njm}(-\mathbf{k}, t'; \mathbf{v}, t; \mathbf{w}, t) \equiv \overline{u_n^{*'}(\mathbf{k})u_j(\mathbf{v})u_m(\mathbf{w})}$ $(\mathbf{k} = \mathbf{v} + \mathbf{w})$

The contribution to S_{njm} from small perturbations in the functions $u_i(\mathbf{k})$, denoted by $\delta u_i(\mathbf{k})$, is given to first order by the expression

(7-146) $\delta S_{njm}(-\mathbf{k}, t'; \mathbf{v}, t; \mathbf{w}, t) = \overline{\delta u_n^{*'}(\mathbf{k})u_j(\mathbf{v})u_m(\mathbf{w})}$
$$+ \overline{u_n^{*'}(\mathbf{k})\delta u_j(\mathbf{v})u_m(\mathbf{w})} + \overline{u_n^{*'}(\mathbf{k})u_j(\mathbf{v})\delta u_m(\mathbf{w})}$$

In order to give a meaning to the $\delta u_i(\mathbf{k})$, we must specify the state we are perturbing about.

We note that in the limit $L \to \infty$, each nonlinear term of the form

$$\frac{i}{2}\beta_{ijm}(\mathbf{k})u_j(\mathbf{k}')u_m(\mathbf{k}'') \qquad (\mathbf{k}' + \mathbf{k}'' = \mathbf{k})$$

may be viewed as an infinitesimal perturbation in Eq. 7-141. The perturbation in $u_n{}^{*\prime}(\mathbf{k})$ *resulting from the term* $-(i/2)\beta_{ijm}(\mathbf{k})u_j{}^*(\mathbf{k}')u_m{}^*(\mathbf{k}'')$ *alone,* denoted by $\delta u_n{}^{*\prime}(\mathbf{k}/\mathbf{k}', \mathbf{k}'')$, may be written

(7-147)

$$\delta u_n{}^{*\prime}(\mathbf{k}/\mathbf{k}', \mathbf{k}'') = \int_{t_0}^{t} \zeta_{ni}{}^*(\mathbf{k}; t', t'') \left[-\frac{i}{2}\beta_{ijm}(\mathbf{k})u_j{}^{*\prime\prime}(\mathbf{k}')u_m{}^{*\prime\prime}(\mathbf{k}'') \right] dt''$$

As Kraichnan stresses and as becomes clear from the definition of $\zeta_{ni}(\mathbf{k}; t', t'')$, $\delta u_n{}^{*\prime}(\mathbf{k}/\mathbf{k}', \mathbf{k}'')$ is not an ordinary perturbation term. The response function, $\zeta_{ni}(\mathbf{k}; t', t'')$, is an implicit functional of all the $u_i(\mathbf{s})$ and thus $\delta u_n{}^{*\prime}(\mathbf{k}/\mathbf{k}', \mathbf{k}'')$ is the change in $u_n{}^{*\prime}(\mathbf{k})$ assuming *all the nonlinear terms* plus the term $-(i/2)\beta_{ijm}(\mathbf{k})u_j{}^{*\prime}(\mathbf{k}')u_m{}^{*\prime}(\mathbf{k}'')$ are acting during the time interval $t_0 - t$. Since

(7-148) $\qquad \left(\dfrac{\partial}{\partial t} + \nu k^2\right)u_i{}^*(\mathbf{k}) = \dfrac{i}{2}\beta_{ijm}(\mathbf{k}) \sum_{\mathbf{k}'+\mathbf{k}''=\mathbf{k}} u_j{}^*(\mathbf{k}')u_m{}^*(\mathbf{k}'')$

the addition of the term

$$-\frac{i}{2}\beta_{ijm}(\mathbf{k})u_j{}^*(\mathbf{k}')u_m{}^*(\mathbf{k}'') \qquad (\mathbf{k}' + \mathbf{k}'' = \mathbf{k})$$

yields an equation with this term absent. The difference in the solution of Eq. 7-148 with and without the above term is $\delta u_i{}^{*\prime}(\mathbf{k}/\mathbf{k}', \mathbf{k}'')$.

Using the expression given in Eq. 7-147, we find that the effect of the entire term

$$\frac{i}{2}\beta_{ijm}(\mathbf{k}) \sum_{\mathbf{k}'+\mathbf{k}''=\mathbf{k}} u_j{}^*(\mathbf{k}')u_m{}^*(\mathbf{k}'')$$

on $u_i(\mathbf{k})$ is given by

(7-149) $\qquad \Delta u_i{}^*(\mathbf{k}) = \sum_{\mathbf{k}'+\mathbf{k}''=\mathbf{k}} \delta u_i{}^{*\prime}(\mathbf{k}/\mathbf{k}', \mathbf{k}'')$

In other words, $u_i^*(\mathbf{k}) + \Delta u_i^*(\mathbf{k})$ is the solution of Eq. 7-148 if no nonlinear terms were present. Similarly, we have

(7-150) $-S_{njm}(-\mathbf{k}, t'; \mathbf{v}, t; \mathbf{w}, t) = \overline{\Delta u_n^{*\prime}(\mathbf{k})u_j(\mathbf{v})u_m(\mathbf{w})}$

$$+ \overline{u_n^{*\prime}(\mathbf{k})\Delta u_j(\mathbf{v})u_m(\mathbf{w})} + \overline{u_n^{*\prime}(\mathbf{k})u_j(\mathbf{v})\Delta u_m(\mathbf{w})}$$

At this point Kraichnan makes a very important assumption. He assumes that to a good approximation $\Delta u_n^{*\prime}(\mathbf{k})$ [and in a like manner $\Delta u_j(\mathbf{v})$ and $\Delta u_m(\mathbf{w})$] may, in Eq. 7-150, be approximated by the following form

(7-151) $\Delta u_n^{*\prime}(\mathbf{k}) = \delta u_n^{*\prime}(\mathbf{k}/\mathbf{v}, \mathbf{w}) + \delta u_n^{*\prime}(\mathbf{k}/\mathbf{w}, \mathbf{v})$

That is, for purposes of calculating S_{njm}, only terms in $\delta u_n^{*\prime}(\mathbf{k}/\mathbf{k}', \mathbf{k}'')$ need be included that satisfy the conditions

$$\mathbf{k}' = \mathbf{v} \quad \text{and} \quad \mathbf{k}'' = \mathbf{w}; \quad \mathbf{k} = \mathbf{v} + \mathbf{w}$$

or

$$\mathbf{k}' = \mathbf{w} \quad \text{and} \quad \mathbf{k}'' = \mathbf{v}; \quad \mathbf{k} = \mathbf{v} + \mathbf{w}$$

(The conditions for $\Delta u_j(\mathbf{v})$ and $\Delta u_m(\mathbf{w})$ are similar in form but have changes in sign.) Kraichnan calls these the direct-interaction terms. Noting that $\beta_{ijm} = \beta_{imj}$, we thus have in this approximation

(7-152) $-S_{njm}(-\mathbf{k}, t'; \mathbf{v}, \mathbf{w}, t)$

$$= -i\beta_{irs}(\mathbf{k}) \int_{t_0}^{t} \overline{[\zeta_{ni}^*(\mathbf{k}; t', t'')u_r^{*\prime\prime}(\mathbf{v})u_s^{*\prime\prime}(\mathbf{w})u_j(\mathbf{v})u_m(\mathbf{w})]} \, dt''$$

$$+ i\beta_{irs}(\mathbf{v}) \int_{t_0}^{t} \overline{[\zeta_{ji}(\mathbf{v}; t, t'')u_r''(\mathbf{k})u_s^{*\prime\prime}(\mathbf{w})u_n^{*\prime}(\mathbf{k})u_m(\mathbf{w})]} \, dt''$$

$$+ i\beta_{isr}(\mathbf{w}) \int_{t_0}^{t} \overline{[\zeta_{mi}(\mathbf{w}; t, t'')u_s''(\mathbf{k})u_r^{*\prime\prime}(\mathbf{v})u_n^{*\prime}(\mathbf{k})u_j(\mathbf{v})]} \, dt''$$

Kraichnan feels that the nonlinear coupling between modes is accomplished principally by direct interaction, and, as a first approximation, only this mechanism need be considered. Higher order approximations could presumably be developed to take into account additional coupling. (See Kraichnan, 1961 for a procedure that may allow this to be accomplished.) It may be thought that since $S_{njm}(-\mathbf{k}, t'; \mathbf{v}, t; \mathbf{w}, t)$ results in the limit from two terms that become infinitesimal, the contribution to Eq. 7-144 would be infinitesimal. This need not be so, however, since the sum

$$\sum_{\mathbf{k'}+\mathbf{k''}=\mathbf{k}} S_{njm}(-\mathbf{k}, t'; \mathbf{k'}, t; \mathbf{k''}, t)$$

appears in this equation rather than a single term. This sum may be finite. A similar circumstance occurs if a conventional perturbation treatment is undertaken about a state in which the nonlinear terms are neglected, and in the unperturbed state the $u_i(\mathbf{k})$ are taken to be statistically independent.

Further Simplifications. It is very difficult to tell a priori if Kraichnan has made a good approximation or not. In order to preserve continuity, we shall proceed with Kraichnan's development and discuss, as much as we are able, the reasonableness of his assumption at the conclusion of this section. With the direct-interaction assumption Eq. 7-144 becomes

(7-153)

$$\left(\frac{\partial}{\partial t} + \nu k^2\right)\overline{u_n'(-\mathbf{k})u_i(\mathbf{k})} = -\frac{i}{2}\beta_{ijm}(\mathbf{k})\sum_{\mathbf{k'}+\mathbf{k''}=\mathbf{k}} S_{njm}(-\mathbf{k}, t'; \mathbf{k'}, t; \mathbf{k''}, t)$$

where $S_{njm}(-\mathbf{k}, t'; \mathbf{k'}, t; \mathbf{k''}, t)$ is given by Eq. 7-152.

Equation 7-153 is still indeterminate as a result of the presence of terms like

$$\overline{\zeta_{ni}{}^*(\mathbf{k}; t', t'')u_r{}^{*''}(\mathbf{v})u_j(\mathbf{v})u_s{}^{*''}(\mathbf{w})u_m(\mathbf{w})}$$

in S_{njm}. To arrive at a satisfactory set of equations, Kraichnan expresses terms like this one in terms of the second-order moment $\overline{u_i'(-\mathbf{k})u_j(\mathbf{k})}$ and the average response function $\overline{\zeta_{ni}(\mathbf{k}; t', t'')}$. He then determines an equation for $\overline{\zeta_{ni}(\mathbf{k}; t', t'')}$.

To simplify the above term, Kraichnan notes that as a result of spatial homogeneity†

(7-154) $\overline{\zeta_{ni}{}^*(\mathbf{k}; t', t'')u_r{}^{*''}(\mathbf{v})u_j(\mathbf{v})u_s{}^{*''}(\mathbf{w})u_m(\mathbf{w})}$

$$= [\overline{\zeta_{ni}{}^*(\mathbf{k}; t', t'')}][\overline{u_r{}^{*''}(\mathbf{v})u_j(\mathbf{v})}][\overline{u_s{}^{*''}(\mathbf{w})u_m(\mathbf{w})}]$$

† This factorization would not follow for the general term

$$\overline{\zeta_{ni}{}''(\mathbf{k}; t', t'')u_r{}^{*''}(\mathbf{v})u_j(\mathbf{v'})u_s{}^{*''}(\mathbf{w})u_m(\mathbf{w'})}$$

where $\mathbf{k} + \mathbf{v} - \mathbf{v'} - \mathbf{w'} - \mathbf{w} = 0$. However, it is correct in the special case where in addition $\mathbf{v'} = \mathbf{v}$ and $\mathbf{w'} = \mathbf{w}$. See Proudman (1962).

The other terms in $S_{njm}(-\mathbf{k}, t'; \mathbf{k}', t; \mathbf{k}'', t)$ are similarly treated. It then remains only to find an equation for $\overline{\zeta_{ni}(\mathbf{k}; t', t'')}$.

Derivation of Equation Governing the Impulse Response. The equation for $\zeta_{ni}(\mathbf{k}; t', t'')$ is derived by first perturbing and then ensemble averaging Eq. 7-141. We find

$$(7\text{-}155) \quad \left(\frac{\partial}{\partial t} + vk^2\right) \overline{\delta u_i(\mathbf{k})} = -i\beta_{ijm}(\mathbf{k}) \sum_{\mathbf{k}'+\mathbf{k}''=\mathbf{k}} \overline{u_j(\mathbf{k}') \, \delta u_m(\mathbf{k}'')}$$

In order to simplify the right-hand side of Eq. 7-155, we proceed as we have previously. We again consider only the direct interaction between the modes $\mathbf{k}$, $\mathbf{k}'$, and $\mathbf{k}''$. The contribution to $\delta u_m(\mathbf{k}'')$ from the nonlinear terms is, in the direct-interaction approximation

$$(7\text{-}156) \quad \delta u_m(\mathbf{k}'') = -i\beta_{nrs}(\mathbf{k}'') \int_{t_0}^{t} \zeta_{mn}(\mathbf{k}''; t, t'')$$
$$\cdot \left[u_r^{*\prime\prime}(\mathbf{k}') \, \delta u_s^{\prime\prime}(\mathbf{k}) + u_s^{*\prime\prime}(\mathbf{k}) \, \delta u_r^{\prime\prime}(\mathbf{k}') \right] dt''$$

Kraichnan next assumes that since $\delta u_i(\mathbf{k})$ represents the original perturbation, $\delta u_i(\mathbf{k}')$ is negligible in comparison to $\delta u_m(\mathbf{k})$. Thus

$$(7\text{-}157) \quad \delta u_m(\mathbf{k}'') = -i\beta_{nrs}(\mathbf{k}'') \int_{t_0}^{t} \zeta_{mn}(\mathbf{k}''; t, t'') u_r^{*\prime\prime}(\mathbf{k}') \, \delta u_s^{\prime\prime}(\mathbf{k}) \, dt''$$

and

$$(7\text{-}158) \quad \left(\frac{\partial}{\partial t} + vk^2\right) \overline{\delta u_i(\mathbf{k})} = -i\beta_{ijm}(\mathbf{k})$$
$$\times \left[-i \sum_{\mathbf{k}'+\mathbf{k}''=\mathbf{k}} \beta_{nrs}(\mathbf{k}'') \int_{t_0}^{t} \overline{\zeta_{mn}(\mathbf{k}''; t, t'') u_j(\mathbf{k}') u_r^{*\prime\prime}(\mathbf{k}') \, \delta u_s^{\prime\prime}(\mathbf{k})} \, dt'' \right]$$

Lastly, factoring the averaged term yields

$$(7\text{-}159) \quad \left(\frac{\partial}{\partial t} + vk^2\right) \overline{\delta u_i(\mathbf{k})} = -\beta_{ijm}(\mathbf{k}) \sum_{\mathbf{k}'+\mathbf{k}''=\mathbf{k}} \beta_{nrs}(\mathbf{k}'')$$
$$\times \int_{t}^{t} [\overline{\zeta_{mn}(\mathbf{k}''; t, t'')}][\overline{u_j(\mathbf{k}') u_r^{*\prime\prime}(\mathbf{k}')}][\overline{\delta u_s^{\prime\prime}(\mathbf{k})}] \, dt''$$

In order to eliminate the functions $\overline{\delta u_i(\mathbf{k})}$ from Eq. 7-159, we consider the definition of $\zeta_{nj}(\mathbf{k}; t, t'')$ given in Eq. 7-143 and let $\delta \xi_j(\mathbf{k}, t') = \alpha_j \delta(t' - t_1)$, where α_j is an arbitrary infinitesimal parameter. With this identification we have

(7-160) $\overline{\delta u_i(\mathbf{k}, t)} = \overline{\zeta_{ij}(\mathbf{k}; t, t_1)}\alpha_j$

Substituting Eq. 7-160 into Eq. 7-159 then yields, finally

(7-161) $\left(\dfrac{\partial}{\partial t} + \nu k^2 \right)\overline{\zeta_{iu}(\mathbf{k}; t, t_1)}$

$$= -\beta_{ijm}(\mathbf{k}) \sum_{\mathbf{k'+k''=k}} \beta_{nrs}(\mathbf{k''}) \int_{t_0}^{t} [\overline{\zeta_{mn}(\mathbf{k''}; t, t'')}][\overline{u_j(\mathbf{k'})u_r^{*''}(\mathbf{k'})}]$$

$$\times [\overline{\zeta_{su}(\mathbf{k}; t'', t_1)}] \, dt''$$

Summary and Isotropic Form of Equations. Equation 7-153 (subject to 7-146, 7-149, 7-150, 7-151, and 7-154) and Eq. 7-161 constitute two integro-differential equations for the determination of $\overline{u_i^*(\mathbf{k})u_j'(\mathbf{k})}$ and $\overline{\zeta_{ij}(\mathbf{k}; t, t'')}$. In the limit $L \to \infty$, the summation over $\mathbf{k'} + \mathbf{k''} + \mathbf{k}$ is replaced by an integration. These equations simplify considerably for isotropic turbulence, and it is the isotropic set that has been given the most attention by Kraichnan. We now list the isotropic equations without derivation as they are given in Kraichnan (1964a). Kraichnan changes his notation slightly in this paper, but we shall use the notation given in the foregoing if a definition has already been introduced. We shall require the following new definitions:

(7-162) $\tfrac{1}{2}\alpha_{ij}(\mathbf{k})U(k; t, t') = \lim_{L \to \infty} \left(\dfrac{L}{2\pi} \right)^3 \overline{u_i(\mathbf{k}, t)u_j^*(\mathbf{k}, t')}$

(Here $k = |\mathbf{k}|$. See Eq. 7-141 for the definition of $\alpha_{ij}(\mathbf{k})$.) We note that $U(k; t, t')$ is real and satisfies the symmetry condition $U(k; t, t') = U(k; t', t)$. From the definition of $u'(\mathbf{k}, t)$ we find (this is a form of the Wiener-Khinchine theorem)

(7-163) $\overline{u_i(\mathbf{x}, t)u_j(\mathbf{x'}, t)} = \dfrac{1}{2} \int \alpha_{ij}(\mathbf{k})U(k; t, t')e^{i\mathbf{k}\cdot(\mathbf{x}-\mathbf{x'})} \, d\mathbf{k}$

The energy spectrum $E(k, t)$ is defined as

(7-164) $$E(k, t) = 2\pi k^2 U(k; t, t)$$

Then $E(t)$, where

(7-165) $$E(t) = \int_0^\infty E(k, t) \, dk$$

is the average kinetic energy/unit mass.

The normalized form of $U(k; t, t')$, denoted by $R(k; t, t')$, is defined as

(7-166) $$R(k; t, t') = \frac{(Uk; t, t')}{[U(k; t, t)U(k; t', t')]^{1/2}}$$

from which it follows that $R(k; t, t) = 1$.

The average response tensor $\overline{\zeta_{ij}}(\mathbf{k}; t, t')$ may now be represented by a single scalar function, $G(k; t, t')$, where

(7-167) $$\overline{\zeta_{ij}(\mathbf{k}; t, t')} = \alpha_{ij}(\mathbf{k})G(k; t, t')$$

Instead of determining equations for $\overline{u_i^*(\mathbf{k}, t)u_j(\mathbf{k}, t')}$ and $\overline{\zeta_{ij}}(\mathbf{k}; t, t')$, we now require equations for the scalar functions $U(k; t, t')$ and $G(k; t, t')$. These equations are

(7-168) $$\left(\frac{\partial}{\partial t} + \nu k^2\right)U(k; t, t') = S(k; t, t')$$

where in the limit $L \to \infty$

$$S(k; t, t') = \pi k \iint_\Delta pq \, dp \, dq$$

$$\times \left[\int_0^{t'} a(k, p, q)G(k; t', s)U(p; t, s)U(q; t, s) \, ds \right.$$

$$\left. - \int_0^t b(k, p, q)U(k; t', s)G(p; t, s)U(q; t, s) \, ds \right]$$

In $S(k; t, t')$ the integration over p and q is subject to the constraint

$\mathbf{p} + \mathbf{q} = \mathbf{k}$. $a(k, p, q)$ and $b(k, p, q)$ are given by the expressions

$$a(k, p, q) = \tfrac{1}{2}(1 - xyz - 2y^2z^2)$$

$$b(k, p, q) = \frac{p}{k}(xy + z^3)$$

where x, y, and z are the cosines of the angles opposite $\mathbf{k}$, $\mathbf{p}$, and $\mathbf{q}$, respectively, in the triangle formed by $\mathbf{k}$, $\mathbf{p}$, and $\mathbf{q}$.

The equation governing $G(k; t, t')$ is

(7-169)
$$\left(\frac{\partial}{\partial t} + \nu k^2\right) G(k; t, t') = H(k; t, t')$$

where

$H(k; t, t')$

$$= -\pi k \iint_{\Delta} pq \, dp \, dq \, b(k, p, q) \int_{t'}^{t} G(k; s, t') G(p; t, s) U(q; t, s) \, ds$$

These equations may be solved subject to the initial condition $U(k; 0, 0)$, for $t > 0$ and $t' > 0$.

Restatement of Key Assumption and Some Comments. At this point it is useful to restate the key assumption under which Eqs. 7-168 and 7-169 were derived. It is assumed that only direct interaction terms contribute importantly to the third-order correlation function, S_{njm}, and the second-order function, $\overline{u_j(\mathbf{k}')\delta u_m(\mathbf{k}'')}$. Kraichnan (1964b) describes his approximation procedure in the following manner:

"The basic idea may be most simply described as follows for the case of homogeneous turbulence: The energy transfer among the Fourier modes is associated with triple correlations among triads of interacting modes. In the direct interaction approximation, it is assumed that the correlation of any given triad of Fourier modes is induced by the continuous direct dynamical interaction of the triad, acting against a relaxation process which destroys the correlation. The relaxation process involves two contributions: viscous decay and dynamical relaxation due to interaction of each of the three modes with all the rest of the Fourier modes. A consistent analytical expression of these ideas yields formulas for triple correlations in terms of two functions, the velocity covariance and the average response function of a Fourier amplitude to infinitesimal disturbances. The approximation then yields closed integrodifferential equations which determine these functions."

As we mentioned above, it is very difficult to tell a priori whether or not the foregoing assumption is reasonable. Kraichnan (1959) attempts to justify his assumption, but this writer did not find all his arguments convincing. He first points out that he expects his approximation to be applicable to flows in which any statistical dependencies that arise between two modes, $\mathbf{k}$ and $\mathbf{k}'$, should occur because of the nonlinear terms in the Navier-Stokes equations and not because of any special initial conditions or external forces. He terms this the "maximal randomness condition." This restriction will certainly rule out some turbulent flows, but it seems to be a reasonable hypothesis for studying decaying homogeneous turbulence as it is usually experimentally treated in flow through grids.

Kraichnan then discusses a "weak dependence principal." It follows from Eq. 7-141 that in the limit $L \to \infty$, the magnitude of each term $u_j(\mathbf{k}')u_m(\mathbf{k}'')$, $(\mathbf{k}' + \mathbf{k}'' = \mathbf{k})$, will become infinitesimal. Since a mode $\mathbf{p} \neq \mathbf{k}$ only occurs twice on the right-hand side of Eq. 7-141 (once as $\mathbf{k}'$ and once as $\mathbf{k}''$), the direct coupling between $\mathbf{p}$ and $\mathbf{k}$ may be termed weak in the limit $L \to \infty$. Now from the maximum randomness hypothesis, all correlation between $\mathbf{p}$ and $\mathbf{k}$ modes should come from the nonlinear interaction. By the weak dependence principle the contribution of the $\mathbf{p}$ mode to the $\mathbf{k}$ mode is infinitesimal, and Kraichnan argues that it is reasonable to assume as a first approximation that the $\mathbf{p}$ mode contributes to the $\mathbf{k}$ mode only directly and not by first coupling to another mode which in turn then contributes to the $\mathbf{k}$ mode.

To this writer it seems unconvincing to expect any physical consequences to accrue from the mathematical fact that $u_j(\mathbf{k}')u_m(\mathbf{k}'')$ becomes infinitesimal as $L \to \infty$. The contribution to $\delta u_i(\mathbf{k})$ resulting from the nondirect interaction gives a quite finite result in general and the fact that $u_j(\mathbf{k}')u_m(\mathbf{k}'') \to 0$ as $L \to \infty$ is of no physical importance. Furthermore, in Wyld's work (Wyld, 1961), which we shall outline shortly, it is shown that other terms of apparently the same order as the direct-interaction contribution appear in the perturbation procedure he uses.

Proudman (1962) makes this point using a Fourier-Stieljes integral formalism. He further points out that in a sense the direct-interaction approximation is somewhat like the cumulant-neglect hypothesis. In the cumulant-neglect approach the fourth-order moment

$$\overline{u_i(\mathbf{k}_1)u_j(\mathbf{k}_2)u_l(\mathbf{k}_3)u_m(\mathbf{k}_4)}$$

(where $\mathbf{k}_1 + \mathbf{k}_2 + \mathbf{k}_3 + \mathbf{k}_4 = 0$, by homogeneity) is replaced by three terms like

$$\overline{u_i(\mathbf{k}_1)u_j(-\mathbf{k}_1)u_l(\mathbf{k}_3)u_m(-\mathbf{k}_3)}$$

thus in effect distinguishing between fourth-order terms where $\mathbf{k}_1 + \mathbf{k}_2 = 0$ and $\mathbf{k}_3 + \mathbf{k}_4 = 0$ and terms where only $\mathbf{k}_1 + \mathbf{k}_2 + \mathbf{k}_3 + \mathbf{k}_4 = 0$. Calling terms where both $\mathbf{k}_1 + \mathbf{k}_2 = 0$ and $\mathbf{k}_3 + \mathbf{k}_4 = 0$ direct-interaction terms, we see a similarity with Kraichnan's approach.

The difference between the cumulant-neglect approach and Kraichnan's is the manner in which the direct-interaction terms are used in the formulation. In the cumulant-neglect analysis all fourth-order terms for which the two relations $\mathbf{k}_1 + \mathbf{k}_2 = 0$ and $\mathbf{k}_3 + \mathbf{k}_4 = 0$ are not satisfied are neglected. In the Kraichnan approach they are partially included. Proudman feels this distinction is probably of no real consequence, but Kraichnan (1962b) differs with this point of view. Kraichnan points out that the character of the energy-transfer rate differs in the two theories and that in the cumulant-neglect theory this leads to the unphysical result of power spectrums that are partially negative. This does not occur in the Kraichnan theory.

To this writer the direct-interaction term does have some intuitive appeal. If Eq. 7-149 is substituted into the first term in Eq. 7-150, we have for this term

$$\sum_{\mathbf{k}+\mathbf{k}'=\mathbf{k}} \overline{\delta u_n{}^{*\prime}(\mathbf{k}/\mathbf{k}', \mathbf{k}'')u_j(\mathbf{v})u_m(\mathbf{w})}$$

$\delta u_n{}^{*\prime}(\mathbf{k}/\mathbf{k}', \mathbf{k}'')$ is the change in $u_n{}^{*\prime}(\mathbf{k})$ resulting from the nonlinear interaction of the modes $\mathbf{k}'$ and $\mathbf{k}''$. It thus would appear as a first guess that this change was correlated most strongly to these modes rather than any other modes. Hence, as a first approximation, we might consider only the terms $\delta u_n{}^{*\prime}(\mathbf{k}/\mathbf{v}, \mathbf{w})$ and $\delta u_n{}^{*\prime}(\mathbf{k}/\mathbf{w}, \mathbf{v})$. At this stage of our understanding we probably cannot say much more about the a priori reasonableness of the Kraichnan theory. A number of consequences of the theory have, however, been adduced, and we shall now turn to some of these results.

Consequences of the Theory. Kraichnan (1961) shows the success of this theory when applied to an harmonic oscillator problem. This is given in a very interesting paper on the dynamics of nonlinear stochastic systems. In this paper he shows the degree of success of various perturbation techniques one may use to treat the problem of an harmonic oscillator with a stochastic frequency parameter. An exact solution to this problem is known, and he demonstrates the shortcomings of the standard perturbation procedure and the cumulant-neglect hypothesis in treating this problem. He shows further that a direct-interaction-type hypothesis yields much more reasonable results. He also is able to show from the type of analysis used in this paper that the direct-interaction hypothesis when applied to the turbulence problem yields physically realizable results. In the direct-interaction approximation the power spectrum will always be positive in contrast to the results that have been obtained for the cumulant neglect hypothesis.

Turning to the consequences of the theory, we note that the result to which Kraichnan pays the most attention, and in fact motivated a later revision of the theory, is the form of the energy spectrum in the inertial range. Analysis given by Kraichnan (1959) shows that the Kolmogorov result given in Eq. 7-116 is replaced by

(7-170) $E(k) = B'(v_0)^{1/2}\bar{\epsilon}^{1/2}k^{-3/2}$

where B' is a constant and

$$v_0 = \frac{2}{3} \int_0^\infty E(k')\,dk'$$

As Kraichnan (1964b) points out, the Kolmogorov result is better supported by experiment. Equation 7-170 in itself is certainly not so far from experimental results as to dismiss the theory. Kraichnan, however, has spent considerable effort probing for the reasons for the discrepancy between his and Kolmogorov's result and has finally modified his equations in order to obtain Kolmogorov's result. The basic reason that the direct-interaction equations will not yield the Kolmogorov result is that the two-point two-time Eulerian correlation function does not distinguish between two effects: (*1*) internal distortion of the small eddies, and (*2*) transport of these small eddies by the larger eddies. The Kolmogorov hypothesis postulates that the small eddies are locally stationary, and hence if it is a correct assumption, any change in the two-point two-time moment $U(k; t, t')$ with t and t' for large wave numbers should result from only the latter effect.

In order to remove convection effects, Kraichnan points out that an appropriate procedure to follow in this case would be to replace Eq. 7-141 by the following equation:

$$(7\text{-}171) \quad \left(\frac{\partial}{\partial t} + \nu k^2\right)u_i(\mathbf{k}) = -i \sum_{k'}^{\infty} [\mathbf{u}(\mathbf{k} - \mathbf{k'}) \cdot \mathbf{k'}]u_i(\mathbf{k'}) - ik_i\pi(\mathbf{k})$$

$[\pi(\mathbf{k})$ is the Fourier coefficient for $p(\mathbf{x})$.] Here the summation over $\mathbf{k'}$ is such that all terms for which $|\mathbf{k} - \mathbf{k'}| < k/\alpha$ or $|\mathbf{k} - \mathbf{k'}| < k'/\alpha$, $\alpha \geqslant 2$, are omitted. To see the effect of this omission, we note that the convection operator $\mathbf{u} \cdot \nabla$ is transformed into the sum

$$\sum_{k'}^{\infty} \mathbf{u}(\mathbf{k} - \mathbf{k'}) \cdot \mathbf{k'}$$

Hence, using a summation $\sum_{k'}^{\infty}$ where $\alpha \geqslant 2$ means that when $|\mathbf{k} - \mathbf{k'}| < k/\alpha$ or k'/α, we have omitted convection of the small eddies by the large eddies. Using the direct interaction approximation in Eq. 7-171, Kraichnan is able to obtain the Kolmogorov result. The details are given in Kraichnan (1964b).

In addition to the inertial range prediction, Kraichnan is able to determine information about the autocorrelation function and response functions for stationary turbulence. Perhaps of more interest, however, are some numerical calculations that he made (Kraichnan, 1964a) for decaying isotropic homogeneous turbulence. He obtained numerical solutions for Eqs. 7-168 and 7-169 for a number of initial spectra. In order to solve these equations, it is necessary to know $U(k; 0, 0)$, or equivalently $E(k, t)$, since $E(k, 0) = 2\pi k^2 U(k; 0, 0)$. The spectra used as initial conditions were

$(A) \qquad E(k, 0) = \dfrac{3}{4}\dfrac{v_0^2}{\Delta k} \qquad k_{\max} - \Delta k \leqslant k \leqslant k_{\max} + \Delta k$

$\qquad\qquad\qquad = 0 \qquad\qquad \text{elsewhere}$

$(B) \qquad E(k, 0) = 16\left(\dfrac{2}{\pi}\right)^{1/2} v_0^2 k_{\max}^{-5} k^4 \exp\left[-2\left(\dfrac{k}{k_{\max}}\right)^2\right]$

$(C) \qquad E(k, 0) = \tfrac{3}{2} v_0^2 k_{\max}^{-2} k \exp\left[-\dfrac{1}{2}\left(\dfrac{k}{k_{\max}}\right)^2\right]$

$(D) \qquad E(k, 0) = \tfrac{3}{2} v_0^2 k_{\max}^{-2} k \exp\left[\dfrac{k}{k_{\max}}\right]$

These spectra were not chosen from experimental data. Spectrum A was presumably chosen to see what happens to the energy if it was initially clustered in a narrow wave-number band. Spectrum B was used previously by Ogura (1963) in his cumulant-neglect study cited in Section 7.3.5. Spectrum C is self-preserving under viscous decay (see Section 7.3.1). Spectrum D was chosen from the results of attempts to find an initial spectrum that would quickly become self-preserving under both viscous and inertial effects. By self-preserving we mean that the spectrum shape is the same for all times if $E(k, t)$ is normalized using a velocity and length that are functions of time, and k is normalized using a length that is a function of time. For velocity and length parameters Kraichnan chooses $u(t)$ the instantaneous rms velocity and $\lambda(t)$ the instantaneous microscale of turbulence. Here

$$\lambda(t) = \left[\frac{5E(t)}{\displaystyle\int_0^\infty k^2 E(k, t)\, dk} \right]^{1/2}$$

For all initial spectra there was transfer of energy to the high wave numbers, but in some cases there was a small transfer to lower wave numbers. When $[E(k, t)]/\{[u(t)]^2\lambda(t)\}$, the normalized spectrum, was plotted vs. $k\lambda(t)$, all the initial spectra seemed to evolve quickly to states that were self-preserving at high wave numbers. For the least peaked spectrum D, the self-preserving property was evident over the entire wave number span.

Since none of the initial spectra were chosen from experimental data, it is difficult to compare these results to experiment. If, however, the initial conditions are overcome by the dynamics of the decay after some time t_0, then the numerically integrated results should correspond to some stage in the decay of turbulence behind a grid. In particular, we may compare this result to experiment by choosing corresponding Reynolds numbers. Kraichnan compared Reynolds numbers defined by the microscale; i.e., he used

(7-172) $$\mathrm{Re} = \frac{u(t)\lambda(t)}{\nu}$$

For spectrum A, the initial condition was so peaked that it influenced the spectrum for very long times. Spectrum D, on the other hand, quickly assumed a self-preserving form (indeed it was chosen for this property), and Kraichnan compared this form to experiments of Steward and Townsend (1951) and found reasonable agreement. The reader is referred to Kraichnan (1964a) to see the curves for both the theoretical and experimental cases.

All of the numerical results are for low Reynolds numbers. As we have pointed out above, Eqs. 7-168 and 7-169 would be expected to yield incorrect results at high Reynolds numbers where an inertial range exists.

Kraichnan (1965a,b) has attempted to obtain the Kolmogorov spectrum by introducing the Lagrangian function $u_i(\mathbf{x}, t/r)$, defined as the velocity a fluid particle at position $\mathbf{x}$ at time t would have had at time r. Using this function, he has obtained a generalized set of equations in the direct-interaction approximation. From these equations he has been able to obtain the Kolmogorov spectrum. We shall not discuss this work here. Instead we shall now consider a formal perturbation procedure set up by Wyld (1961) which, upon neglecting an appropriate set of terms, may be shown to yield the direct-interaction equations for stationary turbulence.

7.4.1.2. Wyld (1961). In our review of Kraichnan's work we did not set up a consistent perturbation procedure and then derive the direct-interaction equations as a first approximation. Rather, attention was focused on the lowest order perturbation only. Kraichnan (1961) presented a more systematic approach to the derivation of these equations, but no unique procedure is given for deriving the next set in the approximation. Wyld (1961) does set up a systematic perturbation scheme, and he is able to derive Kraichnan's direct interaction equations by suitable truncation of these equations. He also derives a set of equations given by Chandrasekhar (1955, 1956), by a lower order truncation. He is not able to show in the derivation of either set of equations under what circumstances the terms neglected should be small.

Wyld treats the Navier-Stokes equations with a forcing term on the right-hand side. That is, he modifies Eq. 7-54a to read

(7-173)

$$\frac{\partial}{\partial t} u_i(\mathbf{x}, t) + u_j(\mathbf{x}, t) \frac{\partial}{\partial x_j} u_i(\mathbf{x}, t) = \nu \nabla^2 u_i(\mathbf{x}, t) - \frac{\partial p(\mathbf{x}, t)}{\partial x_i} + f_i(\mathbf{x}, t)$$

Here, $f_i(\mathbf{x}, t)$ is taken to be a divergenceless random forcing function which prevents the turbulence from decaying and allows us to consider the very special case of turbulence that is homogeneous in space and stationary in time. (Although we did not consider this special case above, Kraichnan, 1959, has derived equations under this restriction.)

Wyld considers his perturbation procedure in terms of the Fourier coefficients of a space-time expansion. That is, he writes the Fourier expansions

$$u_i(\mathbf{x}, t) = \frac{1}{L^{3/2}T^{1/2}} \sum_{\mathbf{k}, \omega} u_i(\mathbf{k}, \omega)e^{i(\mathbf{k}\cdot\mathbf{x}-\omega t)}$$

$$f_i(\mathbf{x}, t) = \frac{1}{L^{3/2}T^{1/2}} \sum_{\mathbf{k}, \omega} f_i(\mathbf{k}, \omega)e^{i(\mathbf{k}\cdot\mathbf{x}-\omega t)}$$

and arrives at the equation

$$(7\text{-}174) \quad (-i\omega + \nu |\mathbf{k}|^2)u_i(\mathbf{k}, \omega) = f_i(\mathbf{k}, \omega)$$

$$-\frac{1}{2} \frac{\beta_{ijm}(\mathbf{k})}{L^{3/2}T^{1/2}} \sum_{\substack{\mathbf{k}'+\mathbf{k}''=\mathbf{k} \\ \omega'+\omega''=\omega}} u_j(\mathbf{k}', \omega)u_m(\mathbf{k}'', \omega'')$$

where, as in Eq. 7-141

$$\beta_{ijm}(\mathbf{k}) = k_m\alpha_{ij}(\mathbf{k}) + k_j\alpha_{im}(\mathbf{k})$$
$$\alpha_{ij}(\mathbf{k}) = \delta_{ij} - k_ik_j/k^2$$

(Note that the definition of the Fourier space coefficients differs from Kraichnan's by the inclusion of an $L^{-3/2}$ factor.)

For simplicity in explaining his procedure, Wyld works instead with the scalar equation

$(7\text{-}175)$

$$(-i\omega + \nu |\mathbf{k}|^2)v(\mathbf{k}, \omega) = f(\mathbf{x}, \omega) + \frac{g}{(L^3T)^{1/2}} \sum_{\substack{k_1+k_2=k \\ \omega_1+\omega_2=\omega}} v(\mathbf{k}_1, \omega_1)v(\mathbf{k}_2, \omega_2)$$

Since the algebra is so lengthy and our main purpose is to illustrate the procedure we shall also explain his method using this equation. It is important to realize that Eq. 7-175 is only for illustrative purposes. After the illustration the appropriate set of approximate equations may be written down for the full Eq. 7-174 by analogy.

For convenience Wyld uses a four vector notation $k = (\mathbf{k}, \omega)$. He also defines the propagator $S(k)$ and an unperturbed velocity by the relations

(7-176)
$$S(k) = \frac{1}{(-i\omega + \nu |\mathbf{k}|^2)}$$

and

(7-177)
$$v_0(k) = S(k)f(k)$$

In the model equation, Eq. 7-175, the mean velocity $v_0(\mathbf{x})$ is not zero, but the mean velocity $\overline{u_i(\mathbf{x}, t)}$ will be set equal to zero.

The perturbation expansion is given by expanding $v(k)$ in powers of g. We write

(7-178)
$$v(k) = v_0(k) + v_1(k) + v_2(k) + \cdots$$

where $v_n(k)$ is of order g^n. Substituting Eq. 7-178 into Eq. 7-175, we find upon comparing like powers of g

(7-179)
$$v_1(k) = 2S(k)\alpha \sum_{k_1+k_2=k} \tfrac{1}{2}v_0(k_1)v_0(k_2)$$

(7-180)
$$v_2(k) = 2S(k)\alpha \sum_{k_1+k_2=k} v_0(k_1)v_1(k_2)$$

$$= 2S(k)\alpha \sum_{k_1+k_2=k} v_0(k_1)2S(k_2)\alpha \sum_{k_3+k_4=k_2} \tfrac{1}{2}v_0(k_3)v_0(k_4)$$

(7-181)
$$v_3(k) = 2S(k)\alpha \sum_{k_1+k_2=k} [v_0(k_1)v_0(k_2) + \tfrac{1}{2}v_1(k_1)v_1(k_2)]$$

$$= 2S(k)\alpha \sum_{k_1+k_2=k} v_0(k_1)2S(k_2)\alpha \sum_{k_3+k_4=k_2} v_0(k_3)$$

$$\cdot 2S(k_4)\alpha \sum_{k_5+k_6=k_4} \tfrac{1}{2}v_0(k_5)v_0(k_6)$$

$$+ 2S(k)\alpha \sum_{k_1+k_2=k} \frac{1}{2}\left[2S(k_1)\alpha \sum_{k_3+k_4=k_1} \tfrac{1}{2}v_0(k_3)v_0(k_4)\right]$$

$$\cdot \left[2S(k_2)\alpha \sum_{k_5+k_6=k_2} \tfrac{1}{2}v_0(k_5)v_0(k_6)\right]$$

$$\cdot$$
$$\cdot$$
$$\cdot$$

where $\alpha = g/(L/T)^{1/2}$.

As we see, it is very cumbersome to write down higher order terms, and for convenience (and indeed almost out of necessity) Wyld introduces a diagram representation that has proved so useful in quantum field theory studies (see Schweber, 1961). He sets up a correspondence between the terms in the perturbation series and tree-like diagrams composed of points and straight lines. He sets the correspondence

$$\text{straight line (propagator)} \leftrightarrow S(k)$$

$$\text{point (vertex)} \qquad\qquad \leftrightarrow \alpha$$

and applies the following rules:

1. Join three elements at each vertex, the elements being either $S(k)$ or $v_0(k)$. For simplicity $v_0(k)$ is not given explicitly. Thus the diagram

$$\line\!\!\!-\!\!\!-\!\!\!-\!\!\!-\!\!\!\circ$$

indicates that $S(k)$ and 2 elements $v_0(k)$ are joined at the vertex.

2. There must be wave number conservation at each vertex where the wave number of the element on the left is equal to the sum of the wave numbers of the elements on the right. Thus in the foregoing simple diagram we should have $S(k_1)$, $v_0(k_2)$ and $v_0(k_3)$, where $k_1 = k_2 + k_3$.

3. For each vertex with one factor $v_0(k)$, the diagram is multiplied by 2. It is also multiplied by 2 for each asymmetric branching of the diagram.

From these rules we see that $v_2(k)$ in Eq. 7-180 and $v_3(k)$ in Eq. 7-181 are given by the diagrams

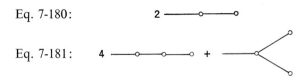

Eq. 7-180:

Eq. 7-181:

Wyld postulates that there is a one-to-one correspondence between all diagrams of this type and the perturbation expansion. He does not prove this, but concludes this from considering all diagrams through sixth order. All conclusions from subsequent diagrams that we shall display have only been critically examined by Wyld through sixth order.

In order to proceed to a statistical analysis, we must know the properties of the correlation function

$$\overline{v_0(k_1)v_0(k_2)\cdots v_0(k_n)}$$

Wyld postulates that the forcing function $f(k)$ and hence $v_0(k)$ are as random as possible and hence obey gaussian statistics. This assumption is along the lines of Kraichnan's maximum randomness principle, which we discussed in the previous section. Using this assumption, all higher moments may be expressed in terms of the second-order moment $U_0(k_1)$ where

(7-182) $$\overline{v_0(k_1)v_0(k_2)} = \delta_{k_1,-k_2}U_0(k_1)$$

All odd moments are zero, and we have for the fourth-order moment, for example, the usual gaussian form

(7-183) $$\overline{v_0(k_1)v_0(k_2)v_0(k_3)v_0(k_4)} = \delta_{k_1,-k_2}\delta_{k_3,-k_4}U_0(k_1)U_0(k_3)$$
$$+ \delta_{k_1,-k_2}\delta_{k_3,-k_4}U_0(k_1)U_0(k_2) + \delta_{k_1,-k_4}\delta_{k_2,-k_3}U_0(k_1)U_0(k_2)$$

In general, the second-order moment $U(k, k')$ defined by

(7-184) $$U(k, k') = \overline{v(k)v(k')}$$

is a function only of k as a result of spatial statistical homogeneity and time stationarity. Thus we have (letting $U(k) \equiv U(k, -k)$)

(7-185) $$U(k) = \overline{v(k)v(-k)} = \overline{v_0(k)v_0(-k)} + \overline{v_0(k)v_2(-k)}$$
$$+ \overline{v_0(k)v_4(-k)} + \cdots + \overline{v_1(k)v_1(-k)} + \overline{v_1(k)v_3(-k)} + \cdots$$
$$+ \overline{v_2(k)v_0(-k)} + \overline{v_2(k)v_2(-k)} + \overline{v_2(k)v_4(-k)} + \cdots$$

Expanding the first two terms in Eq. 7-185, we find

(7-186) $$U(k) = U_0(k) + \overline{2v_0(k)S(-k)\alpha \sum_{k_1+k_2=-k} v_0(k_1)2S(k_2)}$$
$$\cdot \alpha \sum_{k_3+k_4=k_2} \tfrac{1}{2}v_0(k_3)v_0(k_4) + \cdots$$

On using Eq. 7-183, the second term separates into three terms, and we find

(7-187) $$U(k) = U_0(k) + 2S(-k)\alpha U_0(k)S(0)\alpha\alpha\tfrac{1}{2}\sum_{k_3} U_0(k_3)$$
$$+ 2S(-k)\alpha \sum_{k_1+k_2=-k} U_0(k)U_0(k_1)\alpha S(k_2)$$
$$+ 2S(-k)\alpha \sum_{k_1+k_2=-k} U_0(k)U_0(k_1)\alpha S(k_2) + \cdots$$

In order to represent the expansion of all terms in Eq. 7-187 using diagrams, Wyld introduces a new symbol to represent the function $U_0(k)$. He sets the correspondence

$$\text{wavy line} \leftrightarrow U_0(k)$$

Each diagram is now composed of three elements: $U_0(k)$ corresponding to a wavy line; $S(k)$ corresponding to a straight line; and vertex points. The diagrams are constructed so that three lines emerge from each vertex. Any combination of three wavy lines and straight lines may emerge from a vertex point except that at least one line must be straight. There is wave number conservation at each vertex, and there is a sum over all wave numbers not fixed by this conservation. It also should be noted that in the wave number relation the sign of one side may be negative when the summation is carried over all values of the parameter. The zeroth-order diagram consists of non-vertex points and a single wavy line, i.e.,

The second-order diagrams have two vertex points, the fourth-order diagrams have four vertex points, and so on. The three second-order diagrams are

The last two terms written explicitly in Eq. 7-187 correspond to the middle diagram above.* A portion of the term $\overline{v_2(k)v_0(-k)}$ corresponds to the diagram on the right and a portion of the term $\overline{v_1(k)v_1(-k)}$ corresponds to the diagram on the left. The term

$$2S(-k)\alpha U_0(k)S(0)\alpha \tfrac{1}{2} \sum_{k_3} U_0(k_3)$$

and similar terms correspond to contributions from the mean velocity, which is taken to be nonzero in the model. Since in the complete

---

* This may be seen more easily if we write the sum of these terms as follows:

$$4S(-k)\alpha \sum_{k_1+k_2=-k} U_0(k_1)S(k_2)\alpha U_0(k)$$

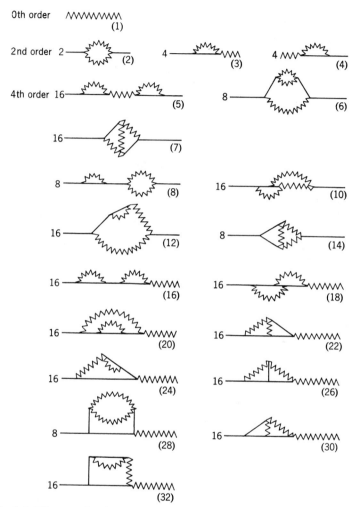

Fig. 7-6. Diagrams for the correlation function $U(k)$ to fourth order. Diagrams 9, 11, . . . , 33 are inversions of diagrams 8, 10, . . . , 32 about a vertical axis. (Reproduced from Wyld, 1961, Fig. 2.)

Navier-Stokes equations the mean velocity is zero, these terms are omitted here. Figure 7-6 is a reproduction of Wyld (1961), Fig. 2 and presents the diagrams to fourth order.

For each diagram there should be a factor of 2 for each vertex and a factor of $\frac{1}{2}$ for each closed loop made up only of wavy lines. There are some other rules for diagrams higher than the fourth-order, but we do not consider these here.

Until this point our procedure has been very straightforward. $U(k)$ could be evaluated by considering each order set of diagrams in their turn. The purpose of this work, however, is to consider approximate solutions for $U(k)$ which contain terms of all orders. The direct-interaction approximation developed by Kraichnan was such a set. It is not easy to see from the perturbation equations just which terms to choose from the higher order sets. Use of some further diagrams, however, does facilitate such a selection, and we now follow Wyld in defining functions which correspond to certain useful sets of diagrams.

Two functions are of special utility: a function $S'(k)$ called a modified propagator, and a function $\Gamma(k, k')$ called a modified vertex function. The modified propagator function corresponds to the sum of complex diagrams that, have a single straight line running through the entire diagram. The zeroth-order diagram is defined as simply $S(k)$. The second-order diagrams have two vertices and the fourth-order diagrams have four vertices. We reproduce here as Fig. 7-7, Fig. 3 of Wyld (1961) to show the nature of these diagrams. The factors $2^0 = 1$, $2^2 = 4$, $2^4 = 16$ are given by the same rules that gave these factors for the $U(k)$ diagrams.

The modified vertex operator $\Gamma(k, k')$ is defined as the sum of all diagrams which have, like the elementary vertex, three external terminals to which lines may be attached. The first-order diagram is degenerate and is the elementary vertex itself. The fifth-order diagrams have two internal elementary vertices. In Fig. 7-8 we reproduce Fig. 4 of Wyld (1961).

The functions $U(k)$, $S'(k)$ and $\Gamma(k, k')$ are connected together by a coupled set of integral equations (in the limit T, $V \to \infty$). The integral equations, however, are in the form of an infinite series, and the equations of Chandrasekhar and Kraichnan are derived by truncating these series at a very low order. We now turn to a derivation of these equations. The derivation is accomplished by inspection of the diagrams in Figs. 7-6, 7-7, and 7-8.

An equation governing $U(k)$ is obtained by reference to Fig. 7-6. The diagrams may be divided into two classes: a class which we call "A," which is the class of those diagrams which may be split in two by severing a single wavy line; and a class "B," which is the class of all

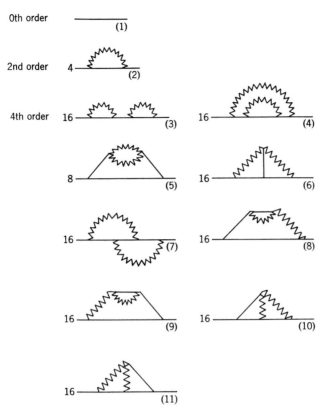

Fig. 7-7. Diagrams for the modified propagator function $S'(k)$ to fourth order. (Reproduced from Wyld (1961) Fig. 3.)

other diagrams. The diagrams in Fig. 7-6 that are in class "A" are diagrams 3, 4, 5 and 16-33. The class "A" diagrams may be readily summed. Wyld has found this sum denoted by $\sum_A$ to be

(7-188) $$\sum_A = S'(k)S^{-1}(k)U_0(k)S^{-1}(k)S'(k)$$

where

$$S^{-1}(k) = \frac{1}{S(k)}$$

In order to verify his result, we need only write

(7-189) $$S'(k) = S(k) + S_2(k) + S_4(k) + \cdots$$

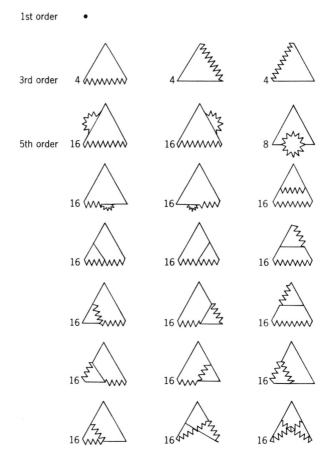

1st order

3rd order

5th order

+2 Rotations of each 5th order diagram
(through 120°, 240°)

Fig. 7-8. Diagrams for the vertex operator $\Gamma(k, k')$ to fifth order. (Reproduced from Wyld, 1961, Fig. 4.)

(where $S_j(k)$ is the sum of all even jth-order diagrams given in Fig. 7-7) and expand the above expression. The first few terms are

$$(7\text{-}190) \quad \sum_A = U_0(k) + U_0(k)S^{-1}(k)S_2(k) + S_2(k)S^{-1}(k)U_0(k) + \cdots$$

The first term corresponds to diagram 1 in Fig. 7-6. The second and third terms correspond to diagrams 3 and 4 in Fig. 7-6. In this manner we may establish a one-to-one correspondence between the terms in Eq. 7-190 and the class "A" diagrams.

Next we note that

(7-191) $$F(k) = S^{-1}(k)U_0(k)S^{-1}(k)$$
$$= |\overline{f(k)}|^2$$

and hence we have

(7-192) $$\sum_A = S'(k)F(k)S'(k)$$

The class "B" diagrams are more difficult to handle and lead to an infinite number of terms even when expressed in terms of $U(k)$, $S'(k)$ and $\Gamma(k, k')$. The summation of class "B" diagrams is accomplished by noting that most of the higher order diagrams can be constructed by taking the lower order diagrams and replacing elementary propagators by modified propagators ($S(k)$ by $S'(k)$), point vertices by modified vertices (α by $\Gamma(k, k')$) and the unperturbed correlation function by the complete correlation function ($U_0(k)$ by $U(k)$). In Fig. 7-6 all fourth-order correlation diagrams with the exception of diagram 7 are generated from diagram 2 by suitable replacements of the elementary propagators, vertices and correlation functions. Similarly, most sixth-order diagrams are obtained from diagrams 2 and 7. In each order there are some diagrams that cannot be determined from the lower-order class and these diagrams are called irreducible.

To see how this works, consider the construction of diagram 8 from diagram 2 in Fig. 7-6. We simply replace in diagram 2 the left straight line ————— by

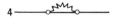

which is the second-order contribution to $S'(k)$ given in Fig. 7-7. The result is the fourth-order diagram 8. We note that in these replacements we replace the elementary elements by specific order portions of the modified elements. If, in the foregoing example, we replaced the left straight line ————— of diagram 2 by diagram 3 of Fig. 7-7, which is

we should find a sixth-order contribution to $U(k)$.

To represent this summation procedure in a diagrammatic manner, Wyld introduces the following symbolism:

thick straight line $\leftrightarrow S'(k)$

solid circle $\leftrightarrow \Gamma(k, k')$

thick wavy line $\leftrightarrow U(k)$

Thus the integral equation for $U(k)$ in terms of $S'(k)$ and $\Gamma(k, k')$ may be represented by the following diagram equation

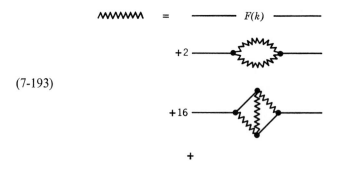

(7-193)

The first term is the sum of class "A" diagrams. The second term is the sum of all diagrams generated by replacing elementary elements in diagram 2 of Fig. 7-6 by modified elements. The third term is the sum of all diagrams generated by replacing elementary elements in diagram 7 of Fig. 7-6 by modified elements. The remaining terms are generated by replacing elementary elements in the higher order irreducible diagrams for the correlation function.

We next require equations for $\Gamma(k, k')$ and $S(k')$. The integral equation for $\Gamma(k, k')$ is determined in the same manner as the equation for $U(k)$ except that in this case we only need consider the equivalent of class "B" diagrams. Referring to Fig. 7-8, Wyld has found all the irreducible diagrams to fifth order. In each such diagram he has replaced elementary vertex points by the modified vertex operator represented by the solid circle. All the third-order diagrams are irreducible, and thus to third-order we find the following symbolic

equation

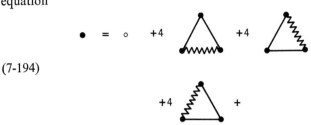

(7-194)

Unfortunately the derivation of an integral equation for $S'(k)$ does not proceed so simply, since a problem of double counting arises. In order to avoid this difficulty, Wyld defined a new function and made use of Ward's Identity used in quantum field theory. This procedure only works for the scalar case, however, and may not be generalized to the full Navier-Stokes equations. A correct procedure is given in Lee (1965). Lee treats the hydromagnetic problem, but the ordinary turbulence problem may be recovered by taking the magnetic field equal to zero.

The problem of double counting is illustrated by considering what would have happened if we had proceeded as in the case of $\Gamma(k, k')$ and written here

(7-195)

Equation 7-195 is obtained by replacing the second-order term in Fig. 7-7 by a generalized diagram. Using Eq. 7-195, we find that diagram 3 of Fig. 7-7 is counted twice.

The above difficulty may be avoided if Eq. 7-195 is replaced by

(7-196)

Lee also shows how the fourth-order term may be modified, but we shall not require this expression here.

The direct-interaction equations of Kraichnan in the steady state case are obtained from Eqs. 7-193, 7-194, and 7-196 by keeping only second-order terms in Eq. 7-193, 0th-order terms in Eq. 7-194 and second-order terms in Eq. 7-196. $S'(k)$ is analogous to the impulse response function. The set he used is thus equivalent to

$$(7\text{-}197) \quad \text{〰〰} = \text{——} F(k) \text{——} +2 \text{——⬦——}$$

$$(7\text{-}198) \quad \bullet = \circ$$

$$(7\text{-}199) \quad \text{——} = \text{——} +4 \text{——⬦——}$$

when constructed in terms of the full Navier-Stokes equations. The reader will find the full correct set in Lee (1965).

As Wyld points out, it is very difficult to show that the terms omitted in Kraichnan's approximation are indeed negligible. In fact we shall next turn to some work by Shut'ko (1965) in which he retains one second-order term in Eq. 7-194 and claims to obtain the Kolmogorov spectrum for the steady state equations.

We have presented Wyld's approach in such detail in spite of the fact that there were virtually no physical ideas present because the writer feels that this type of approach may have promise in all statistical continuum theories. It has already proved very valuable in quantum field studies wherein a physical interpretation may be given to the diagrams. Wyld states that this approach applied to the turbulence problem seems to be a perturbation in orders of complexity of the interaction, and even if this cannot be precisely formulated, it has intuitive appeal. Some variation of this formulism should certainly be attempted for the much simpler heterogeneous mixture problems described in Chapter 5.

7.4.1.3. Shut'ko (1965). Shut'ko (1965) takes as his basic equations the diagrammatic set*

$$(7\text{-}201) \quad \text{〰〰} = \text{——} F(k) \text{——} +2 \text{——⬦——}$$

$$(7\text{-}202) \quad \bullet = \circ \quad +4 \quad \triangle$$

$$(7\text{-}203) \quad \text{——} = \text{——} +4 \text{——⬦——}$$

* Note that Eqs. 3 and 4 of Shut'ko's paper are inappropriate. The set he uses in his final derivation is, however, equivalent to Eqs. 7-201 through 7-203 with the

This set is a generalization of Kraichnan's equations through the addition of the second-order vertex term in Eq. 7-202. Shut'ko states without proof that the other two second-order vertex terms are negligible. The corresponding integral equations for $U(k)$, $S'(k)$ and $\Gamma(k, k')$ are written explicitly in Shut'ko's paper for the case of isotropic turbulence.

The main point of Shut'ko's development is the claim that inclusion of the term $\Gamma(k, k')$ modifies the inertial spectrum obtained by Kraichnan (Eq. 7-170)

(7-204) $$E(k) = B'(v_0)^{1/2}\bar{\epsilon}^{1/2}k^{-3/2}$$

and yields the Kolmogorov spectrum (Eq. 7-116)

(7-205) $$E(k) = B\bar{\epsilon}^{2/3}k^{-5/3}$$

(We should point out here that in Wyld's development and Shut'ko's work we are considering stationary turbulence rather than decaying turbulence. We expect, however, that if Kolmogorov's assertion is correct, the spectral form for the inertial region should be the same in both cases.)

Shut'ko shows that $\Gamma(k, k')$ has the following properties:

(7-206) $$\Gamma(k, k') \approx 1; \quad k' \sim k; \quad k \to \infty$$

$$\Gamma(k, k') \to 0; \quad k' \ll k; \quad k \to \infty$$

by considering the asymptotic forms of Eqs. 7-201 to 7-203, as $k \to \infty$.

In the Kraichnan solution the vertex function is a constant as $k \to \infty$ for all k'. Hence the effect of the velocity v_0 defined by the relation (see Eq. 7-170)

$$v_0 = \frac{2}{3} \int_0^\infty E(k')\, dk'$$

---

exception of one vertex point in the second-order term in Eq. 7-203. Shut'ko uses instead the term

(7-200)

His final conclusion does not appear to the writer to be dependent on this discrepancy but since his arguments are so abbreviated it is difficult to make a definite statement on this point.

is important for determining the character of the large wave number eddies. v_0 characterizes the velocity of the energy-containing eddies. In the Shut'ko equations $\Gamma(k, k') \to 0$ for $k' \ll k$ as $k \to \infty$, and hence Shut'ko states that the energy-containing eddies do not affect the spectrum of the large wave number eddies (except for energy transfer, of course). Shut'ko then reasons that v_0 in Eq. 7-204 should be replaced by $B''[kE(k)]^{1/2}$, thus yielding a Kolmogorov spectrum.

Shut'ko's paper is brief and his final statements leading to the Kolmogorov spectrum are open to question. It is not really explained why v_0 may be replaced by $B''[kE(k)]^{1/2}$. Nevertheless Eqs. 7-201 to 7-203 are worthy of study and a more careful analysis of their properties should be made.

7.4.1.4. Further Remarks. The utility of the work presented in this section (7.4.1) and in 7.3.5 is discussed in general terms by Kraichnan (1965c). He states (as we have indicated above) that approximate procedures like his own and Wyld's are not based on a firm foundation since at present there is no way to calculate the importance of the neglected terms. He feels that in view of this uncertainty the approximate schemes should be careful to preserve fundamental invariance properties (e.g., conservation of energy) although this is by no means sufficient.* The reader is referred to this paper as a very readable yet perceptive account of the problems encountered in this type of work.

It is thus not clear at this time of what value these procedures may be in turbulence theory. We reiterate that we have included them not only because they are presently being actively studied in turbulence theory but also because it may be possible to apply them successfully in other statistical continuum theories. A recent example of the success of a procedure like Wyld's is given by Brown (1967) who calculates the form of the coherence function for electromagnetic radiation propagating in a random medium (compare to Beran, 1966).

7.4.2. Functional Approaches

The functional equation was first derived by Hopf (1952), and we have discussed this derivation and the derivation of a more general

---

* The reader should note his remarks on Shut'ko's work.

functional in Section 3.1.4. In this section we shall first discuss a solution of the Hopf equation obtained by Hopf and Titt (1953). We shall then present some work by Edwards (1964) and Tatarski (1962) in which attempts are made to solve the Hopf equation. Edwards work attempts to obtain an approximate solution by introducing the notions of turbulent diffusivity and turbulent viscosity. Tatarski, using techniques previously applied in quantum field theory, develops a formal procedure for solving the Hopf equation.

7.4.2.1. Hopf (1952), Hopf and Titt (1953). The work of Hopf is well summarized in Hopf (1962). His most interesting result is in the limit $\nu = 0$. In this particular case he was able to solve the functional equation for the case of homogeneous isotropic turbulence.

It has proved simpler to treat $M_H[y_i(\mathbf{x})]$ in terms of the variable

$$z_i(\mathbf{k}) = \int_{-\infty}^{\infty} e^{-i\mathbf{x}\cdot\mathbf{k}} y_i(\mathbf{x})\, d\mathbf{x}$$

the Fourier transform of $y_i(\mathbf{x})$. Since $y_i(\mathbf{x})$ is real, we require $z_i^*(\mathbf{k}) = z_i(-\mathbf{k})$. (See Section 3.1.4 for the discussion of $M_H[y_i(\mathbf{x})]$.) In terms of $M_H[z_i(\mathbf{k})]$, Hopf has shown that for homogeneous isotropic turbulence a stationary solution of the following form exists when $\nu = 0$:

(7-207) $$M_H[z_i(\mathbf{k})] = w\left[A \int \tilde{z}_i(\mathbf{k})\tilde{z}_i(-\mathbf{k})\, d\mathbf{k} \right]$$

where

$$\tilde{z}_i = \left[\delta_{ij} - \frac{k_i k_j}{k^2} \right] z_j$$

and A is a constant. Here w is an arbitrary function with a continuous second derivative. Hopf and Titt (1953) were then able to show that there is *not* a more general solution of the form

$$M_H[z_i(\mathbf{k})] = w\left[\int f(|\mathbf{k}|)\tilde{z}_i(\mathbf{k})\tilde{z}_i(-\mathbf{k})\, d\mathbf{k} \right]$$

That is, the only possible solution is $f(|\mathbf{k}|)$ equal to a constant.

This particular solution is of interest since the second-order moment may be simply derived from Eq. 7-207 using Eq. 2-86. We find

(7-208) $$\frac{\delta}{\delta z_j(\mathbf{k})}\left[\frac{\delta M_H}{\delta z_i(\mathbf{k})}\right]\Bigg|_{z=0} = 2w'(0)\alpha_{ij}(\mathbf{k''})\,\delta(\mathbf{k}+\mathbf{k''})$$

$$\left(\alpha_{ij}(\mathbf{k}) = \delta_{ij} - \frac{k_i k_j}{k^2}\right)$$

For homogeneous isotropic turbulence, this implies that the energy spectrum in wave number space, a second-order moment, is a constant, since it is proportional to

$$\frac{\delta}{\delta z_j(\mathbf{k})}\left[\frac{\delta M_H}{\delta z_i(\mathbf{k})}\right]\Bigg|_{z=0}$$

(upon discarding the delta function). The lack of dependence upon $|\mathbf{k}|$ is at variance with the Kolmogorov spectrum. Thus we have the interesting, if negative, result that the spectrum of turbulence cannot be obtained by assuming local stationarity, neglecting viscosity and demanding a nonsingular solution.

We might mention here that Lewis and Kraichnan (1962) solve the functional equations governing turbulent decay in its final stages. They are successful in obtaining a solution, since, as we have pointed out, the Navier-Stokes equations may be linearized in this regime by neglect of the inertial and pressure terms.

7.4.2.2. Edwards (1964).   Edwards (1964) begins his investigations with the Liouville-type equation, Eq. 3-66, written in terms of

(7-209) $$u_m(\mathbf{k}, t) = \int u_m(\mathbf{x}, t)e^{-i\mathbf{k}\cdot\mathbf{x}}\,d\mathbf{x}$$

and including a forcing function $\mathscr{F}(\mathbf{k}, t)$. $\mathscr{F}(\mathbf{k}, t)$ is chosen to provide stationary turbulence, and he takes the probability density functional associated with $\mathscr{F}(\mathbf{k}, t)$ to have the form

(7-210) $P[\mathscr{F}(k, t)]$

$$= \mathscr{N}\exp\left[-\left(\frac{2\pi}{L}\right)^3\sum_{\mathbf{k}}\int_0^T\int_0^T\mathscr{F}(\mathbf{k}, t)g^{-1}(\mathbf{k}, t-t')\mathscr{F}(\mathbf{k}, t')\,dt\,dt'\right]$$

where $\mathcal{N}$ is a normalization constant and

$$\int_{-\infty}^{\infty} g(\mathbf{k}, t - \tau)g^{-1}(\mathbf{k}, \tau - t')\, d\tau = \delta(t - t')$$

$g(\mathbf{k}, t - t')$ is defined by the equation

(7-211) $$g(\mathbf{k}, t - t') = \left(\frac{2\pi}{L}\right)^3 \langle \mathcal{F}(\mathbf{k}, t)\mathcal{F}(-\mathbf{k}, t')\rangle$$

The brackets indicate averaging with respect to $P[\mathcal{F}(\mathbf{k}, t)]$. For simplicity he further assumes that $g(\mathbf{k}, t - t')$ has the delta function form

(7-212) $$g(\mathbf{k}, t - t') = h(\mathbf{k})\delta(t - t')$$

since it is expected that the characteristic correlation times associated with $u(\mathbf{x}, t)$ will be long compared to the characteristic times associated with the forcing function. Edwards then averages $P_H[u_i(\mathbf{k}), t]$ over all realizations of the force $\mathcal{F}(\mathbf{k}, t)$.* We denote this function by $\langle P \rangle$. For the choice of $g(\mathbf{k}, t - t')$ given in Eq. 7-212, the expression for $\langle P \rangle$ simplifies, and he finds for the stationary problem

(7-213) $$\sum_{\mathbf{k},\alpha} \frac{\partial}{\partial u_\alpha(\mathbf{k})} \left(\left[\frac{L}{2\pi}\right]^3 \sum_{\alpha'} \mathscr{D}_{\alpha\alpha'}(\mathbf{k})h(\mathbf{k}) \frac{\partial}{\partial u_{\alpha'}(\mathbf{k})} + \nu k^2 u_\alpha(\mathbf{k}) \right.$$
$$\left. - \sum_{\beta,\gamma,\mathbf{j},\mathbf{l}} M_{\alpha\beta\gamma}(-\mathbf{k}, \mathbf{j}, \mathbf{l})u_\beta(\mathbf{j})u_\gamma(\mathbf{l}) \right)\langle P \rangle = 0$$

where

$$\mathscr{D}_{\alpha\beta}(\mathbf{k}) = \delta_{\alpha\beta} - \frac{k_\alpha k_\beta}{k^2}$$

$$M_{\alpha\beta\gamma}(\mathbf{k}, \mathbf{j}, \mathbf{l}) = \frac{1}{iL^3}\left(k_\beta \mathscr{D}_{\alpha\gamma}(\mathbf{k}) + k_\gamma \mathscr{D}_{\gamma\beta}(\mathbf{k})\right)\delta(\mathbf{k}, \mathbf{j}, \mathbf{l})$$

$\delta(\mathbf{k}, \mathbf{j}, \mathbf{l}) = 0$ unless $\mathbf{k} + \mathbf{j} + \mathbf{l} = 0$ when it is equal to one. Edwards also describes the equation governing the probability density functional associated with the four-dimensional transform of $u_\alpha(\mathbf{x}, t)$, but we shall not discuss this here.

* Prior to this averaging P_H has here the form of a delta functional with $u_i(\mathbf{k}, t)$ determined by a specific realization of $\mathcal{F}(\mathbf{k}, t)$.

In order to solve Eq. 7-213, Edwards introduces the notions of a turbulent diffusion and turbulent viscosity. These types of ideas were discussed previously in the phenomonological mixing length theories and also in Heisenberg's work. Edwards' intent is to introduce these ideas systematically. For this purpose Edwards rewrites Eq. 7-213 in the following form:

$$(7\text{-}214) \quad \left[\sum_{\mathbf{k},\alpha} \frac{\partial}{\partial u_\alpha(\mathbf{k})} \left(\sum_\beta \frac{\partial}{\partial u_\beta(\mathbf{k})} \left\{ \frac{L^3}{(2\pi)^3} \mathscr{D}_{\alpha\beta}(\mathbf{k})\, d(\mathbf{k}) \right\} + \omega(\mathbf{k})u_\alpha(\mathbf{k}) \right) \right.$$

$$- \sum_{\alpha,\beta,\gamma,\mathbf{k},\mathbf{j},\mathbf{l}} M_{\alpha\beta\gamma}(-\mathbf{k},\mathbf{j},\mathbf{l}) u_\beta(\mathbf{j}) u_\gamma(\mathbf{l}) \frac{\partial}{\partial u_\alpha(\mathbf{k})}$$

$$\left. - \sum_{\mathbf{k},\alpha} \frac{\partial}{\partial u_\alpha(\mathbf{k})} \left(\sum_\beta \frac{\partial}{\partial u_\beta(\mathbf{k})} \left(\frac{L}{2\pi} \right)^3 \mathscr{D}_{\alpha\beta}(\mathbf{k})S(\mathbf{k}) + R(\mathbf{k})u_\alpha(\mathbf{k}) \right) \right] \langle P \rangle = 0$$

where

$$d(\mathbf{k}) = h(\mathbf{k}) + S(\mathbf{k})$$
$$\omega(\mathbf{k}) = \nu k^2 + R(\mathbf{k})$$

in which the terms with $S(\mathbf{k})$ and $R(\mathbf{k})$ have just been added and subtracted.

If the last term is neglected, then Eq. 7-214 is written in a form in which $d(\mathbf{k})$ may be considered a total diffusion coefficient and $\omega(\mathbf{k})$, a total viscosity. To exploit this physical notion, Edwards considers the expansion of $\langle P \rangle$ in terms of some arbitrary parameter M and supposes that in this expansion $S(\mathbf{k})$ and $R(\mathbf{k})$ are of order M^2. Writing

$$(7\text{-}215) \qquad \langle P \rangle = \langle P_0 \rangle + \langle P_1 \rangle + \langle P_2 \rangle + \cdots$$

and denoting the operator

$$\sum_{\mathbf{k},\alpha} \frac{\partial}{\partial u_\alpha(\mathbf{k})} \left[\sum_\beta \frac{\partial}{\partial u_\beta(\mathbf{k})} \left[\frac{L^3}{(2\pi)^3} \right] \mathscr{D}_{\alpha\beta}(\mathbf{k})\, d(\mathbf{k}) + \omega(\mathbf{k})u_\alpha(\mathbf{k}) \right]$$

by $\mathscr{K}$ we find

$$(7\text{-}216) \qquad \mathscr{K} \langle P_0 \rangle = 0$$

$$\mathscr{K} \langle P_1 \rangle = \sum_{\alpha,\beta,\gamma,\mathbf{k},\mathbf{j},\mathbf{l}} M_{\alpha\beta\gamma}(\mathbf{k},\mathbf{j},\mathbf{l}) u_\beta(\mathbf{j}) u_\gamma(\mathbf{l}) \frac{\partial}{\partial u_\alpha(-\mathbf{k})} \langle P_0 \rangle$$

.
.
.

The sequence of equations given in Eq. 7-216 is solved by Edwards using a Hermite polynomial expansion of the $\langle P_n \rangle$ in terms of $\langle P_0 \rangle$. The solution for $\langle P_0 \rangle$ is

$$(7\text{-}217) \quad \langle P_0 \rangle = \prod_k A_k \exp\left[-\sum_{\alpha,k} \left(\frac{2\pi}{L}\right)^3 u_\alpha(\mathbf{k})u_\alpha(-\mathbf{k})/q(\mathbf{k}) \right]$$

where A_k is a normalization constant and

$$q(\mathbf{k}) = \frac{d(\mathbf{k})}{\omega(\mathbf{k})}$$

The coefficients $S(\mathbf{k})$ and $R(\mathbf{k})$ are determined by specifying that $\langle u_\alpha(\mathbf{k})u_\beta(-\mathbf{k})\rangle$ should be determined form $\langle P_0 \rangle$ alone. Thus we have the condition

$$(7\text{-}218) \quad \int (\langle P_1 \rangle + \langle P_2 \rangle + \cdots)u_\alpha(\mathbf{k})u_\beta(-\mathbf{k}) \prod_j du_\gamma(\mathbf{j}) = 0$$

and we set each order equal to zero.

The algebra associated with carrying out the above steps is very lengthy, but Edwards demonstrates that it is manageable. We refer the reader to his paper for the details. He solves for the correlation function $\langle u_\alpha(\mathbf{k})u_\alpha(-\mathbf{k})\rangle$ for a number of simple power inputs. In particular, if $h(\mathbf{k}) = h\,|\mathbf{k}|^{-\alpha}$, then he finds that

$$(7\text{-}219) \quad q(\mathbf{k}) = \tfrac{1}{2}\langle u_\alpha(\mathbf{k})u_\alpha(-\mathbf{k})\rangle = B\,|\mathbf{k}|^{-(1/3)(5+2\alpha)} \quad (B = \text{constant})$$

in the limit of large Reynolds numbers.

Representing the steady state decay problem in terms of generalized diffusion and viscosity coefficients certainly has intuitive appeal, but it is difficult to determine how good an approximation one obtains by taking only the lower order terms. In this connection Kraichnan (1964c) points out that Edwards' procedure may be applied to a model for which the direct interaction equations are an exact solution (see Kraichnan, 1961 for this model). It is then possible to see by numerical procedures how close Edwards' theory is to the true solution in this case. This seems a useful test, since there is no reason to expect that the model is less easy to approximate than the true physical problem. Using this test Kraichnan (1964c) finds that the Edwards equations to lowest-useful order provide too small an energy transfer for given spectral levels.

In a later paper (Edwards, 1965) Edwards points out the similarity between the equation governing $q(\mathbf{k})$ and the Boltzmann equation. In terms of the Boltzmann analogy $1/\omega(\mathbf{k})$ would be identified with a collision time. Since in turbulence there is really a continuum of "collision" times Edwards feels that to develop the analogy it is more appropriate to work with the probability density functional associated with $\mathbf{u}(\mathbf{k}, t)$ rather than with $\mathbf{u}(\mathbf{k})$ at time t. Using this formulism he is able to develop a Boltzmann-type equation for $q(\mathbf{k})$.* If this line of reasoning is pursued, it remains next to develop an independent equation governing $\omega(\mathbf{k})$.

As of the writing of this book, Edwards' approach is under active investigation. No doubt the validity of his assumptions will be considerably clarified in the next few years. From the point of view of this book we found his application of the functional equations of particular interest.

7.4.2.3. Tatarski (1962).

Tatarski (1962) attempts to obtain an integral solution of the Hopf equation (Eq. 3-61) using the techniques of quantum field theory. This type of approach was first given by Rosen (1960a,b), but we will discuss Tatarski's development, since it is somewhat easier to follow. Tatarski's analysis is basically a mathematical development with little physical discussion. The interest in his work stems from the iteration techniques employed, and hence the mathematics will be outlined in some detail.

Tatarski begins with the Hopf equation expressed in terms of a function simply related to the Fourier transform of $u_i(\mathbf{x}, t)$. The transform is denoted by $u_i(\mathbf{k}, t)$. The function $u_i(\mathbf{k}, t)$ does not exist for an unbounded volume unless some limiting procedure is defined, but we shall assume such a limiting procedure is implicit in the definition of the transform. In a compressed notation, $u_i(\mathbf{k}, t)$ satisfies the following equation (in addition to the divergence condition)

$$(7\text{-}220) \qquad \frac{\partial}{\partial t} u_i(\mathbf{k}, t) = Q_i[u_i(\mathbf{s}, t); \mathbf{k}] - \nu k^2 u_i(\mathbf{k}, t)$$

---

* Professor Edwards has informed the writer that Eq. 4.18 of Edwards (1965) is incorrectly presented. The kernel should be

$$L(\mathbf{k}, \mathbf{j}, \mathbf{l})q(\mathbf{l})q(\mathbf{k}) - L(\mathbf{j}, \mathbf{k}, \mathbf{l})q(\mathbf{l})q(\mathbf{j})$$

where

$$Q_i[u_i(\mathbf{k}, t); \mathbf{k}] = B_{l,ij} \int q_l(\mathbf{s}, t) q_j(\mathbf{k} - \mathbf{s}, t) \, ds$$

$$B_{l,ij} = -ik_l(\delta_{ij} - k_i k_j/k^2)$$

It is then convenient to define the function*

$$g_i(\mathbf{k}, t) = u_i(\mathbf{k}, t) \exp [\nu k^2 t]$$

which satisfies the equation

(7-221) $$\frac{\partial}{\partial t} g_i(\mathbf{k}, t) = \exp [-\nu k^2 t] Q_i[\exp [-\nu s^2 t] g(\mathbf{s}, t); \mathbf{k}]$$

The characteristic functional associated with $g_i(\mathbf{k}, t)$ is defined as

(7-222) $$M[p_i(\mathbf{s}), t] = \int \exp \left[2\pi i \int p_j(\mathbf{s}) g_j(\mathbf{s}, t) \, ds \right] P[g_i(\mathbf{s})] \, dg_i(\mathbf{s})$$

$$\equiv \left\langle \exp \left[2\pi i \int p_j(\mathbf{s}) g_j(\mathbf{s}, t) \, ds \right] \right\rangle$$

$$\equiv \langle Z[p_j(\mathbf{s}); g_j(\mathbf{s}, t)] \rangle$$

where $g_i(\mathbf{s}) = g_i(\mathbf{s}, 0)$.

An equation for $M[p_i(\mathbf{s}), t]$ is then derived by differentiation of Eq. 7-222 with respect to t. We find, using Eq. 7-221,

(7-223) $$\frac{\partial M}{\partial t} = 2\pi i \int \exp [\nu k^2 t] p_i(\mathbf{k}) \langle Z[p_j(\mathbf{s}); g_j(\mathbf{s}, t)]$$

$$\times Q_i[\exp [-\nu s^2 t] g_i(\mathbf{s}, t); \mathbf{k}] \rangle \, dk$$

This equation may then be expressed in terms of functional derivatives

$$D_i(\mathbf{k}, t) = \exp [-\nu k^2 t] \frac{\delta}{\delta p_i(\mathbf{k})}$$

to yield the Hopf-like equation

(7-224) $$2\pi i \frac{\partial M[p(\mathbf{k}), t]}{\partial t} = \int dk\, p_i(\mathbf{k}, t) Q_i[D(\mathbf{s}, t); \mathbf{k}] M[p(\mathbf{k}), t]$$

* This function has no relation to the function $g(\mathbf{k}, t - t')$ defined in Eq. 7-211.

where

$$p_i(\mathbf{k}, t) = \exp[\nu k^2 t] p_i(\mathbf{k})$$

The boundary condition for $M[p_i(\mathbf{k}), t]$ is determined from the condition $P[g_i(\mathbf{k})]$. In addition we find

(7-225) $k_i D_i(\mathbf{k}, 0) M[p_j(\mathbf{k}), 0] = 0$

from the divergence condition.

We also note that $D_i(\mathbf{k}, t)$ and $p_j(\mathbf{k}', t')$ satisfy the commutation relation

(7-226) $[D_i(\mathbf{k}, t), p_j(\mathbf{k}', t')] = \exp[-\nu k^2(t - t')] \delta_{ij} \delta(\mathbf{k} - \mathbf{k}')$

Equation 7-224 may be considered as a Schroedinger equation for a particular vector Bose field with Hamiltonian

$$H(t) = \int d\mathbf{k} p_i(\mathbf{k}, t) Q_i[D(\mathbf{s}, t); \mathbf{k}]$$

The methods developed in quantum field theory may now be used to attempt to solve this equation by iteration. Up to this point no approximations have been made. We may write

(7-227) $M[p_i(\mathbf{x}), t] = S(t) M[p_i(\mathbf{x}), 0] = \left[1 + \left(\dfrac{1}{2\pi i} \displaystyle\int_0^t d\tau_1 H(\tau_1) \right) \right.$

$$+ \cdots + \left(\frac{1}{(2\pi i)^m} \int_0^t d\tau_1 \int_0^{\tau_1} d\tau_2 \cdots \int_0^{\tau_m} d\tau_m H(\tau_1) \cdots \right.$$

$$\left. \times H(\tau_m) \right) + \cdots \bigg] M[p_i(\mathbf{x}), 0]$$

(see Schweber, 1961). If $M[p_i(\mathbf{x}), 0]$ is written in terms of a functional Taylor series (see Eq. 2-59), then quantum mechanically Eq. 7-227 may be interpreted in terms of various particle states by considering only a finite number of terms in the series. Since we demand that

$$|M[p_i(\mathbf{x}), 0]| \leqslant 1$$

no analogous interpretation is possible in the turbulent problem, and we must consider only series with an infinite number of terms.

The function $S(t)$, called the scattering matrix in quantum field theory, may be written in the exponential form

$$(7\text{-}228) \qquad S(t) = T \exp \left[-\frac{i}{2\pi} \int_0^t H(\tau)\, d\tau \right] \equiv TK$$

T is a chronological operator which orders the $H(\tau)$ operators so that when the exponential term is expanded, the $H(\tau)$ terms with the latest times are to the left. By expanding the exponential term, the reader will see what the properties of τ must be in order to recover the series expansion in Eq. 7-227. For a thorough discussion of chronological operators and the normal form operators which we shall define below, we refer the reader to Schweber (1961).

$S(t)$ may also be written in the following manner:

$$(7\text{-}229) \qquad S(t) = N\{(\exp \Delta) \cdot K\}$$

where Δ is the operator

$$\Delta = \int d\mathbf{k} \int_0^t d\tau_2 \int_0^{\tau_2} d\tau_1 \exp\left[-\nu k^2(\tau_2 - \tau_1) \right] \frac{\delta}{\delta p_i(\mathbf{k}, \tau_1)} \frac{\delta}{\delta D_i(\mathbf{k}, \tau_2)}$$

and N is a normal form operator. The normal form of a sequence of operators is a form in which all creation operators are to the left and all destruction operators are to the right. In this problem the $p_i(\mathbf{k}, t)$ are identified with creation operators, and the $D_i(\mathbf{k}, t)$ are identified with destruction operators.

From Eqs. 7-222 and 7-229 we find then

$$(7\text{-}230) \qquad M[p_i(\mathbf{s}), t] = \langle \{N[(\exp \Delta)K]\}Z[p_i(\mathbf{s}); u_i(\mathbf{s})] \rangle$$

Since the $D_i(\mathbf{k}, t)$ operators are to the right, they act only on Z. The effect of $D_i(\mathbf{k}, t)$ operating on the exponential form Z is simply to multiply the exponential term by

$$2\pi i \tilde{q}_i(\mathbf{k}, t) \equiv 2\pi i \exp\left[-\nu k^2 t \right] u_i(\mathbf{k})$$

Similarly, when $\delta/\delta D_i(\mathbf{k}, t)$ operates on K, $\delta/\delta D_i(\mathbf{k}, t)$ should be replaced by

$$\frac{1}{2\pi i} \frac{\delta}{\delta \tilde{q}_i(\mathbf{k}, t)}$$

Using the notation that a tilde symbol indicates that all $D_i(\mathbf{k}, t)$ and $\delta/\delta D_i(\mathbf{k}, t)$ operators have been replaced according to the above rules, we have then

$$(7\text{-}231) \quad M[p_i(\mathbf{s}), t] = \langle \{(\exp \tilde{\Delta}) \tilde{K}_t[p_i(\mathbf{s}, \tau); \tilde{q}_i(\mathbf{s}, \tau)]\} Z[p_i(\mathbf{s}); u_i(\mathbf{s})] \rangle$$

where

$$\tilde{K}_t[p_i(\mathbf{s}, \tau); \tilde{q}_i(\mathbf{s}, \tau)] = \exp\left[-\frac{i}{2\pi} \int_0^t \tilde{H}(p_i(\mathbf{s}, t'); \tilde{q}_i(\mathbf{s}, t')) \, dt' \right]$$

In order to proceed further, Tatarski introduces an integral representation for $\tilde{K}_t$ which allows one to operate with $\tilde{\Delta}$. We note that

$$(7\text{-}232) \quad \int F[\phi(\eta)] \, \delta[\phi(\eta) - f(\eta)] \, d\phi(\eta) = F[f(\eta)]$$

and

$$(7\text{-}233) \quad \delta[\phi(\eta)] = \int \exp\left[2\pi i \int f(\eta) \phi(\eta) \, d\eta \right] df(\eta)$$

where the integration over the functional $\phi(\eta)$ is suitably defined. (See Chapter 2, Sec. 2.2.4 or Tatarski's paper.) Generalizing these formulas, we may write the identity

$$(7\text{-}234) \quad \tilde{K}_t[p_i(\mathbf{s}, \tau); \tilde{q}_i(\mathbf{s}, \tau)] = \int d\mathbf{a}(\mathbf{s}, \tau) \int d\mathbf{A}(\mathbf{s}, \tau) \tilde{K}_t[p_i(\mathbf{s}, \tau); a_i(\mathbf{s}, \tau)]$$

$$\cdot \exp\left[2\pi i \int d\mathbf{k} \int_0^t d\tau A_i(\mathbf{k}, \tau)(\tilde{q}_i(\mathbf{k}, \tau) - a_i(\mathbf{k}, \tau)) \right]$$

It can then be shown that

$$(7\text{-}235) \quad \tilde{S}_t[p_i(\mathbf{s}, \tau); \tilde{q}_i(\mathbf{s}, \tau)] \equiv (\exp \tilde{\Delta}) K_t[p_i(\mathbf{s}, \tau); \tilde{q}_i(\mathbf{s}, \tau)]$$

$$= \int d\mathbf{a}(\mathbf{s}, \tau) \int d\mathbf{A}(\mathbf{s}, \tau) \tilde{K}_t[p_i(\mathbf{s}, t) + L(A_i(\mathbf{s}, \tau'); \tau); a_i(\mathbf{s}, \tau)]$$

$$\cdot \exp\left[2\pi i \int d\mathbf{k} \int_0^t dz A_i(\mathbf{k}, \tau)[\tilde{q}_i(\mathbf{k}, \tau) - a_i(\mathbf{k}, \tau)] \right]$$

where

$$L_i(A_i(\mathbf{s}, \tau); \tau') = \int_{\tau'}^t \exp\left[-\nu k^2 (\tau - \tau') \right] A_i(\mathbf{s}, \tau) \, d\tau$$

The next step is to integrate over $a_i(\mathbf{s}, \tau)$. That is, perform the integration over $a_i(\mathbf{s}, \tau)$ in the expression

$$(7\text{-}236) \quad G_t[p_i(\mathbf{s}, \tau); A_i(\mathbf{s}, \tau)] \equiv \int d\mathbf{a}(\mathbf{s}, \tau) \widetilde{K}_t[p_i(\mathbf{s}, \tau)$$

$$+ L(A_i(\mathbf{s}, \tau'); \tau); a_i(\mathbf{s}, \tau)] \exp \left[-2\pi i \int d\mathbf{k} \int_0^t d\tau A_i(\mathbf{k}, \tau) a_i(\mathbf{k}, \tau) \right]$$

where

$$(7\text{-}237) \quad M[p_i(\mathbf{s}), t] = \left\langle G_t[p_i(\mathbf{s}, \tau); A_i(\mathbf{s}, \tau)] \exp \left\{ 2\pi i \int d\mathbf{k} p_i(\mathbf{k}t) u_i(\mathbf{k}) \right. \right.$$

$$\left. \left. + \int_0^t d\tau A_i(\mathbf{k}, \tau) \exp\left[-\nu k^2 \tau \right] u_i(\mathbf{k}) \right\} dA(\mathbf{k}, \tau) \right\rangle$$

In writing down Eq. 7-237, we have used the definition of

$$Z[p_i(\mathbf{s}), u_i(\mathbf{s})].$$

We shall not give the details for the integration given in Eq. 7-236 but refer the reader to Tatarski's paper, since the details are too cumbersome to put down here. Instead we write now a final expression for $M[p_i(\mathbf{s}), t]$ that may be found from Eq. 7-237 by averaging over $u_i(\mathbf{k})$ in this equation. Tatarski's final expression is

$$(7\text{-}238) \quad M[p_i(\mathbf{s}), t] = \int G_t[p_i(\mathbf{s}) \exp[-\nu s^2(t - \tau)]; A_i(\mathbf{s}, \tau)]$$

$$\cdot M[p_i(\mathbf{s}) \exp[-\nu s^2 t] + L(A_i(\mathbf{s}, \tau); 0)] dA(s, \tau)$$

Without reference to the specific form of $G_t[p_i(\mathbf{s}, \tau); A_i(\mathbf{s}, \tau)]$, Tatarski concludes from this equation that $M[p_i(\mathbf{s}), t]$ is independent of $M[p_i(\mathbf{s}), 0]$ when the Reynolds number approaches infinity. He reasons that in this case $M[p_i(\mathbf{s}), 0]$ is almost a delta functional about the point $p_i(\mathbf{s}) = 0$, and hence the change in $M[p_i(\mathbf{s}), t]$ will depend upon G_t rather than $M[p_i(\mathbf{s}), 0]$.

From the expression for $M[p_i(\mathbf{s}), t]$ given in Eq. 7-238, we may find $\langle u_i(\mathbf{k}_1, t) u_j(\mathbf{k}_2, t) \rangle$ by functional differentiation in the usual manner. Possibly by manipulation of the resultant expression, the general character of the decay of this function may be inferred without performing the integrations in Eq. 7-238. Rosen (1960a,b) shows how this may be done by assuming a gaussian form for $M[p_i(\mathbf{s}), 0]$. Unfortunately, there is an error in the later portions of his work.

7.4.3. Deissler (1965a)

The work of Deissler (1965a) is concerned with the problem of shear-flow turbulence rather than homogeneous turbulence. We wish to outline the basic idea of his paper here, since it appears to the writer that Deissler has considered a method of attack that warranted attention many years ago and may eventually prove more useful for understanding turbulence than consideration of the homogeneous problem. In the homogeneous problem the basic problem considered is the change in turbulent statistics with time or the determination of these statistics in the steady state from the statistics of some forcing function. In either case, we have no turbulence, except in a very degenerate sense, if third-order terms are neglected in setting up a determinate problem. In the steady state shear problem there is an intermediate course, since the effects of the third-order terms may be partially included through the spatially variable mean velocity without being forced into an indeterminacy.

Equation 7-56 is indeterminate, since third-order terms like

$$\overline{u_j(\mathbf{x}_2, t)u_k(\mathbf{x}_2, t)u_i(\mathbf{x}_1, t)}$$

are present in the equation determining

$$\overline{u_i(\mathbf{x}_1, t)u_k(\mathbf{x}_2, t)}$$

In steady state shear turbulence there is a spatially variable mean velocity, $\overline{u_i(\mathbf{x})}$, and we may write

(7-239) $$u_i(\mathbf{x}, t) = \overline{u_i(\mathbf{x})} + u_i'(\mathbf{x}, t)$$

where $\overline{u_i'(\mathbf{x}, t)} = 0$.

Thus the third-order term cited above gives

(7-240) $$\overline{u_j(\mathbf{x}_2, t)u_k(\mathbf{x}_2, t)u_i(\mathbf{x}_1, t)} = [\overline{u_j(\mathbf{x}_2)}][\overline{u_k(\mathbf{x}_2)}][\overline{u_i(\mathbf{x}_1)}]$$

$$+ [\overline{u_j(\mathbf{x}_2)}][\overline{u_k'(\mathbf{x}_2, t)u_i'(\mathbf{x}_1, t)}] + [\overline{u_k(\mathbf{x}_2)}][\overline{u_j'(\mathbf{x}_2, t)u_i'(\mathbf{x}_1, t)}]$$

$$+ [\overline{u_i(\mathbf{x}_1)}][\overline{u_j'(\mathbf{x}_2, t)u_k'(\mathbf{x}_2, t)}] + \overline{u_j'(\mathbf{x}_2, t)u_k'(\mathbf{x}_2, t)u_i'(\mathbf{x}_1, t)}$$

Deissler neglects the term

$$\overline{u_j'(\mathbf{x}_2, t)u_k'(\mathbf{x}_2, t)u_i'(\mathbf{x}_1, t)}$$

in Eq. 7-240 and in other similar expressions. He is thus able to find a determinate set of equations for turbulent Couette flow. He retains pressure–velocity correlations and obtains an equation for $u_i(\mathbf{x})$ by averaging Eq. 7-54a.

The resultant equations are nonlinear, and since, in addition, there is not much symmetry, they are very difficult to treat. Deissler makes some attempt at treating these equations by power series expansions for

$$\overline{u_i'(\mathbf{x}_1, t)u_j'(\mathbf{x}_2, t)}$$

for small values of $\mathbf{x}_1 - \mathbf{x}_2$. This is not too satisfactory a procedure since the boundary condition

$$u_i(\mathbf{x}, t) = 0$$

at the walls is presumably very important in this problem. Based on his assumptions, he does show that there is a critical value below which turbulence does not exist and also that pressure-velocity correlations and terms like $[\overline{u_j'(\mathbf{x}_2)}][\overline{u_k'(\mathbf{x}_2, t)u_i'(\mathbf{x}_1, t)}]$ are essential for a turbulent solution. We refer the reader to his paper for details of his method.

A considerable amount of work must be spent in analyzing the Deissler equations before it is clear how much of the turbulent shear flow problem is contained within them. At the writing of this book, this is a very open question, and these equations thus deserve detailed attention.

7.4.4. Recent Papers of Interest

Space precludes reporting on all recent work in turbulence. We think the following papers may, however, be of interest to the reader, and in concluding this chapter we list the authors and titles with no discussion.

Eschenroeder, A. (1965), "Solution of the Inertial Energy Spectrum of Isotropic Turbulence," *Phys. Fluids*, **8**, 598.
Favre, A., Ed. (1962), *Mechanics of Turbulence*, Gordon and Breach, New York. Papers presented at 1961 Marseille Conference.

414 Statistical Continuum Theories

Favre, A. (1965), "Review of Space-Time Correlations in Turbulent Fluids," *J. Appl. Mech.*, **32**, 241.

Frenkiel, F., and P. Kelbanoff (1965), "Two-Dimensional Probability Distribution in a Turbulent Field," *Phys. Fluids*, **8**, 2291.

Frenkiel, F., and P. Kelbanoff (1967), "Higher-Order Correlations in a Turbulent Field," *Phys. Fluids*, **10**, 507.

Herring, J. (1965), "Self-Consistent Field Approach to Turbulence Theory," *Phys. Fluids*, **8**, 2219.

Herring, J. (1966), "Self-Consistent Field Approach to Nonstationary Turbulence," *Phys. Fluids*, **9**, 2106.

Imamura, T., W. Meecham, and A. Siegal (1965), "Symbolic Calculus of the Wiener Process and Wiener-Hermite Functionals," *J. Math. Phys.*, **6**, 695.

Kraichnan, R. (1966), "Isotropic Turbulence and Inertial Range Structure," *Phys. Fluids*, **9**, 1728.

Lee, J. (1966), "Comparison of Closure Approximation Theories in Turbulent Mixing," *Phys. Fluids*, **9**, 363.

Lumley, J. (1966), "Invariants in Turbulent Flow", *Phys. Fluids*, **9**, 2111.

Lundgren, T. (1967), "Distribution Functions in the Statistical Theory of Turbulence," *Phys. Fluids*, **10**, 969.

Novikov, E. (1963), "Random Force Method in Turbulence Theory," *Soviet Phys. JETP (English Transl.)*, **17**, 1449.

Novikov, E. (1965), "Functionals and the Random Force Method in Turbulence Theory," *Soviet Phys. JETP (English Transl.)*, **20**, 1290.

O'Brien, E. (1966), "Closure Approximations Applied to Stochastically Distributed Second Order Reactants," *Phys. Fluids*, **9**, 1561.

Orszag, S., and M. Kruskal, (1966), "Theory of Turbulence," *Phys. Rev. Letters*, **16**, 441.

Pao, Y. (1965), "Structure of Turbulent Velocity and Scalar Fields at Large Wavenumbers," *Phys. Fluids*, **8**, 1063.

Saffman, P. (1967), "The Large Scale Structure of Homogeneous Turbulence, *J. Fluid Mech.*, **27**, 581.

Siegel, A., T. Imamura, and W. Meecham (1965), "Wiener-Hermite Expansion in Model Turbulence in the Late Decay Stage," *J. Math. Phys.*, **6**, 707.

Bibliography

Adomian, G. (1963). *Rev. Mod. Phys.*, **35**, 185.

Aris, R. (1956). *Proc. Roy. Soc. (London)*, **A235**, 67.

Batchelor, G. (1953). *The Theory of Homogeneous Turbulence*, Cambridge Univ. Press, London and New York,

Batchelor, G., and I. Proudman (1956). *Phil. Trans. Roy. Soc. London*, **248A**, 369.

Beran, M. (1955). Ph.D. Thesis, Dept. of Applied Science, Harvard University, Cambridge, Massachusetts.

Beran, M. (1957). *J. Chem. Phys.*, **27**, 270.

Beran, M. (1965a). *Nuovo Cimento Ser. X*, **38**, 771.

Beran, M. (1965b). *Trans. Rheology Soc.*, Pt. 9, No. 1, 339.

Beran, M. (1965c). *Nuovo Cimento Suppl.*, **3**, 448.

Beran, M. (1966). *J. Opt. Soc. Am.*, **56**, 1475.

Beran, M. (1967). *Am. J. Phys.*, **35**, 242.

Beran, M., and P. Corson (1965). *J. Math. Phys.*, **6**, 271.

Beran, M., and J. Molyneux (1963). *Nuovo Cimento*, **30**, 1406.

Beran, M., and J. Molyneux (1966). *Quart. Appl. Math.*, **24**, 107.

Beran, M., and G. Parrent, Jr. (1964). *Theory of Partial Coherence*, Prentice-Hall, Englewood Cliffs, New Jersey.

Betchov, R. (1956). *J. Fluid Mech.*, **1**, 497.

Birkhoff, G. D. (1931). *Proc. Natl. Acad. Sci. U.S.*, **17**, 650, 656.

Blanc-Lapierre, A., and P. Dumontet (1955). *Rev. Opt.*, **34**, 1.

Born, M., and E. Wolf (1959). *Principles of Optics*, Macmillan (Pergamon), New York.

Bourret, R. (1960). *Nuovo Cimento*, **18**, 347.

Bourret, R. (1962). *Nuovo Cimento*, **26**, 1.

Boussinesq, J. (1877). *Mem. Prés. par div. sàvants à l'acad. sci., Paris*, **23**, 46.

Brown, W. F. (1955). *J. Chem. Phys.*, **23**, 1514.

Brown, W. F. (1962), *Magnetostatic Principles in Ferromagnetism*, North-Holland Publ., Amsterdam.

Brown, W. F. (1965). *Trans. Rheology Soc.*, Pt. 9, No. 1, 357.

Brown, W. P. (1967). *IEEE Trans. Antennas Propagation AP-15*, 81.

Brull, M. A., and A. Soler (1966). *Quart. Appl. Math.*, **24**, 143.

Budiansky, B. (1965). *J. Mech. Phys. Solids*, **13**, 223.

Burgess, R. (1965). *Fluctuation Phenomena in Solids*, Academic Press, New York.

Carman, P. (1956). *Flow of Gases Through Porous Media*, Academic Press, New York.

Chandrasekhar, S. (1949). *Proc. Roy. Soc. (London)*, **A200**, 20.

Chandrasekhar, S. (1955). *Proc. Roy. Soc. (London)*, **A229**, 1.

Chandrasekhar, S. (1956). *Phys. Rev.*, **102**, 941.

Chandrasekhar, S. (1961). *Hydrodynamic and Hydromagnetic Stability*, Oxford Univ. Press (*Clarendon*), London and New York.

Childs, E., and N. Collis-George (1950). *Proc. Roy. Soc.* (*London*), **201A**, 392.

Collins, R. (1961). *Flow of Fluids Through Porous Materials*, Reinhold, New York.

Courant, R., and D. Hilbert (1953). *Methods of Mathematical Physics*, Vol. I, Interscience, New York.

Cramér, H. (1946). *Mathematical Methods of Statistics*, Princeton Univ. Press, Princeton, N.J.

Davenport, W., Jr., and W. Root (1958). *An Introduction to the Theory of Random Signals and Noise*, McGraw-Hill, New York.

Deissler, R. (1965a). *Phys. Fluids*, **8**, 391.

Deissler, R. (1965b). *Phys. Fluids*, **8**, 2106.

De Loor, G. (1956). Thesis, Univ. of Leiden, Leiden.

Edwards, S. (1964). *J. Fluid Mech.*, **18**, 239.

Edwards, S. (1965). *Intern. Conf. Plasma Physics, Trieste*, International Atomic Energy Association, Vienna, 595.

Edwards, S., and G. Parrent, Jr. (1959). *Optica Acta*, **6**, 367.

Einstein, A. (1906). *Investigations on the Theory of Brownian Motion*, Dover, New York, 1956.

Eschenroeder, A. (1965). *Phys. Fluids*, **8**, 598.

Evans, G. (1964). *Functionals and Their Applications*, Dover, New York.

Farquhar, I. (1964). *Ergodic Theory in Statistical Mechanics*, Interscience, New York.

Favre, A., Ed. (1962). *Mechanics of Turbulence*, Gordon and Breach, New York.

Favre, A. (1965). *J. Appl. Mech.*, **32**, 241.

Feller, W. (1950). *Probability Theory and Its Applications*, Wiley, New York.

Fermi, E. (1923). *Z. Physik*, **24**, 261.

Frenkiel, F., and P. Klebanoff (1965). *Phys. Fluids*, **8**, 2291.

Frenkiel, F., and P. Klebanoff (1967). *Phys. Fluids*, **10**, 507.

Friedrichs, K., H. Shapiro et al. (1957). *Integration of Functionals*, Seminar, New York Univ., Inst. Math. Sciences.

Frisch, H. (1965). *Trans. Rheology Soc.*, Pt. 9, No. 1, 293.

Furutsu, K. (1963). *J. Res. Natl. Bur. Std.*, **67D**, 303.

Gabor, D. (1946). *J. Inst. Elec. Engrs.* (*London*), **93**, 429.

Gelfand, I., and A. Yaglom (1960). *J. Math. Phys.*, **1**, 48.

Gilbert, C. (1962). *Ann. Math. Stat.*, **33**, 958.

Glauber, R. (1964). *Proc. Third Intern. Conf. Quantum Electronics*, P. Grivet and N. Bloembergen, Eds., Columbia Univ. Press, New York, 111.

Goldstein, S. (1938). *Modern Developments in Fluid Dynamics*, Oxford Univ. Press (*Clarendon*), London and New York.

Grant, H., R. Stewart, and A. Moilliet (1962). *J. Fluid Mech.*, **12**, 241.

Hardy, G. (1952). *A Course of Pure Mathematics*, Cambridge Univ. Press, London and New York.

Hashin, Z., and S. Shtrikman (1962). *J. Appl. Phys.*, **33**, 3125.

Hashin, Z., and S. Shtrikman (1963a). *Phys. Rev.*, **130**, 129.

Hashin, Z., and S. Shtrikman (1963b). *J. Mech. Phys. Solids*, **11**, 127.

Hashin, Z. (1964). *Appl. Mech. Rev.*, **17**, 1.
Hashin, Z. (1967). *Intern. J. Eng. Sci.*, **5**, 213.
Heisenberg, W. (1948a). *Z. Physik*, **124**, 628.
Heisenberg, W. (1948b). *Proc. Roy. Soc. (London)*, **195**, 402.
Herring, J. (1965). *Phys. Fluids*, **8**, 2219.
Herring, J. (1966). *Phys. Fluids*, **9**, 2106.
Hildebrand, F. (1962). *Advanced Calculus for Applications*, Prentice-Hall, Englewood Cliffs, N.J.
Hill, R. (1965). *J. Mech. Phys. Solids*, **13**, 213.
Hinze, J. (1959). *Turbulence*, McGraw-Hill, New York.
Hirschfelder, J., C. Curtiss, and B. Bird (1954). *Molecular Theory of Gases and Liquids*, Wiley, New York.
Hoeffing, W., and H. Robbins (1948). *Duke Univ. Math. J.*, **15**, 773.
Hoffman, R. (1964). *Proc. Symp. Appl. Math.*, **16**, 117 (Am. Math. Soc., Providence, R.I.).
Hopf, E. (1952). *J. Ratl. Mech. Anal.*, **1**, 87.
Hopf, E. (1962). *Proc. Symp. Appl. Math.*, **13**, 157 (Am. Math. Soc., Providence, R.I.).
Hopf, E., and E. Titt (1953). *J. Ratl. Mech. Anal.*, **2**, 587.
Imamura, T., W. Meecham, and A. Siegal (1965). *J. Math. Phys.*, **6**, 695.
Kadomtsev, B. (1965). *Plasma Turbulence*, Academic Press, London.
Kampé De Fériet, J. (1962). *Proc. Symp. Appl. Math.*, **13**, 165 (Am. Math. Soc., Providence, R.I.).
Karal, F., and J. B. Keller (1964). *J. Math. Phys.*, **5**, 537.
Kármán, T. von (1937a). *Proc. Natl. Acad. Sci. U.S.*, **23**, 98.
Kármán, T. von (1937b). *J. Aeron. Sci.*, **4**, 131.
Kármán, T. von, and L. Howarth (1938). *Proc. Roy. Soc. (London)*, **164**, Ser. A, 192.
Keller, J. B. (1964). *Proc. Symp. Appl. Math.*, **16**, 145 (Am. Math. Soc., Providence, R.I.).
Kendall, M., and P. Moran (1963). *Geometrical Probability (Griffen's Statistical Monograph Courses, No. 10)*, Griffen and Co., London.
Kerner, E. (1956). *Proc. Phys. Soc. (London)*, **B69**, 802.
Kestelman, H. (1960). *Modern Theories of Integration*, Dover, New York.
Kolmogorov, A. (1941). *Compt. Rend. Acad. Sci. URSS*, **30**, 301. English translation in *Turbulence*, S. Friedlander and L. Topper, Eds., Interscience, New York.
Kolmogorov, A. (1950). *Foundations of the Theory of Probability*, Chelsea, New York. Original work published in 1938.
Kolmogorov, A. (1962). *J. Fluid Mech.*, **13**, 82.
Kovásnay, L. (1948). *J. Aeron. Sci.*, **15**, 745.
Kozeny, J. (1927). *Sitzber. Deutsch Akad. Wiss. Berlin, Wien. Abt. IIa*, **136**, 271.
Kraichnan, R. (1957). *Phys. Rev.*, **107**, 1485.
Kraichnan, R. (1958a). *Phys. Rev.*, **109**, 1407; *Errata*, **111**, 1747.
Kraichnan, R. (1958b). *Phys. Fluids*, **1**, 358.
Kraichnan, R. (1959). *J. Fluid Mech.*, **5**, 497.
Kraichnan, R. (1961). *J. Math. Phys.*, **2**, 124.

Kraichnan, R. (1962a). *Proc. Symp. Appl. Math.*, **13**, 199 (Am. Math. Soc., Providence, R.I.).
Kraichnan, R. (1962b). *Mecanique de la Turbulence*, Marseille Conf., 1961, A. Favre, Ed., Editions du Centre National de la Recherche Scientifique, Paris.
Kraichnan, R. (1964a). *Phys. Fluids*, **7**, 1030.
Kraichnan, R. (1964b). *Phys. Fluids*, **7**, 1723.
Kraichnan, R. (1964c). *Phys. Fluids*, **7**, 1163.
Kraichnan, R. (1965a). *Phys. Fluids*, **8**, 575.
Kraichnan, R. (1965b). *Phys. Fluids*, **8**, 995.
Kraichnan, R. (1965c). Symp. Dynamics Fluids Plasmas, College Park, Oct. 1965.
Kraichnan, R. (1966). *Phys. Fluids*, **9**, 1728.
Landau, L., and E. Lifshitz (1960). *Electrodynamics of Continuous Media*, Macmillan (Pergamon), New York.
Landauer, R. (1952). *J. Appl. Phys.*, **23**, 779.
Laufer, J. (1951). N.A.C.A. Tech. Rept. No. 1053, p. 1247.
Lee, D. (1965). *Phys. Fluids*, **8**, 1911.
Lee, J. (1966). *Phys. Fluids*, **9**, 363.
Lee, L. (1965). *Ann. Phys.*, **32**, 292.
Lewis, R., and R. Kraichnan (1962). *Commun. Pure Appl. Math.*, **15**, 397.
Lin, C. (1955). *The Theory of Hydrodynamic Stability*, Cambridge Univ. Press, London and New York.
Loève, M. (1962). *Probability Theory*, Van Nostrand, Princeton, N.J.
Lumley, J. (1966). *Phys. Fluids*, **9**, 2111.
Lumley, J., and H. Panofsky (1964). *The Structure of Atmospheric Turbulence*, Interscience, New York.
Lundgren, T. (1967). *Phys. Fluids*, **10**, 969.
Marshall, T. (1957). *Nature*, **180**, 664.
Maruyana, G. (1949). *Mem. Fac. Sci., Kyushyu Univ.*, **4**.
Mehta, C., E. Wolf, and A. Balachandran (1966). *J. Math. Phys.*, **7**, 133.
Michelson, A. (1890). *Phil. Mag.* (5), **30**, 1.
Michelson, A., and F. Pease (1921). *Astrophys. J.*, **53**, 29.
Middleton, D. (1960). *Introduction to Statistical Communications Theory*, McGraw-Hill, New York.
Millionshtchikov, M. (1941a). *Compt. Rend. Acad. Sci. URSS*, **32**, 615.
Millionshtchikov, M. (1941b). *Compt. Rend. Acad. Sci. URSS*, **32**, 619.
Molyneux, J. (1964). Ph.D. Thesis, Dept. of Mech. Eng., Univ. of Pennsylvania, Philadelphia, Pennsylvania.
Molyneux, J., and M. Beran (1965). *J. Math. Mech.*, **14**, 337.
Novikov, E. (1963). *Soviet Phys. JETP (English Transl.)*, **17**, 1449.
Novikov, E. (1965). *Soviet Phys. JETP (English Transl.)*, **20**, 1449.
O'Brien, E. (1966). *Phys. Fluids*, **9**, 1561.
Obukhoff, A. (1941). *Compt. Rend. Acad. Sci. URSS*, **32**, 19.
Obukhoff, A. (1962). *J. Fluid Mech.*, **13**, 77.
Ogura, Y. (1963). *J. Fluid Mech.*, **16**, 33.
O'Neill, E. (1963). *Introduction to Statistical Optics*, Addison-Wesley, Reading, Mass.

Orszag, S., and M. Krushal (1966). *Phys. Rev. Letters*, **16**, 441.
Pao, Y. (1965). *Phys. Fluids*, **8**, 1063.
Parrent, G., Jr., and E. Marathay (1965). Private communication.
Paul, B. (1960). *Trans. AIME*, **218**, 36.
Poreh, M., and C. Elata (1966). *Israel J. Technol.*, **4**, 214.
Prager, S. (1960). *J. Chem. Phys.* **33**, 122.
Prager, S. (1961). *Phys. Fluids*, **4**, 1477.
Proudman, I. (1962). *Mécanique de la Turbulence*, Marseille Conf. 1961, A. Favre, Ed., Editions du Centre National de la Recherche Scientifique, Paris.
Proudman, I., and W. Reid (1954). *Phil. Trans. Roy. Soc. London*, **A247**, 926.
Reid, W. (1960). *Phys. Fluids*, **3**, 72.
Reynolds, O. (1901). *Scientific Papers of Osborne Reynolds*, Vol. II, Cambridge Univ. Press, London and New York.
Richardson, J. (1964). *Proc. Symp. Appl. Math.*, **16**, 290 (Am. Math. Soc., Providence, R.I.).
Roman, P., and E. Wolf (1960). *Nuovo Cimento*, **17**, 462.
Rosen, G. (1960a). *Phys. Fluids*, **3**, 519.
Rosen, G. (1960b). *Phys. Fluids*, **3**, 525.
Saffman, P. (1959). *J. Fluid Mech.*, **6**, 321.
Saffman, P. (1960). *J. Fluid Mech.*, **7**, 194.
Saffman, P. (1967). *J. Fluid Mech.*, **27**, 581.
Scheidegger, A. (1954). *J. Appl. Phys.*, **25**, 994.
Scheidegger, A. (1956). *Can. J. Phys.*, **34**, 692.
Scheidegger, A. (1960). *The Physics of Flow Through Porous Media*, Macmillan, New York.
Scheidegger, A. (1965). *Trans. Rheology Soc.*, Pt. 9, No. 1, 313.
Schweber, S. (1961). *An Introduction to Relativistic Quantum Field Theory*, Harper, New York.
Shut'ko, A. (1965). *Soviet Phys. Doklady (English Transl.)*, **9**, 857.
Siegal, A., T. Imamura, and W. Meecham (1965). *J. Math. Phys.*, **6**, 707.
Stratton, J. (1941). *Electromagnetic Theory*, McGraw-Hill, New York.
Stepanow, N. (1912). *Z. Anorg. Allgem. Chem.*, **78**, 1.
Stewart, R., and A. Townsend (1951). *Phil. Trans. Roy. Soc. London*, **A243**, 359.
Tatarski, V. (1961). *Wave Propagation in a Turbulent Medium*, McGraw-Hill, New York.
Tatarski, V. (1962). *Soviet Phys. JETP (English Transl.)*, **15**, 961.
Tatsumi, T. (1957). *Proc. Roy. Soc. (London)*, **A239**, 16.
Taylor, G. I. (1921). *Proc. London Math. Soc.*, **20**, 196.
Taylor, G. I. (1935). *Proc. Roy. Soc. (London)*, **A151**, 421.
Taylor, G. I. (1936). *Proc. Roy. Soc. (London)*, **A156**, 307.
Taylor, G. I. (1953). *Proc. Roy. Soc. (London)*, **A219**, 186.
Ter Haar, D. (1960). *Elements of Statistical Mechanics*, Holt, New York.
Townsend, A. (1956). *The Structure of Turbulent Shear Flow*, Cambridge Univ. Press, London and New York.
Truesdell, C. (1961). *Ergodic Theories* (Proc. Intern. School Phys., "E. Fermi" XIV Course), Academic Press, New York, p. 21.
Umekawa, S., and O. Sherby (1966). *J. Mech. Phys. Solids*, **14**, 65.

Volterra, V. (1959). *Theory of Functionals and of Integral and Integro-Differential Equations*, Dover, New York.

Weissberg, W., and S. Prager (1962). *Phys. Fluids*, **5**, 1390.

Wiener, O. (1912). *Abhandl. Math.-Phys. Kl. Königl. Sachsischen Ges.*, **32**, 509.

Wolf, E. (1955). *Proc. Roy. Soc. (London)*, **A230**, 246.

Wyld, H. (1961). *Ann. Phys.*, **14**, 143.

Wylie, M., and G. Gardner (1958a). *World Oil*, **146**, 121.

Wylie, M., and G. Gardner (1958b). *Nature*, **181**, 477.

Yaglom, A. (1962). *An Introduction to Mathematical Stationary Random Functions*, Prentice-Hall, Englewood Cliffs, N.J.

Subject Index

A

Analytic signal, 44, 158
Angular diameter, stars, 174
  two-point objects, 151
Axially symmetric tensors, 138, 225, 230, 252

B

Blackbody radiation, 176
Boltzmann's equation, 406

C

Capillary models, 264, 275
van Cittert-Zernike theorem, 174
Coherence, blackbody radiation, 176
  coherent and incoherent fields, 149
  far-field approximation, 169
  functional solution, 85
  functions, 44, 145, 155
  governing equations, 158
  Green's functions, 85, 163
  quasi-monochromatic radiation, 147, 166
  radiation from a plane finite surface, 165
  star, measurement of angular diameter, 174
  visibility, 144
Conditional probability, 21
Conductivity. *See* Permittivity.
Cumulant neglect hypothesis, 117, 121, 361

D

Darcy's law, 262
Decay of correlation functions, 172, 231, 234, 240, 353, 368
Diagrammatic techniques, 388
Dielectric constant. *See* Permittivity.
Dilute suspensions, 200, 247
Direct interaction equations, 369, 398
Dispersion in porous media, 268, 288
  effect of molecular diffusion, 304
Displacement field. *See* Permittivity.

E

Eddy "size," 344
Eddy viscosity, 318, 323, 360, 404
Effective constants, bounds, 131, 141, 245, 246, 288
  definitions, 126, 131, 184, 191
  determination from perturbation solutions, 229, 235, 240
  dilute suspensions, 200, 247
  n-phase materials, 197
  self-consistent approximation, 199
  simple models, 192
Elasticity, effective constants, 182, 212, 240
  fluctuations, 240
  statistical moment equations, 236
Electric field fluctuations, 229, 232, 235
Ensemble, concept of, 18
  variational principle, 128
Ergodic hypothesis, 41
Expectations, 30

421

F

Functionals, 56
  characteristic, 71
  continuity, 57
  delta, 63, 79, 90, 410
  differentiation, 62
  governing equations, harmonic oscillator, 75
    Maxwell's equations, 81
    Navier-Stokes equations, 87, 400
  integration, 67
  linear, 59
  probability density, 70
  Taylor series, 60

G

Guassian processes, 36, 49, 72, 179, 271, 362, 389, 402, 412
Geometry, heterogeneous media, 202
  porous media, 258

H

Harmonic oscillator, functional equations, 75
  introduction, 6
  moment equations, 96, 104
  other treatments, 117, 125, 382
Heterogeneous media, effective constants. *See* Effective constants.
  geometry, 202
  statistical moment equations, 215
    elastic case, 236
    electrostatic case, 216
    scalar permittivity, 230, 232
    tensor permittivity, 225, 250
  variational principles, 126, 241
Hilbert transform, 43, 146
Homogeneity, heterogeneous media, 112, 128, 182, 211
  turbulence, 337
Hydraulic radius, 265

I

Inclusion, 186, 199, 200, 247
Incoherent radiation, 149
Isotropic, direct interaction equations, 378
  equations for turbulence, 343, 349
  radiation field, 176
  tensors, 177, 218, 338

K

Karhunen-Loève theorem, 55
Kolmogorov's hypothesis, 355, 382, 402
Kozeny equation, 266, 277

L

Lambertian source, 175
Liouville's equation, 92, 403

M

Maxwell's equations, 81, 155
Mixing lengths, 318, 323, 330
Moments, definitions, 32, 35
  different type, 94
  equations, 93, 104, 158, 215, 334
  Fourier transforms of, 112, 343
  solutions, 116

N

n-phase materials, 197, 199
Navier-Stokes equations, 87, 101, 109, 263, 316, 370, 385, 406

P

Permeability, 262, 278, 283
Permittivity, bounds, 131, 141, 245
  cumulant neglect hypothesis, 121
  effective constants, 210, 229, 232, 235

functional equation, 82
moment equations, 99, 105, 216
one-dimensional problem, 10, 193
perturbation solution, 118, 222
variational principles, standard, 126, 241
    Brown, Hashin, Shtrikman-type, 132, 247
Perturbation theory, 114, 118, 222, 385
Poisson point model, 207
Polarization, 132
Polycrystal, 189, 217, 224, 250
Porosity, 259, 263
Porous media, flow through, correlation lengths, 260
    Darcy's law, 262
    description, 258
    dispersion, 268, 288
    Green's function, 278, 281
    permeability, 262, 278, 286
    random capillary model, 275
    spherical arrangement, 259, 273
    variational principle, 283
Power spectra, 44
    smoothing procedure, 48
Probability theory, axiomatization, 18
    characteristic functionals, 71
    characteristic functions, 31
    characterization of a two-phase medium, 204
    conditional probability, 21
    convergence, 33, 53
    correlation functions, 35, 43
    density functionals, 70
    density functions, 22
    description of porous media, 258
    distribution functions, 26
    ergodic hypothesis, 41
    gaussian processes, 49, 72
    mathematical expectations, 30
    moments, 32, 37
    power spectra, 43
    semiinvariants, 34
    stationary processes, 38
    transformation of variables, 28
Propagation of radiation through random media, 85, 118, 154, 180, 400

Q

Quasi-monochromatic radiation, 147, 166

R

Radiation, 83, 162
Reynolds' equation, 316
Reynolds' number, 267, 303, 313, 327, 357

S

Self-consistent approximation, 199
Semiinvariants, 34, 122, 124
Similarity hypothesis, 331, 384
Stability, 317
Star, measurement of angular diameter, 174
Stationary processes, 38, 156
Strain fluctuations, 240
Stress fluctuations, 240
Symmetric materials, 245, 246, 256

T

Taylor pipe dispersion problem, 289
Taylor series, 60, 95
Tchebycheff's inequality, 53
Tortuosity, 266
Turbulence, analogy to quantum field theory, 408
    cumulant neglect hypothesis, 361, 381
    direct interaction equations, 369, 398
    eddy "size," 344
    eddy viscosity, 318, 323, 360
    energy transfer, 354, 381
    experiments in channel flow, 327
    final period of decay, 350, 402
    functional approaches, 400
    Heisenberg's theory, 358
    homogeneous, 337

homogeneous and isotropic, 338
inertial range, 357
Kolmogorov's hypothesis, 355
Lagrangian fields, 370, 383, 385
lateral correlation function, 342
Loitsianski's invariant, 367
longitudinal correlation function, 342
mixing lengths, 318, 323, 330
Reynolds' equation, 316
Reynolds' number, 267, 303, 313,
    327, 357
Reynolds' studies, 312
shear flow, 312, 412
similarity hypothesis, 323, 331, 384
stability, 317
statistical moment equations, 101,
    109, 334
vorticity, 366
Wyld's perturbation procedure, 385
Turbulent diffusion, 125, 314, 335, 363,
    404

V

Variational principles, 126
    heterogeneous media, 241, 247
    porous media, 283
Viscosity, eddy, 318, 323, 360, 404
    kinematic, 319
Visibility, 144
Volume fractions, 185

W

Wiener-Khinchin theorem, 46

Y

Young's interference experiment, 143